PEARSON

ALWAYS LEARNING

Margaret L. Lial • Raymond N. Greenwell • Nathan P. Ri~~tchey~~

Finite Mathema~~tics~~

Custom Edition for Northeastern Illinois University

Taken from:
Finite Mathematics and Calculus with Applications, Ninth Edition
by Margaret L. Lial, Raymond N. Greenwell, Nathan P. Ritchey

Taken from:

Finite Mathematics and Calculus with Applications, Ninth Edition
by Margaret L. Lial, Raymond N. Greenwell, Nathan P. Ritchey
Copyright © 2012, 2009, 2005, 2002 by Pearson Education, Inc.
Published by Addison-Wesley
Boston, Massachusetts 02116

This special edition published in cooperation with Pearson Learning Solutions.

All trademarks, service marks, registered trademarks, and registered service marks are the property of their respective owners and are used herein for identification purposes only.

Pearson Learning Solutions, 501 Boylston Street, Suite 900, Boston, MA 02116
A Pearson Education Company
www.pearsoned.com

Printed in the United States of America

1 2 3 4 5 6 7 8 9 10 V092 17 16 15 14 13 12

000200010271681806

CM

ISBN 10: 1-256-78345-5
ISBN 13: 978-1-256-78345-9

Contents

Special Topics to Accompany Finite Mathematics and Calculus with Applications

The following material is provided free to adopters at
www.pearsonhighered.com/mathstatsresources:

Digraphs and Networks
   Graphs and Digraphs
   Dominance Digraphs
   Communication Digraphs
   Networks
Review Exercises

Linear Functions

Over short time intervals, many changes in the economy are well modeled by linear functions. In an exercise in the first section of this chapter, we will examine a linear model that predicts the number of cellular telephone users in the United States. Such predictions are important tools for cellular telephone company executives and planners.

Before using mathematics to solve a real-world problem, we must usually set up a **mathematical model**, a mathematical description of the situation. In this chapter we look at some mathematics of *linear* models, which are used for data whose graphs can be approximated by straight lines. Linear models have an immense number of applications, because even when the underlying phenomenon is not linear, a linear model often provides an approximation that is sufficiently accurate and much simpler to use.

1.1 Slopes and Equations of Lines

APPLY IT How fast has tuition at public colleges been increasing in recent years, and how well can we predict tuition in the future?
In Example 14 of this section, we will answer these questions using the equation of a line.

There are many everyday situations in which two quantities are related. For example, if a bank account pays 6% simple interest per year, then the interest I that a deposit of P dollars would earn in one year is given by

$$I = 0.06 \cdot P, \quad \text{or} \quad I = 0.06P.$$

The formula $I = 0.06P$ describes the relationship between interest and the amount of money deposited.

Using this formula, we see, for example, that if $P = \$100$, then $I = \$6$, and if $P = \$200$, then $I = \$12$. These corresponding pairs of numbers can be written as **ordered pairs**, $(100, 6)$ and $(200, 12)$, whose order is important. The first number denotes the value of P and the second number the value of I.

Ordered pairs are graphed with the perpendicular number lines of a **Cartesian coordinate system**, shown in Figure 1.* The horizontal number line, or **x-axis**, represents the first components of the ordered pairs, while the vertical or **y-axis** represents the second components. The point where the number lines cross is the zero point on both lines; this point is called the **origin**.

Each point on the xy-plane corresponds to an ordered pair of numbers, where the x-value is written first. From now on, we will refer to the point corresponding to the ordered pair (x, y) as "the point (x, y)."

Locate the point $(-2, 4)$ on the coordinate system by starting at the origin and counting 2 units to the left on the horizontal axis and 4 units upward, parallel to the vertical axis. This point is shown in Figure 1, along with several other sample points. The number -2 is the **x-coordinate** and the number 4 is the **y-coordinate** of the point $(-2, 4)$.

The x-axis and y-axis divide the plane into four parts, or **quadrants**. For example, quadrant I includes all those points whose x- and y-coordinates are both positive. The quadrants are numbered as shown in Figure 1. The points on the axes themselves belong to no quadrant. The set of points corresponding to the ordered pairs of an equation is the **graph** of the equation.

The x- and y-values of the points where the graph of an equation crosses the axes are called the **x-intercept** and **y-intercept**, respectively.** See Figure 2.

*The name "Cartesian" honors René Descartes (1596–1650), one of the greatest mathematicians of the seventeenth century. According to legend, Descartes was lying in bed when he noticed an insect crawling on the ceiling and realized that if he could determine the distance from the bug to each of two perpendicular walls, he could describe its position at any given moment. The same idea can be used to locate a point in a plane.
**Some people prefer to define the intercepts as ordered pairs, rather than as numbers.

FIGURE 1

FIGURE 2

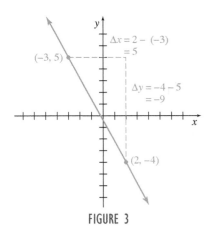

FIGURE 3

Slope of a Line

An important characteristic of a straight line is its *slope*, a number that represents the "steepness" of the line. To see how slope is defined, look at the line in Figure 3. The line goes through the points $(x_1, y_1) = (-3, 5)$ and $(x_2, y_2) = (2, -4)$. The difference in the two x-values,

$$x_2 - x_1 = 2 - (-3) = 5$$

in this example, is called the **change in x**. The symbol Δx (read "delta x") is used to represent the change in x. In the same way, Δy represents the **change in y**. In our example,

$$\Delta y = y_2 - y_1$$
$$= -4 - 5$$
$$= -9.$$

These symbols, Δx and Δy, are used in the following definition of slope.

Slope of a Line

The **slope** of a line is defined as the vertical change (the "rise") over the horizontal change (the "run") as one travels along the line. In symbols, taking two different points (x_1, y_1) and (x_2, y_2) on the line, the slope is

$$m = \frac{\text{Change in } y}{\text{Change in } x} = \frac{\Delta y}{\Delta x} = \frac{y_2 - y_1}{x_2 - x_1},$$

where $x_1 \neq x_2$.

By this definition, the slope of the line in Figure 3 is

$$m = \frac{\Delta y}{\Delta x} = \frac{-4 - 5}{2 - (-3)} = -\frac{9}{5}.$$

The slope of a line tells how fast y changes for each unit of change in x.

NOTE Using similar triangles, it can be shown that the slope of a line is independent of the choice of points on the line. That is, the same slope will be obtained for *any* choice of two different points on the line.

EXAMPLE 1 **Slope**

Find the slope of the line through each pair of points.

(a) $(7, 6)$ and $(-4, 5)$

SOLUTION Let $(x_1, y_1) = (7, 6)$ and $(x_2, y_2) = (-4, 5)$. Use the definition of slope.

$$m = \frac{\Delta y}{\Delta x} = \frac{5 - 6}{-4 - 7} = \frac{-1}{-11} = \frac{1}{11}$$

(b) $(5, -3)$ and $(-2, -3)$

SOLUTION Let $(x_1, y_1) = (5, -3)$ and $(x_2, y_2) = (-2, -3)$. Then

$$m = \frac{-3 - (-3)}{-2 - 5} = \frac{0}{-7} = 0.$$

Lines with zero slope are horizontal (parallel to the x-axis).

(c) $(2, -4)$ and $(2, 3)$

SOLUTION Let $(x_1, y_1) = (2, -4)$ and $(x_2, y_2) = (2, 3)$. Then

$$m = \frac{3 - (-4)}{2 - 2} = \frac{7}{0},$$

which is undefined. This happens when the line is vertical (parallel to the y-axis).

YOUR TURN 1 Find the slope of the line through $(1, 5)$ and $(4, 6)$.

TRY YOUR TURN 1

CAUTION The phrase "no slope" should be avoided; specify instead whether the slope is zero or undefined.

In finding the slope of the line in Example 1(a), we could have let $(x_1, y_1) = (-4, 5)$ and $(x_2, y_2) = (7, 6)$. In that case,

$$m = \frac{6 - 5}{7 - (-4)} = \frac{1}{11},$$

the same answer as before. The order in which coordinates are subtracted does not matter, as long as it is done consistently.

Figure 4 shows examples of lines with different slopes. Lines with positive slopes go up from left to right, while lines with negative slopes go down from left to right.

It might help you to compare slope with the percent grade of a hill. If a sign says a hill has a 10% grade uphill, this means the slope is 0.10, or 1/10, so the hill rises 1 foot for every 10 feet horizontally. A 15% grade downhill means the slope is -0.15.

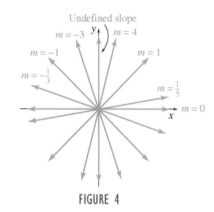

FIGURE 4

Equations of a Line

An equation in two first-degree variables, such as $4x + 7y = 20$, has a line as its graph, so it is called a **linear equation**. In the rest of this section, we consider various forms of the equation of a line.

Suppose a line has a slope m and y-intercept b. This means that it goes through the point $(0, b)$. If (x, y) is any other point on the line, then the definition of slope tells us that

$$m = \frac{y - b}{x - 0}.$$

FOR REVIEW

For review on solving a linear equation, see Section R.4.

We can simplify this equation by multiplying both sides by x and adding b to both sides. The result is

$$y = mx + b,$$

which we call the *slope-intercept* form of a line. This is the most common form for writing the equation of a line.

Slope-Intercept Form

If a line has slope m and y-intercept b, then the equation of the line in **slope-intercept form** is

$$y = mx + b.$$

When $b = 0$, we say that y is **proportional** to x.

EXAMPLE 2   Equation of a Line

Find an equation in slope-intercept form for each line.

(a) Through $(0, -3)$ with slope $3/4$

SOLUTION   We recognize $(0, -3)$ as the y-intercept because it's the point with 0 as its x-coordinate, so $b = -3$. The slope is $3/4$, so $m = 3/4$. Substituting these values into $y = mx + b$ gives

$$y = \frac{3}{4}x - 3.$$

(b) With x-intercept 7 and y-intercept 2

SOLUTION   Notice that $b = 2$. To find m, use the definition of slope after writing the x-intercept as $(7, 0)$ (because the y-coordinate is 0 where the line crosses the x-axis) and the y-intercept as $(0, 2)$.

$$m = \frac{0 - 2}{7 - 0} = -\frac{2}{7}$$

YOUR TURN 2 Find the equation of the line with x-intercept -4 and y-intercept 6.

Substituting these values into $y = mx + b$, we have

$$y = -\frac{2}{7}x + 2.$$

TRY YOUR TURN 2

EXAMPLE 3   Finding the Slope

Find the slope of the line whose equation is $3x - 4y = 12$.

SOLUTION   To find the slope, solve the equation for y.

$$3x - 4y = 12$$
$$-4y = -3x + 12 \qquad \text{Subtract } 3x \text{ from both sides.}$$
$$y = \frac{3}{4}x - 3 \qquad \text{Divide both sides by } -4.$$

YOUR TURN 3 Find the slope of the line whose equation is $8x + 3y = 5$.

The coefficient of x is $3/4$, which is the slope of the line. Notice that this is the same line as in Example 2 (a).

TRY YOUR TURN 3

The slope-intercept form of the equation of a line involves the slope and the y-intercept. Sometimes, however, the slope of a line is known, together with one point (perhaps *not* the y-intercept) that the line goes through. The *point-slope form* of the equation of a line is used to find the equation in this case. Let (x_1, y_1) be any fixed point on the line, and let (x, y) represent any other point on the line. If m is the slope of the line, then by the definition of slope,

$$\frac{y - y_1}{x - x_1} = m,$$

or

$$y - y_1 = m(x - x_1). \qquad \text{Multiply both sides by } x - x_1.$$

> **Point-Slope Form**
>
> If a line has slope m and passes through the point (x_1, y_1), then an equation of the line is given by
>
> $$y - y_1 = m(x - x_1),$$
>
> the **point-slope form** of the equation of a line.

EXAMPLE 4 **Point-Slope Form**

Find an equation of the line that passes through the point $(3, -7)$ and has slope $m = 5/4$.

SOLUTION Use the point-slope form.

$$y - y_1 = m(x - x_1)$$

$$y - (-7) = \frac{5}{4}(x - 3) \qquad y_1 = -7, m = \tfrac{5}{4}, x_1 = 3$$

$$y + 7 = \frac{5}{4}(x - 3)$$

$$4y + 28 = 5(x - 3) \qquad \text{Multiply both sides by 4.}$$

$$4y + 28 = 5x - 15 \qquad \text{Distribute.}$$

$$4y = 5x - 43 \qquad \text{Combine constants.}$$

$$y = \frac{5}{4}x - \frac{43}{4} \qquad \text{Divide both sides by 4.}$$

FOR REVIEW

See Section R.4 for details on eliminating denominators in an equation.

The equation of the same line can be given in many forms. To avoid confusion, the linear equations used in the rest of this section will be written in slope-intercept form, $y = mx + b$, which is often the most useful form.

The point-slope form also can be useful to find an equation of a line if we know two different points that the line goes through, as in the next example.

EXAMPLE 5 **Using Point-Slope Form to Find an Equation**

Find an equation of the line through $(5, 4)$ and $(-10, -2)$.

SOLUTION Begin by using the definition of slope to find the slope of the line that passes through the given points.

$$\text{Slope} = m = \frac{-2 - 4}{-10 - 5} = \frac{-6}{-15} = \frac{2}{5}$$

Either $(5, 4)$ or $(-10, -2)$ can be used in the point-slope form with $m = 2/5$. If $(x_1, y_1) = (5, 4)$, then

$$y - y_1 = m(x - x_1)$$

$$y - 4 = \frac{2}{5}(x - 5) \qquad y_1 = 4, m = \tfrac{2}{5}, x_1 = 5$$

$$5y - 20 = 2(x - 5) \qquad \text{Multiply both sides by 5.}$$

$$5y - 20 = 2x - 10 \qquad \text{Distributive property}$$

$$5y = 2x + 10 \qquad \text{Add 20 to both sides.}$$

$$y = \frac{2}{5}x + 2 \qquad \text{Divide by 5 to put in slope-intercept form.}$$

YOUR TURN 4 Find the equation of the line through $(2, 9)$ and $(5, 3)$. Put your answer in slope-intercept form.

Check that the same result is found if $(x_1, y_1) = (-10, -2)$. **TRY YOUR TURN 4**

EXAMPLE 6   Horizontal Line

Find an equation of the line through $(8, -4)$ and $(-2, -4)$.

SOLUTION   Find the slope.

$$m = \frac{-4 - (-4)}{-2 - 8} = \frac{0}{-10} = 0$$

Choose, say, $(8, -4)$ as (x_1, y_1).

$$y - y_1 = m(x - x_1)$$
$$y - (-4) = 0(x - 8) \qquad y_1 = -4, m = 0, x_1 = 8$$
$$y + 4 = 0 \qquad\qquad 0(x - 8) = 0$$
$$y = -4$$

Plotting the given ordered pairs and drawing a line through the points show that the equation $y = -4$ represents a horizontal line. See Figure 5(a). Every horizontal line has a slope of zero and an equation of the form $y = k$, where k is the y-value of all ordered pairs on the line.

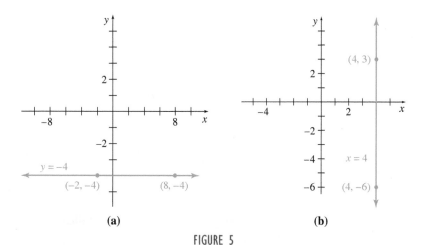

(a)   (b)

FIGURE 5

EXAMPLE 7   Vertical Line

Find an equation of the line through $(4, 3)$ and $(4, -6)$.

SOLUTION   The slope of the line is

$$m = \frac{-6 - 3}{4 - 4} = \frac{-9}{0},$$

which is undefined. Since both ordered pairs have x-coordinate 4, the equation is $x = 4$. Because the slope is undefined, the equation of this line cannot be written in the slope-intercept form.

Again, plotting the given ordered pairs and drawing a line through them show that the graph of $x = 4$ is a vertical line. See Figure 5(b).

Slope of Horizontal and Vertical Lines

The slope of a horizontal line is 0.

The slope of a vertical line is undefined.

The different forms of linear equations discussed in this section are summarized below. The slope-intercept and point-slope forms are equivalent ways to express the equation of a nonvertical line. The slope-intercept form is simpler for a final answer, but you may find the point-slope form easier to use when you know the slope of a line and a point through which the line passes. The slope-intercept form is often considered the standard form. Any line that is not vertical has a unique slope-intercept form but can have many point-slope forms for its equation.

Equations of Lines

Equation	Description
$y = mx + b$	**Slope-intercept form:** slope m, y-intercept b
$y - y_1 = m(x - x_1)$	**Point-slope form:** slope m, line passes through (x_1, y_1)
$x = k$	**Vertical line:** x-intercept k, no y-intercept (except when $k = 0$), undefined slope
$y = k$	**Horizontal line:** y-intercept k, no x-intercept (except when $k = 0$), slope 0

Parallel and Perpendicular Lines

One application of slope involves deciding whether two lines are parallel, which means that they never intersect. Since two parallel lines are equally "steep," they should have the same slope. Also, two lines with the same "steepness" are parallel.

Parallel Lines

Two lines are **parallel** if and only if they have the same slope, or if they are both vertical.

EXAMPLE 8   Parallel Line

Find the equation of the line that passes through the point $(3, 5)$ and is parallel to the line $2x + 5y = 4$.

SOLUTION   The slope of $2x + 5y = 4$ can be found by writing the equation in slope-intercept form.

$$2x + 5y = 4$$

$$y = -\frac{2}{5}x + \frac{4}{5} \qquad \text{Subtract } 2x \text{ from both sides and divide both sides by 5.}$$

This result shows that the slope is $-2/5$. Since the lines are parallel, $-2/5$ is also the slope of the line whose equation we want. This line passes through $(3, 5)$. Substituting $m = -2/5$, $x_1 = 3$, and $y_1 = 5$ into the point-slope form gives

$$y - y_1 = m(x - x_1)$$

$$y - 5 = -\frac{2}{5}(x - 3) = -\frac{2}{5}x + \frac{6}{5}$$

$$y = -\frac{2}{5}x + \frac{6}{5} + 5$$

$$y = -\frac{2}{5}x + \frac{31}{5}. \qquad \text{Multiply 5 by } 5/5 \text{ to get a common denominator.}$$

TRY YOUR TURN 5

YOUR TURN 5   Find the equation of the line that passes through the point $(4, 5)$ and is parallel to the line $3x - 6y = 7$. Put your answer in slope-intercept form.

As already mentioned, two nonvertical lines are parallel if and only if they have the same slope. Two lines having slopes with a product of -1 are perpendicular. A proof of this fact, which depends on similar triangles from geometry, is given as Exercise 43 in this section.

Perpendicular Lines

Two lines are **perpendicular** if and only if the product of their slopes is -1, or if one is vertical and the other horizontal.

EXAMPLE 9 Perpendicular Line

Find the equation of the line L passing through the point $(3, 7)$ and perpendicular to the line having the equation $5x - y = 4$.

SOLUTION To find the slope, write $5x - y = 4$ in slope-intercept form:

$$y = 5x - 4.$$

The slope is 5. Since the lines are perpendicular, if line L has slope m, then

$$5m = -1$$

$$m = -\frac{1}{5}.$$

Now substitute $m = -1/5$, $x_1 = 3$, and $y_1 = 7$ into the point-slope form.

$$y - 7 = -\frac{1}{5}(x - 3)$$

$$y - 7 = -\frac{1}{5}x + \frac{3}{5}$$

$$y = -\frac{1}{5}x + \frac{3}{5} + 7 \cdot \frac{5}{5} \qquad \text{Add 7 to both sides and get a common denominator.}$$

$$y = -\frac{1}{5}x + \frac{38}{5}$$

YOUR TURN 6 Find the equation of the line passing through the point $(3, 2)$ and perpendicular to the line having the equation $2x + 3y = 4$.

TRY YOUR TURN 6

The next example uses the equation of a line to analyze real-world data. In this example, we are looking at how one variable changes over time. To simplify the arithmetic, we will *rescale* the variable representing time, although computers and calculators have made rescaling less important than in the past. Here it allows us to work with smaller numbers, and, as you will see, find the y-intercept of the line more easily. We will use rescaling on many examples throughout this book. When we do, it is important to be consistent.

EXAMPLE 10 Prevalence of Cigarette Smoking

In recent years, the percentage of the U.S. population age 18 and older who smoke has decreased at a roughly constant rate, from 24.1% in 1998 to 20.6% in 2008. *Source: Centers for Disease Control and Prevention.*

(a) Find the equation describing this linear relationship.

SOLUTION Let t represent time in years, with $t = 0$ representing 1990. With this rescaling, the year 1998 corresponds to $t = 8$ and the year 2008 corresponds to $t = 2008 - 1990 = 18$. Let y represent the percentage of the population who smoke. The two ordered pairs representing the given information are then $(8, 24.1)$ and $(18, 20.6)$. The slope of the line through these points is

$$m = \frac{20.6 - 24.1}{18 - 8} = \frac{-3.5}{10} = -0.35.$$

This means that, on average, the percentage of the adult population who smoke is decreasing by about 0.35% per year.

Using $m = -0.35$ in the point-slope form, and choosing $(t_1, y_1) = (8, 24.1)$, gives the required equation.

$$y - 24.1 = -0.35\,(t - 8)$$
$$y - 24.1 = -0.35\,t + 2.8$$
$$y = -0.35\,t + 26.9$$

We could have used the other point $(18, 20.6)$ and found the same answer. Instead, we'll use this to check our answer by observing that $-0.35(18) + 26.9 = 20.6$, which agrees with the y-value at $t = 18$.

(b) One objective of Healthy People 2010 (a campaign of the U.S. Department of Health and Human Services) was to reduce the percentage of U.S. adults who smoke to 12% or less by the year 2010. If this decline in smoking continued at the same rate, did they meet this objective?

SOLUTION Using the same rescaling, $t = 20$ corresponds to the year 2010. Substituting this value into the above equation gives

$$y = -0.35(20) + 26.9 = 19.9.$$

Continuing at this rate, an estimated 19.9% of the adult population still smoked in 2010, and the objective of Healthy People 2010 was not met.

Notice that if the formula from part (b) of Example 10 is valid for all nonnegative t, then eventually y becomes 0:

$$-0.35\,t + 26.9 = 0$$
$$-0.35\,t = -26.9 \qquad \text{Subtract 26.9 from both sides.}$$
$$t = \frac{-26.9}{-0.35} = 76.857 \approx 77^{*}, \qquad \text{Divide both sides by } -0.35.$$

which indicates that 77 years from 1990 (in the year 2067), 0% of the U.S. adult population will smoke. Of course, it is still possible that in 2067 there will be adults who smoke; the trend of recent years may not continue. Most equations are valid for some specific set of numbers. It is highly speculative to extrapolate beyond those values.

On the other hand, people in business and government often need to make some prediction about what will happen in the future, so a tentative conclusion based on past trends may be better than no conclusion at all. There are also circumstances, particularly in the physical sciences, in which theoretical reasons imply that the trend will continue.

(a)

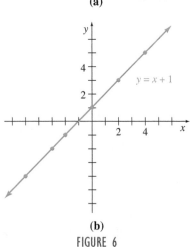

(b)

FIGURE 6

Graph of a Line

We can graph the linear equation defined by $y = x + 1$ by finding several ordered pairs that satisfy the equation. For example, if $x = 2$, then $y = 2 + 1 = 3$, giving the ordered pair $(2, 3)$. Also, $(0, 1)$, $(4, 5)$, $(-2, -1)$, $(-5, -4)$, $(-3, -2)$, among many others, satisfy the equation.

To graph $y = x + 1$, we begin by locating the ordered pairs obtained above, as shown in Figure 6(a). All the points of this graph appear to lie on a straight line, as in Figure 6(b). This straight line is the graph of $y = x + 1$.

It can be shown that every equation of the form $ax + by = c$ has a straight line as its graph, assuming a and b are not both 0. Although just two points are needed to determine a line, it is a good idea to plot a third point as a check. It is often convenient to use the x- and y-intercepts as the two points, as in the following example.

*The symbol $\approx$ means "is approximately equal to."

EXAMPLE 11 **Graph of a Line**

Graph $3x + 2y = 12$.

SOLUTION   To find the y-intercept, let $x = 0$.

$$3(0) + 2y = 12$$
$$2y = 12 \qquad \text{Divide both sides by 2.}$$
$$y = 6$$

Similarly, find the x-intercept by letting $y = 0$, which gives $x = 4$. Verify that when $x = 2$, the result is $y = 3$. These three points are plotted in Figure 7(a). A line is drawn through them in Figure 7(b).

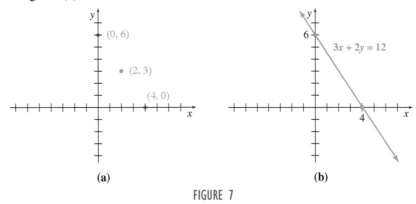

(a)   (b)

FIGURE 7

Not every line has two distinct intercepts; the graph in the next example does not cross the x-axis, and so it has no x-intercept.

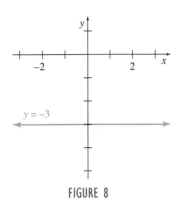

FIGURE 8

EXAMPLE 12 **Graph of a Horizontal Line**

Graph $y = -3$.

SOLUTION   The equation $y = -3$, or equivalently, $y = 0x - 3$, always gives the same y-value, -3, for any value of x. Therefore, no value of x will make $y = 0$, so the graph has no x-intercept. As we saw in Example 6, the graph of such an equation is a horizontal line parallel to the x-axis. In this case the y-intercept is -3, as shown in Figure 8.

The graph in Example 12 has only one intercept. Another type of linear equation with coinciding intercepts is graphed in Example 13.

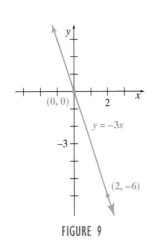

FIGURE 9

EXAMPLE 13 **Graph of a Line Through the Origin**

Graph $y = -3x$.

SOLUTION   Begin by looking for the x-intercept. If $y = 0$, then

$$y = -3x$$
$$0 = -3x \qquad \text{Let } y = 0.$$
$$0 = x. \qquad \text{Divide both sides by } -3.$$

We have the ordered pair $(0, 0)$. Starting with $x = 0$ gives exactly the same ordered pair, $(0, 0)$. Two points are needed to determine a straight line, and the intercepts have led to only one point. To get a second point, we choose some other value of x (or y). For example, if $x = 2$, then

$$y = -3x = -3(2) = -6, \qquad \text{Let } x = 2.$$

giving the ordered pair $(2, -6)$. These two ordered pairs, $(0, 0)$ and $(2, -6)$, were used to get the graph shown in Figure 9.

Linear equations allow us to set up simple mathematical models for real-life situations. In almost every case, linear (or any other reasonably simple) equations provide only approximations to real-world situations. Nevertheless, these are often remarkably useful approximations.

EXAMPLE 14 Tuition

APPLY IT

The table on the left lists the average annual cost (in dollars) of tuition and fees at public four-year colleges for selected years. *Source: The College Board.*

(a) Plot the cost of public colleges by letting $t = 0$ correspond to 2000. Are the data *exactly* linear? Could the data be *approximated* by a linear equation?

SOLUTION The data is plotted in Figure 10(a) in a figure known as a **scatterplot**. Although it is not exactly linear, it is approximately linear and could be approximated by a linear equation.

Cost of Public College	
Year	**Tuition and Fees**
2000	3508
2001	3766
2002	4098
2003	4645
2004	5126
2005	5492
2006	5804
2007	6191
2008	6591
2009	7020

(a)

(b)

FIGURE 10

(b) Use the points (0, 3508) and (9, 7020) to determine an equation that models the data.

SOLUTION We first find the slope of the line as follows:

$$m = \frac{7020 - 3508}{9 - 0} = \frac{3512}{9} \approx 390.2.$$

We have rounded to four digits, noting that we cannot expect more accuracy in our answer than in our data, which is accurate to four digits. Using the slope-intercept form of the line, $y = mt + b$, with $m = 390.2$ and $b = 3508$, gives

$$y = 390.2t + 3508.$$

TECHNOLOGY NOTE | A graphing calculator plot of this line and the data points are shown in Figure 10(b). Notice that the points closely fit the line. More details on how to construct this graphing calculator plot are given at the end of this example.

(c) Discuss the accuracy of using this equation to estimate the cost of public colleges in the year 2030.

SOLUTION The year 2030 corresponds to the year $t = 30$, for which the equation predicts a cost of

$$y = 390.2(30) + 3508 = 15,214, \quad \text{or} \quad \$15,214.$$

The year 2030 is many years in the future, however. Many factors could affect the tuition, and the actual figure for 2030 could turn out to be very different from our prediction.

TECHNOLOGY NOTE You can plot data with a TI-84 Plus graphing calculator using the following steps.

1. Store the data in lists.
2. Define the stat plot.
3. Turn off $Y =$ functions (unless you also want to graph a function).
4. Turn on the plot you want to display.
5. Define the viewing window.
6. Display the graph.

Consult the calculator's instruction booklet or the *Graphing Calculator and Excel Spreadsheet Manual*, available with this book, for specific instructions. See the calculator-generated graph in Figure 10(b), which includes the points and line from Example 14. Notice how the line closely approximates the data.

1.1 EXERCISES

Find the slope of each line.

1. Through $(4, 5)$ and $(-1, 2)$

2. Through $(5, -4)$ and $(1, 3)$

3. Through $(8, 4)$ and $(8, -7)$

4. Through $(1, 5)$ and $(-2, 5)$

5. $y = x$
6. $y = 3x - 2$

7. $5x - 9y = 11$
8. $4x + 7y = 1$

9. $x = 5$
10. The x-axis

11. $y = 8$
12. $y = -6$

13. A line parallel to $6x - 3y = 12$

14. A line perpendicular to $8x = 2y - 5$

In Exercises 15–24, find an equation in slope-intercept form for each line.

15. Through $(1, 3)$, $m = -2$

16. Through $(2, 4)$, $m = -1$

17. Through $(-5, -7)$, $m = 0$

18. Through $(-8, 1)$, with undefined slope

19. Through $(4, 2)$ and $(1, 3)$

20. Through $(8, -1)$ and $(4, 3)$

21. Through $(2/3, 1/2)$ and $(1/4, -2)$

22. Through $(-2, 3/4)$ and $(2/3, 5/2)$

23. Through $(-8, 4)$ and $(-8, 6)$

24. Through $(-1, 3)$ and $(0, 3)$

In Exercises 25–34, find an equation for each line in the form $ax + by = c$, where a, b, and c are integers with no factor common to all three and $a \geq 0$.

25. x-intercept -6, y-intercept -3

26. x-intercept -2, y-intercept 4

27. Vertical, through $(-6, 5)$

28. Horizontal, through $(8, 7)$

29. Through $(-4, 6)$, parallel to $3x + 2y = 13$

30. Through $(2, -5)$, parallel to $2x - y = -4$

31. Through $(3, -4)$, perpendicular to $x + y = 4$

32. Through $(-2, 6)$, perpendicular to $2x - 3y = 5$

33. The line with y-intercept 4 and perpendicular to $x + 5y = 7$

34. The line with x-intercept $-2/3$ and perpendicular to $2x - y = 4$

35. Do the points $(4, 3)$, $(2, 0)$, and $(-18, -12)$ lie on the same line? Explain why or why not. (*Hint:* Find the slopes between the points.)

36. Find k so that the line through $(4, -1)$ and $(k, 2)$ is
    a. parallel to $2x + 3y = 6$,
    b. perpendicular to $5x - 2y = -1$.

37. Use slopes to show that the quadrilateral with vertices at $(1, 3)$, $(-5/2, 2)$, $(-7/2, 4)$, and $(2, 1)$ is a parallelogram.

38. Use slopes to show that the square with vertices at $(-2, 5)$, $(4, 5)$, $(4, -1)$, and $(-2, -1)$ has diagonals that are perpendicular.

For the lines in Exercises 39 and 40, which of the following is closest to the slope of the line? (a) 1 (b) 2 (c) 3 (d) 21 (e) 22 (f) −3

39.

40.

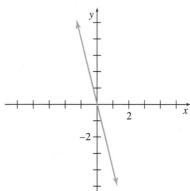

In Exercises 41 and 42, estimate the slope of the lines.

41.

42.

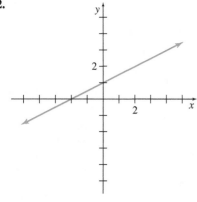

43. To show that two perpendicular lines, neither of which is vertical, have slopes with a product of −1, go through the following steps. Let line L_1 have equation $y = m_1 x + b_1$, and let L_2 have equation $y = m_2 x + b_2$, with $m_1 > 0$ and $m_2 < 0$. Assume that L_1 and L_2 are perpendicular, and use right triangle *MPN* shown in the figure. Prove each of the following statements.

a. *MQ* has length m_1.

b. *QN* has length $-m_2$.

c. Triangles *MPQ* and *PNQ* are similar.

d. $m_1/1 = 1/(-m_2)$ and $m_1 m_2 = -1$

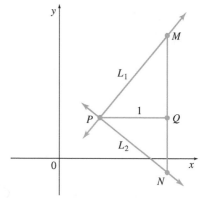

44. Consider the equation $\dfrac{x}{a} + \dfrac{y}{b} = 1$.

a. Show that this equation represents a line by writing it in the form $y = mx + b$.

b. Find the *x*- and *y*-intercepts of this line.

c. Explain in your own words why the equation in this exercise is known as the intercept form of a line.

Graph each equation.

45. $y = x - 1$ **46.** $y = 4x + 5$

47. $y = -4x + 9$ **48.** $y = -6x + 12$

49. $2x - 3y = 12$ **50.** $3x - y = -9$

51. $3y - 7x = -21$ **52.** $5y + 6x = 11$

53. $y = -2$ **54.** $x = 4$

55. $x + 5 = 0$ **56.** $y + 8 = 0$

57. $y = 2x$ **58.** $y = -5x$

59. $x + 4y = 0$ **60.** $3x - 5y = 0$

APPLICATIONS

Business and Economics

61. Sales The sales of a small company were $27,000 in its second year of operation and $63,000 in its fifth year. Let *y* represent sales in the *x*th year of operation. Assume that the data can be approximated by a straight line.

a. Find the slope of the sales line, and give an equation for the line in the form $y = mx + b$.

b. Use your answer from part a to find out how many years must pass before the sales surpass $100,000.

62. Use of Cellular Telephones The following table shows the subscribership of cellular telephones in the United States (in millions) for even-numbered years between 2000 and 2008. *Source: Time Almanac 2010.*

Year	2000	2002	2004	2006	2008
Subscribers (in millions)	109.48	140.77	182.14	233.04	270.33

a. Plot the data by letting $t = 0$ correspond to 2000. Discuss how well the data fit a straight line.

b. Determine a linear equation that approximates the number of subscribers using the points $(0, 109.48)$ and $(8, 270.33)$.

c. Repeat part b using the points $(2, 140.77)$ and $(8, 270.33)$.

d. Discuss why your answers to parts b and c are similar but not identical.

e. Using your equations from parts b and c, approximate the number of cellular phone subscribers in the year 2007. Compare your result with the actual value of 255.40 million.

63. Consumer Price Index The Consumer Price Index (CPI) is a measure of the change in the cost of goods over time. The index was 100 for the three-year period centered on 1983. For simplicity, we will assume that the CPI was exactly 100 in 1983. Then the CPI of 215.3 in 2008 indicates that an item that cost $1.00 in 1983 would cost $2.15 in 2008. The CPI has been increasing approximately linearly over the last few decades. *Source: Time Almanac 2010.*

a. Use this information to determine an equation for the CPI in terms of t, which represents the years since 1980.

b. Based on the answer to part a, what was the predicted value of the CPI in 2000? Compare this estimate with the actual CPI of 172.2.

c. Describe the rate at which the annual CPI is changing.

Life Sciences

64. HIV Infection The time interval between a person's initial infection with HIV and that person's eventual development of AIDS symptoms is an important issue. The method of infection with HIV affects the time interval before AIDS develops. One study of HIV patients who were infected by intravenous drug use found that 17% of the patients had AIDS after 4 years, and 33% had developed the disease after 7 years. The relationship between the time interval and the percentage of patients with AIDS can be modeled accurately with a linear equation. *Source: Epidemiologic Review.*

a. Write a linear equation $y = mt + b$ that models this data, using the ordered pairs $(4, 0.17)$ and $(7, 0.33)$.

b. Use your equation from part a to predict the number of years before half of these patients will have AIDS.

65. Exercise Heart Rate To achieve the maximum benefit for the heart when exercising, your heart rate (in beats per minute) should be in the target heart rate zone. The lower limit of this zone is found by taking 70% of the difference between 220 and your age. The upper limit is found by using 85%. *Source: Physical Fitness.*

a. Find formulas for the upper and lower limits (u and l) as linear equations involving the age x.

b. What is the target heart rate zone for a 20-year-old?

c. What is the target heart rate zone for a 40-year-old?

d. Two women in an aerobics class stop to take their pulse and are surprised to find that they have the same pulse. One woman is 36 years older than the other and is working at the upper limit of her target heart rate zone. The younger woman is working at the lower limit of her target heart rate zone. What are the ages of the two women, and what is their pulse?

e. Run for 10 minutes, take your pulse, and see if it is in your target heart rate zone. (After all, this is listed as an exercise!)

66. Ponies Trotting A 1991 study found that the peak vertical force on a trotting Shetland pony increased linearly with the pony's speed, and that when the force reached a critical level, the pony switched from a trot to a gallop. For one pony, the critical force was 1.16 times its body weight. It experienced a force of 0.75 times its body weight at a speed of 2 meters per second and a force of 0.93 times its body weight at 3 meters per second. At what speed did the pony switch from a trot to a gallop? *Source: Science.*

67. Life Expectancy Some scientists believe there is a limit to how long humans can live. One supporting argument is that during the last century, life expectancy from age 65 has increased more slowly than life expectancy from birth, so eventually these two will be equal, at which point, according to these scientists, life expectancy should increase no further. In 1900, life expectancy at birth was 46 yr, and life expectancy at age 65 was 76 yr. In 2004, these figures had risen to 77.8 and 83.7, respectively. In both cases, the increase in life expectancy has been linear. Using these assumptions and the data given, find the maximum life expectancy for humans. *Source: Science.*

Social Sciences

68. Child Mortality Rate The mortality rate for children under 5 years of age around the world has been declining in a roughly linear fashion in recent years. The rate per 1000 live births was 90 in 1990 and 65 in 2008. *Source: World Health Organization.*

a. Determine a linear equation that approximates the mortality rate in terms of time t, where t represents the number of years since 1900.

b. If this trend continues, in what year will the mortality rate first drop to 50 or below per 1000 live births?

69. Health Insurance The percentage of adults in the United States without health insurance increased at a roughly linear rate from 1999, when it was 17.2%, to 2008, when it was 20.3%. *Source: The New York Times.*

a. Determine a linear equation that approximates the percentage of adults in the United States without health insurance in terms of time t, where t represents the number of years since 1990.

b. If this trend were to continue, in what year would the percentage of adults without health insurance be at least 25%?

70. Marriage The following table lists the U.S. median age at first marriage for men and women. The age at which both groups marry for the first time seems to be increasing at a roughly linear rate in recent decades. Let t correspond to the number of years since 1980. *Source: U.S. Census Bureau.*

Age at First Marriage						
Year	1980	1985	1990	1995	2000	2005
Men	24.7	25.5	26.1	26.9	26.8	27.1
Women	22.0	23.3	23.9	24.5	25.1	25.3

a. Find a linear equation that approximates the data for men, using the data for the years 1980 and 2005.

b. Repeat part a using the data for women.

c. Which group seems to have the faster increase in median age at first marriage?

d. In what year will the men's median age at first marriage reach 30?

e. When the men's median age at first marriage is 30, what will the median age be for women?

71. Immigration In 1950, there were 249,187 immigrants admitted to the United States. In 2008, the number was 1,107,126. *Source: 2008 Yearbook of Immigration Statistics.*

a. Assuming that the change in immigration is linear, write an equation expressing the number of immigrants, y, in terms of t, the number of years after 1900.

b. Use your result in part a to predict the number of immigrants admitted to the United States in 2015.

c. Considering the value of the y-intercept in your answer to part a, discuss the validity of using this equation to model the number of immigrants throughout the entire 20th century.

Physical Sciences

72. Global Warming In 1990, the Intergovernmental Panel on Climate Change predicted that the average temperature on Earth would rise 0.3°C per decade in the absence of international controls on greenhouse emissions. Let t measure the time in years since 1970, when the average global temperature was 15°C. *Source: Science News.*

a. Find a linear equation giving the average global temperature in degrees Celsius in terms of t, the number of years since 1970.

b. Scientists have estimated that the sea level will rise by 65 cm if the average global temperature rises to 19°C. According to your answer to part a, when would this occur?

73. Galactic Distance The table lists the distances (in megaparsecs where 1 megaparsec ≈ 3.1×10^{19} km) and velocities (in kilometers per second) of four galaxies moving rapidly away from Earth. *Source: Astronomical Methods and Calculations, and Fundamental Astronomy.*

Galaxy	Distance	Velocity
Virga	15	1600
Ursa Minor	200	15,000
Corona Borealis	290	24,000
Bootes	520	40,000

a. Plot the data points letting x represent distance and y represent velocity. Do the points lie in an approximately linear pattern?

b. Write a linear equation $y = mx$ to model this data, using the ordered pair $(520, 40{,}000)$.

c. The galaxy Hydra has a velocity of 60,000 km per sec. Use your equation to approximate how far away it is from Earth.

d. The value of m in the equation is called the *Hubble constant*. The Hubble constant can be used to estimate the age of the universe A (in years) using the formula

$$A = \frac{9.5 \times 10^{11}}{m}.$$

Approximate A using your value of m.

General Interest

74. News/Talk Radio From 2001 to 2007, the number of stations carrying news/talk radio increased at a roughly linear rate, from 1139 in 2001 to 1370 in 2007. *Source: State of the Media.*

a. Find a linear equation expressing the number of stations carrying news/talk radio, y, in terms of t, the years since 2000.

b. Use your answer from part a to predict the number of stations carrying news/talk radio in 2008. Compare with the actual number of 2046. Discuss how the linear trend from 2001 to 2007 might have changed in 2008.

75. Tuition The table lists the annual cost (in dollars) of tuition and fees at private four-year colleges for selected years. (See Example 14.) *Source: The College Board.*

Year	Tuition and Fees
2000	16,072
2002	18,060
2004	20,045
2006	22,308
2008	25,177
2009	26,273

a. Sketch a graph of the data. Do the data appear to lie roughly along a straight line?

b. Let $t = 0$ correspond to the year 2000. Use the points $(0, 16{,}072)$ and $(9, 26{,}273)$ to determine a linear equation that models the data. What does the slope of the graph of the equation indicate?

c. Discuss the accuracy of using this equation to estimate the cost of private college in 2025.

YOUR TURN ANSWERS

1. 1/3

2. $y = (3/2)x + 6$

3. $-8/3$

4. $y = -2x + 13$

5. $y = (1/2)x + 3$

6. $y = (3/2)x - 5/2$

1.2 Linear Functions and Applications

APPLY IT **How many units must be sold for a firm to break even?**
In Example 6 in this section, this question will be answered using a linear function.

As we saw in the previous section, many situations involve two variables related by a linear equation. For such a relationship, when we express the variable y in terms of x, we say that y is a **linear function** of x. This means that for any allowed value of x (the **independent variable**), we can use the equation to find the corresponding value of y (the **dependent variable**). Examples of equations defining linear functions include $y = 2x + 3$, $y = -5$, and $2x - 3y = 7$, which can be written as $y = (2/3)x - (7/3)$. Equations in the form $x = k$, where k is a constant, do not define linear functions. All other linear equations define linear functions.

$f(x)$ Notation

Letters such as f, g, or h are often used to name functions. For example, f might be used to name the function defined by

$$y = 5 - 3x.$$

To show that this function is named f, it is common to replace y with $f(x)$ (read "f of x") to get

$$f(x) = 5 - 3x.$$

By choosing 2 as a value of x, $f(x)$ becomes $5 - 3 \cdot 2 = 5 - 6 = -1$, written

$$f(2) = -1.$$

The corresponding ordered pair is $(2, -1)$. In a similar manner,

$$f(-4) = 5 - 3(-4) = 17, \qquad f(0) = 5, \qquad f(-6) = 23,$$

and so on.

EXAMPLE 1   Function Notation

Let $g(x) = -4x + 5$. Find $g(3)$, $g(0)$, $g(-2)$, and $g(b)$.

SOLUTION   To find $g(3)$, substitute 3 for x.

$$g(3) = -4(3) + 5 = -12 + 5 = -7$$

Similarly,

$$g(0) = -4(0) + 5 = 0 + 5 = 5,$$
$$g(-2) = -4(-2) + 5 = 8 + 5 = 13,$$

and

$$g(b) = -4b + 5.$$

YOUR TURN 1
Calculate $g(-5)$.

TRY YOUR TURN 1

We summarize the discussion below.

> ### Linear Function
> A relationship f defined by
>
> $$y = f(x) = mx + b,$$
>
> for real numbers m and b, is a **linear function**.

Supply and Demand

Linear functions are often good choices for supply and demand curves. Typically, as the price of an item increases, consumers are less likely to buy an increasingly expensive item, and so the demand for the item decreases. On the other hand, as the price of an item increases, producers are more likely to see a profit in selling the item, and so the supply of the item increases. The increase in the quantity supplied and decrease in the quantity demanded can eventually result in a surplus, which causes the price to fall. These countervailing trends tend to move the price, as well as the quantity supplied and demanded toward an equilibrium value.

For example, during the late 1980s and early 1990s, the consumer demand for cranberries (and all of their healthy benefits) soared. The quantity demanded surpassed the quantity supplied, causing a shortage, and cranberry prices rose dramatically. As prices increased, growers wanted to increase their profits, so they planted more acres of cranberries. Unfortunately, cranberries take 3 to 5 years from planting until they can first be harvested. As growers waited and prices increased, consumer demand decreased. When the cranberries were finally harvested, the supply overwhelmed the demand and a huge surplus occurred, causing the price of cranberries to drop in the late 1990s. *Source: Agricultural Marketing Resource Center.* Other factors were involved in this situation, but the relationship between price, supply, and demand was nonetheless typical.

Although economists consider price to be the independent variable, they have the unfortunate habit of plotting price, usually denoted by p, on the vertical axis, while everyone else graphs the independent variable on the horizontal axis. This custom was started by the English economist Alfred Marshall (1842–1924). In order to abide by this custom, we will write p, the price, as a function of q, the quantity produced, and plot p on the vertical axis. But remember, it is really *price* that determines how much consumers demand and producers supply, not the other way around.

Supply and demand functions are not necessarily linear, the simplest kind of function. Yet most functions are approximately linear if a small enough piece of the graph is taken, allowing applied mathematicians to often use linear functions for simplicity. That approach will be taken in this chapter.

EXAMPLE 2   Supply and Demand

Suppose that Greg Tobin, manager of a giant supermarket chain, has studied the supply and demand for watermelons. He has noticed that the demand increases as the price decreases. He has determined that the quantity (in thousands) demanded weekly, q, and the price (in dollars) per watermelon, p, are related by the linear function

$$p = D(q) = 9 - 0.75q. \quad \text{Demand function}$$

(a) Find the quantity demanded at a price of \$5.25 per watermelon and at a price of \$3.75 per watermelon.

SOLUTION   To find the quantity demanded at a price of \$5.25 per watermelon, replace p in the demand function with 5.25 and solve for q.

$$5.25 = 9 - 0.75q$$
$$-3.75 = -0.75q \quad \text{Subtract 9 from both sides.}$$
$$5 = q \quad \text{Divide both sides by } -0.75.$$

Thus, at a price of \$5.25, the quantity demanded is 5000 watermelons.

Similarly, replace p with 3.75 to find the demand when the price is \$3.75. Verify that this leads to $q = 7$. When the price is lowered from \$5.25 to \$3.75 per watermelon, the quantity demanded increases from 5000 to 7000 watermelons.

(b) Greg also noticed that the quantity of watermelons supplied decreased as the price decreased. Price p and supply q are related by the linear function

$$p = S(q) = 0.75q. \quad \text{Supply function}$$

Find the quantity supplied at a price of \$5.25 per watermelon and at a price of \$3.00 per watermelon.

SOLUTION Substitute 5.25 for p in the supply function, $p = 0.75q$, to find that $q = 7$, so the quantity supplied is 7000 watermelons. Similarly, replacing p with 3 in the supply equation gives a quantity supplied of 4000 watermelons. If the price decreases from \$5.25 to \$3.00 per watermelon, the quantity supplied also decreases, from 7000 to 4000 watermelons.

(c) Graph both functions on the same axes.

YOUR TURN 2 Find the quantity of watermelon demanded and supplied at a price of \$3.30 per watermelon.

SOLUTION The results of part (a) are written as the ordered pairs (5, 5.25) and (7, 3.75). The line through those points is the graph of the demand function, $p = 9 - 0.75q$, shown in red in Figure 11(a). We used the ordered pairs (7, 5.25) and (4, 3) from the work in part (b) to graph the supply function, $p = 0.75q$, shown in blue in Figure 11(a).

TRY YOUR TURN 2

🔲 TECHNOLOGY NOTE A calculator-generated graph of the lines representing the supply and demand functions in Example 2 is shown in Figure 11(b). To get this graph, the equation of each line, using x and y instead of q and p, was entered, along with an appropriate window. A special menu choice gives the coordinates of the intersection point, as shown at the bottom of the graph.

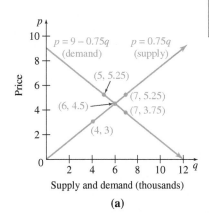

NOTE Not all supply and demand problems will have the same scale on both axes. It helps to consider the intercepts of both the supply graph and the demand graph to decide what scale to use. For example, in Figure 11, the y-intercept of the demand function is 9, so the scale should allow values from 0 to at least 9 on the vertical axis. The x-intercept of the demand function is 12, so the values on the x-axis must go from 0 to 12.

(a)

(b)

FIGURE 11

As shown in the graphs of Figure 11, both the supply graph and the demand graph pass through the point (6, 4.5). If the price of a watermelon is more than \$4.50, the quantity supplied will exceed the quantity demanded and there will be a **surplus** of watermelons. At a price less than \$4.50, the quantity demanded will exceed the quantity supplied and there will be a **shortage** of watermelons. Only at a price of \$4.50 will quantity demanded and supplied be equal. For this reason, \$4.50 is called the *equilibrium price*. When the price is \$4.50, quantity demanded and supplied both equal 6000 watermelons, the *equilibrium quantity*. In general, the **equilibrium price** of the commodity is the price found at the point where the supply and demand graphs for that commodity intersect. The **equilibrium quantity** is the quantity demanded and supplied at that same point. Figure 12 illustrates a general supply and demand situation.

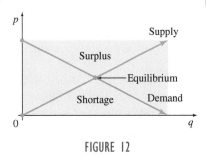

FIGURE 12

YOUR TURN 3 Repeat Example 3 using the demand equation $D(q) = 10 - 0.85q$ and the supply equation $S(q) = 0.4q$.

EXAMPLE 3 Equilibrium Quantity

Use algebra to find the equilibrium quantity and price for the watermelons in Example 2.

SOLUTION The equilibrium quantity is found when the prices from both supply and demand are equal. Set the two expressions for p equal to each other and solve.

$$9 - 0.75q = 0.75q$$
$$9 = 1.5q \quad \text{Add 0.75}q \text{ to both sides.}$$
$$6 = q$$

The equilibrium quantity is 6000 watermelons, the same answer found earlier.

The equilibrium price can be found by plugging the value of $q = 6$ into either the demand or the supply function. Using the demand function,

$$p = D(6) = 9 - 0.75(6) = 4.5.$$

The equilibrium price is \$4.50, as we found earlier. Check your work by also plugging $q = 6$ into the supply function.

TRY YOUR TURN 3

⊞ **TECHNOLOGY NOTE** You may prefer to find the equilibrium quantity by solving the equation with your calculator. Or, if your calculator has a TABLE feature, you can use it to find the value of q that makes the two expressions equal.

Another important issue is how, in practice, the equations of the supply and demand functions can be found. Data need to be collected, and if they lie perfectly along a line, then the equation can easily be found with any two points. What usually happens, however, is that the data are scattered, and there is no line that goes through all the points. In this case we must find a line that approximates the linear trend of the data as closely as possible (assuming the points lie approximately along a line) as in Example 14 in the previous section. This is usually done by the *method of least squares*, also referred to as *linear regression*. We will discuss this method in Section 1.3.

Cost Analysis

The cost of manufacturing an item commonly consists of two parts. The first is a **fixed cost** for designing the product, setting up a factory, training workers, and so on. Within broad limits, the fixed cost is constant for a particular product and does not change as more items are made. The second part is a *cost per item* for labor, materials, packing, shipping, and so on. The total value of this second cost *does* depend on the number of items made.

EXAMPLE 4 Cost Analysis

A small company decides to produce video games. The owners find that the fixed cost for creating the game is $5000, after which they must spend $12 to produce each individual copy of the game. Find a formula $C(x)$ for the cost as a linear function of x, the number of games produced.

SOLUTION Notice that $C(0) = 5000$, since $5000 must be spent even if no games are produced. Also, $C(1) = 5000 + 12 = 5012$, and $C(2) = 5000 + 2 \cdot 12 = 5024$. In general,

$$C(x) = 5000 + 12x,$$

because every time x increases by 1, the cost should increase by $12. The number 12 is also the slope of the graph of the cost function; the slope gives us the cost to produce one additional item.

In economics, **marginal cost** is the rate of change of cost $C(x)$ at a level of production x and is equal to the slope of the cost function at x. It approximates the cost of producing one additional item. In fact, some books define the marginal cost to be the cost of producing one additional item. With *linear functions*, these two definitions are equivalent, and the marginal cost, which is equal to the slope of the cost function, is *constant*. For instance, in the video game example, the marginal cost of each game is $12. For other types of functions, these two definitions are only approximately equal. Marginal cost is important to management in making decisions in areas such as cost control, pricing, and production planning.

The work in Example 4 can be generalized. Suppose the total cost to make x items is given by the linear cost function $C(x) = mx + b$. The fixed cost is found by letting $x = 0$:

$$C(0) = m \cdot 0 + b = b;$$

thus, the fixed cost is b dollars. The additional cost of each additional item, the marginal cost, is m, the slope of the line $C(x) = mx + b$.

Linear Cost Function

In a cost function of the form $C(x) = mx + b$, the m represents the marginal cost and b the fixed cost. Conversely, if the fixed cost of producing an item is b and the marginal cost is m, then the **linear cost function** $C(x)$ for producing x items is $C(x) = mx + b$.

EXAMPLE 5   Cost Function

The marginal cost to make x batches of a prescription medication is $10 per batch, while the cost to produce 100 batches is $1500. Find the cost function $C(x)$, given that it is linear.

SOLUTION   Since the cost function is linear, it can be expressed in the form $C(x) = mx + b$. The marginal cost is $10 per batch, which gives the value for m. Using $x = 100$ and $C(x) = 1500$ in the point-slope form of the line gives

$$C(x) - 1500 = 10(x - 100)$$
$$C(x) - 1500 = 10x - 1000$$
$$C(x) = 10x + 500. \qquad \text{Add 1500 to both sides.}$$

YOUR TURN 4 Repeat Example 5, using a marginal cost of $15 per batch and a cost of $1930 to produce 80 batches.

The cost function is given by $C(x) = 10x + 500$, where the fixed cost is $500.

TRY YOUR TURN 4

Break-Even Analysis

The **revenue** $R(x)$ from selling x units of an item is the product of the price per unit p and the number of units sold (demand) x, so that

$$R(x) = px.$$

The corresponding **profit** $P(x)$ is the difference between revenue $R(x)$ and cost $C(x)$. That is,

$$P(x) = R(x) - C(x).$$

A company can make a profit only if the revenue received from its customers exceeds the cost of producing and selling its goods and services. The number of units at which revenue just equals cost is the **break-even quantity**; the corresponding ordered pair gives the **break-even point**.

EXAMPLE 6   Break-Even Analysis

APPLY IT

A firm producing poultry feed finds that the total cost $C(x)$ in dollars of producing and selling x units is given by

$$C(x) = 20x + 100.$$

Management plans to charge $24 per unit for the feed.

(a) How many units must be sold for the firm to break even?

SOLUTION   The firm will break even (no profit and no loss) as long as revenue just equals cost, or $R(x) = C(x)$. From the given information, since $R(x) = px$ and $p = \$24$,

$$R(x) = 24x.$$

Substituting for $R(x)$ and $C(x)$ in the equation $R(x) = C(x)$ gives

$$24x = 20x + 100,$$

FIGURE 13

from which $x = 25$. The firm breaks even by selling 25 units, which is the break-even quantity. The graphs of $C(x) = 20x + 100$ and $R(x) = 24x$ are shown in Figure 13.

The break-even point (where $x = 25$) is shown on the graph. If the company sells more than 25 units (if $x > 25$), it makes a profit. If it sells fewer than 25 units, it loses money.

(b) What is the profit if 100 units of feed are sold?

SOLUTION Use the formula for profit $P(x)$.

$$P(x) = R(x) - C(x)$$
$$= 24x - (20x + 100)$$
$$= 4x - 100$$

Then $P(100) = 4(100) - 100 = 300$. The firm will make a profit of $300 from the sale of 100 units of feed.

(c) How many units must be sold to produce a profit of $900?

SOLUTION Let $P(x) = 900$ in the equation $P(x) = 4x - 100$ and solve for x.

$$900 = 4x - 100$$
$$1000 = 4x$$
$$x = 250$$

Sales of 250 units will produce $900 profit. **TRY YOUR TURN 5**

YOUR TURN 5 Repeat Example 6(c), using a cost function $C(x) = 35x + 250$, a charge of $58 per unit, and a profit of $8030.

Temperature One of the most common linear relationships found in everyday situations deals with temperature. Recall that water freezes at 32° Fahrenheit and 0° Celsius, while it boils at 212° Fahrenheit and 100° Celsius.* The ordered pairs $(0, 32)$ and $(100, 212)$ are graphed in Figure 14 on axes showing Fahrenheit (F) as a function of Celsius (C). The line joining them is the graph of the function.

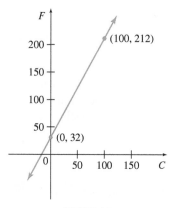

FIGURE 14

EXAMPLE 7 **Temperature**

Derive an equation relating F and C.

SOLUTION To derive the required linear equation, first find the slope using the given ordered pairs, $(0, 32)$ and $(100, 212)$.

$$m = \frac{212 - 32}{100 - 0} = \frac{9}{5}$$

*Gabriel Fahrenheit (1686–1736), a German physicist, invented his scale with 0° representing the temperature of an equal mixture of ice and ammonium chloride (a type of salt), and 96° as the temperature of the human body. (It is often said, erroneously, that Fahrenheit set 100° as the temperature of the human body. Fahrenheit's own words are quoted in *A History of the Thermometer and Its Use in Meteorology* by W. E. Knowles, Middleton: The Johns Hopkins Press, 1966, p. 75.) The Swedish astronomer Anders Celsius (1701–1744) set 0° and 100° as the freezing and boiling points of water.

The F-intercept of the graph is 32, so by the slope-intercept form, the equation of the line is

$$F = \frac{9}{5}C + 32.$$

With simple algebra this equation can be rewritten to give C in terms of F:

$$C = \frac{5}{9}(F - 32).$$

1.2 EXERCISES

For Exercises 1–10, let $f(x) = 7 - 5x$ and $g(x) = 2x - 3$. Find the following.

1. $f(2)$ **2.** $f(4)$

3. $f(-3)$ **4.** $f(-1)$

5. $g(1.5)$ **6.** $g(2.5)$

7. $g(-1/2)$ **8.** $g(-3/4)$

9. $f(t)$ **10.** $g(k^2)$

In Exercises 11–14, decide whether the statement is true or false.

11. To find the x-intercept of the graph of a linear function, we solve $y = f(x) = 0$, and to find the y-intercept, we evaluate $f(0)$.

12. The graph of $f(x) = -5$ is a vertical line.

13. The slope of the graph of a linear function cannot be undefined.

14. The graph of $f(x) = ax$ is a straight line that passes through the origin.

15. Describe what fixed costs and marginal costs mean to a company.

16. In a few sentences, explain why the price of a commodity not already at its equilibrium price should move in that direction.

17. Explain why a linear function may not be adequate for describing the supply and demand functions.

18. In your own words, describe the break-even quantity, how to find it, and what it indicates.

Write a linear cost function for each situation. Identify all variables used.

19. A Lake Tahoe resort charges a snowboard rental fee of $10 plus $2.25 per hour.

20. An Internet site for downloading music charges a $10 registration fee plus 99 cents per downloaded song.

21. A parking garage charges 2 dollars plus 75 cents per half-hour.

22. For a one-day rental, a car rental firm charges $44 plus 28 cents per mile.

Assume that each situation can be expressed as a linear cost function. Find the cost function in each case.

23. Fixed cost: $100; 50 items cost $1600 to produce.

24. Fixed cost: $35; 8 items cost $395 to produce.

25. Marginal cost: $75; 50 items cost $4300 to produce.

26. Marginal cost: $120; 700 items cost $96,500 to produce.

APPLICATIONS

Business and Economics

27. Supply and Demand Suppose that the demand and price for a certain model of a youth wristwatch are related by

$$p = D(q) = 16 - 1.25q,$$

where p is the price (in dollars) and q is the quantity demanded (in hundreds). Find the price at each level of demand.

a. 0 watches   **b.** 400 watches   **c.** 800 watches

Find the quantity demanded for the watch at each price.

d. $8   **e.** $10   **f.** $12

g. Graph $p = 16 - 1.25q$.

Suppose the price and supply of the watch are related by

$$p = S(q) = 0.75q,$$

where p is the price (in dollars) and q is the quantity supplied (in hundreds) of watches. Find the quantity supplied at each price.

h. $0   **i.** $10   **j.** $20

k. Graph $p = 0.75q$ on the same axis used for part g.

l. Find the equilibrium quantity and the equilibrium price.

28. Supply and Demand Suppose that the demand and price for strawberries are related by

$$p = D(q) = 5 - 0.25q,$$

where p is the price (in dollars) and q is the quantity demanded (in hundreds of quarts). Find the price at each level of demand.

a. 0 quarts   **b.** 400 quarts   **c.** 840 quarts

Find the quantity demanded for the strawberries at each price.

d. $4.50   **e.** $3.25   **f.** $2.40

g. Graph $p = 5 - 0.25q$.

Suppose the price and supply of strawberries are related by

$$p = S(q) = 0.25q,$$

where p is the price (in dollars) and q is the quantity supplied (in hundreds of quarts) of strawberries. Find the quantity supplied at each price.

h. $0   **i.** $2   **j.** $4.50

k. Graph $p = 0.75q$ on the same axis used for part g.

l. Find the equilibrium quantity and the equilibrium price.

29. Supply and Demand Let the supply and demand functions for butter pecan ice cream be given by

$$p = S(q) = \frac{2}{5}q \quad \text{and} \quad p = D(q) = 100 - \frac{2}{5}q,$$

where p is the price in dollars and q is the number of 10-gallon tubs.

a. Graph these on the same axes.

b. Find the equilibrium quantity and the equilibrium price. (*Hint:* The way to divide by a fraction is to multiply by its reciprocal.)

30. Supply and Demand Let the supply and demand functions for sugar be given by

$$p = S(q) = 1.4q - 0.6 \quad \text{and}$$
$$p = D(q) = -2q + 3.2,$$

where p is the price per pound and q is the quantity in thousands of pounds.

a. Graph these on the same axes.

b. Find the equilibrium quantity and the equilibrium price.

31. Supply and Demand Suppose that the supply function for honey is $p = S(q) = 0.3q + 2.7$, where p is the price in dollars for an 8-oz container and q is the quantity in barrels. Suppose also that the equilibrium price is $4.50 and the demand is 2 barrels when the price is $6.10. Find an equation for the demand function, assuming it is linear.

32. Supply and Demand Suppose that the supply function for walnuts is $p = S(q) = 0.25q + 3.6$, where p is the price in dollars per pound and q is the quantity in bushels. Suppose also that the equilibrium price is $5.85, and the demand is 4 bushels when the price is $7.60. Find an equation for the demand function, assuming it is linear.

33. T-Shirt Cost Joanne Wendelken sells silk-screened T-shirts at community festivals and crafts fairs. Her marginal cost to produce one T-shirt is $3.50. Her total cost to produce 60 T-shirts is $300, and she sells them for $9 each.

a. Find the linear cost function for Joanne's T-shirt production.

b. How many T-shirts must she produce and sell in order to break even?

c. How many T-shirts must she produce and sell to make a profit of $500?

34. Publishing Costs Alfred Juarez owns a small publishing house specializing in Latin American poetry. His fixed cost to produce a typical poetry volume is $525, and his total cost to produce 1000 copies of the book is $2675. His books sell for $4.95 each.

a. Find the linear cost function for Alfred's book production.

b. How many poetry books must he produce and sell in order to break even?

c. How many books must he produce and sell to make a profit of $1000?

35. Marginal Cost of Coffee The manager of a restaurant found that the cost to produce 100 cups of coffee is $11.02, while the cost to produce 400 cups is $40.12. Assume the cost $C(x)$ is a linear function of x, the number of cups produced.

a. Find a formula for $C(x)$.

b. What is the fixed cost?

c. Find the total cost of producing 1000 cups.

d. Find the total cost of producing 1001 cups.

e. Find the marginal cost of the 1001st cup.

f. What is the marginal cost of *any* cup and what does this mean to the manager?

36. Marginal Cost of a New Plant In deciding whether to set up a new manufacturing plant, company analysts have decided that a linear function is a reasonable estimation for the total cost $C(x)$ in dollars to produce x items. They estimate the cost to produce 10,000 items as $547,500, and the cost to produce 50,000 items as $737,500.

a. Find a formula for $C(x)$.

b. Find the fixed cost.

c. Find the total cost to produce 100,000 items.

d. Find the marginal cost of the items to be produced in this plant and what does this mean to the manager?

37. Break-Even Analysis Producing x units of tacos costs $C(x) = 5x + 20$; revenue is $R(x) = 15x$, where $C(x)$ and $R(x)$ are in dollars.

a. What is the break-even quantity?

b. What is the profit from 100 units?

c. How many units will produce a profit of $500?

38. Break-Even Analysis To produce x units of a religious medal costs $C(x) = 12x + 39$. The revenue is $R(x) = 25x$. Both $C(x)$ and $R(x)$ are in dollars.

a. Find the break-even quantity.

b. Find the profit from 250 units.

c. Find the number of units that must be produced for a profit of $130.

Break-Even Analysis **You are the manager of a firm. You are considering the manufacture of a new product, so you ask the accounting department for cost estimates and the sales department for sales estimates. After you receive the data, you must decide whether to go ahead with production of the new product. Analyze the data in Exercises 39–42 (find a break-even**

quantity) and then decide what you would do in each case. Also write the profit function.

39. $C(x) = 85x + 900$; $R(x) = 105x$; no more than 38 units can be sold.

40. $C(x) = 105x + 6000$; $R(x) = 250x$; no more than 400 units can be sold.

41. $C(x) = 70x + 500$; $R(x) = 60x$ (*Hint*: What does a negative break-even quantity mean?)

42. $C(x) = 1000x + 5000$; $R(x) = 900x$

43. Break-Even Analysis Suppose that the fixed cost for a product is $400 and the break-even quantity is 80. Find the marginal profit (the slope of the linear profit function).

44. Break-Even Analysis Suppose that the fixed cost for a product is $650 and the break-even quantity is 25. Find the marginal profit (the slope of the linear profit function).

Physical Sciences

45. Temperature Use the formula for conversion between Fahrenheit and Celsius derived in Example 7 to convert each temperature.

a. 58°F to Celsius

b. −20°F to Celsius

c. 50°C to Fahrenheit

46. Body Temperature You may have heard that the average temperature of the human body is 98.6°. Recent experiments show that the actual figure is closer to 98.2°. The figure of 98.6 comes from experiments done by Carl Wunderlich in 1868. But Wunderlich measured the temperatures in degrees Celsius and rounded the average to the nearest degree, giving 37°C as the average temperature. *Source: Science News.*

a. What is the Fahrenheit equivalent of 37°C?

b. Given that Wunderlich rounded to the nearest degree Celsius, his experiments tell us that the actual average human body temperature is somewhere between 36.5°C and 37.5°C. Find what this range corresponds to in degrees Fahrenheit.

47. Temperature Find the temperature at which the Celsius and Fahrenheit temperatures are numerically equal.

General Interest

48. Education Cost The 2009–2010 budget for the California State University system projected a fixed cost of $486,000 at each of five off-campus centers, plus a marginal cost of $1140 per student. *Source: California State University.*

a. Find a formula for the cost at each center, $C(x)$, as a linear function of x, the number of students.

b. The budget projected 500 students at each center. Calculate the total cost at each center.

c. Suppose, due to budget cuts, that each center is limited to $1 million. What is the maximum number of students that each center can then support?

YOUR TURN ANSWERS

1. 25   **2.** 7600 and 4400
3. 8000 watermelons and $3.20 per watermelon
4. $C(x) = 15x + 730$ **5.** 360

1.3 The Least Squares Line

APPLY IT How has the accidental death rate in the United States changed over time? *In Example 1 in this section, we show how to answer such questions using the method of least squares.*

We use past data to find trends and to make tentative predictions about the future. The only assumption we make is that the data are related linearly—that is, if we plot pairs of data, the resulting points will lie close to some line. This method cannot give exact answers. The best we can expect is that, if we are careful, we will get a reasonable approximation.

The table lists the number of accidental deaths per 100,000 people in the United States through the past century. *Source: National Center for Health Statistics.* If you were a manager at an insurance company, these data could be very important. You might need to make some predictions about how much you will pay out next year in accidental death benefits, and even a very tentative prediction based on past trends is better than no prediction at all.

The first step is to draw a scatterplot, as we have done in Figure 15 on the next page. Notice that the points lie approximately along a line, which means that a linear function may give a good approximation of the data. If we select two points and find the line that passes through them, as we did in Section 1.1, we will get a different line for each pair of points, and in some cases the lines will be very different. We want to draw one line that is simultaneously close to all the points on the graph, but many such lines are possible, depending upon how we define the phrase "simultaneously close to all the points." How do we decide on the best possible line? Before going on, you might want to try drawing the line you think is best on Figure 15.

Accidental Death Rate	
Year	Death Rate
1910	84.4
1920	71.2
1930	80.5
1940	73.4
1950	60.3
1960	52.1
1970	56.2
1980	46.5
1990	36.9
2000	34.0

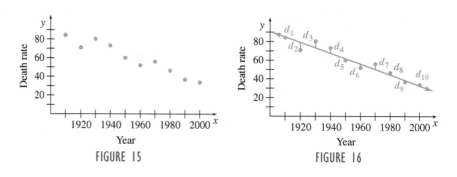

FIGURE 15 FIGURE 16

The line used most often in applications is that in which the sum of the squares of the vertical distances from the data points to the line is as small as possible. Such a line is called the **least squares line**. The least squares line for the data in Figure 15 is drawn in Figure 16. How does the line compare with the one you drew on Figure 15? It may not be exactly the same, but should appear similar.

In Figure 16, the vertical distances from the points to the line are indicated by d_1, d_2, and so on, up through d_{10} (read "d-sub-one, d-sub-two, d-sub-three," and so on). For n points, corresponding to the n pairs of data, the least squares line is found by minimizing the sum $(d_1)^2 + (d_2)^2 + (d_3)^2 + \cdots + (d_n)^2$.

We often use **summation notation** to write the sum of a list of numbers. The Greek letter sigma, Σ, is used to indicate "the sum of." For example, we write the sum $x_1 + x_2 + \cdots + x_n$, where n is the number of data points, as

$$x_1 + x_2 + \cdots + x_n = \Sigma x.$$

Similarly, Σxy means $x_1 y_1 + x_2 y_2 + \cdots + x_n y_n$, and so on.

> **CAUTION** Note that Σx^2 means $x_1^2 + x_2^2 + \cdots + x_n^2$, which is *not* the same as squaring Σx. When we square Σx, we write it as $(\Sigma x)^2$.

For the least squares line, the sum of the distances we are to minimize, $d_1^2 + d_2^2 + \cdots + d_n^2$, is written as

$$d_1^2 + d_2^2 + \cdots + d_n^2 = \Sigma d^2.$$

To calculate the distances, we let $(x_1, y_1), (x_2, y_2), \cdots, (x_n, y_n)$ be the actual data points and we let the least squares line be $Y = mx + b$. We use Y in the equation instead of y to distinguish the predicted values (Y) from the y-value of the given data points. The predicted value of Y at x_1 is $Y_1 = mx_1 + b$, and the distance, d_1, between the actual y-value y_1 and the predicted value Y_1 is

$$d_1 = |Y_1 - y_1| = |mx_1 + b - y_1|.$$

Likewise,

$$d_2 = |Y_2 - y_2| = |mx_2 + b - y_2|,$$

and

$$d_n = |Y_n - y_n| = |mx_n + b - y_n|.$$

The sum to be minimized becomes

$$\Sigma d^2 = (mx_1 + b - y_1)^2 + (mx_2 + b - y_2)^2 + \cdots + (mx_n + b - y_n)^2$$
$$= \Sigma (mx + b - y)^2,$$

where $(x_1, y_1), (x_2, y_2), \ldots, (x_n, y_n)$ are known and m and b are to be found.

The method of minimizing this sum requires advanced techniques and is not given here. To obtain the equation for the least squares line, a system of equations must be solved, producing the following formulas for determining the slope m and y-intercept b.*

Least Squares Line

The **least squares line** $Y = mx + b$ that gives the best fit to the data points $(x_1, y_1), (x_2, y_2), \ldots, (x_n, y_n)$ has slope m and y-intercept b given by

$$m = \frac{n(\Sigma xy) - (\Sigma x)(\Sigma y)}{n(\Sigma x^2) - (\Sigma x)^2} \quad \text{and} \quad b = \frac{\Sigma y - m(\Sigma x)}{n}.$$

EXAMPLE 1   Least Squares Line

APPLY IT   Calculate the least squares line for the accidental death rate data.

SOLUTION

Method 1
Calculating by Hand

To find the least squares line for the given data, we first find the required sums. To reduce the size of the numbers, we rescale the year data. Let x represent the years since 1900, so that, for example, $x = 10$ corresponds to the year 1910. Let y represent the death rate. We then calculate the values in the xy, x^2, and y^2 columns and find their totals. (The column headed y^2 will be used later.) Note that the number of data points is $n = 10$.

Least Squares Calculations				
x	y	xy	x^2	y^2
10	84.4	844	100	7123.36
20	71.2	1424	400	5069.44
30	80.5	2415	900	6480.25
40	73.4	2936	1600	5387.56
50	60.3	3015	2500	3636.09
60	52.1	3126	3600	2714.41
70	56.2	3934	4900	3158.44
80	46.5	3720	6400	2162.25
90	36.9	3321	8100	1361.61
100	34.0	3400	10,000	1156.00
$\Sigma x = 550$	$\Sigma y = 595.5$	$\Sigma xy = 28,135$	$\Sigma x^2 = 38,500$	$\Sigma y^2 = 38,249.41$

Putting the column totals into the formula for the slope m, we get

$$m = \frac{n(\Sigma xy) - (\Sigma x)(\Sigma y)}{n(\Sigma x^2) - (\Sigma x)^2} \qquad \text{Formula for } m$$

$$= \frac{10(28,135) - (550)(595.5)}{10(38,500) - (550)^2} \qquad \text{Substitute from the table.}$$

$$= \frac{281,350 - 327,525}{385,000 - 302,500} \qquad \text{Multiply.}$$

$$= \frac{-46,175}{82,500} \qquad \text{Subtract.}$$

$$= -0.5596970 \approx -0.560.$$

*See Exercise 9 at the end of this section.

The significance of m is that the death rate per 100,000 people is tending to drop (because of the negative) at a rate of 0.560 per year.

Now substitute the value of m and the column totals in the formula for b:

$$b = \frac{\Sigma y - m(\Sigma x)}{n} \qquad \text{Formula for } b$$

$$= \frac{595.5 - (-0.559697)(550)}{10} \qquad \text{Substitute.}$$

$$= \frac{595.5 - (-307.83335)}{10} \qquad \text{Multiply.}$$

$$= \frac{903.33335}{10} = 90.333335 \approx 90.3$$

Substitute m and b into the least squares line, $Y = mx + b$; the least squares line that best fits the 10 data points has equation

$$Y = -0.560x + 90.3.$$

This gives a mathematical description of the relationship between the year and the number of accidental deaths per 100,000 people. The equation can be used to predict y from a given value of x, as we will show in Example 2. As we mentioned before, however, caution must be exercised when using the least squares equation to predict data points that are far from the range of points on which the equation was modeled.

CAUTION In computing m and b, we rounded the final answer to three digits because the original data were known only to three digits. It is important, however, *not* to round any of the intermediate results (such as Σx^2) because round-off error may have a detrimental effect on the accuracy of the answer. Similarly, it is important not to use a rounded-off value of m when computing b.

Method 2
Graphing Calculator

The calculations for finding the least squares line are often tedious, even with the aid of a calculator. Fortunately, many calculators can calculate the least squares line with just a few keystrokes. For purposes of illustration, we will show how the least squares line in the previous example is found with a TI-84 Plus graphing calculator.

We begin by entering the data into the calculator. We will be using the first two lists, called L_1 and L_2. Choosing the STAT menu, then choosing the fourth entry ClrList, we enter L_1, L_2, to indicate the lists to be cleared. Now we press STAT again and choose the first entry EDIT, which brings up the blank lists. As before, we will only use the last two digits of the year, putting the numbers in L_1. We put the death rate in L_2, giving the two screens shown in Figure 17.

L1	**L2**	L3	2
10	84.4	------	
20	71.2		
30	80.5		
40	73.4		
50	60.3		
60	52.1		
70	56.2		

L2=(84.4, 71.2, 8...

L1	L2	L3	1
50	60.3		
60	52.1		
70	56.2		
80	46.5		
90	36.9		
100	34		
■		------	

L1(11)=

FIGURE 17

Quit the editor, press STAT again, and choose CALC instead of EDIT. Then choose item 4 LinReg($ax + b$) to get the values of a (the slope) and b (the y-intercept) for the least squares line, as shown in Figure 18. With a and b rounded to three decimal places, the least squares line is $Y = -0.560x + 90.3$. A graph of the data points and the line is shown in Figure 19.

```
LinReg
 y=ax+b
 a=⁻.5596969697
 b=90.33333333

 ■
```

FIGURE 18

FIGURE 19

For more details on finding the least squares line with a graphing calculator, see the *Graphing Calculator and Excel Spreadsheet Manual* available with this book.

⊞ **Method 3**
Spreadsheet

YOUR TURN 1 Repeat Example 1, deleting the last pair of data (100, 34.0) and changing the second to last pair to (90, 40.2).

Many computer spreadsheet programs can also find the least squares line. Figure 20 shows the scatterplot and least squares line for the accidental death rate data using an Excel spreadsheet. The scatterplot was found using the Marked Scatter chart from the Gallery and the line was found using the Add Trendline command under the Chart menu. For details, see the *Graphing Calculator and Excel Spreadsheet Manual* available with this book.

TRY YOUR TURN 1 ▮

FIGURE 20

▮ **EXAMPLE 2** **Least Squares Line**

What do we predict the accidental death rate to be in 2012?

SOLUTION Use the least squares line equation given above with $x = 112$.

$$Y = -0.560x + 90.3$$
$$= -0.56(112) + 90.3$$
$$= 27.6$$

The accidental death rate in 2012 is predicted to be about 27.6 per 100,000 population. In this case, we will have to wait until the 2012 data become available to see how accurate our prediction is. We have observed, however, that the accidental death rate began to go up after 2000 and was 40.6 per 100,000 population in 2006. This illustrates the danger of extrapolating beyond the data. ▬

▮ **EXAMPLE 3** **Least Squares Line**

In what year is the death rate predicted to drop below 26 per 100,000 population?

SOLUTION   Let $Y = 26$ in the equation above and solve for x.

$$26 = -0.560x + 90.3$$

$$-64.3 = -0.560x \qquad \text{Subtract 90.3 from both sides.}$$

$$x = 115 \qquad \text{Divide both sides by } -0.560.$$

This corresponds to the year 2015 (115 years after 1900), when our equation predicts the death rate to be $-0.560(115) + 90.3 = 25.9$ per 100,000 population.

Correlation

Although the least squares line can always be found, it may not be a good model. For example, if the data points are widely scattered, no straight line will model the data accurately. One measure of how well the original data fits a straight line is the **correlation coefficient,** denoted by r, which can be calculated by the following formula.

Correlation Coefficient

$$r = \frac{n(\Sigma xy) - (\Sigma x)(\Sigma y)}{\sqrt{n(\Sigma x^2) - (\Sigma x)^2} \cdot \sqrt{n(\Sigma y^2) - (\Sigma y)^2}}$$

Although the expression for r looks daunting, remember that each of the summations, Σx, Σy, Σxy, and so on, are just the totals from a table like the one we prepared for the data on accidental deaths. Also, with a calculator, the arithmetic is no problem! Furthermore, statistics software and many calculators can calculate the correlation coefficient for you.

The correlation coefficient measures the strength of the linear relationship between two variables. It was developed by statistics pioneer Karl Pearson (1857–1936). The correlation coefficient r is between 1 and -1 or is equal to 1 or -1. Values of exactly 1 or -1 indicate that the data points lie *exactly* on the least squares line. If $r = 1$, the least squares line has a positive slope; $r = -1$ gives a negative slope. If $r = 0$, there is no linear correlation between the data points (but some *nonlinear* function might provide an excellent fit for the data). A correlation coefficient of zero may also indicate that the data fit a horizontal line. To investigate what is happening, it is always helpful to sketch a scatterplot of the data. Some scatterplots that correspond to these values of r are shown in Figure 21.

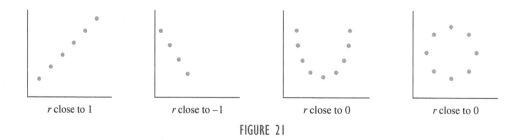

| r close to 1 | r close to -1 | r close to 0 | r close to 0 |

FIGURE 21

A value of r close to 1 or -1 indicates the presence of a linear relationship. The exact value of r necessary to conclude that there is a linear relationship depends upon n, the number of data points, as well as how confident we want to be of our conclusion. For details, consult a text on statistics.*

*For example, see *Introductory Statistics*, 8th edition, by Neil A. Weiss, Boston, Mass.: Pearson, 2008.

EXAMPLE 4   Correlation Coefficient

Find r for the data on accidental death rates in Example 1.

SOLUTION

From the table in Example 1,

$\Sigma x = 550, \Sigma y = 595.5, \Sigma xy = 28{,}135, \Sigma x^2 = 38{,}500,$

$\Sigma y^2 = 38{,}249.41,$ and $n = 10.$

Substituting these values into the formula for r gives

$$r = \frac{n(\Sigma xy)-(\Sigma x)(\Sigma y)}{\sqrt{n(\Sigma x^2)-(\Sigma x)^2}\cdot\sqrt{n(\Sigma y^2)-(\Sigma y)^2}}$$

Formula for r

$$= \frac{10(28{,}135)-(550)(595.5)}{\sqrt{10(38{,}500)-(550)^2}\cdot\sqrt{10(38{,}249.41)-(595.5)^2}}$$

Substitute.

$$= \frac{281{,}350-327{,}525}{\sqrt{385{,}000-302{,}500}\cdot\sqrt{382{,}494.1-354{,}620.25}}$$

Multiply.

$$= \frac{-46{,}175}{\sqrt{82{,}500}\cdot\sqrt{27{,}873.85}}$$

Subtract.

$$= \frac{-46{,}175}{47{,}954.06787}$$

Take square roots and multiply.

$$= -0.9629005849 \approx -0.963.$$

This is a high correlation, which agrees with our observation that the data fit a line quite well.

Most calculators that give the least squares line will also give the correlation coefficient. To do this on the TI-84 Plus, press the second function CATALOG and go down the list to the entry DiagnosticOn. Press ENTER at that point, then press STAT, CALC, and choose item 4 to get the display in Figure 22. The result is the same as we got by hand. The command DiagnosticOn need only be entered once, and the correlation coefficient will always appear in the future.

```
LinReg
 y=ax+b
 a=⁻.5596969697
 b=90.33333333
 r²=.9271775365
 r=⁻.962900585
■
```

FIGURE 22

Many computer spreadsheet programs have a built-in command to find the correlation coefficient. For example, in Excel, use the command "= CORREL(A1:A10,B1:B10)" to find the correlation of the 10 data points stored in columns A and B. For more details, see the *Graphing Calculator and Excel Spreadsheet Manual* available with this text.

YOUR TURN 2 Repeat Example 4, deleting the last pair of data (100, 34.0) and changing the second to last pair to (90, 40.2).

TRY YOUR TURN 2

The square of the correlation coefficient gives the fraction of the variation in y that is explained by the linear relationship between x and y. Consider Example 4, where $r^2 = (-0.963)^2 = 0.927$. This means that 92.7% of the variation in y is explained by the linear relationship found earlier in Example 1. The remaining 7.3% comes from the scattering of the points about the line.

EXAMPLE 5   Average Expenditure per Pupil Versus Test Scores

Many states and school districts debate whether or not increasing the amount of money spent per student will guarantee academic success. The following scatterplot shows the average eighth grade reading score on the National Assessment of Education Progress (NAEP) for the 50 states and the District of Columbia in 2007 plotted against the average expenditure per pupil in 2007. Explore how the correlation coefficient is affected by the inclusion of the District of Columbia, which spent $14,324 per pupil and had a NAEP score of 241. *Source: U.S. Census Bureau and National Center for Education Statistics.*

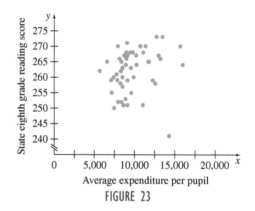

FIGURE 23

SOLUTION   A spreadsheet was used to create a plot of the points shown in Figure 23. Washington D.C. corresponds to the red point in the lower right, which is noticeably separate from all the other points. Using the original data, the correlation coefficient when Washington D.C. is included is 0.1981, indicating that there is not a strong linear correlation. Excluding Washington D.C. raises the correlation coefficient to 0.3745, which is a somewhat stronger indication of a linear correlation. This illustrates that one extreme data point that is separate from the others, known as an **outlier**, can have a strong effect on the correlation coefficient.

Even if the correlation between average expenditure per pupil and reading score in Example 5 was high, this would not prove that spending more per pupil causes high reading scores. To prove this would require further research. It is a common statistical fallacy to assume that correlation implies causation. Perhaps the correlation is due to a third underlying variable. In Example 5, perhaps states with wealthier families spend more per pupil, and the students read better because wealthier families have greater access to reading material. Determining the truth requires careful research methods that are beyond the scope of this textbook.

1.3   EXERCISES

1. Suppose a positive linear correlation is found between two quantities. Does this mean that one of the quantities increasing causes the other to increase? If not, what does it mean?

2. Given a set of points, the least squares line formed by letting x be the independent variable will not necessarily be the same as the least squares line formed by letting y be the independent variable. Give an example to show why this is true.

3. For the following table of data,

x	1	2	3	4	5	6	7	8	9	10
y	0	0.5	1	2	2.5	3	3	4	4.5	5

   a. draw a scatterplot.

   b. calculate the correlation coefficient.

c. calculate the least squares line and graph it on the scatterplot.

d. predict the y-value when x is 11.

The following problem is reprinted from the November 1989 Actuarial Examination on Applied Statistical Methods. *Source: Society of Actuaries.*

4. You are given

X	6.8	7.0	7.1	7.2	7.4
Y	0.8	1.2	0.9	0.9	1.5

Determine r^2, the coefficient of determination for the regression of Y on X. Choose one of the following. (*Note:* The coefficient of determination is defined as the square of the correlation coefficient.)

a. 0.3 **b.** 0.4 **c.** 0.5 **d.** 0.6 **e.** 0.7

5. Consider the following table of data.

x	1	1	2	2	9
y	1	2	1	2	9

a. Calculate the least squares line and the correlation coefficient.

b. Repeat part a, but this time delete the last point.

c. Draw a graph of the data, and use it to explain the dramatic difference between the answers to parts a and b.

6. Consider the following table of data.

x	1	2	3	4	9
y	1	2	3	4	-20

a. Calculate the least squares line and the correlation coefficient.

b. Repeat part a, but this time delete the last point.

c. Draw a graph of the data, and use it to explain the dramatic difference between the answers to parts a and b.

7. Consider the following table of data.

x	1	2	3	4
y	1	1	1	1.1

a. Calculate the correlation coefficient.

b. Sketch a graph of the data.

c. Based on how closely the data fits a straight line, is your answer to part a surprising? Discuss the extent to which the correlation coefficient describes how well the data fit a horizontal line.

8. Consider the following table of data.

x	0	1	2	3	4
y	4	1	0	1	4

a. Calculate the least squares line and the correlation coefficient.

b. Sketch a graph of the data.

c. Comparing your answers to parts a and b, does a correlation coefficient of 0 mean that there is no relationship between the x and y values? Would some curve other than a line fit the data better? Explain.

9. The formulas for the least squares line were found by solving the system of equations

$$nb + (\Sigma x)m = \Sigma y$$
$$(\Sigma x)b + (\Sigma x^2)m = \Sigma xy.$$

Solve the above system for b and m to show that

$$m = \frac{n(\Sigma xy) - (\Sigma x)(\Sigma y)}{n(\Sigma x^2) - (\Sigma x)^2} \quad \text{and}$$

$$b = \frac{\Sigma y - m(\Sigma x)}{n}.$$

APPLICATIONS

Business and Economics

10. Consumer Durable Goods The total value of consumer durable goods has grown at an approximately linear rate in recent years. The annual data for the years 2002 through 2008 can be summarized as follows, where x represents the years since 2000 and y the total value of consumer durable goods in trillions of dollars. *Source: Bureau of Economic Analysis.*

$n = 7$	$\Sigma x = 35$	$\Sigma x^2 = 203$
$\Sigma y = 28.4269$	$\Sigma y^2 = 116.3396$	$\Sigma xy = 147.1399$

a. Find an equation for the least squares line.

b. Use your result from part **a** to predict the total value of consumer durable goods in the year 2015.

c. If this growth continues linearly, in what year will the total value of consumer durable goods first reach at least 6 trillion dollars?

d. Find and interpret the correlation coefficient.

11. Decrease in Banks The number of banks in the United States has been dropping steadily since 1984, and the trend in recent years has been roughly linear. The annual data for the years 1999 through 2008 can be summarized as follows, where x represents the years since 1990 and y the number of banks, in thousands, in the United States. *Source: FDIC.*

$n = 10$	$\Sigma x = 235$	$\Sigma x^2 = 5605$
$\Sigma y = 77.564$	$\Sigma y^2 = 603.60324$	$\Sigma xy = 1810.095$

a. Find an equation for the least squares line.

b. Use your result from part a to predict the number of U.S. banks in the year 2020.

c. If this trend continues linearly, in what year will the number of U.S. banks drop below 6000?

d. Find and interpret the correlation coefficient.

12. Digital Cable Subscribers The number of subscribers to digital cable television has been growing steadily, as shown by the following table. *Source: National Cable and Telecommunications Association.*

Year	2000	2002	2004	2006	2008
Customers (in millions)	8.5	19.3	25.4	32.6	40.4

a. Find an equation for the least squares line, letting x equal the number of years since 2000.

b. Based on your answer to part a, at approximately what rate is the number of subscribers to digital cable television growing per year?

c. Use your result from part a to predict the number of digital cable subscribers in the year 2012.

d. If this trend continues linearly, in what year will the number of digital cable subscribers first exceed 70 million?

e. Find and interpret the correlation coefficient.

13. **Consumer Credit** The total amount of consumer credit has been increasing steadily in recent years. The following table gives the total U.S. outstanding consumer credit. *Source: Federal Reserve.*

Year	2004	2005	2006	2007	2008
Consumer credit (in billions of dollars)	2219.5	2319.8	2415.0	2551.9	2592.1

a. Find an equation for the least squares line, letting x equal the number of years since 2000.

b. Based on your answer to part a, at approximately what rate is the consumer credit growing per year?

c. Use your result from part a to predict the amount of consumer credit in the year 2015.

d. If this trend continues linearly, in what year will the total debt first exceed $4000 billion?

e. Find and interpret the correlation coefficient.

14. **New Car Sales** New car sales have increased at a roughly linear rate. Sales, in millions of vehicles, from 2000 to 2007, are given in the table below. *Source: National Automobile Dealers Association.* Let x represent the number of years since 2000.

Year	Sales
2000	17.3
2001	17.1
2002	16.8
2003	16.6
2004	16.9
2005	16.9
2006	16.5
2007	16.1

a. Find the equation of the least squares line and the correlation coefficient.

b. Find the equation of the least squares line using only the data for every other year starting with 2000, 2002, and so on. Find the correlation coefficient.

c. Compare your results for parts a and b. What do you find? Why do you think this happens?

15. **Air Fares** In 2006, for passengers who made early reservations, American Airlines offered lower prices on one-way fares from New York to various cities. Fourteen of the cities are listed in the following table, with the distances from New York to the cities included. *Source: American Airlines.*

a. Plot the data. Do the data points lie in a linear pattern?

b. Find the correlation coefficient. Combining this with your answer to part a, does the cost of a ticket tend to go up with the distance flown?

c. Find the equation of the least squares line, and use it to find the approximate marginal cost per mile to fly.

d. For similar data in a January 2000 *New York Times* ad, the equation of the least squares line was $Y = 113 + 0.0243x$. *Source: The New York Times.* Use this information and your answer to part b to compare the cost of flying American Airlines for these two time periods.

e. Identify the outlier in the scatterplot. Discuss the reason why there would be a difference in price to this city.

City	Distance (x) (miles)	Price (y) (dollars)
Boston	206	95
Chicago	802	138
Denver	1771	228
Kansas City	1198	209
Little Rock	1238	269
Los Angeles	2786	309
Minneapolis	1207	202
Nashville	892	217
Phoenix	2411	109
Portland	2885	434
Reno	2705	399
St. Louis	948	206
San Diego	2762	239
Seattle	2815	329

Life Sciences

16. **Bird Eggs** The average length and width of various bird eggs are given in the following table. *Source: National Council of Teachers of Mathematics.*

Bird Name	Width (cm)	Length (cm)
Canada goose	5.8	8.6
Robin	1.5	1.9
Turtledove	2.3	3.1
Hummingbird	1.0	1.0
Raven	3.3	5.0

a. Plot the points, putting the length on the *y*-axis and the width on the *x*-axis. Do the data appear to be linear?

b. Find the least squares line, and plot it on the same graph as the data.

c. Suppose there are birds with eggs even smaller than those of hummingbirds. Would the equation found in part b continue to make sense for all positive widths, no matter how small? Explain.

d. Find the correlation coefficient.

17. Size of Hunting Parties   In the 1960s, the famous researcher Jane Goodall observed that chimpanzees hunt and eat meat as part of their regular diet. Sometimes chimpanzees hunt alone, while other times they form hunting parties. The following table summarizes research on chimpanzee hunting parties, giving the size of the hunting party and the percentage of successful hunts. *Source: American Scientist and Mathematics Teacher.*

Number of Chimps in Hunting Party	Percentage of Successful Hunts
1	20
2	30
3	28
4	42
5	40
6	58
7	45
8	62
9	65
10	63
12	75
13	75
14	78
15	75
16	82

a. Plot the data. Do the data points lie in a linear pattern?

b. Find the correlation coefficient. Combining this with your answer to part a, does the percentage of successful hunts tend to increase with the size of the hunting party?

c. Find the equation of the least squares line, and graph it on your scatterplot.

18. Crickets Chirping   Biologists have observed a linear relationship between the temperature and the frequency with which a cricket chirps. The following data were measured for the striped ground cricket. *Source: The Song of Insects.*

Temperature °F (*x*)	Chirps Per Second (*y*)
88.6	20.0
71.6	16.0
93.3	19.8
84.3	18.4
80.6	17.1
75.2	15.5
69.7	14.7
82.0	17.1
69.4	15.4
83.3	16.2
79.6	15.0
82.6	17.2
80.6	16.0
83.5	17.0
76.3	14.4

a. Find the equation for the least squares line for the data.

b. Use the results of part a to determine how many chirps per second you would expect to hear from the striped ground cricket if the temperature were 73°F.

c. Use the results of part a to determine what the temperature is when the striped ground crickets are chirping at a rate of 18 times per sec.

d. Find the correlation coefficient.

Social Sciences

19. Pupil-Teacher Ratios   The following table gives the national average pupil-teacher ratio in public schools over selected years. *Source: National Center for Education Statistics.*

Year	Ratio
1990	17.4
1994	17.7
1998	16.9
2002	16.2
2006	15.8

a. Find the equation for the least squares line. Let *x* correspond to the number of years since 1990 and let *y* correspond to the average number of pupils per 1 teacher.

b. Use your answer from part a to predict the pupil-teacher ratio in 2020. Does this seem realistic?

c. Calculate and interpret the correlation coefficient.

20. Poverty Levels The following table lists how poverty level income cutoffs (in dollars) for a family of four have changed over time. *Source: U.S. Census Bureau.*

Year	Income
1980	8414
1985	10,989
1990	13,359
1995	15,569
2000	17,604
2005	19,961
2008	22,207

Let x represent the year, with $x = 0$ corresponding to 1980 and y represent the income in thousands of dollars.

a. Plot the data. Do the data appear to lie along a straight line?

b. Calculate the correlation coefficient. Does your result agree with your answer to part a?

c. Find the equation of the least squares line.

d. Use your answer from part c to predict the poverty level in the year 2018.

21. Ideal Partner Height In an introductory statistics course at Cornell University, 147 undergraduates were asked their own height and the ideal height for their ideal spouse or partner. For this exercise, we are including the data for only a representative sample of 10 of the students, as given in the following table. All heights are in inches. *Source: Chance.*

Height	Ideal Partner's Height
59	66
62	71
66	72
68	73
71	75
67	63
70	63
71	67
73	66
75	66

a. Find the regression line and correlation coefficient for this data. What strange phenomenon do you observe?

b. The first five data pairs are for female students and the second five for male students. Find the regression line and correlation coefficient for each set of data.

c. Plot all the data on one graph, using different types of points to distinguish the data for the males and for the females. Using this plot and the results from part b, explain the strange phenomenon that you observed in part a.

22. SAT Scores At Hofstra University, all students take the math SAT before entrance, and most students take a mathematics placement test before registration. Recently, one professor collected the following data for 19 students in his Finite Mathematics class:

Math SAT	Placement Test	Math SAT	Placement Test	Math SAT	Placement Test
540	20	580	8	440	10
510	16	680	15	520	11
490	10	560	8	620	11
560	8	560	13	680	8
470	12	500	14	550	8
600	11	470	10	620	7
540	10				

a. Find an equation for the least squares line. Let x be the math SAT and y be the placement test score.

b. Use your answer from part a to predict the mathematics placement test score for a student with a math SAT score of 420.

c. Use your answer from part a to predict the mathematics placement test score for a student with a math SAT score of 620.

d. Calculate the correlation coefficient.

e. Based on your answer to part d, what can you conclude about the relationship between a student's math SAT and mathematics placement test score?

Physical Sciences

23. Length of a Pendulum Grandfather clocks use pendulums to keep accurate time. The relationship between the length of a pendulum L and the time T for one complete oscillation can be determined from the data in the table.* *Source: Gary Rockswold.*

L (ft)	T (sec)
1.0	1.11
1.5	1.36
2.0	1.57
2.5	1.76
3.0	1.92
3.5	2.08
4.0	2.22

a. Plot the data from the table with L as the horizontal axis and T as the vertical axis.

b. Find the least squares line equation and graph it simultaneously, if possible, with the data points. Does it seem to fit the data?

c. Find the correlation coefficient and interpret it. Does it confirm your answer to part b?

24. Air Conditioning While shopping for an air conditioner, Adam Bryer consulted the following table, which gives a machine's BTUs and the square footage (ft^2) that it would cool.

---

*The actual relationship is $L = 0.81T^2$, which is not a linear relationship. This illustration that even if the relationship is not linear, a line can give a good approximation.

ft² (x)	BTUs (y)
150	5000
175	5500
215	6000
250	6500
280	7000
310	7500
350	8000
370	8500
420	9000
450	9500

a. Find the equation for the least squares line for the data.

b. To check the fit of the data to the line, use the results from part a to find the BTUs required to cool a room of 150 ft², 280 ft², and 420 ft². How well does the actual data agree with the predicted values?

c. Suppose Adam's room measures 230 ft². Use the results from part a to decide how many BTUs it requires. If air conditioners are available only with the BTU choices in the table, which would Adam choose?

d. Why do you think the table gives ft² instead of ft³, which would give the volume of the room?

General Interest

25. Football The following data give the expected points for a football team with first down and 10 yards to go from various points on the field. *Source: Operations Research.* (*Note:* $\sum x = 500$, $\sum x^2 = 33{,}250$, $\sum y = 20.668$, $\sum y^2 = 91.927042$, $\sum xy = 399.16$.)

Yards from Goal (x)	Expected Points (y)
5	6.041
15	4.572
25	3.681
35	3.167
45	2.392
55	1.538
65	0.923
75	0.236
85	−0.637
95	−1.245

a. Calculate the correlation coefficient. Does there appear to be a linear correlation?

b. Find the equation of the least squares line.

c. Use your answer from part a to predict the expected points when a team is at the 50-yd line.

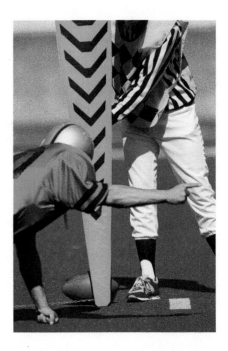

26. Athletic Records The table shows the men's and women's outdoor world records (in seconds) in the 800-m run. *Source: Nature, Track and Field Athletics, Statistics in Sports, and The World Almanac and Book of Facts.*

Year	Men's Record	Women's Record
1905	113.4	—
1915	111.9	—
1925	111.9	144
1935	109.7	135.6
1945	106.6	132
1955	105.7	125
1965	104.3	118
1975	103.7	117.48
1985	101.73	113.28
1995	101.11	113.28
2005	101.11	113.28

Let x be the year, with $x = 0$ corresponding to 1900.

a. Find the equation for the least squares line for the men's record (y) in terms of the year (x).

b. Find the equation for the least squares line for the women's record.

c. Suppose the men's and women's records continue to improve as predicted by the equations found in parts a and b. In what year will the women's record catch up with the men's record? Do you believe that will happen? Why or why not?

d. Calculate the correlation coefficient for both the men's and the women's record. What do these numbers tell you?

e. Draw a plot of the data, and discuss to what extent a linear function describes the trend in the data.

27. Running If you think a marathon is a long race, consider the Hardrock 100, a 100.5 mile running race held in southwestern Colorado. The chart at right lists the times that the 2008 winner, Kyle Skaggs, arrived at various mileage points along the way. *Source: www.run100s.com.*

a. What was Skagg's average speed?

b. Graph the data, plotting time on the *x*-axis and distance on the *y*-axis. You will need to convert the time from hours and minutes into hours. Do the data appear to lie approximately on a straight line?

c. Find the equation for the least squares line, fitting distance as a linear function of time.

d. Calculate the correlation coefficient. Does it indicate a good fit of the least squares line to the data?

e. Based on your answer to part d, what is a good value for Skagg's average speed? Compare this with your answer to part a. Which answer do you think is better? Explain your reasoning.

Time (hr:min)	Miles
0	0
2:19	11.5
3:43	18.9
5:36	27.8
7:05	32.8
7:30	36.0
8:30	43.9
10:36	51.5
11:56	58.4
15:14	71.8
17:49	80.9
18:58	85.2
20:50	91.3
23:23	100.5

YOUR TURN ANSWERS

1. $Y = -0.535x + 89.5$ **2.** -0.949

CHAPTER REVIEW

SUMMARY

In this chapter we studied linear functions, whose graphs are straight lines. We developed the slope-intercept and point-slope formulas, which can be used to find the equation of a line, given a point and the slope or given two points. We saw that lines have many applications in virtually every discipline. Lines are used through the rest of this book, so fluency in their use is important. We concluded the chapter by introducing the method of least squares, which is used to find an equation of the line that best fits a given set of data.

Slope of a Line   The slope of a line is defined as the vertical change (the "rise") over the horizontal change (the "run") as one travels along the line. In symbols, taking two different points (x_1, y_1) and (x_2, y_2) on the line, the slope is

$$m = \frac{y_2 - y_1}{x_2 - x_1},$$

where $x_1 \neq x_2$.

Equations of Lines

Equation	Description
$y = mx + b$	Slope intercept form: slope m and y-intercept b.
$y - y_1 = m(x - x_1)$	Point-slope form: slope m and line passes through (x_1, y_1).
$x = k$	Vertical line: x-intercept k, no y-intercept (except when $k = 0$), undefined slope.
$y = k$	Horizontal line: y-intercept k, no x-intercept (except when $k = 0$), slope 0.

Parallel Lines   Two lines are parallel if and only if they have the same slope, or if they are both vertical.

Perpendicular Lines   Two lines are perpendicular if and only if the product of their slopes is -1, or if one is vertical and the other horizontal.

Linear Function   A relationship f defined by

$$y = f(x) = mx + b,$$

for real numbers m and b, is a linear function.

Linear Cost Function   In a cost function of the form $C(x) = mx + b$, the m represents the marginal cost and b represents the fixed cost.

Least Squares Line   The least squares line $Y = mx + b$ that gives the best fit to the data points $(x_1, y_1), (x_2, y_2), \ldots, (x_n, y_n)$ has slope m and y-intercept b given by the equations

$$m = \frac{n(\Sigma xy) - (\Sigma x)(\Sigma y)}{n(\Sigma x^2) - (\Sigma x)^2}$$

$$b = \frac{\Sigma y - m(\Sigma x)}{n}$$

Correlation Coefficient
$$r = \frac{n(\Sigma xy) - (\Sigma x)(\Sigma y)}{\sqrt{n(\Sigma x^2) - (\Sigma x)^2} \ \sqrt{n(\Sigma y^2) - (\Sigma y)^2}}$$

KEY TERMS

To understand the concepts presented in this chapter, you should know the meaning and use of the following terms.
For easy reference, the section in the chapter where a word (or expression) was first used is provided.

mathematical model
1.1
ordered pair
Cartesian coordinate system
axes
origin
coordinates
quadrants
graph
intercepts

slope
linear equation
slope-intercept form
proportional
point-slope form
parallel
perpendicular
scatterplot
1.2
linear function

independent variable
dependent variable
surplus
shortage
equilibrium price
equilibrium quantity
fixed cost
marginal cost
linear cost function
revenue

profit
break-even quantity
break-even point
1.3
least squares line
summation notation
correlation coefficient
outlier

REVIEW EXERCISES

CONCEPT CHECK

Determine whether each statement is true or false, and explain why.

1. A given line can have more than one slope.

2. The equation $y = 3x + 4$ represents the equation of a line with slope 4.

3. The line $y = -2x + 5$ intersects the point $(3, -1)$.

4. The line that intersects the points $(2, 3)$ and $(2, 5)$ is a horizontal line.

5. The line that intersects the points $(4, 6)$ and $(5, 6)$ is a horizontal line.

6. The x-intercept of the line $y = 8x + 9$ is 9.

7. The function $f(x) = \pi x + 4$ represents a linear function.

8. The function $f(x) = 2x^2 + 3$ represents a linear function.

9. The lines $y = 3x + 17$ and $y = -3x + 8$ are perpendicular.

10. The lines $4x + 3y = 8$ and $4x + y = 5$ are parallel.

11. A correlation coefficient of zero indicates a perfect fit with the data.

12. It is not possible to get a correlation coefficient of -1.5 for a set of data.

PRACTICE AND EXPLORATIONS

13. What is marginal cost? Fixed cost?

14. What six quantities are needed to compute a correlation coefficient?

Find the slope for each line that has a slope.

15. Through $(-3, 7)$ and $(2, 12)$

16. Through $(4, -1)$ and $(3, -3)$

17. Through the origin and $(11, -2)$

18. Through the origin and $(0, 7)$

19. $4x + 3y = 6$ **20.** $4x - y = 7$

21. $y + 4 = 9$ **22.** $3y - 1 = 14$

23. $y = 5x + 4$ **24.** $x = 5y$

Find an equation in the form $y = mx + b$ for each line.

25. Through $(5, -1)$; slope $= 2/3$

26. Through $(8, 0)$; slope $= -1/4$

27. Through $(-6, 3)$ and $(2, -5)$

28. Through $(2, -3)$ and $(-3, 4)$

29. Through $(2, -10)$, perpendicular to a line with undefined slope

30. Through $(-2, 5)$; slope $= 0$

Find an equation for each line in the form $ax + by = c$, where a, b, and c are integers with no factor common to all three and $a \geq 0$.

31. Through $(3, -4)$, parallel to $4x - 2y = 9$

32. Through $(0, 5)$, perpendicular to $8x + 5y = 3$

33. Through $(-1, 4)$; undefined slope

34. Through $(7, -6)$, parallel to a line with undefined slope

35. Through $(3, -5)$, parallel to $y = 4$

36. Through $(-3, 5)$, perpendicular to $y = -2$

Graph each linear equation defined as follows.

37. $y = 4x + 3$ **38.** $y = 6 - 2x$

39. $3x - 5y = 15$ **40.** $4x + 6y = 12$

41. $x - 3 = 0$ **42.** $y = 1$

43. $y = 2x$ **44.** $x + 3y = 0$

APPLICATIONS

Business and Economics

45. Profit To manufacture x thousand computer chips requires fixed expenditures of $352 plus $42 per thousand chips. Receipts from the sale of x thousand chips amount to $130 per thousand.

  a. Write an expression for expenditures.

  b. Write an expression for receipts.

  c. For profit to be made, receipts must be greater than expenditures. How many chips must be sold to produce a profit?

46. Supply and Demand The supply and demand for crabmeat in a local fish store are related by the equations

$$\text{Supply: } p = S(q) = 6q + 3$$

and

$$\text{Demand: } p = D(q) = 19 - 2q,$$

where p represents the price in dollars per pound and q represents the quantity of crabmeat in pounds per day. Find the quantity supplied and demanded at each of the following prices.

  a. $10   **b.** $15   **c.** $18

  d. Graph both the supply and the demand functions on the same axes.

  e. Find the equilibrium price.

  f. Find the equilibrium quantity.

47. Supply For a new diet pill, 60 pills will be supplied at a price of $40, while 100 pills will be supplied at a price of $60. Write a linear supply function for this product.

48. Demand The demand for the diet pills in Exercise 47 is 50 pills at a price of $47.50 and 80 pills at a price of $32.50. Determine a linear demand function for these pills.

49. Supply and Demand Find the equilibrium price and quantity for the diet pills in Exercises 47 and 48.

Cost **In Exercises 50–53, find a linear cost function.**

50. Eight units cost $300; fixed cost is $60.

51. Fixed cost is $2000; 36 units cost $8480.

52. Twelve units cost $445; 50 units cost $1585.

53. Thirty units cost $1500; 120 units cost $5640.

54. Break-Even Analysis The cost of producing x cartons of CDs is $C(x)$ dollars, where $C(x) = 200x + 1000$. The CDs sell for $400 per carton.

  a. Find the break-even quantity.

  b. What revenue will the company receive if it sells just that number of cartons?

55. Break-Even Analysis The cost function for flavored coffee at an upscale coffeehouse is given in dollars by $C(x) = 3x + 160$, where x is in pounds. The coffee sells for $7 per pound.

  a. Find the break-even quantity.

  b. What will the revenue be at that point?

56. U.S. Imports from China The United States is China's largest export market. Imports from China have grown from about 102 billion dollars in 2001 to 338 billion dollars in 2008. This growth has been approximately linear. Use the given data pairs to write a linear equation that describes this growth in imports over the years. Let $t = 1$ represent 2001 and $t = 8$ represent 2008. *Source: TradeStats Express*^{TM}.

57. U.S. Exports to China U.S. exports to China have grown (although at a slower rate than imports) since 2001. In 2001, about 19.1 billion dollars of goods were exported to China. By 2008, this amount had grown to 69.7 billion dollars. Write a linear equation describing the number of exports each year, with $t = 1$ representing 2001 and $t = 8$ representing 2008. *Source: TradeStats Express*^{TM}.

58. Median Income The U.S. Census Bureau reported that the median income for all U.S. households in 2008 was $50,303. In 1988, the median income (in 2008 dollars) was $47,614. The median income is approximately linear and is a function of time. Find a formula for the median income, I, as a function of the year t, where t is the number of years since 1900. *Source: U.S Census Bureau.*

59. New Car Cost The average new car cost (in dollars) for selected years from 1980 to 2005 is given in the table. *Source: Chicago Tribute and National Automobile Dealers Association.*

Year	1980	1985	1990	1995	2000	2005
Cost	7500	12,000	16,000	20,450	24,900	28,400

a. Find a linear equation for the average new car cost in terms of x, the number of years since 1980, using the data for 1980 and 2005.

b. Repeat part a, using the data for 1995 and 2005.

c. Find the equation of the least squares line using all the data.

d. Use a graphing calculator to plot the data and the three lines from parts a-c.

e. Discuss which of the three lines found in parts a–c best describes the data, as well as to what extent a linear model accurately describes the data.

f. Calculate the correlation coefficient.

Life Sciences

60. World Health In general, people tend to live longer in countries that have a greater supply of food. Listed below is the 2003–2005 daily calorie supply and 2005 life expectancy at birth for 10 randomly selected countries. *Source: Food and Agriculture Organization.*

Country	Calories (x)	Life Expectancy (y)
Belize	2818	75.4
Cambodia	2155	59.4
France	3602	80.4
India	2358	62.7
Mexico	3265	75.5
New Zealand	3235	79.8
Peru	2450	72.5
Sweden	3120	80.5
Tanzania	2010	53.7
United States	3826	78.7

a. Find the correlation coefficient. Do the data seem to fit a straight line?

b. Draw a scatterplot of the data. Combining this with your results from part a, do the data seem to fit a straight line?

c. Find the equation of the least squares line.

d. Use your answer from part c to predict the life expectancy in the United Kingdom, which has a daily calorie supply of 3426. Compare your answer with the actual value of 79.0 years.

e. Briefly explain why countries with a higher daily calorie supply might tend to have a longer life expectancy. Is this trend likely to continue to higher calorie levels? Do you think that an American who eats 5000 calories a day is likely to live longer than one who eats 3600 calories? Why or why not?

f. (For the ambitious!) Find the correlation coefficient and least squares line using the data for a larger sample of countries, as found in an almanac or other reference. Is the result in general agreement with the previous results?

61. Blood Sugar and Cholesterol Levels The following data show the connection between blood sugar levels and cholesterol levels for eight different patients.

Patient	Blood Sugar Level (x)	Cholesterol Level (y)
1	130	170
2	138	160
3	142	173
4	159	181
5	165	201
6	200	192
7	210	240
8	250	290

For the data given in the preceding table, $\Sigma x = 1394$, $\Sigma y = 1607$, $\Sigma xy = 291{,}990$, $\Sigma x^2 = 255{,}214$, and $\Sigma y^2 = 336{,}155$.

a. Find the equation of the least squares line.

b. Predict the cholesterol level for a person whose blood sugar level is 190.

c. Find the correlation coefficient.

Social Sciences

62. Beef Consumption The per capita consumption of beef in the United States decreased from 115.7 lb in 1974 to 92.9 lb in 2007. Assume a linear function describes the decrease. Write a linear equation defining the function. Let t represent the number of years since 1950 and y represent the number of pounds of red meat consumed. *Source: U.S. Department of Agriculture.*

63. Marital Status More people are staying single longer in the United States. In 1995, the number of never-married adults, age 15 and over, was 55.0 million. By 2009, it was 72.1 million. Assume the data increase linearly, and write an equation that defines a linear function for this data. Let t represent the number of years since 1990. *Source: U.S. Census Bureau.*

64. Poverty The following table gives the number of families under the poverty level in the U.S. in recent years. *Source: U.S. Census Bureau.*

Year	Families Below Poverty Level (in thousands)
2000	6400
2001	6813
2002	7229
2003	7607
2004	7623
2005	7657
2006	7668
2007	7835
2008	8147

a. Find a linear equation for the number of families below poverty level (in thousands) in terms of x, the number of years since 2000, using the data for 2000 and 2008.

b. Repeat part a, using the data for 2004 and 2008.

c. Find the equation of the least squares line using all the data. Then plot the data and the three lines from parts a–c on a graphing calculator.

d. Discuss which of the three lines found in parts a–c best describes the data, as well as to what extent a linear model accurately describes the data.

e. Calculate the correlation coefficient.

65. Governors' Salaries In general, the larger a state's population, the more the governor earns. Listed in the table below are the estimated 2008 populations (in millions) and the salary of the governor (in thousands of dollars) for eight randomly selected states. *Source: U.S. Census Bureau and Alaska Department of Administration.*

State	AZ	DE	MD	MA	NY	PA	TN	WY
Population (x)	6.50	0.88	5.54	6.45	19.30	12.39	5.92	0.53
Governor's Salary (y)	95	133	150	141	179	170	160	105

a. Find the correlation coefficient. Do the data seem to fit a straight line?

b. Draw a scatterplot of the data. Compare this with your answer from part a.

c. Find the equation for the least squares line.

d. Based on your answer to part c, how much does a governor's salary increase, on average, for each additional million in population?

e. Use your answer from part c to predict the governor's salary in your state. Based on your answers from parts a and b, would this prediction be very accurate? Compare with the actual salary, as listed in an almanac or other reference.

f. (For the ambitious!) Find the correlation coefficient and least squares line using the data for all 50 states, as found in an almanac or other reference. Is the result in general agreement with the previous results?

66. Movies A mathematician exploring the relationship between ratings of movies, their year of release, and their length discovered a paradox. Rather than list the data set of 100 movies in the original research, we have created a sample of size 10 that captures the properties of the original dataset. In the following table, the rating is a score from 1 to 10, and the length is in minutes. *Source: Journal of Statistics Education.*

Year	Rating	Length
2001	10	120
2003	5	85
2004	3	100
2004	6	105
2005	4	110
2005	8	115
2006	6	135
2007	2	105
2007	5	125
2008	6	130

a. Find the correlation coefficient between the years since 2000 and the length.

b. Find the correlation coefficient between the length and the rating.

c. Given that you found a positive correlation between the year and the length in part a, and a positive correlation between the length and the rating in part b, what would you expect about the correlation between the year and the rating? Calculate this correlation. Are you surprised?

d. Discuss the paradoxical result in part c. Write out in words what each correlation tells you. Try to explain what is happening. You may want to look at a scatterplot between the year and the rating, and consider which points on the scatterplot represent movies of length no more than 110 minutes, and which represent movies of length 115 minutes or more.

EXTENDED APPLICATION

USING EXTRAPOLATION TO PREDICT LIFE EXPECTANCY

One reason for developing a mathematical model is to make predictions. If your model is a least squares line, you can predict the y-value corresponding to some new x by substituting this x into an equation of the form $Y = mx + b$. (We use a capital Y to remind us that we're getting a predicted value rather than an actual data value.) Data analysts distinguish between two very different kinds of prediction, *interpolation*, and *extrapolation*. An interpolation uses a new x inside the x range of your original data. For example, if you have inflation data at 5-year intervals from 1950 to 2000, estimating the rate of inflation in 1957 is an interpolation problem. But if you use the same data to estimate what the inflation rate was in 1920, or what it will be in 2020, you are extrapolating.

In general, interpolation is much safer than extrapolation, because data that are approximately linear over a short interval may be nonlinear over a larger interval. One way to detect nonlinearity is to look at *residuals*, which are the differences between the actual data values and the values predicted by the line of best fit. Here is a simple example:

FIGURE 24

FIGURE 25

The regression equation for the linear fit in Figure 24 is $Y = 3.431 + 1.334x$. Since the r-value for this regression line is 0.93, our linear model fits the data very well. But we might notice that the predictions are a bit low at the ends and high in the middle. We can get a better look at this pattern by plotting the residuals. To find them, we put each value of the independent variable into the regression equation, calculate

the predicted value Y, and subtract it from the actual y-value. The residual plot is shown in Figure 25, with the vertical axis rescaled to exaggerate the pattern. The residuals indicate that our data have a nonlinear, U-shaped component that is not captured by the linear fit. Extrapolating from this data set is probably not a good idea; our linear prediction for the value of y when x is 10 may be much too low.

EXERCISES

The following table gives the life expectancy at birth of females born in the United States in various years from 1970 to 2005. **Source: National Center for Health Statistics.**

Year of Birth	Life Expectancy (years)
1970	74.7
1975	76.6
1980	77.4
1985	78.2
1990	78.8
1995	78.9
2000	79.3
2005	79.9

1. Find an equation for the least squares line for these data, using year of birth as the independent variable.

2. Use your regression equation to guess a value for the life expectancy of females born in 1900.

3. Compare your answer with the actual life expectancy for females born in 1900, which was 48.3 years. Are you surprised?

4. Find the life expectancy predicted by your regression equation for each year in the table, and subtract it from the actual value in the second column. This gives you a table of residuals. Plot your residuals as points on a graph.

5. Now look at the residuals as a fresh data set, and see if you can sketch the graph of a smooth function that fits the residuals well. How easy do you think it will be to predict the life expectancy at birth of females born in 2015?

6. What will happen if you try linear regression on the *residuals*? If you're not sure, use your calculator or software to find the regression equation for the residuals. Why does this result make sense?

7. Since most of the females born in 1995 are still alive, how did the Public Health Service come up with a life expectancy of 78.9 years for these women?

8. Go to the website WolframAlpha.com and enter: "linear fit {1970,74.7}, {1975,76.6}, etc.," putting in all the data from the table. Discuss how the solution compares with the solutions provided by a graphing calculator and by Microsoft Excel.

DIRECTIONS FOR GROUP PROJECT

Assume that you and your group (3–5 students) are preparing a report for a local health agency that is interested in using linear regression to predict life expectancy. Using the questions above as a guide, write a report that addresses the spirit of each question and any issues related to that question. The report should be mathematically sound, grammatically correct, and professionally crafted. Provide recommendations as to whether the health agency should proceed with the linear equation or whether it should seek other means of making such predictions.

2

Systems of Linear Equations and Matrices

The synchronized movements of band members marching on a field can be modeled using matrix arithmetic. An exercise in Section 5 in this chapter shows how multiplication by a matrix inverse transforms the original positions of the marchers into their new coordinates as they change direction.

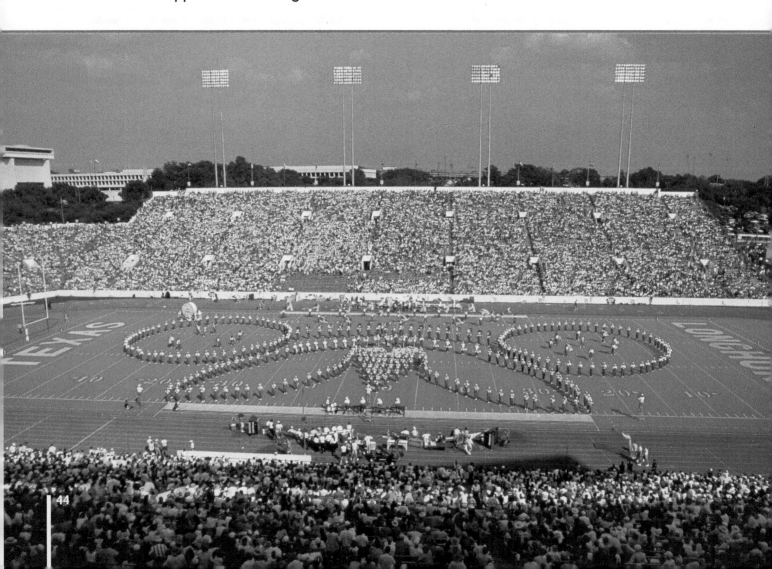

Many mathematical models require finding the solutions of two or more equations. The solutions must satisfy *all* of the equations in the model. A set of equations related in this way is called a **system of equations**. In this chapter we will discuss systems of equations, introduce the idea of a *matrix*, and then show how matrices are used to solve systems of equations.

2.1 Solution of Linear Systems by the Echelon Method

APPLY IT   How much of each ingredient should be used in an animal feed to meet dietary requirements?

APPLY IT   Suppose that an animal feed is made from two ingredients: corn and soybeans. One serving of each ingredient provides the number of grams of protein and fiber shown in the table. For example, the entries in the first column, 3 and 11, indicate that one serving of corn provides 3 g of protein and 11 g of fiber.

Nutritional Content of Ingredients		
	Corn	Soybeans
Protein	3	10
Fiber	11	4

Now suppose we want to know how many servings of corn and soybeans should be used to make a feed that contains 115 g of protein and 95 g of fiber. Let x represent the number of servings of corn used and y the number of servings of soybeans. Each serving of corn provides 3 g of protein, so the amount of protein provided by x servings of corn is $3x$. Similarly, the amount of protein provided by y servings of soybeans is $10y$. Since the total amount of protein is to be 115 g,

$$3x + 10y = 115.$$

The feed must supply 95 g of fiber, so

$$11x + 4y = 95.$$

Solving this problem means finding values of x and y that satisfy this system of equations. Verify that $x = 5$ and $y = 10$ is a solution of the system, since these numbers satisfy both equations. In fact, this is the only solution of this system. Many practical problems lead to such a system of *first-degree equations*.

A **first-degree equation in n unknowns** is any equation of the form

$$a_1x_1 + a_2x_2 + \cdots + a_nx_n = k,$$

where $a_1, a_2, \ldots, a_n$ and k are real numbers and $x_1, x_2, \ldots, x_n$ represent variables.* Each of the two equations from the animal feed problem is a first-degree equation. For example, the first equation

$$3x + 10y = 115$$

---

*a_1 is read "a-sub-one." The notation $a_1, a_2, \ldots, a_n$ represents n real-number coefficients (some of which may be equal), and the notation $x_1, x_2, \ldots, x_n$ represents n different variables, or unknowns.

is a first-degree equation with $n = 2$ where

$$a_1 = 3, \qquad a_2 = 10, \qquad k = 115,$$

and the variables are x and y. We use x_1, x_2, etc., rather than x, y, etc., in the general case because we might have any number of variables. When n is no more than 4, we usually use x, y, z, and w to represent x_1, x_2, x_3, and x_4.

A *solution* of the first-degree equation

$$a_1x_1 + a_2x_2 + \cdots + a_nx_n = k$$

is a sequence of numbers $s_1, s_2, \ldots, s_n$ such that

$$a_1s_1 + a_2s_2 + \cdots + a_ns_n = k.$$

A solution of an equation is usually written in parentheses as $(s_1, s_2, \ldots, s_n)$. For example, $(1, 6, 2)$ is a solution of the equation $3x_1 + 2x_2 - 4x_3 = 7$, since $3(1) + 2(6) - 4(2) = 7$. This is an extension of the idea of an ordered pair, which was introduced in Chapter 1. A solution of a first-degree equation in two unknowns is an ordered pair, and the graph of the equation is a straight line. For this reason, all first-degree equations are also called linear equations.

Because the graph of a linear equation in two unknowns is a straight line, there are three possibilities for the solutions of a system of two linear equations in two unknowns.

Types of Solutions for Two Equations in Two Unknowns

1. The two graphs are lines intersecting at a single point. The system has a **unique solution**, and it is given by the coordinates of this point. See Figure 1(a).

2. The graphs are distinct parallel lines. When this is the case, the system is **inconsistent**; that is, there is no solution common to both equations. See Figure 1(b).

3. The graphs are the same line. In this case, the equations are said to be **dependent**, since any solution of one equation is also a solution of the other. There are infinitely many solutions. See Figure 1(c).

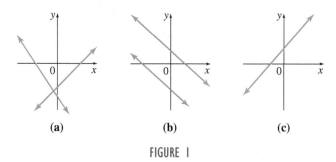

(a)   (b)   (c)

FIGURE 1

In larger systems, with more variables or more equations (or both, as is usually the case), there also may be exactly one solution, no solution, or infinitely many solutions. With more than two variables, the geometrical interpretation becomes more complicated, so we will only consider the geometry of two variables in two unknowns. We will, however, look at the algebra of two equations in three unknowns. In the next section, we will show how to handle any number of equations in any number of unknowns.

In Chapter 1, we used the graphing method and the substitution method to find the solution to a pair of equations describing the supply and demand for a commodity. The graphing method does not necessarily give an exact answer, and the substitution method becomes awkward with larger systems. In this section we will demonstrate a method to determine solutions using the addition property of equality to eliminate variables. This method forms the basis of the more general method presented in the next section.

Transformations

To solve a linear system of equations, we use properties of algebra to change, or transform, the system into a simpler *equivalent* system. An **equivalent system** is one that has the same solution(s) as the given system. Algebraic properties are the basis of the following transformations.

Transformations of a System

The following transformations can be applied to a system of equations to get an equivalent system:

1. exchanging any two equations;
2. multiplying both sides of an equation by any nonzero real number;
3. replacing any equation by a nonzero multiple of that equation plus a nonzero multiple of any other equation.

Use of these transformations leads to an equivalent system because each transformation can be reversed or "undone," allowing a return to the original system.

The Echelon Method

A systematic approach for solving systems of equations using the three transformations is called the **echelon method**. The goal of the echelon method is to use the transformations to rewrite the equations of the system until the system has a triangular form.

For a system of two equations in two variables, for example, the system should be transformed into the form

$$x + ay = b$$
$$y = c,$$

where a, b, and c are constants. Then the value for y from the second equation can be substituted into the first equation to find x. This is called **back substitution**. In a similar manner, a system of three equations in three variables should be transformed into the form

$$x + ay + bz = c$$
$$y + dz = e,$$
$$z = f.$$

EXAMPLE 1 Solving a System of Equations with a Unique Solution

Solve the system of equations from the animal feed example that began this section:

$$3x + 10y = 115 \tag{1}$$
$$11x + 4y = 95. \tag{2}$$

SOLUTION We first use transformation 3 to eliminate the x-term from equation (2). We multiply equation (1) by 11 and add the results to -3 times equation (2).

FOR REVIEW
For review of how to combine like terms using properties of real numbers, see Section R.1.

$$11(3x + 10y) = 11 \cdot 115 \qquad \rightarrow \qquad 33x + 110y = 1265$$
$$-3(11x + 4y) = -3 \cdot 95 \qquad \qquad \underline{-33x - 12y = -285}$$
$$98y = 980$$

We will indicate this process by the notation $11R_1 + (-3)R_2 \rightarrow R_2$. (R stands for the row.) The new system is

$$3x + 10y = 115 \tag{1}$$
$$11R_1 + (-3)R_2 \rightarrow R_2 \qquad 98y = 980 \tag{3}$$

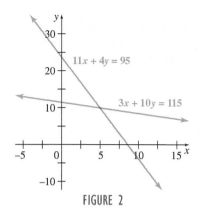

FIGURE 2

YOUR TURN 1

Solve the system

$2x + 3y = 12$

$3x - 4y = 1.$

FOR REVIEW

For review on graphing lines, see Section 1.1.

Now we use transformation 2 to make the coefficient of the first term in each row equal to 1. Here, we must multiply equation (1) by 1/3 and equation (3) by 1/98 to accomplish this. We get the system

$$\tfrac{1}{3}R_1 \to R_1 \qquad x + \frac{10}{3}y = \frac{115}{3}$$

$$\tfrac{1}{98}R_2 \to R_2 \qquad\qquad\quad y = 10.$$

Back-substitution gives

$$x + \frac{10}{3}(10) = \frac{115}{3} \qquad \text{Substitute } y = 10.$$

$$x + \frac{100}{3} = \frac{115}{3}$$

$$x = \frac{115}{3} - \frac{100}{3}$$

$$= \frac{15}{3} = 5.$$

The solution of the system is (5, 10). The graphs of the two equations in Figure 2 suggest that (5, 10) satisfies both equations in the system.   **TRY YOUR TURN 1**

The echelon method, as illustrated in Example 1, is a specific case of a procedure known as the *elimination method*. The elimination method allows for any variable to be eliminated. For example, the variable y in Equations (1) and (2) could be eliminated by calculating $2R_1 - 5R_2$. In the echelon method, the goal is to get the system into the specific form described just before Example 1.

EXAMPLE 2 **Solving a System of Equations with No Solution**

Solve the system

$$2x - 3y = 6 \tag{1}$$

$$-4x + 6y = 8. \tag{2}$$

SOLUTION Eliminate x in equation (2) to get the system

$$2x - 3y = 6 \tag{1}$$

$$2R_1 + R_2 \to R_2 \qquad\quad 0 = 20. \tag{3}$$

In equation (3), both variables have been eliminated, leaving a *false statement*. This means it is impossible to have values of x and y that satisfy both equations, because this leads to a contradiction. To see why this occurs, see Figure 3, where we have shown that the graph of the system consists of two parallel lines. A solution would be a point lying on both lines, which is impossible. We conclude that the system is inconsistent and has no solution.

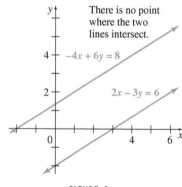

FIGURE 3

EXAMPLE 3 Solving a System of Equations with an Infinite Number of Solutions

Solve the system

$$3x - y = 4 \qquad (1)$$
$$-6x + 2y = -8. \qquad (2)$$

SOLUTION We use transformation 3 to eliminate x in equation (2), getting the system

$$3x - y = 4 \qquad (1)$$
$$2R_1 + R_2 \to R_2 \qquad 0 = 0. \qquad (3)$$

The system becomes

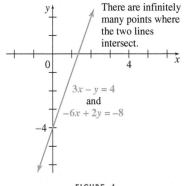

There are infinitely many points where the two lines intersect.

$3x - y = 4$
and
$-6x + 2y = -8$

FIGURE 4

$$\tfrac{1}{3}R_1 \to R_1 \qquad x - \frac{1}{3}y = \frac{4}{3} \qquad (4)$$
$$0 = 0. \qquad (3)$$

In equation (3), both variables have been eliminated, leaving a *true statement*. If we graph the original equations of the system on the same axes, as shown in Figure 4, we see that the graphs are the same line, and any point on the line will satisfy the system. This indicates that one equation was simply a multiple of the other. This system is dependent and has an infinite number of solutions.

We will express the solutions in terms of y, where y can be any real number. The variable y in this case is called a **parameter**. (We could also let x be the parameter. In this text, we will follow the common practice of letting the rightmost variable be the parameter.) Solving equation (4) for x gives $x = (1/3)y + 4/3 = (y + 4)/3$, and all ordered pairs of the form

$$\left(\frac{y + 4}{3}, y\right)$$

are solutions. For example, if we let $y = 5$, then $x = (5 + 4)/3 = 3$ and one solution is $(3, 5)$. Similarly, letting $y = -10$ and $y = 3$ gives the solutions $(-2, -10)$ and $(7/3, 3)$.

Note that the original two equations are solved not only by the particular solutions like $(3, 5)$, $(-2, -10)$, and $(7/3, 3)$ but also by the general solution $(x, y) = ((y + 4)/3, y)$. For example, substituting this general solution into the first equation gives

$$3\left(\frac{y + 4}{3}\right) - y = y + 4 - y = 4,$$

which verifies that this general solution is indeed a solution.

In some applications, x and y must be nonnegative integers. For instance, in Example 3, if x and y represent the number of male and female workers in a factory, it makes no sense to have $x = 7/3$ or $x = -2$. To make both x and y nonnegative, we solve the inequalities

$$\frac{y + 4}{3} \geq 0 \qquad \text{and} \qquad y \geq 0,$$

yielding

$$y \geq -4 \qquad \text{and} \qquad y \geq 0.$$

To make these last two inequalities true, we require $y \geq 0$, from which $y \geq -4$ automatically follows. Furthermore, to ensure $(y + 4)/3$ is an integer, it is necessary that y be 2 more than a whole-number multiple of 3. Therefore, the possible values of y are 2, 5, 8, 11, and so on, and the corresponding values of x are 2, 3, 4, 5, and so on.

The echelon method can be generalized to systems with more equations and unknowns. Because systems with three or more equations are more complicated, however, we will postpone those to the next section, where we will show a procedure for solving them based on the echelon system. Meanwhile, we summarize the echelon method here. To solve a linear system in n variables, perform the following steps using the three transformations given earlier.

Echelon Method of Solving a Linear System

1. If possible, arrange the equations so that there is an x_1-term in the first equation, an x_2-term in the second equation, and so on.
2. Eliminate the x_1-term in all equations after the first equation.
3. Eliminate the x_2-term in all equations after the second equation.
4. Eliminate the x_3-term in all equations after the third equation.
5. Continue in this way until the last equation has the form $ax_n = k$, for constants a and k, if possible.
6. Multiply each equation by the reciprocal of the coefficient of its first term.
7. Use back-substitution to find the value of each variable.

Applications

The mathematical techniques in this text will be useful to you only if you are able to apply them to practical problems. To do this, always begin by reading the problem carefully. Next, identify what must be found. Let each unknown quantity be represented by a variable. (It is a good idea to *write down* exactly what each variable represents.) Now reread the problem, looking for all necessary data. Write those down, too. Finally, look for one or more sentences that lead to equations or inequalities. The next example illustrates these steps.

EXAMPLE 4   Flight Time

A flight leaves New York at 8 P.M. and arrives in Paris at 9 A.M. (Paris time). This 13-hour difference includes the flight time plus the change in time zones. The return flight leaves Paris at 1 P.M. and arrives in New York at 3 P.M. (New York time). This 2-hour difference includes the flight time *minus* time zones, plus an extra hour due to the fact that flying westward is against the wind. Find the actual flight time eastward and the difference in time zones.

SOLUTION   Let x be the flight time eastward and y be the difference in time zones. For the trip east, the flight time plus the change in time zones is 13 hours, so

$$x + y = 13.$$

For the trip west, the flight time (which is $x + 1$ hours due to the wind) minus the time zone is 2 hours, so

$$(x + 1) - y = 2.$$

Subtract 1 from both sides of this equation, and then solve the system

$$x + y = 13$$
$$x - y = \ \ 1$$

YOUR TURN 2 Solve Example 4 for the case in which there is a 16-hour time difference on the trip from New York, a 2-hour difference on the return trip, and no wind.

using the echelon method.

$$\begin{aligned} &x + y = 13 \\ R_1 + (-1)R_2 \rightarrow R_2 \quad &2y = 12 \end{aligned}$$

Dividing the last equation by 2 gives $y = 6$. Substituting this into the first equation gives $x + 6 = 13$, so $x = 7$. Therefore, the flight time eastward is 7 hours, and the difference in time zones is 6 hours.

TRY YOUR TURN 2

EXAMPLE 5 **Integral Solutions**

A restaurant owner orders a replacement set of knives, forks, and spoons. The box arrives containing 40 utensils and weighing 141.3 oz (ignoring the weight of the box). A knife, fork, and spoon weigh 3.9 oz, 3.6 oz, and 3.0 oz, respectively.

(a) How many solutions are there for the number of knives, forks, and spoons in the box?

SOLUTION Let

$$x = \text{the number of knives};$$
$$y = \text{the number of forks};$$
$$z = \text{the number of spoons}.$$

A chart is useful for organizing the information in a problem of this type.

Number and Weight of Utensils				
	Knives	Forks	Spoons	Total
Number	x	y	z	40
Weight	3.9	3.6	3.0	141.3

Because the box contains 40 utensils,

$$x + y + z = 40.$$

The x knives weigh $3.9x$ ounces, the y forks weigh $3.6y$ ounces, and the z spoons weigh $3.0z$ ounces. Since the total weight is 141.3 oz, we have the system

$$x + \quad y + \quad z = \quad 40$$
$$3.9x + 3.6y + 3.0z = 141.3.$$

Solve using the echelon method.

$$x + \quad y + \quad z = 40$$
$$3.9\text{R}_1 + (-1)\text{R}_2 \rightarrow \text{R}_2 \qquad 0.3y + 0.9z = 14.7$$

We do not have a third equation to solve for z, as we did in Example 4. We could thus let z be any real number, and then use this value of z in the second equation to find a corresponding value of y. These values of y and z could be put into the first equation to find a corresponding value of x. This system, then, has an infinite number of solutions. Letting z be the parameter, solve the second equation for y to get

$$y = \frac{14.7 - 0.9z}{0.3} = 49 - 3z.$$

Substituting this into the first equation, we get

$$x + (49 - 3z) + z = 40.$$

Solving this for x gives

$$x = 2z - 9.$$

Thus, the solutions are $(2z - 9, 49 - 3z, z)$, where z is any real number.

Now that we have solved for x and y in terms of z, let us investigate what values z can take on. This application demands that the solutions be nonnegative integers. The number of forks cannot be negative, so set

$$49 - 3z \geq 0.$$

Solving for z gives

$$z \leq \frac{49}{3} \approx 16.33.$$

Also, the number of knives cannot be negative, so set

$$2z - 9 \geq 0.$$

Solving for z gives

$$z \geq \frac{9}{2} = 4.5.$$

Therefore, the permissible values of z are 5, 6, 7, . . . , 16, for a total of 12 solutions.

YOUR TURN 3 Find the solution with the largest number of spoons.

(b) Find the solution with the smallest number of spoons.

SOLUTION The smallest value of z is $z = 5$, from which we find $x = 2(5) - 9 = 1$ and $y = 49 - 3(5) = 34$. This solution has 1 knife, 34 forks, and 5 spoons.

TRY YOUR TURN 3

2.1 EXERCISES

Use the echelon method to solve each system of two equations in two unknowns. Check your answers.

1. $x + y = 5$
$\quad 2x - 2y = 2$

2. $4x + y = 9$
$\quad 3x - y = 5$

3. $3x - 2y = -3$
$\quad 5x - y = 2$

4. $2x + 7y = -8$
$\quad -2x + 3y = -12$

5. $3x + 2y = -6$
$\quad 5x - 2y = -10$

6. $-3x + y = 4$
$\quad 2x - 2y = -4$

7. $6x - 2y = -4$
$\quad 3x + 4y = 8$

8. $4m + 3n = -1$
$\quad 2m + 5n = 3$

9. $5p + 11q = -7$
$\quad 3p - 8q = 25$

10. $12s - 5t = 9$
$\quad 3s - 8t = -18$

11. $6x + 7y = -2$
$\quad 7x - 6y = 26$

12. $3a - 8b = 14$
$\quad a - 2b = 2$

13. $3x + 2y = 5$
$\quad 6x + 4y = 8$

14. $9x - 5y = 1$
$\quad -18x + 10y = 1$

15. $3x - 2y = -4$
$\quad -6x + 4y = 8$

16. $3x + 5y + 2 = 0$
$\quad 9x + 15y + 6 = 0$

17. $x - \dfrac{3y}{2} = \dfrac{5}{2}$
$\quad \dfrac{4x}{3} + \dfrac{2y}{3} = 6$

18. $\dfrac{x}{5} + 3y = 31$
$\quad 2x - \dfrac{y}{5} = 8$

19. $\dfrac{x}{2} + y = \dfrac{3}{2}$
$\quad \dfrac{x}{3} + y = \dfrac{1}{3}$

20. $\dfrac{x}{9} + \dfrac{y}{6} = \dfrac{1}{3}$
$\quad 2x + \dfrac{8y}{5} = \dfrac{2}{5}$

21. An inconsistent system has _____ solutions.

22. The solution of a system with two dependent equations in two variables is _____.

For each of the following systems of equations in echelon form, tell how many solutions there are in nonnegative integers.

23. $x + 2y + 3z = 90$
$\quad 3y + 4z = 36$

24. $x - 7y + 4z = 75$
$\quad 2y + 7z = 60$

25. $3x + 2y + 4z = 80$
$\quad y - 3z = 10$

26. $4x + 2y + 3z = 72$
$\quad 2y - 3z = 12$

27. Describe what a parameter is and why it is used in systems of equations with an infinite number of solutions.

28. In your own words, describe the echelon method as used to solve a system of two equations in three variables.

Solve each system of equations. Let z be the parameter.

29. $2x + 3y - z = 1$
$\quad 3x + 5y + z = 3$

30. $3x + y - z = 0$
$\quad 2x - y + 3z = -7$

31. $x + 2y + 3z = 11$
$\quad 2x - y + z = 2$

32. $-x + y - z = -7$
$\quad 2x + 3y + z = 7$

33. In Exercise 9 in Section 1.3, you were asked to solve the system of least squares line equations

$$nb + (\Sigma x)m = \Sigma y$$
$$(\Sigma x)b + (\Sigma x^2)m = \Sigma xy$$

by the method of substitution. Now solve the system by the echelon method to get

$$m = \frac{n(\Sigma xy) - (\Sigma x)(\Sigma y)}{n(\Sigma x^2) - (\Sigma x)^2}$$

$$b = \frac{\Sigma y - m(\Sigma x)}{n}.$$

34. The examples in this section did not use the first transformation. How might this transformation be used in the echelon method?

APPLICATIONS

Business and Economics

35. Groceries If 20 lb of rice and 10 lb of potatoes cost $16.20, and 30 lb of rice and 12 lb of potatoes cost $23.04, how much will 10 lb of rice and 50 lb of potatoes cost?

36. Sales An apparel shop sells skirts for $45 and blouses for $35. Its entire stock is worth $51,750. But sales are slow and only half the skirts and two-thirds of the blouses are sold, for a total of $30,600. How many skirts and blouses are left in the store?

37. Sales A theater charges $8 for main floor seats and $5 for balcony seats. If all seats are sold, the ticket income is $4200. At one show, 25% of the main floor seats and 40% of the balcony seats were sold and ticket income was $1200. How many seats are on the main floor and how many are in the balcony?

38. Stock Lorri Morgan has $16,000 invested in Disney and Exxon stock. The Disney stock currently sells for $30 a share and the Exxon stock for $70 a share. Her stockbroker points out that if Disney stock goes up 50% and Exxon stock goes up by $35 a share, her stock will be worth $25,500. Is this possible? If so, tell how many shares of each stock she owns. If not, explain why not.

39. Production A company produces two models of bicycles, model 201 and model 301. Model 201 requires 2 hours of assembly time and model 301 requires 3 hours of assembly time. The parts for model 201 cost $18 per bike and the parts for model 301 cost $27 per bike. If the company has a total of 34 hours of assembly time and $335 available per day for these two models, how many of each should be made in a day to use up all available time and money? If it is not possible, explain why not.

40. Banking A bank teller has a total of 70 bills in five-, ten-, and twenty-dollar denominations. The total value of the money is $960.

   a. Find the total number of solutions.

   b. Find the solution with the smallest number of five-dollar bills.

   c. Find the solution with the largest number of five-dollar bills.

41. Production Felsted Furniture makes dining room furniture. A buffet requires 30 hours for construction and 10 hours for finishing. A chair requires 10 hours for construction and 10 hours for finishing. A table requires 10 hours for construction and 30 hours for finishing. The construction department has 350 hours of labor and the finishing department has 150 hours of labor available each week. How many pieces of each type of furniture should be produced each week if the factory is to run at full capacity?

42. Rug Cleaning Machines Kelly Karpet Kleaners sells rug cleaning machines. The EZ model weighs 10 lb and comes in a 10-cubic-ft box. The compact model weighs 20 lb and comes in an 8-cubic-ft box. The commercial model weighs 60 lb and comes in a 28-cubic-ft box. Each of their delivery vans has 248 cubic ft of space and can hold a maximum of 440 lb. In order for a van to be fully loaded, how many of each model should it carry?

43. Production Turley Tailor, Inc. makes long-sleeve, short-sleeve, and sleeveless blouses. A long-sleeve blouse requires 1.5 hours of cutting and 1.2 hours of sewing. A short-sleeve blouse requires 1 hour of cutting and 0.9 hour of sewing. A sleeveless blouse requires 0.5 hour of cutting and 0.6 hour of sewing. There are 380 hours of labor available in the cutting department each day and 330 hours in the sewing department. If the plant is to run at full capacity, how many of each type of blouse should be made each day?

44. Broadway Economics When Neil Simon opens a new play, he has to decide whether to open the show on Broadway or Off Broadway. For example, in his play *London Suite*, he decided to open it Off Broadway. From information provided by Emanuel Azenberg, his producer, the following equations were developed:

$$43{,}500x - y = 1{,}295{,}000$$
$$27{,}000x - y = 440{,}000,$$

where x represents the number of weeks that the show has run and y represents the profit or loss from the show (first equation is for Broadway and second equation is for Off Broadway). *Source: The Mathematics Teacher.*

   a. Solve this system of equations to determine when the profit/loss from the show will be equal for each venue. What is the profit at that point?

   b. Discuss which venue is favorable for the show.

Life Sciences

45. Birds The date of the first sighting of robins has been occurring earlier each spring over the past 25 years at the Rocky Mountain Biological Laboratory. Scientists from this laboratory have developed two linear equations that estimate the date of the first sighting of robins:

$$y = 759 - 0.338x$$
$$y = 1637 - 0.779x,$$

where x is the year and y is the estimated number of days into the year when a robin can be expected. *Source: Proceedings of the National Academy of Science.*

   a. Compare the date of first sighting in 2000 for each of these equations. (*Hint:* 2000 was a leap year.)

   b. Solve this system of equations to find the year in which the two estimates agree.

Physical Sciences

46. Stopping Distance The stopping distance of a car traveling 25 mph is 61.7 ft, and for a car traveling 35 mph it is 106 ft. The stopping distance in feet can be described by the equation $y = ax^2 + bx$, where x is the speed in mph. *Source: National Traffic Safety Institute.*

   a. Find the values of a and b.

   b. Use your answers from part a to find the stopping distance for a car traveling 55 mph.

General Interest

47. Basketball Wilt Chamberlain holds the record for the highest number of points scored in a single NBA basketball game.

Chamberlain scored 100 points for Philadelphia against the New York Knicks on March 2, 1962. This is an amazing feat, considering he scored all of his points without the help of three-point shots. Chamberlain made a total of 64 baskets, consisting of field goals (worth two points) and foul shots (worth one point). Find the number of field goals and the number of foul shots that Chamberlain made. *Source: ESPN.*

48. The 24® Game The object of the 24® Game, created by Robert Sun, is to combine four numbers, using addition, subtraction, multiplication, and/or division, to get the number 24. For example, the numbers 2, 5, 5, 4 can be combined as $2(5 + 5) + 4 = 24$. For the algebra edition of the game and the game card shown to the right, the object is to find single-digit positive integer values x and y so the four numbers $x + y$, $3x + 2y$, 8, and 9 can be combined to make 24. *Source: Suntex.*

a. Using the game card, write a system of equations that, when solved, can be used to make 24 from the game card. What is the solution to this system, and how can it be used to make 24 on the game card?

b. Repeat part a and develop a second system of equations.

YOUR TURN ANSWERS

1. (3, 2)
2. Flight time is 9 hours, difference in time zones is 7 hours.
3. 23 knives, 1 fork, and 16 spoons

2.2 Solution of Linear Systems by the Gauss-Jordan Method

APPLY IT How can an auto manufacturer with more than one factory and several dealers decide how many cars to send to each dealer from each factory? *Questions like this are called transportation problems; they frequently lead to a system of equations that must be satisfied. In Exercise 52 in this section we use a further refinement of the echelon method to answer this question.*

When we use the echelon method, since the variables are in the same order in each equation, we really need to keep track of just the coefficients and the constants. For example, consider the following system of three equations in three unknowns.

$$2x + y - z = 2$$
$$x + 3y + 2z = 1$$
$$x + y + z = 2$$

This system can be written in an abbreviated form as

Such a rectangular array of numbers enclosed by brackets is called a **matrix** (plural: **matrices**).* Each number in the array is an **element** or **entry**. To separate the constants in

---

*The word matrix, Latin for "womb," was coined by James Joseph Sylvester (1814–1897) and made popular by his friend Arthur Cayley (1821–1895). Both mathematicians were English, although Sylvester spent much of his life in the United States.

the last column of the matrix from the coefficients of the variables, we use a vertical line, producing the following **augmented matrix**.

$$\begin{bmatrix} 2 & 1 & -1 & 2 \\ 1 & 3 & 2 & 1 \\ 1 & 1 & 1 & 2 \end{bmatrix}$$

The rows of the augmented matrix can be transformed in the same way as the equations of the system, since the matrix is just a shortened form of the system. The following **row operations** on the augmented matrix correspond to the transformations of systems of equations given earlier.

Row Operations

For any augmented matrix of a system of equations, the following operations produce the augmented matrix of an equivalent system:

1. interchanging any two rows;
2. multiplying the elements of a row by any nonzero real number;
3. adding a nonzero multiple of the elements of one row to the corresponding elements of a nonzero multiple of some other row.

In steps 2 and 3, we are replacing a row with a new, modified row, which the old row helped to form, just as we replaced an equation with a new, modified equation in the previous section.

Row operations, like the transformations of systems of equations, are reversible. If they are used to change matrix A to matrix B, then it is possible to use row operations to transform B back into A. In addition to their use in solving equations, row operations are very important in the simplex method to be described in Chapter 4.

In the examples in this section, we will use the same notation as in Section 1 to show the row operation used. For example, the notation R_1 indicates row 1 of the previous matrix, and $-3R_1 + R_2$ means that row 1 is multiplied by -3 and added to row 2.

By the first row operation, interchanging two rows, the matrix

$$\begin{bmatrix} 0 & 1 & 2 & 3 \\ -2 & -6 & -10 & -12 \\ 2 & 1 & -2 & -5 \end{bmatrix} \quad \text{becomes} \quad \begin{bmatrix} -2 & -6 & -10 & -12 \\ 0 & 1 & 2 & 3 \\ 2 & 1 & -2 & -5 \end{bmatrix} \quad \begin{matrix} \text{Interchange } R_1 \\ \text{and } R_2 \end{matrix}$$

by interchanging the first two rows. Row 3 is left unchanged.

The second row operation, multiplying a row by a number, allows us to change

$$\begin{bmatrix} -2 & -6 & -10 & -12 \\ 0 & 1 & 2 & 3 \\ 2 & 1 & -2 & -5 \end{bmatrix} \quad \text{to} \quad \begin{bmatrix} 1 & 3 & 5 & 6 \\ 0 & 1 & 2 & 3 \\ 2 & 1 & -2 & -5 \end{bmatrix} \quad (-1/2)R_1 \rightarrow R_1$$

by multiplying the elements of row 1 of the original matrix by $-1/2$. Note that rows 2 and 3 are left unchanged.

Using the third row operation, adding a multiple of one row to another, we change

$$\begin{bmatrix} 1 & 3 & 5 & 6 \\ 0 & 1 & 2 & 3 \\ 2 & 1 & -2 & -5 \end{bmatrix} \quad \text{to} \quad \begin{bmatrix} 1 & 3 & 5 & 6 \\ 0 & 1 & 2 & 3 \\ 0 & -5 & -12 & -17 \end{bmatrix} \quad -2R_1 + R_3 \rightarrow R_3$$

by first multiplying each element in row 1 of the original matrix by -2 and then adding the results to the corresponding elements in the third row of that matrix. Work as follows.

$$\begin{bmatrix} 1 & 3 & 5 & | & 6 \\ 0 & 1 & 2 & | & 3 \\ (-2)1 + 2 & (-2)3 + 1 & (-2)5 - 2 & | & (-2)6 - 5 \end{bmatrix} = \begin{bmatrix} 1 & 3 & 5 & | & 6 \\ 0 & 1 & 2 & | & 3 \\ 0 & -5 & -12 & | & -17 \end{bmatrix}$$

Notice that rows 1 and 2 are left unchanged, *even though the elements of row 1 were used to transform row 3.*

The Gauss-Jordan Method

The **Gauss-Jordan method** is an extension of the echelon method of solving systems.* Before the Gauss-Jordan method can be used, the system must be in proper form: the terms with variables should be on the left and the constants on the right in each equation, with the variables in the same order in each equation.

The system is then written as an augmented matrix. Using row operations, the goal is to transform the matrix so that it has zeros above and below a diagonal of 1's on the left of the vertical bar. Once this is accomplished, the final solution can be read directly from the last matrix. The following example illustrates the use of the Gauss-Jordan method to solve a system of equations.

EXAMPLE 1 Gauss-Jordan Method

Solve the system

$$3x - 4y = 1 \tag{1}$$

$$5x + 2y = 19. \tag{2}$$

SOLUTION

Method 1
1's on Diagonal

The system is already in the proper form to use the Gauss-Jordan method. Our goal is to transform this matrix, if possible, into the form

$$\begin{bmatrix} 1 & 0 & | & m \\ 0 & 1 & | & n \end{bmatrix},$$

where m and n are real numbers. To begin, we change the 3 in the first row to 1 using the second row operation. (Notice that the same notation is used to indicate each transformation, as in the previous section.)

$$\begin{bmatrix} 3 & -4 & | & 1 \\ 5 & 2 & | & 19 \end{bmatrix} \quad \text{Augmented matrix}$$

$$\tfrac{1}{3}R_1 \rightarrow R_1 \quad \begin{bmatrix} 1 & -\tfrac{4}{3} & | & \tfrac{1}{3} \\ 5 & 2 & | & 19 \end{bmatrix}$$

Using the third row operation, we change the 5 in row 2 to 0.

$$-5R_1 + R_2 \rightarrow R_2 \quad \begin{bmatrix} 1 & -\tfrac{4}{3} & | & \tfrac{1}{3} \\ 0 & \tfrac{26}{3} & | & \tfrac{52}{3} \end{bmatrix}$$

We now change 26/3 in row 2 to 1 to complete the diagonal of 1's.

$$\tfrac{3}{26}R_2 \rightarrow R_2 \quad \begin{bmatrix} 1 & -\tfrac{4}{3} & | & \tfrac{1}{3} \\ 0 & 1 & | & 2 \end{bmatrix}$$

*The great German mathematician Carl Friedrich Gauss (1777–1855), sometimes referred to as the "Prince of Mathematicians," originally developed his elimination method for use in finding least squares coefficients. (See Section 1.3.) The German geodesist Wilhelm Jordan (1842–1899) improved his method and used it in surveying problems. Gauss's method had been known to the Chinese at least 1800 years earlier and was described in the *Jiuahang Suanshu (Nine Chapters on the Mathematical Art).*

The final transformation is to change the $-4/3$ in row 1 to 0.

$$\tfrac{4}{3}R_2 + R_1 \rightarrow R_1 \quad \begin{bmatrix} 1 & 0 & | & 3 \\ 0 & 1 & | & 2 \end{bmatrix}$$

The last matrix corresponds to the system

$$x = 3$$
$$y = 2,$$

so we can read the solution directly from the last column of the final matrix. Check that $(3, 2)$ is the solution by substitution in the equations of the original matrix.

Method 2
Fraction-Free

An alternate form of Gauss-Jordan is to first transform the matrix so that it contains zeros above and below the main diagonal. Then, use the second transformation to get the required 1's. When doing calculations by hand, this second method simplifies the calculations by avoiding fractions and decimals. We will use this method when doing calculations by hand throughout the remainder of this chapter.

To begin, we change the 5 in row 2 to 0.

$$\begin{bmatrix} 3 & -4 & | & 1 \\ 5 & 2 & | & 19 \end{bmatrix} \quad \text{Augmented matrix}$$

$$5R_1 + (-3)R_2 \rightarrow R_2 \quad \begin{bmatrix} 3 & -4 & | & 1 \\ 0 & -26 & | & -52 \end{bmatrix}$$

We change the -4 in row 1 to 0.

$$-4R_2 + 26R_1 \rightarrow R_1 \quad \begin{bmatrix} 78 & 0 & | & 234 \\ 0 & -26 & | & -52 \end{bmatrix}$$

Then we change the first nonzero number in each row to 1.

$$\tfrac{1}{78}R_1 \rightarrow R_1 \quad \begin{bmatrix} 1 & 0 & | & 3 \\ 0 & 1 & | & 2 \end{bmatrix}$$
$$-\tfrac{1}{26}R_2 \rightarrow R_2$$

YOUR TURN 1 Use the Gauss-Jordan method to solve the system
$4x + 5y = 10$
$7x + 8y = 19.$

The solution is read directly from this last matrix: $x = 3$ and $y = 2$, or $(3, 2)$.

TRY YOUR TURN 1

NOTE   If your solution does not check, the most efficient way to find the error is to substitute back through the equations that correspond to each matrix, starting with the last matrix. When you find a system that is not satisfied by your (incorrect) answers, you have probably reached the matrix just before the error occurred. Look for the error in the transformation to the next matrix. For example, if you erroneously wrote the 2 as -2 in the final matrix of the fraction-free method of Example 2, you would find that $(3, -2)$ was not a solution of the system represented by the previous matrix because $-26(-2) \neq -52$, telling you that your error occurred between this matrix and the final one.

When the Gauss-Jordan method is used to solve a system, the final matrix always will have zeros above and below the diagonal of 1's on the left of the vertical bar. To transform the matrix, it is best to work column by column from left to right. Such an orderly method avoids confusion and going around in circles. For each column, first perform the steps that give the zeros. When all columns have zeros in place, multiply each row by the reciprocal of the coefficient of the remaining nonzero number in that row to get the required 1's. With dependent equations or inconsistent systems, it will not be possible to get the complete diagonal of 1's.

We will demonstrate the method in an example with three variables and three equations, after which we will summarize the steps.

> **EXAMPLE 2** **Gauss-Jordan Method**

Use the Gauss-Jordan method to solve the system

$$x + 5z = -6 + y$$
$$3x + 3y = 10 + z$$
$$x + 3y + 2z = 5.$$

Method 1
Calculating by Hand

SOLUTION

First, rewrite the system in proper form, as follows.

$$x - y + 5z = -6$$
$$3x + 3y - z = 10$$
$$x + 3y + 2z = 5$$

Begin to find the solution by writing the augmented matrix of the linear system.

$$\begin{bmatrix} 1 & -1 & 5 & | & -6 \\ 3 & 3 & -1 & | & 10 \\ 1 & 3 & 2 & | & 5 \end{bmatrix}$$

Row transformations will be used to rewrite this matrix in the form

$$\begin{bmatrix} 1 & 0 & 0 & | & m \\ 0 & 1 & 0 & | & n \\ 0 & 0 & 1 & | & p \end{bmatrix},$$

where m, n, and p are real numbers (if this form is possible). From this final form of the matrix, the solution can be read: $x = m$, $y = n$, $z = p$, or (m, n, p).

In the first column, we need zeros in the second and third rows. Multiply the first row by -3 and add to the second row to get a zero there. Then multiply the first row by -1 and add to the third row to get that zero.

$$\begin{matrix} \\ -3R_1 + R_2 \rightarrow R_2 \\ -1R_1 + R_3 \rightarrow R_3 \end{matrix} \begin{bmatrix} 1 & -1 & 5 & | & -6 \\ 0 & 6 & -16 & | & 28 \\ 0 & 4 & -3 & | & 11 \end{bmatrix}$$

Now get zeros in the second column in a similar way. We want zeros in the first and third rows. Row 2 will not change.

$$\begin{matrix} R_2 + 6R_1 \rightarrow R_1 \\ \\ 2R_2 + (-3)R_3 \rightarrow R_3 \end{matrix} \begin{bmatrix} 6 & 0 & 14 & | & -8 \\ 0 & 6 & -16 & | & 28 \\ 0 & 0 & -23 & | & 23 \end{bmatrix}$$

In transforming the third row, you may have used the operation $4R_2 + (-6)R_3 \rightarrow R_3$ instead of $2R_2 + (-3)R_3 \rightarrow R_3$. This is perfectly fine; the last row would then have -46 and 46 in place of -23 and 23. To avoid errors, it helps to keep the numbers as small as possible. We observe at this point that all of the numbers can be reduced in size by multiplying each row by an appropriate constant. This next step is not essential, but it simplifies the arithmetic.

$$\begin{matrix} \frac{1}{2}R_1 \rightarrow R_1 \\ \frac{1}{2}R_2 \rightarrow R_2 \\ -\frac{1}{23}R_3 \rightarrow R_3 \end{matrix} \begin{bmatrix} 3 & 0 & 7 & | & -4 \\ 0 & 3 & -8 & | & 14 \\ 0 & 0 & 1 & | & -1 \end{bmatrix}$$

Next, we want zeros in the first and second rows of the third column. Row 3 will not change.

$$\begin{matrix} -7R_3 + R_1 \rightarrow R_1 \\ 8R_3 + R_2 \rightarrow R_2 \\ \\ \end{matrix} \begin{bmatrix} 3 & 0 & 0 & | & 3 \\ 0 & 3 & 0 & | & 6 \\ 0 & 0 & 1 & | & -1 \end{bmatrix}$$

Finally, get 1's in each row by multiplying the row by the reciprocal of (or dividing the row by) the number in the diagonal position.

$$\begin{array}{c} \frac{1}{3}R_1 \to R_1 \\ \frac{1}{3}R_2 \to R_2 \\ \, \end{array} \begin{bmatrix} 1 & 0 & 0 & | & 1 \\ 0 & 1 & 0 & | & 2 \\ 0 & 0 & 1 & | & -1 \end{bmatrix}$$

The linear system associated with the final augmented matrix is

$$\begin{aligned} x &= 1 \\ y &= 2 \\ z &= -1, \end{aligned}$$

and the solution is $(1, 2, -1)$. Verify that this is the solution to the original system of equations.

CAUTION   Notice that we have performed two or three operations on the same matrix in one step. This is permissible as long as we do not use a row that we are changing as part of another row operation. For example, when we changed row 2 in the first step, we could not use row 2 to transform row 3 in the same step. To avoid difficulty, use *only* row 1 to get zeros in column 1, row 2 to get zeros in column 2, and so on.

Method 2
Graphing Calculator

The row operations of the Gauss-Jordan method can also be done on a graphing calculator. For example, Figure 5 shows the result when the augmented matrix is entered into a TI-84 Plus. Figures 6 and 7 show how row operations can be used to get zeros in rows 2 and 3 of the first column.

Calculators typically do not allow any multiple of a row to be added to any multiple of another row, such as in the operation $2R_2 + 6R_1 \to R_1$. They normally allow a multiple of a row to be added only to another unmodified row. To get around this restriction, we can convert the diagonal element to a 1 before changing the other elements in the column to 0, as we did in the first method of Example 1. In this example, we change the 6 in row 2, column 2, to a 1 by dividing by 6. The result is shown in Figure 8. (The right side of the matrix is not visible but can be seen by pressing the right arrow key.) Notice that this operation introduces decimals. Converting to fractions is preferable on calculators that have that option; 1/3 is certainly more concise than 0.3333333333. Figure 9 shows such a conversion on the TI-84 Plus.

FIGURE 5

FIGURE 6

FIGURE 7

FIGURE 8

FIGURE 9

When performing row operations without a graphing calculator, it is best to avoid fractions and decimals, because these make the operations more difficult and more prone to error. A calculator, on the other hand, encounters no such difficulties.

Continuing in the same manner, the solution $(1, 2, -1)$ is found as shown in Figure 10.

FIGURE 10

Some calculators can do the entire Gauss-Jordan process with a single command; on the TI-84 Plus, for example, this is done with the `rref` command. This is very useful in practice, although it does not show any of the intermediate steps. For more details, see the *Graphing Calculator and Excel Spreadsheet Manual* available with this book.

Method 3
Spreadsheet

The Gauss-Jordan method can be done using a spreadsheet either by using a macro or by developing the pivot steps using formulas with the copy and paste commands. However, spreadsheets also have built-in methods to solve systems of equations. Although these solvers do not usually employ the Gauss-Jordan method for solving systems of equations, they are, nonetheless, efficient and practical to use.

The Solver included with Excel can solve systems of equations that are both linear and nonlinear. The Solver is located in the Tools menu and requires that cells be identified ahead of time for each variable in the problem. It also requires that the left-hand side of each equation be placed in the spreadsheet as a formula. For example, to solve the above problem, we could identify cells A1, B1, and C1 for the variables x, y, and z, respectively. The Solver requires that we place a guess for the answer in these cells. It is convenient to place a zero in each of these cells. The left-hand side of each equation must be placed in a cell. We could choose A3, A4, and A5 to hold each of these formulas. Thus, in cell A3, we would type "=A1 - B1 + 5*C1" and put the other two equations in cells A4 and A5.

We now click on the Tools menu and choose Solver. (In some versions, it may be necessary to install the Solver. For more details, see the *Graphing Calculator and Excel Spreadsheet Manual* available with this book.) Since this solver attempts to find a solution that is best in some way, we are required to identify a cell with a formula in it that we want to optimize. In this case, it is convenient to use the cell with the left-hand side of the first constraint in it, A3. Figure 11 illustrates the Solver box and the items placed in it.

FIGURE 11

To obtain a solution, click on Solve. The approximate solution is located in cells A1, B1, and C1, and these correspond to x, y, and z, respectively.

YOUR TURN 2 Use the Gauss-Jordan method to solve the system
$$x + 2y + 3z = 2$$
$$2x + 2y - 3z = 27$$
$$3x + 2y + 5z = 10.$$

TRY YOUR TURN 2

In summary, the Gauss-Jordan method of solving a linear system requires the following steps.

Gauss-Jordan Method of Solving a Linear System

1. Write each equation so that variable terms are in the same order on the left side of the equal sign and constants are on the right.

2. Write the augmented matrix that corresponds to the system.

3. Use row operations to transform the first column so that all elements except the element in the first row are zero.

4. Use row operations to transform the second column so that all elements except the element in the second row are zero.

5. Use row operations to transform the third column so that all elements except the element in the third row are zero.

6. Continue in this way, when possible, until the last row is written in the form

$$[0 \quad 0 \quad 0 \quad \cdots \quad 0 \quad j \mid k],$$

where j and k are constants with $j \neq 0$. When this is not possible, continue until every row has more zeros on the left than the previous row (except possibly for any rows of all zero at the bottom of the matrix), and the first nonzero entry in each row is the only nonzero entry in its column.

7. Multiply each row by the reciprocal of the nonzero element in that row.

Systems without a Unique Solution
In the previous examples, we were able to get the last row in the form $[0 \quad 0 \quad 0 \quad \cdots \quad 0 \quad j \mid k]$, where j and k are constants with $j \neq 0$. We will now look at examples where this is not the case.

EXAMPLE 3 **Solving a System of Equations with No Solution**

Use the Gauss-Jordan method to solve the system

$$x - 2y = 2$$
$$3x - 6y = 5.$$

SOLUTION Begin by writing the augmented matrix.

$$\begin{bmatrix} 1 & -2 & | & 2 \\ 3 & -6 & | & 5 \end{bmatrix}$$

To get a zero for the second element in column 1, multiply the numbers in row 1 by -3 and add the results to the corresponding elements in row 2.

$$-3R_1 + R_2 \rightarrow R_2 \quad \begin{bmatrix} 1 & -2 & | & 2 \\ 0 & 0 & | & -1 \end{bmatrix}$$

This matrix corresponds to the system

$$x - 2y = 2$$
$$0x + 0y = -1.$$

Since the second equation is $0 = -1$, the system is inconsistent and, therefore, has no solution. The row $[0 \quad 0 \mid k]$ for any nonzero k is a signal that the given system is inconsistent.

| EXAMPLE 4 | **Solving a System of Equations with an Infinite Number of Solutions** |

Use the Gauss-Jordan method to solve the system

$$
\begin{aligned}
x + 2y - z &= 0 \\
3x - y + z &= 6 \\
-2x - 4y + 2z &= 0.
\end{aligned}
$$

SOLUTION The augmented matrix is

$$
\begin{bmatrix}
1 & 2 & -1 & 0 \\
3 & -1 & 1 & 6 \\
-2 & -4 & 2 & 0
\end{bmatrix}.
$$

We first get zeros in the second and third rows of column 1.

$$
\begin{matrix}
-3R_1 + R_2 \rightarrow R_2 \\
2R_1 + R_3 \rightarrow R_3
\end{matrix}
\quad
\begin{bmatrix}
1 & 2 & -1 & 0 \\
0 & -7 & 4 & 6 \\
0 & 0 & 0 & 0
\end{bmatrix}
$$

To continue, we get a zero in the first row of column 2 using the second row, as usual.

$$
2R_2 + 7R_1 \rightarrow R_1
\quad
\begin{bmatrix}
7 & 0 & 1 & 12 \\
0 & -7 & 4 & 6 \\
0 & 0 & 0 & 0
\end{bmatrix}
$$

We cannot get a zero for the first-row, third-column element without changing the form of the first two columns. We must multiply each of the first two rows by the reciprocal of the first nonzero number.

$$
\begin{matrix}
\frac{1}{7}R_1 \rightarrow R_1 \\
-\frac{1}{7}R_2 \rightarrow R_2
\end{matrix}
\quad
\begin{bmatrix}
1 & 0 & \frac{1}{7} & \frac{12}{7} \\
0 & 1 & -\frac{4}{7} & -\frac{6}{7} \\
0 & 0 & 0 & 0
\end{bmatrix}
$$

To complete the solution, write the equations that correspond to the first two rows of the matrix.

$$
x + \frac{1}{7}z = \frac{12}{7}
$$

$$
y - \frac{4}{7}z = -\frac{6}{7}
$$

Because both equations involve z, let z be the parameter. There are an infinite number of solutions, corresponding to the infinite number of values of z. Solve the first equation for x and the second for y to get

$$
x = \frac{12 - z}{7} \quad \text{and} \quad y = \frac{4z - 6}{7}.
$$

As shown in the previous section, the general solution is written

$$
\left(\frac{12 - z}{7}, \frac{4z - 6}{7}, z \right),
$$

where z is any real number. For example, $z = 2$ and $z = 12$ lead to the solutions $(10/7, 2/7, 2)$ and $(0, 6, 12)$.

EXAMPLE 5 Solving a System of Equations with an Infinite Number of Solutions

Consider the following system of equations.

$$x + 2y + 3z - w = 4$$
$$2x + 3y \quad\quad + w = -3$$
$$3x + 5y + 3z \quad\quad = 1$$

(a) Set this up as an augmented matrix, and verify that the result after the Gauss-Jordan method is

$$\begin{bmatrix} 1 & 0 & -9 & 5 & | & -18 \\ 0 & 1 & 6 & -3 & | & 11 \\ 0 & 0 & 0 & 0 & | & 0 \end{bmatrix}$$

(b) Find the solution to this system of equations.

SOLUTION To complete the solution, write the equations that correspond to the first two rows of the matrix.

$$x \quad - 9z + 5w = -18$$
$$y + 6z - 3w = 11$$

Because both equations involve both z and w, let z and w be parameters. There are an infinite number of solutions, corresponding to the infinite number of values of z and w. Solve the first equation for x and the second for y to get

$$x = -18 + 9z - 5w \quad\quad \text{and} \quad\quad y = 11 - 6z + 3w.$$

YOUR TURN 3 Use the Gauss-Jordan method to solve the system
$$2x - 2y + 3z - 4w = 6$$
$$3x + 2y + 5z - 3w = 7$$
$$4x + y + 2z - 2w = 8.$$

In an analogous manner to problems with a single parameter, the general solution is written

$$(-18 + 9z - 5w, 11 - 6z + 3w, z, w),$$

where z and w are any real numbers. For example, $z = 1$ and $w = -2$ leads to the solution $(1, -1, 1, -2)$. **TRY YOUR TURN 3**

Although the examples have used only systems with two equations in two unknowns, three equations in three unknowns, or three equations in four unknowns, the Gauss-Jordan method can be used for any system with n equations and m unknowns. The method becomes tedious with more than three equations in three unknowns; on the other hand, it is very suitable for use with graphing calculators and computers, which can solve fairly large systems quickly. Sophisticated computer programs modify the method to reduce round-off error. Other methods used for special types of large matrices are studied in a course on numerical analysis.

EXAMPLE 6 Soda Sales

A convenience store sells 23 sodas one summer afternoon in 12-, 16-, and 20-oz cups (small, medium, and large). The total volume of soda sold was 376 oz.

(a) Suppose that the prices for a small, medium, and large soda are $1, $1.25, and $1.40, respectively, and that the total sales were $28.45. How many of each size did the store sell?

SOLUTION As in Example 6 of the previous section, we will organize the information in a table.

	Soda Sales			
	Small	Medium	Large	Total
Number	x	y	z	23
Volume	12	16	20	376
Price	1.00	1.25	1.40	28.45

The three rows of the table lead to three equations: one for the total number of sodas, one for the volume, and one for the price.

$$x + y + z = 23$$
$$12x + 16y + 20z = 376$$
$$1.00x + 1.25y + 1.40z = 28.45$$

Set this up as an augmented matrix, and verify that the result after the Gauss-Jordan method is

$$\begin{bmatrix} 1 & 0 & 0 & | & 6 \\ 0 & 1 & 0 & | & 9 \\ 0 & 0 & 1 & | & 8 \end{bmatrix}.$$

The store sold 6 small, 9 medium, and 8 large sodas.

(b) Suppose the prices for small, medium, and large sodas are changed to $1, $2, and $3, respectively, but all other information is kept the same. How many of each size did the store sell?

SOLUTION Change the third equation to

$$x + 2y + 3z = 28.45$$

and go through the Gauss-Jordan method again. The result is

$$\begin{bmatrix} 1 & 0 & -1 & | & -2 \\ 0 & 1 & 2 & | & 25 \\ 0 & 0 & 0 & | & -19.55 \end{bmatrix}.$$

(If you do the row operations in a different order in this example, you will have different numbers in the last column.) The last row of this matrix says that $0 = -19.55$, so the system is inconsistent and has no solution. (In retrospect, this is clear, because each soda sells for a whole number of dollars, and the total amount of money is not a whole number of dollars. In general, however, it is not easy to tell whether a system of equations has a solution or not by just looking at it.)

(c) Suppose the prices are the same as in part (b), but the total revenue is $48. Now how many of each size did the store sell?

SOLUTION The third equation becomes

$$x + 2y + 3z = 48,$$

and the Gauss-Jordan method leads to

$$\begin{bmatrix} 1 & 0 & -1 & | & -2 \\ 0 & 1 & 2 & | & 25 \\ 0 & 0 & 0 & | & 0 \end{bmatrix}.$$

The system is dependent, similar to Example 4. Let z be the parameter, and solve the first two equations for x and y, yielding

$$x = z - 2 \quad \text{and} \quad y = 25 - 2z.$$

Remember that in this problem, x, y, and z must be nonnegative integers. From the equation for x, we must have

$$z \geq 2,$$

and from the equation for y, we must have

$$25 - 2z \geq 0,$$

from which we find

$$z \leq 12.5.$$

Therefore, we have 11 solutions corresponding to $z = 2, 3, \ldots, 12$.

(**d**) Give the solutions from part (c) that have the smallest and largest numbers of large sodas.

SOLUTION   For the smallest number of large sodas, let $z = 2$, giving $x = 2 - 2 = 0$ and $y = 25 - 2(2) = 21$. There are 0 small, 21 medium, and 2 large sodas.

For the largest number of large sodas, let $z = 12$, giving $x = 12 - 2 = 10$ and $y = 25 - 2(12) = 1$. There are 10 small, 1 medium, and 12 large sodas.

2.2   EXERCISES

Write the augmented matrix for each system. Do not solve.

1. $3x + y = 6$
$2x + 5y = 15$

2. $4x - 2y = 8$
$-7y = -12$

3. $2x + y + z = 3$
$3x - 4y + 2z = -7$
$x + y + z = 2$

4. $2x - 5y + 3z = 4$
$-4x + 2y - 7z = -5$
$3x - y = 8$

Write the system of equations associated with each augmented matrix.

5. $\begin{bmatrix} 1 & 0 & | & 2 \\ 0 & 1 & | & 3 \end{bmatrix}$

6. $\begin{bmatrix} 1 & 0 & | & 5 \\ 0 & 1 & | & -3 \end{bmatrix}$

7. $\begin{bmatrix} 1 & 0 & 0 & | & 4 \\ 0 & 1 & 0 & | & -5 \\ 0 & 0 & 1 & | & 1 \end{bmatrix}$

8. $\begin{bmatrix} 1 & 0 & 0 & | & 4 \\ 0 & 1 & 0 & | & 2 \\ 0 & 0 & 1 & | & 3 \end{bmatrix}$

9. _____ on a matrix correspond to transformations of a system of equations.

10. Describe in your own words what $2R_1 + R_3 \rightarrow R_3$ means.

Use the indicated row operations to change each matrix.

11. Replace R_2 by $R_1 + (-3)R_2$.
$\begin{bmatrix} 3 & 7 & 4 & | & 10 \\ 1 & 2 & 3 & | & 6 \\ 0 & 4 & 5 & | & 11 \end{bmatrix}$

12. Replace R_3 by $(-1)R_1 + 3R_3$.
$\begin{bmatrix} 3 & 2 & 6 & | & 18 \\ 2 & -2 & 5 & | & 7 \\ 1 & 0 & 5 & | & 20 \end{bmatrix}$

13. Replace R_1 by $(-2)R_2 + R_1$.
$\begin{bmatrix} 1 & 6 & 4 & | & 7 \\ 0 & 3 & 2 & | & 5 \\ 0 & 5 & 3 & | & 7 \end{bmatrix}$

14. Replace R_1 by $R_3 + (-3)R_1$.
$\begin{bmatrix} 1 & 0 & 4 & | & 21 \\ 0 & 6 & 5 & | & 30 \\ 0 & 0 & 12 & | & 15 \end{bmatrix}$

15. Replace R_1 by $\frac{1}{3}R_1$.
$\begin{bmatrix} 3 & 0 & 0 & | & 18 \\ 0 & 5 & 0 & | & 9 \\ 0 & 0 & 4 & | & 8 \end{bmatrix}$

16. Replace R_3 by $\frac{1}{6}R_3$.
$\begin{bmatrix} 1 & 0 & 0 & | & 30 \\ 0 & 1 & 0 & | & 17 \\ 0 & 0 & 6 & | & 162 \end{bmatrix}$

Use the Gauss-Jordan method to solve each system of equations.

17. $x + y = 5$
$3x + 2y = 12$

18. $x + 2y = 5$
$2x + y = -2$

19. $x + y = 7$
$4x + 3y = 22$

20. $4x - 2y = 3$
$-2x + 3y = 1$

21. $2x - 3y = 2$
$4x - 6y = 1$

22. $2x + 3y = 9$
$4x + 6y = 7$

23. $6x - 3y = 1$
$-12x + 6y = -2$

24. $x - y = 1$
$-x + y = -1$

25. $y = x - 3$
$y = 1 + z$
$z = 4 - x$

26. $x = 1 - y$
$2x = z$
$2z = -2 - y$

27. $2x - 2y = -5$
$2y + z = 0$
$2x + z = -7$

28. $x - z = -3$
$y + z = 9$
$-2x + 3y + 5z = 33$

29. $4x + 4y - 4z = 24$
$2x - y + z = -9$
$x - 2y + 3z = 1$

30. $x + 2y - 7z = -2$
$-2x - 5y + 2z = 1$
$3x + 5y + 4z = -9$

31. $3x + 5y - z = 0$
$4x - y + 2z = 1$
$7x + 4y + z = 1$

32. $3x - 6y + 3z = 11$
$2x + y - z = 2$
$5x - 5y + 2z = 6$

33.
$$5x - 4y + 2z = 6$$
$$5x + 3y - z = 11$$
$$15x - 5y + 3z = 23$$

34.
$$3x + 2y - z = -16$$
$$6x - 4y + 3z = 12$$
$$5x - 2y + 2z = 4$$

35.
$$2x + 3y + z = 9$$
$$4x + 6y + 2z = 18$$
$$-\frac{1}{2}x - \frac{3}{4}y - \frac{1}{4}z = -\frac{9}{4}$$

36.
$$3x - 5y - 2z = -9$$
$$-4x + 3y + z = 11$$
$$8x - 5y + 4z = 6$$

37.
$$x + 2y - w = 3$$
$$2x + 4z + 2w = -6$$
$$x + 2y - z = 6$$
$$2x - y + z + w = -3$$

38.
$$x + 3y - 2z - w = 9$$
$$2x + 4y + 2w = 10$$
$$-3x - 5y + 2z - w = -15$$
$$x - y - 3z + 2w = 6$$

39.
$$x + y - z + 2w = -20$$
$$2x - y + z + w = 11$$
$$3x - 2y + z - 2w = 27$$

40.
$$4x - 3y + z + w = 21$$
$$-2x - y + 2z + 7w = 2$$
$$10x - 5z - 20w = 15$$

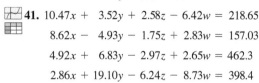

41.
$$10.47x + 3.52y + 2.58z - 6.42w = 218.65$$
$$8.62x - 4.93y - 1.75z + 2.83w = 157.03$$
$$4.92x + 6.83y - 2.97z + 2.65w = 462.3$$
$$2.86x + 19.10y - 6.24z - 8.73w = 398.4$$

42.
$$28.6x + 94.5y + 16.0z - 2.94w = 198.3$$
$$16.7x + 44.3y - 27.3z + 8.9w = 254.7$$
$$12.5x - 38.7y + 92.5z + 22.4w = 562.7$$
$$40.1x - 28.3y + 17.5z - 10.2w = 375.4$$

43. On National Public Radio, the "Weekend Edition" program on Sunday, July 29, 2001, posed the following puzzle: Draw a three-by-three square (three boxes across by three boxes down). Put the fraction 3/8 in the first square in the first row. Put the fraction 1/4 in the last square in the second row. The object is to put a fraction in each of the remaining boxes, so the three numbers in each row, each column, and each of the long diagonals add up to 1. Solve this puzzle by letting seven variables represent the seven unknown fractions, writing eight equations for the eight sums, and solving by the Gauss-Jordan method.

APPLICATIONS

Business and Economics

44. Surveys The president of Sam's Supermarkets plans to hire two public relations firms to survey 500 customers by phone, 750 by mail, and 250 by in-person interviews. The Garcia firm has personnel to do 10 phone surveys, 30 mail surveys, and 5 interviews per hour. The Wong firm can handle 20 phone surveys, 10 mail surveys, and 10 interviews per hour. For how many hours should each firm be hired to produce the exact number of surveys needed?

45. Investments Katherine Chong invests $10,000 received from her grandmother in three ways. With one part, she buys U.S. savings bonds at an interest rate of 2.5% per year. She uses the second part, which amounts to twice the first, to buy mutual funds that offer a return of 6% per year. She puts the rest of the money into a money market account paying 4.5% annual interest. The first year her investments bring a return of $470. How much did she invest in each way?

46. Office Technology Pyro-Tech, Inc. is upgrading office technology by purchasing inkjet printers, LCD monitors, and additional memory chips. The total number of pieces of hardware purchased is 46. The cost of each inkjet printer is $109, the cost of each LD monitor is $129, and the cost of each memory chip is $89. The total amount of money spent on new hardware came to $4774. They purchased two times as many memory chips as they did LCD monitors. Determine the number of each that was purchased. *Source: Nathan Borchelt.*

47. Manufacturing Fred's Furniture Factory has 1950 machine hours available each week in the cutting department, 1490 hours in the assembly department, and 2160 in the finishing department. Manufacturing a chair requires 0.2 hours of cutting, 0.3 hours of assembly, and 0.1 hours of finishing. A cabinet requires 0.5 hours of cutting, 0.4 hours of assembly, and 0.6 hours of finishing. A buffet requires 0.3 hours of cutting, 0.1 hours of assembly, and 0.4 hours of finishing. How many chairs, cabinets, and buffets should be produced in order to use all the available production capacity?

48. Manufacturing Nadir, Inc. produces three models of television sets: deluxe, super-deluxe, and ultra. Each deluxe set requires 2 hours of electronics work, 3 hours of assembly time, and 5 hours of finishing time. Each super-deluxe requires 1, 3, and 2 hours of electronics, assembly, and finishing time, respectively. Each ultra requires 2, 2, and 6 hours of the same work, respectively.

a. There are 54 hours available for electronics, 72 hours available for assembly, and 148 hours available for finishing per week. How many of each model should be produced each week if all available time is to be used?

b. Suppose everything is the same as in part a, but a super-deluxe set requires 1, rather than 2, hours of finishing time. How many solutions are there now?

c. Suppose everything is the same as in part b, but the total hours available for finishing changes from 148 hours to 144 hours. Now how many solutions are there?

49. Transportation An electronics company produces three models of stereo speakers, models A, B, and C, and can deliver them by truck, van, or SUV. A truck holds 2 boxes of model A, 2 of model B, and 3 of model C. A van holds 3 boxes of model A, 4 boxes of model B, and 2 boxes of model C. An SUV holds 3 boxes of model A, 5 boxes of model B, and 1 box of model C.

a. If 25 boxes of model A, 33 boxes of model B, and 22 boxes of model C are to be delivered, how many vehicles of each type should be used so that all operate at full capacity?

b. Model C has been discontinued. If 25 boxes of model A and 33 boxes of model B are to be delivered, how many vehicles of each type should be used so that all operate at full capacity?

50. Truck Rental   The U-Drive Rent-A-Truck company plans to spend $7 million on 200 new vehicles. Each commercial van will cost $35,000, each small truck $30,000, and each large truck $50,000. Past experience shows that they need twice as many vans as small trucks. How many of each type of vehicle can they buy?

51. Loans   To get the necessary funds for a planned expansion, a small company took out three loans totaling $25,000. Company owners were able to get interest rates of 8%, 9%, and 10%. They borrowed $1000 more at 9% than they borrowed at 10%. The total annual interest on the loans was $2190.

a. How much did they borrow at each rate?

b. Suppose we drop the condition that they borrowed $1000 more at 9% than at 10%. What can you say about the amount borrowed at 10%? What is the solution if the amount borrowed at 10% is $5000?

c. Suppose the bank sets a maximum of $10,000 at the lowest interest rate of 8%. Is a solution possible that still meets all of the original conditions?

d. Explain why $10,000 at 8%, $8000 at 9%, and $7000 at 10% is not a feasible solution for part c.

52. APPLY IT Transportation   An auto manufacturer sends cars from two plants, I and II, to dealerships A and B located in a midwestern city. Plant I has a total of 28 cars to send, and plant II has 8. Dealer A needs 20 cars, and dealer B needs 16. Transportation costs per car, based on the distance of each dealership from each plant, are $220 from I to A, $300 from I to B, $400 from II to A, and $180 from II to B. The manufacturer wants to limit transportation costs to $10,640. How many cars should be sent from each plant to each of the two dealerships?

53. Transportation   A manufacturer purchases a part for use at both of its plants — one at Roseville, California, the other at Akron, Ohio. The part is available in limited quantities from two suppliers. Each supplier has 75 units available. The Roseville plant needs 40 units, and the Akron plant requires 75 units. The first supplier charges $70 per unit delivered to Roseville and $90 per unit delivered to Akron. Corresponding costs from the second supplier are $80 and $120. The manufacturer wants to order a total of 75 units from the first, less expensive supplier, with the remaining 40 units to come from the second supplier. If the company spends $10,750 to purchase the required number of units for the two plants, find the number of units that should be sent from each supplier to each plant.

54. Packaging   A company produces three combinations of mixed vegetables that sell in 1-kg packages. Italian style combines 0.3 kg of zucchini, 0.3 of broccoli, and 0.4 of carrots. French style combines 0.6 kg of broccoli and 0.4 of carrots. Oriental style combines 0.2 kg of zucchini, 0.5 of broccoli, and 0.3 of carrots. The company has a stock of 16,200 kg of zucchini, 41,400 kg of broccoli, and 29,400 kg of carrots. How many packages of each style should it prepare to use up existing supplies?

55. Tents   L.L. Bean makes three sizes of Ultra Dome tents: two-person, four-person, and six-person models, which cost $129,

$179, and $229, respectively. A two-person tent provides 40 ft^2 of floor space, while a four-person and a six-person model provide 64 ft^2 and 88 ft^2 of floor space, respectively. *Source: L. L. Bean.* A recent order by an organization that takes children camping ordered enough tents to hold 200 people and provide 3200 ft^2 of floor space. The total cost was $8950, and we wish to know how many tents of each size were ordered.

a. How many solutions are there to this problem?

b. What is the solution with the most four-person tents?

c. What is the solution with the most two-person tents?

d. Discuss the company's pricing strategy that led to a system of equations that is dependent. Do you think that this is a coincidence or an example of logical thinking?

Life Sciences

56. Animal Breeding   An animal breeder can buy four types of food for Vietnamese pot-bellied pigs. Each case of Brand A contains 25 units of fiber, 30 units of protein, and 30 units of fat. Each case of Brand B contains 50 units of fiber, 30 units of protein, and 20 units of fat. Each case of Brand C contains 75 units of fiber, 30 units of protein, and 20 units of fat. Each case of Brand D contains 100 units of fiber, 60 units of protein, and 30 units of fat. How many cases of each should the breeder mix together to obtain a food that provides 1200 units of fiber, 600 units of protein, and 400 units of fat?

57. Dietetics   A hospital dietician is planning a special diet for a certain patient. The total amount per meal of food groups A, B, and C must equal 400 grams. The diet should include one-third as much of group A as of group B, and the sum of the amounts of group A and group C should equal twice the amount of group B.

a. How many grams of each food group should be included?

b. Suppose we drop the requirement that the diet include one-third as much of group A as of group B. Describe the set of all possible solutions.

c. Suppose that, in addition to the conditions given in the original problem, foods A and B cost 2 cents per gram and food C costs 3 cents per gram, and that a meal must cost $8. Is a solution possible?

58. Bacterial Food Requirements   Three species of bacteria are fed three foods, I, II, and III. A bacterium of the first species consumes 1.3 units each of foods I and II and 2.3 units of food III each day. A bacterium of the second species consumes 1.1 units of food I, 2.4 units of food II, and 3.7 units of food III each day. A bacterium of the third species consumes 8.1 units of I, 2.9 units of II, and 5.1 units of III each day. If 16,000 units of I, 28,000 units of II, and 44,000 units of III are supplied each day, how many of each species can be maintained in this environment?

59. Fish Food Requirements   A lake is stocked each spring with three species of fish, A, B, and C. Three foods, I, II, and III, are available in the lake. Each fish of species A requires an average of 1.32 units of food I, 2.9 units of food II, and 1.75 units of food III each day. Species B fish each require 2.1 units of food I, 0.95 unit of food II, and 0.6 unit of food III daily. Species C fish require 0.86, 1.52, and 2.01 units of I, II, and III per day, respectively. If 490 units of food I, 897 units of food II, and

653 units of food III are available daily, how many of each species should be stocked?

60. Agriculture According to data from a Texas agricultural report, the amount of nitrogen (in lb/acre), phosphate (in lb/acre), and labor (in hr/acre) needed to grow honeydews, yellow onions, and lettuce is given by the following table. *Source: The AMATYC Review.*

	Honeydews	Yellow Onions	Lettuce
Nitrogen	120	150	180
Phosphate	180	80	80
Labor	4.97	4.45	4.65

a. If the farmer has 220 acres, 29,100 lb of nitrogen, 32,600 lb of phosphate, and 480 hours of labor, is it possible to use all resources completely? If so, how many acres should he allot for each crop?

b. Suppose everything is the same as in part a, except that 1061 hours of labor are available. Is it possible to use all resources completely? If so, how many acres should he allot for each crop?

61. Archimedes' Problem Bovinum Archimedes is credited with the authorship of a famous problem involving the number of cattle of the sun god. A simplified version of the problem is stated as follows:

> *The sun god had a herd of cattle consisting of bulls and cows, one part of which was white, a second black, a third spotted, and a fourth brown.*
>
> *Among the bulls, the number of white ones was one-half plus one-third the number of the black greater than the brown; the number of the black, one-quarter plus one-fifth the number of the spotted greater than the brown; the number of the spotted, one-sixth and one-seventh the number of the white greater than the brown.*
>
> *Among the cows, the number of white ones was one-third plus one-quarter of the total black cattle; the number of the black, one-quarter plus one-fifth the total of the spotted cattle; the number of the spotted, one-fifth plus one-sixth the total of the brown cattle; the number of the brown, one-sixth plus one-seventh the total of the white cattle.*
>
> *What was the composition of the herd?*

Source: 100 Great Problems of Elementary Mathematics.
The problem can be solved by converting the statements into two systems of equations, using X, Y, Z, and T for the number of white, black, spotted, and brown bulls, respectively, and x, y, z, and t for the number of white, black, spotted, and brown cows, respectively. For example, the first statement can be written as $X = (1/2 + 1/3)Y + T$ and then reduced. The result is the following two systems of equations:

$$6X - 5Y = 6T \qquad 12x - 7y = 7Y$$
$$20Y - 9Z = 20T \quad \text{and} \quad 20y - 9z = 9Z$$
$$42Z - 13X = 42T \qquad 30z - 11t = 11T$$
$$-13x + 42t = 13X$$

a. Show that these two systems of equations represent Archimedes' Problem Bovinum.

b. If it is known that the number of brown bulls, T, is 4,149,387, use the Gauss-Jordan method to first find a solution to the 3×3 system and then use these values and the Gauss-Jordan method to find a solution to the 4×4 system of equations.

62. Health The U.S. National Center for Health Statistics tracks the major causes of death in the United States. After a steady increase, the death rate by cancer has decreased since the early 1990s. The table lists the age-adjusted death rate per 100,000 people for 4 years. *Source: The New York Times 2010 Almanac.*

Year	Rate
1980	183.9
1990	203.3
2000	196.5
2006	187.0

a. If the relationship between the death rate R and the year t is expressed as $R = at^2 + bt + c$, where $t = 0$ corresponds to 1980, use data from 1980, 1990, and 2000 and a linear system of equations to determine the constants a, b, and c.

b. Use the equation from part a to predict the rate in 2006, and compare the result with the actual data.

c. If the relationship between the death rate R and the year t is expressed as $R = at^3 + bt^2 + ct + d$, where $t = 0$ corresponds to 1980, use all four data points and a linear system of equations to determine the constants a, b, c, and d.

d. Discuss the appropriateness of the functions used in parts a and c to model this data.

Social Sciences

63. Modeling War One of the factors that contribute to the success or failure of a particular army during war is its ability to get new troops ready for service. It is possible to analyze the rate of change in the number of troops of two hypothetical armies with the following simplified model,

$$\text{Rate of increase (RED ARMY)} = 200{,}000 - 0.5r - 0.3b$$
$$\text{Rate of increase (BLUE ARMY)} = 350{,}000 - 0.5r - 0.7b,$$

where r is the number of soldiers in the Red Army at a given time and b is the number of soldiers in the Blue Army at a given time. The factors 0.5 and 0.7 represent each army's efficiency of bringing new soldiers to the fight. *Source: Journal of Peace Research.*

a. Solve this system of equations to determine the number of soldiers in each army when the rate of increase for each is zero.

b. Describe what might be going on in a war when the rate of increase is zero.

64. Traffic Control At rush hours, substantial traffic congestion is encountered at the traffic intersections shown in the figure on the next page. (The streets are one-way, as shown by the arrows.)

The city wishes to improve the signals at these corners so as to speed the flow of traffic. The traffic engineers first gather data. As the figure shows, 700 cars per hour come down M Street to intersection A, and 300 cars per hour come down 10th Street to intersection A. A total of x_1 of these cars leave A on M Street, and x_4 cars leave A on 10th Street. The number of cars entering A must equal the number leaving, so that

$$x_1 + x_4 = 700 + 300$$

or

$$x_1 + x_4 = 1000.$$

For intersection B, x_1 cars enter on M Street and x_2 on 11th Street. The figure shows that 900 cars leave B on 11th and 200 on M. Thus,

$$x_1 + x_2 = 900 + 200$$
$$x_1 + x_2 = 1100.$$

a. Write two equations representing the traffic entering and leaving intersections C and D.

b. Use the four equations to set up an augmented matrix, and solve the system by the Gauss-Jordan method, using x_4 as the parameter.

c. Based on your solution to part b, what are the largest and smallest possible values for the number of cars leaving intersection A on 10th Street?

d. Answer the question in part c for the other three variables.

e. Verify that you could have discarded any one of the four original equations without changing the solution. What does this tell you about the original problem?

General Interest

65. Snack Food   According to the nutrition labels on the package, a single serving of Oreos® has 10 g of fat, 36 g of carbohydrates, 2 g of protein, and 240 calories. The figures for a single serving of Twix® are 14 g, 37 g, 3 g, and 280 calories. The figures for a single serving of trail mix are 20 g, 23 g, 11 g, and 295 calories. How many calories are in each gram of fat, carbohydrate, and protein? *Source: The Mathematics Teacher.* *

*For a discussion of some complications that can come up in solving linear systems, read the original article: Szydlik, Stephen D., "The Problem with the Snack Food Problem," *The Mathematics Teacher*, Vol. 103, No. 1, Aug. 2009, p. 18–28.

66. Basketball   Kobe Bryant has the second highest single game point total in the NBA. Bryant scored 81 points for the Los Angeles Lakers on January 22, 2006, against the Toronto Raptors. Bryant made a total of 46 baskets, including foul shots (worth one point), field goals (worth two points), and three-point shots (worth three points). The number of field goal shots he made is equal to three times the number of three pointers he made. Find the number of foul shots, field goals, and three pointers Bryant made. *Source: ESPN.*

67. Toys   One hundred toys are to be given out to a group of children. A ball costs $2, a doll costs $3, and a car costs $4. A total of $295 was spent on the toys.

a. A ball weighs 12 oz, a doll 16 oz, and a car 18 oz. The total weight of all the toys is 1542 oz. Find how many of each toy there are.

b. Now suppose the weight of a ball, doll, and car are 11, 15, and 19 oz, respectively. If the total weight is still 1542 oz, how many solutions are there now?

c. Keep the weights as in part b, but change the total weight to 1480 oz. How many solutions are there?

d. Give the solution to part c that has the smallest number of cars.

e. Give the solution to part c that has the largest number of cars.

68. Ice Cream   Researchers have determined that the amount of sugar contained in ice cream helps to determine the overall "degree of like" that a consumer has toward that particular flavor. They have also determined that too much or too little sugar will have the same negative affect on the "degree of like" and that this relationship follows a quadratic function. In an experiment conducted at Pennsylvania State University, the following condensed table was obtained. *Source: Journal of Food Science.*

Percentage of Sugar	Degree of Like
8	5.4
13	6.3
18	5.6

a. Use this information and the Gauss-Jordan method to determine the coefficients a, b, c, of the quadratic equation

$$y = ax^2 + bx + c,$$

where y is the "degree of like" and x is the percentage of sugar in the ice cream mix.

b. Repeat part a by using the quadratic regression feature on a graphing calculator. Compare your answers.

69. Lights Out   The Tiger Electronics' game, Lights Out, consists of five rows of five lighted buttons. When a button is pushed, it changes the on/off status of it and the status of all of its vertical and horizontal neighbors. For any given situation where some of the lights are on and some are off, the goal of the game is to push buttons until all of the lights are turned off. It turns out that for any given array of lights, solving a system of equations can be used to develop a strategy for turning the lights out. The following system of equations can be used to solve the problem for a simplified version of

the game with 2 rows of 2 buttons where all of the lights are initially turned on:

$$x_{11} + x_{12} + x_{21} = 1$$
$$x_{11} + x_{12} + x_{22} = 1$$
$$x_{11} + x_{21} + x_{22} = 1$$
$$x_{12} + x_{21} + x_{22} = 1,$$

where $x_{ij} = 1$ if the light in row i, column j, is on and $x_{ij} = 0$ when it is off. The order in which the buttons are pushed does not matter, so we are only seeking which buttons should be pushed. *Source: Mathematics Magazine.*

a. Solve this system of equations and determine a strategy to turn the lights out. (*Hint:* While doing row operations, if an odd number is found, immediately replace this value with a 1; if an even number is found, then immediately replace that number with a zero. This is called modulo 2 arithmetic, and it is necessary in problems dealing with on/off switches.)

b. Resolve the equation with the right side changed to (0, 1, 1, 0).

70. Baseball   Ichiro Suzuki holds the American League record for the most hits in a single baseball season. In 2004, Suzuki had a total of 262 hits for the Seattle Mariners. He hit three fewer triples than home runs, and he hit three times as many doubles as home runs. Suzuki also hit 45 times as many singles as triples. Find the number of singles, doubles, triples, and home runs hit by Suzuki during the season. *Source: Baseball Almanac.*

YOUR TURN ANSWERS

1. $(5, -2)$ **2.** $(7, 2, -3)$
3. $(17/9 + w/3, -4/9 - 2w/3, 4/9 + 2w/3, w)$

2.3 Addition and Subtraction of Matrices

APPLY IT   A company sends monthly shipments to its warehouses in several cities. How might the company keep track of the shipments to each warehouse most efficiently?

In the previous section, matrices were used to store information about systems of linear equations. In this section, we begin to study calculations with matrices, which we will use in Examples 1, 5, and 7 to answer the question posed above.

The use of matrices has gained increasing importance in the fields of management, natural science, and social science because matrices provide a convenient way to organize data, as Example 1 demonstrates.

EXAMPLE 1   **Furniture Shipments**

The EZ Life Company manufactures sofas and armchairs in three models, A, B, and C. The company has regional warehouses in New York, Chicago, and San Francisco. In its August shipment, the company sends 10 model-A sofas, 12 model-B sofas, 5 model-C sofas, 15 model-A chairs, 20 model-B chairs, and 8 model-C chairs to each warehouse. Use a matrix to organize this information.

APPLY IT   **SOLUTION**   To organize this data, we might tabulate the data in a chart.

Number of Furniture Pieces			
	Model		
	A	B	C
Furniture Type *Sofas*	10	12	5
Chairs	15	20	8

With the understanding that the numbers in each row refer to the furniture type (sofa, chair) and the numbers in each column refer to the model (A, B, C), the same information can be given by a matrix, as follows.

$$M = \begin{bmatrix} 10 & 12 & 5 \\ 15 & 20 & 8 \end{bmatrix}$$

Matrices often are named with capital letters, as in Example 1. Matrices are classified by **size**; that is, by the number of rows and columns they contain. For example, matrix M above has two rows and three columns. This matrix is a 2×3 (read "2 by 3") matrix. By definition, a matrix with m rows and n columns is an $m \times n$ matrix. The number of rows is always given first.

EXAMPLE 2 Matrix Size

(a) The matrix $\begin{bmatrix} -3 & 5 \\ 2 & 0 \\ 5 & -1 \end{bmatrix}$ is a 3×2 matrix.

(b) $\begin{bmatrix} 0.5 & 8 & 0.9 \\ 0 & 5.1 & -3 \\ -4 & 0 & 5 \end{bmatrix}$ is a 3×3 matrix.

(c) $\begin{bmatrix} 1 & 6 & 5 & -2 & 5 \end{bmatrix}$ is a 1×5 matrix.

(d) $\begin{bmatrix} 3 \\ -5 \\ 0 \\ 2 \end{bmatrix}$ is a 4×1 matrix.

A matrix with the same number of rows as columns is called a **square matrix**. The matrix in Example 2(b) is a square matrix.

A matrix containing only one row is called a **row matrix** or a **row vector**. The matrix in Example 2(c) is a row matrix, as are

$$\begin{bmatrix} 5 & 8 \end{bmatrix}, \qquad \begin{bmatrix} 6 & -9 & 2 \end{bmatrix}, \qquad \text{and} \qquad \begin{bmatrix} -4 & 0 & 0 & 0 \end{bmatrix}.$$

A matrix of only one column, as in Example 2(d), is a **column matrix** or a **column vector**.

Equality for matrices is defined as follows.

Matrix Equality

Two matrices are equal if they are the same size and if each pair of corresponding elements is equal.

By this definition,

$$\begin{bmatrix} 2 & 1 \\ 3 & -5 \end{bmatrix} \qquad \text{and} \qquad \begin{bmatrix} 1 & 2 \\ -5 & 3 \end{bmatrix}$$

are not equal (even though they contain the same elements and are the same size) since the corresponding elements differ.

EXAMPLE 3 Matrix Equality

(a) From the definition of matrix equality given above, the only way that the statement

$$\begin{bmatrix} 2 & 1 \\ p & q \end{bmatrix} = \begin{bmatrix} x & y \\ -1 & 0 \end{bmatrix}$$

can be true is if $2 = x$, $1 = y$, $p = -1$, and $q = 0$.

(b) The statement

$$\begin{bmatrix} x \\ y \end{bmatrix} = \begin{bmatrix} 1 \\ -3 \\ 0 \end{bmatrix}$$

can never be true, since the two matrices are different sizes. (One is 2×1 and the other is 3×1.)

Addition

The matrix given in Example 1,

$$M = \begin{bmatrix} 10 & 12 & 5 \\ 15 & 20 & 8 \end{bmatrix},$$

shows the August shipment from the EZ Life plant to each of its warehouses. If matrix N below gives the September shipment to the New York warehouse, what is the total shipment of each item of furniture to the New York warehouse for these two months?

$$N = \begin{bmatrix} 45 & 35 & 20 \\ 65 & 40 & 35 \end{bmatrix}$$

If 10 model-A sofas were shipped in August and 45 in September, then altogether $10 + 45 = 55$ model-A sofas were shipped in the two months. The other corresponding entries can be added in a similar way to get a new matrix Q, which represents the total shipment for the two months.

$$Q = \begin{bmatrix} 55 & 47 & 25 \\ 80 & 60 & 43 \end{bmatrix}$$

It is convenient to refer to Q as the sum of M and N.

The way these two matrices were added illustrates the following definition of addition of matrices.

Adding Matrices

The sum of two $m \times n$ matrices X and Y is the $m \times n$ matrix $X + Y$ in which each element is the sum of the corresponding elements of X and Y.

| CAUTION | It is important to remember that only matrices that are the same size can be added.

EXAMPLE 4 Adding Matrices

Find each sum, if possible.

SOLUTION

YOUR TURN 1 Find each sum, if possible.

(a) $\begin{bmatrix} 3 & 4 & 5 & 6 \\ 1 & 2 & 3 & 4 \end{bmatrix} + \begin{bmatrix} 1 & -2 & 4 \\ -2 & -4 & 8 \end{bmatrix}$

(b) $\begin{bmatrix} 3 & 4 & 5 \\ 1 & 2 & 3 \end{bmatrix} + \begin{bmatrix} 1 & -2 & 4 \\ -2 & -4 & 8 \end{bmatrix}$

(a) $\begin{bmatrix} 5 & -6 \\ 8 & 9 \end{bmatrix} + \begin{bmatrix} -4 & 6 \\ 8 & -3 \end{bmatrix} = \begin{bmatrix} 5 + (-4) & -6 + 6 \\ 8 + 8 & 9 + (-3) \end{bmatrix} = \begin{bmatrix} 1 & 0 \\ 16 & 6 \end{bmatrix}$

(b) The matrices

$$A = \begin{bmatrix} 5 & -8 \\ 6 & 2 \end{bmatrix} \quad \text{and} \quad B = \begin{bmatrix} 3 & -9 & 1 \\ 4 & 2 & -5 \end{bmatrix}$$

are different sizes. Therefore, the sum $A + B$ does not exist.   **TRY YOUR TURN 1**

EXAMPLE 5 Furniture Shipments

The September shipments from the EZ Life Company to the New York, San Francisco, and Chicago warehouses are given in matrices N, S, and C below.

$$N = \begin{bmatrix} 45 & 35 & 20 \\ 65 & 40 & 35 \end{bmatrix} \quad S = \begin{bmatrix} 30 & 32 & 28 \\ 43 & 47 & 30 \end{bmatrix} \quad C = \begin{bmatrix} 22 & 25 & 38 \\ 31 & 34 & 35 \end{bmatrix}$$

What was the total amount shipped to the three warehouses in September?

APPLY IT

SOLUTION The total of the September shipments is represented by the sum of the three matrices N, S, and C.

$$N + S + C = \begin{bmatrix} 45 & 35 & 20 \\ 65 & 40 & 35 \end{bmatrix} + \begin{bmatrix} 30 & 32 & 28 \\ 43 & 47 & 30 \end{bmatrix} + \begin{bmatrix} 22 & 25 & 38 \\ 31 & 34 & 35 \end{bmatrix}$$

$$= \begin{bmatrix} 97 & 92 & 86 \\ 139 & 121 & 100 \end{bmatrix}$$

For example, this sum shows that the total number of model-C sofas shipped to the three warehouses in September was 86.

Subtraction Subtraction of matrices is defined similarly to addition.

Subtracting Matrices
The difference of two $m \times n$ matrices X and Y is the $m \times n$ matrix $X - Y$ in which each element is found by subtracting the corresponding elements of X and Y.

EXAMPLE 6 Subtracting Matrices

Subtract each pair of matrices, if possible.
SOLUTION

(a) $\begin{bmatrix} 8 & 6 & -4 \\ -2 & 7 & 5 \end{bmatrix} - \begin{bmatrix} 3 & 5 & -8 \\ -4 & 2 & 9 \end{bmatrix} = \begin{bmatrix} 8-3 & 6-5 & -4-(-8) \\ -2-(-4) & 7-2 & 5-9 \end{bmatrix} = \begin{bmatrix} 5 & 1 & 4 \\ 2 & 5 & -4 \end{bmatrix}.$

(b) The matrices

$$\begin{bmatrix} -2 & 5 \\ 0 & 1 \end{bmatrix} \quad \text{and} \quad \begin{bmatrix} 3 \\ 5 \end{bmatrix}$$

YOUR TURN 2 Calculate

$\begin{bmatrix} 3 & 4 & 5 \\ 1 & 2 & 3 \end{bmatrix} - \begin{bmatrix} 1 & -2 & 4 \\ -2 & -4 & 8 \end{bmatrix}.$

are different sizes and cannot be subtracted.   **TRY YOUR TURN 2**

EXAMPLE 7 Furniture Shipments

APPLY IT

During September the Chicago warehouse of the EZ Life Company shipped out the following numbers of each model.

$$K = \begin{bmatrix} 5 & 10 & 8 \\ 11 & 14 & 15 \end{bmatrix}$$

What was the Chicago warehouse inventory on October 1, taking into account only the number of items received and sent out during the month?

Method 1
Calculating by Hand

SOLUTION The number of each kind of item received during September is given by matrix C from Example 5; the number of each model sent out during September is given by matrix K. The October 1 inventory will be represented by the matrix $C - K$:

[A]-[B]
$\begin{bmatrix} 17 & 15 & 30 \\ 20 & 20 & 20 \end{bmatrix}$

$$\begin{bmatrix} 22 & 25 & 38 \\ 31 & 34 & 35 \end{bmatrix} - \begin{bmatrix} 5 & 10 & 8 \\ 11 & 14 & 15 \end{bmatrix} = \begin{bmatrix} 17 & 15 & 30 \\ 20 & 20 & 20 \end{bmatrix}.$$

FIGURE 12

Method 2
Graphing Calculator

Matrix operations are easily performed on a graphing calculator. Figure 12 shows the previous operation; the matrices A and B were already entered into the calculator.

TECHNOLOGY NOTE

Spreadsheet programs are designed to effectively organize data that can be represented in rows and columns. Accordingly, matrix operations are also easily performed on spreadsheets. See the *Graphing Calculator and Excel Spreadsheet Manual* available with this book for details.

2.3 EXERCISES

Decide whether each statement is true or false. If false, tell why.

1. $\begin{bmatrix} 1 & 3 \\ 5 & 7 \end{bmatrix} = \begin{bmatrix} 1 & 5 \\ 3 & 7 \end{bmatrix}$

2. $\begin{bmatrix} 1 \\ 2 \\ 3 \end{bmatrix} = \begin{bmatrix} 1 & 2 & 3 \end{bmatrix}$

3. $\begin{bmatrix} x \\ y \end{bmatrix} = \begin{bmatrix} -2 \\ 8 \end{bmatrix}$ if $x = -2$ and $y = 8$.

4. $\begin{bmatrix} 3 & 5 & 2 & 8 \\ 1 & -1 & 4 & 0 \end{bmatrix}$ is a 4 × 2 matrix.

5. $\begin{bmatrix} 1 & 9 & -4 \\ 3 & 7 & 2 \\ -1 & 1 & 0 \end{bmatrix}$ is a square matrix.

6. $\begin{bmatrix} 2 & 4 & -1 \\ 3 & 7 & 5 \\ 0 & 0 & 0 \end{bmatrix} = \begin{bmatrix} 2 & 4 & -1 \\ 3 & 7 & 5 \end{bmatrix}$

Find the size of each matrix. Identify any square, column, or row matrices.

7. $\begin{bmatrix} -4 & 8 \\ 2 & 3 \end{bmatrix}$

8. $\begin{bmatrix} 2 & -3 & 7 \\ 1 & 0 & 4 \end{bmatrix}$

9. $\begin{bmatrix} -6 & 8 & 0 & 0 \\ 4 & 1 & 9 & 2 \\ 3 & -5 & 7 & 1 \end{bmatrix}$

10. $\begin{bmatrix} 8 & -2 & 4 & 6 & 3 \end{bmatrix}$

11. $\begin{bmatrix} -7 \\ 5 \end{bmatrix}$

12. $\begin{bmatrix} -9 \end{bmatrix}$

13. The sum of an $n \times m$ matrix and an $m \times n$ matrix, where $m \neq n$, is _____.

14. If A is a 5 × 2 matrix and $A + K = A$, what do you know about K?

Find the values of the variables in each equation.

15. $\begin{bmatrix} 3 & 4 \\ -8 & 1 \end{bmatrix} = \begin{bmatrix} 3 & x \\ y & z \end{bmatrix}$

16. $\begin{bmatrix} -5 \\ y \end{bmatrix} = \begin{bmatrix} -5 \\ 8 \end{bmatrix}$

17. $\begin{bmatrix} s-4 & t+2 \\ -5 & 7 \end{bmatrix} = \begin{bmatrix} 6 & 2 \\ -5 & r \end{bmatrix}$

18. $\begin{bmatrix} 9 & 7 \\ r & 0 \end{bmatrix} = \begin{bmatrix} m-3 & n+5 \\ 8 & 0 \end{bmatrix}$

19. $\begin{bmatrix} a+2 & 3b & 4c \\ d & 7f & 8 \end{bmatrix} + \begin{bmatrix} -7 & 2b & 6 \\ -3d & -6 & -2 \end{bmatrix} = \begin{bmatrix} 15 & 25 & 6 \\ -8 & 1 & 6 \end{bmatrix}$

20. $\begin{bmatrix} a+2 & 3z+1 & 5m \\ 4k & 0 & 3 \end{bmatrix} + \begin{bmatrix} 3a & 2z & 5m \\ 2k & 5 & 6 \end{bmatrix} = \begin{bmatrix} 10 & -14 & 80 \\ 10 & 5 & 9 \end{bmatrix}$

Perform the indicated operations, where possible.

21. $\begin{bmatrix} 2 & 4 & 5 & -7 \\ 6 & -3 & 12 & 0 \end{bmatrix} + \begin{bmatrix} 8 & 0 & -10 & 1 \\ -2 & 8 & -9 & 11 \end{bmatrix}$

22. $\begin{bmatrix} 1 & 5 \\ 2 & -3 \\ 3 & 7 \end{bmatrix} + \begin{bmatrix} 2 & 3 \\ 8 & 5 \\ -1 & 9 \end{bmatrix}$

23. $\begin{bmatrix} 1 & 3 & -2 \\ 4 & 7 & 1 \end{bmatrix} + \begin{bmatrix} 3 & 0 \\ 6 & 4 \\ -5 & 2 \end{bmatrix}$

24. $\begin{bmatrix} 8 & 0 & -3 \\ 1 & 19 & -5 \end{bmatrix} - \begin{bmatrix} 1 & -5 & 2 \\ 3 & 9 & -8 \end{bmatrix}$

25. $\begin{bmatrix} 2 & 8 & 12 & 0 \\ 7 & 4 & -1 & 5 \\ 1 & 2 & 0 & 10 \end{bmatrix} - \begin{bmatrix} 1 & 3 & 6 & 9 \\ 2 & -3 & -3 & 4 \\ 8 & 0 & -2 & 17 \end{bmatrix}$

26. $\begin{bmatrix} 2 & 1 \\ 5 & -3 \\ -7 & 2 \\ 9 & 0 \end{bmatrix} + \begin{bmatrix} 1 & -8 & 0 \\ 5 & 3 & 2 \\ -6 & 7 & -5 \\ 2 & -1 & 0 \end{bmatrix}$

27. $\begin{bmatrix} 2 & 3 \\ -2 & 4 \end{bmatrix} + \begin{bmatrix} 4 & 3 \\ 7 & 8 \end{bmatrix} - \begin{bmatrix} 3 & 2 \\ 1 & 4 \end{bmatrix}$

28. $\begin{bmatrix} 4 & 3 \\ 1 & 2 \end{bmatrix} - \begin{bmatrix} 1 & 1 \\ 1 & 0 \end{bmatrix} + \begin{bmatrix} 1 & 1 \\ 1 & 4 \end{bmatrix}$

29. $\begin{bmatrix} 2 & -1 \\ 0 & 13 \end{bmatrix} - \begin{bmatrix} 4 & 8 \\ -5 & 7 \end{bmatrix} + \begin{bmatrix} 12 & 7 \\ 5 & 3 \end{bmatrix}$

30. $\begin{bmatrix} 5 & 8 \\ -3 & 1 \end{bmatrix} + \begin{bmatrix} 0 & 1 \\ -2 & -2 \end{bmatrix} + \begin{bmatrix} -5 & -8 \\ 6 & 1 \end{bmatrix}$

31. $\begin{bmatrix} -4x+2y & -3x+y \\ 6x-3y & 2x-5y \end{bmatrix} + \begin{bmatrix} -8x+6y & 2x \\ 3y-5x & 6x+4y \end{bmatrix}$

32. $\begin{bmatrix} 4k-8y \\ 6z-3x \\ 2k+5a \\ -4m+2n \end{bmatrix} - \begin{bmatrix} 5k+6y \\ 2z+5x \\ 4k+6a \\ 4m-2n \end{bmatrix}$

33. For matrices $X = \begin{bmatrix} x & y \\ z & w \end{bmatrix}$ and $0 = \begin{bmatrix} 0 & 0 \\ 0 & 0 \end{bmatrix}$, find the matrix $0 - X$.

Using matrices $O = \begin{bmatrix} 0 & 0 \\ 0 & 0 \end{bmatrix}$, $P = \begin{bmatrix} m & n \\ p & q \end{bmatrix}$, $T = \begin{bmatrix} r & s \\ t & u \end{bmatrix}$, and $X = \begin{bmatrix} x & y \\ z & w \end{bmatrix}$, verify the statements in Exercises 34–37.

34. $X + T = T + X$ (commutative property of addition of matrices)

35. $X + (T + P) = (X + T) + P$ (associative property of addition of matrices)

36. $X - X = O$ (inverse property of addition of matrices)

37. $P + O = P$ (identity property of addition of matrices)

38. Which of the above properties are valid for matrices that are not square?

APPLICATIONS

Business and Economics

39. **Management** A toy company has plants in Boston, Chicago, and Seattle that manufacture toy phones and calculators. The following matrix gives the production costs (in dollars) for each item at the Boston plant:

	Phones	Calculators
Material	4.27	6.94
Labor	3.45	3.65

a. In Chicago, a phone costs $4.05 for material and $3.27 for labor; a calculator costs $7.01 for material and $3.51 for labor. In Seattle, material costs are $4.40 for a phone and $6.90 for a calculator; labor costs are $3.54 for a phone and $3.76 for a calculator. Write the production cost matrices for Chicago and Seattle.

b. Suppose labor costs increase by $0.11 per item in Chicago and material costs there increase by $0.37 for a phone and $0.42 for a calculator. What is the new production cost matrix for Chicago?

40. Management There are three convenience stores in Folsom. This week, store I sold 88 loaves of bread, 48 qt of milk, 16 jars of peanut butter, and 112 lb of cold cuts. Store II sold 105 loaves of bread, 72 qt of milk, 21 jars of peanut butter, and 147 lb of cold cuts. Store III sold 60 loaves of bread, 40 qt of milk, no peanut butter, and 50 lb of cold cuts.

a. Use a 4×3 matrix to express the sales information for the three stores.

b. During the following week, sales on these products at store I increased by 25%; sales at store II increased by 1/3; and sales at store III increased by 10%. Write the sales matrix for that week.

c. Write a matrix that represents total sales over the two-week period.

Life Sciences

41. Dietetics A dietician prepares a diet specifying the amounts a patient should eat of four basic food groups: group I, meats; group II, fruits and vegetables; group III, breads and starches; group IV, milk products. Amounts are given in "exchanges" that represent 1 oz (meat), 1/2 cup (fruits and vegetables), 1 slice (bread), 8 oz (milk), or other suitable measurements.

a. The number of "exchanges" for breakfast for each of the four food groups, respectively, are 2, 1, 2, and 1; for lunch, 3, 2, 2, and 1; and for dinner, 4, 3, 2, and 1. Write a 3×4 matrix using this information.

b. The amounts of fat, carbohydrates, and protein (in appropriate units) in each food group, respectively, are as follows.

Fat: 5, 0, 0, 10

Carbohydrates: 0, 10, 15, 12

Protein: 7, 1, 2, 8

Use this information to write a 4×3 matrix.

c. There are 8 calories per exchange of fat, 4 calories per exchange of carbohydrates, and 5 calories per exchange of protein. Summarize this data in a 3×1 matrix.

42. Animal Growth At the beginning of a laboratory experiment, five baby rats measured 5.6, 6.4, 6.9, 7.6, and 6.1 cm in length, and weighed 144, 138, 149, 152, and 146 g, respectively.

a. Write a 2×5 matrix using this information.

b. At the end of two weeks, their lengths (in centimeters) were 10.2, 11.4, 11.4, 12.7, and 10.8 and their weights (in grams) were 196, 196, 225, 250, and 230. Write a 2×5 matrix with this information.

c. Use matrix subtraction and the matrices found in parts a and b to write a matrix that gives the amount of change in length and weight for each rat.

d. During the third week, the rats grew by the amounts shown in the matrix below.

$$\begin{array}{c} \text{Length} \\ \text{Weight} \end{array} \begin{bmatrix} 1.8 & 1.5 & 2.3 & 1.8 & 2.0 \\ 25 & 22 & 29 & 33 & 20 \end{bmatrix}$$

What were their lengths and weights at the end of this week?

43. Testing Medication A drug company is testing 200 patients to see if Painfree (a new headache medicine) is effective. Half the patients receive Painfree and half receive a placebo. The data on the first 50 patients is summarized in this matrix:

$$\begin{array}{c} \\ \text{Painfree} \\ \text{Placebo} \end{array} \overset{\text{Pain Relief Obtained}}{\begin{array}{cc} \text{Yes} & \text{No} \end{array}} \begin{bmatrix} 22 & 3 \\ 8 & 17 \end{bmatrix}.$$

a. Of those who took the placebo, how many got relief?

b. Of those who took the new medication, how many got no relief?

c. The test was repeated on three more groups of 50 patients each, with the results summarized by these matrices.

$$\begin{bmatrix} 21 & 4 \\ 6 & 19 \end{bmatrix} \quad \begin{bmatrix} 19 & 6 \\ 10 & 15 \end{bmatrix} \quad \begin{bmatrix} 23 & 2 \\ 3 & 22 \end{bmatrix}$$

Find the total results for all 200 patients.

d. On the basis of these results, does it appear that Painfree is effective?

44. Motorcycle Helmets The following table shows the percentage of motorcyclists in various regions of the country who used helmets compliant with federal safety regulations and the percentage who used helmets that were noncompliant in two recent years. *Source: NHTSA.*

2008	Compliant	Noncompliant
Northeast	45	8
Midwest	67	16
South	61	14
West	71	5

2009	Compliant	Noncompliant
Northeast	61	15
Midwest	67	8
South	65	6
West	83	4

a. Write two matrices for the 2008 and 2009 helmet usage.

b. Use the two matrices from part a to write a matrix showing the change in helmet usage from 2008 to 2009.

c. Analyze the results from part b and discuss the extent to which changes from 2008 to 2009 differ from one region to another.

45. Life Expectancy The following table gives the life expectancy of African American males and females and white American males and females at the beginning of each decade since 1970. *Source: The New York Times 2010 Almanac.*

Year	African American Male	African American Female	White American Male	White American Female
1970	60.0	68.3	68.0	75.6
1980	63.8	72.5	70.7	78.1
1990	64.5	73.6	72.7	79.4
2000	68.3	75.2	74.9	80.1

a. Write a matrix for the life expectancy of African Americans.

b. Write a matrix for the life expectancy of white Americans.

c. Use the matrices from parts a and b to write a matrix showing the difference between the two groups.

d. Analyze the results from part c and discuss any noticeable trends.

46. Educational Attainment The table below gives the educational attainment of the U.S. population 25 years and older since 1970. *Source: U. S. Census Bureau.*

Year	Male: Percentage with 4 Years of High School or More	Male: Percentage with 4 Years of College or More	Female: Percentage with 4 Years of High School or More	Female: Percentage with 4 Years of College or More
1970	55.0	14.1	55.4	8.2
1980	69.2	20.9	68.1	13.6
1990	77.7	24.4	77.5	18.4
2000	84.2	27.8	84.0	23.6
2008	85.9	30.1	87.2	28.8

a. Write a matrix for the educational attainment of males.

b. Write a matrix for the educational attainment of females.

c. Use the matrices from parts a and b to write a matrix showing the difference in educational attainment between males and females since 1970.

47. Educational Attainment The following table gives the educational attainment of African Americans and Hispanic Americans 25 years and older since 1980. *Source: U. S. Census Bureau.*

a. Write a matrix for the educational attainment of African Americans.

b. Write a matrix for the educational attainment of Hispanic Americans.

Year	African American: Percentage with 4 Years of High School or More	African American: Percentage with 4 Years of College or More	Hispanic American: Percentage with 4 Years of High School or More	Hispanic American: Percentage with 4 Years of College or More
1980	51.2	7.9	45.3	7.9
1985	59.8	11.1	47.9	8.5
1990	66.2	11.3	50.8	9.2
1995	73.8	13.2	53.4	9.3
2000	78.5	16.5	57.0	10.6
2008	83.0	19.6	62.3	13.3

c. Use the matrices from parts a and b to write a matrix showing the difference in educational attainment between African and Hispanic Americans.

General Interest

48. Animal Interactions When two kittens named Cauchy and Cliché were introduced into a household with Jamie (an older cat) and Musk (a dog), the interactions among animals were complicated. The two kittens liked each other and Jamie, but didn't like Musk. Musk liked everybody, but Jamie didn't like any of the other animals.

a. Write a 4 × 4 matrix in which rows (and columns) 1, 2, 3, and 4 refer to Musk, Jamie, Cauchy, and Cliché. Make an element a 1 if the animal for that row likes the animal for that column, and otherwise make the element a 0. Assume every animal likes herself.

b. Within a few days, Cauchy and Cliché decided that they liked Musk after all. Write a 4 × 4 matrix, as you did in part a, representing the new situation.

1. (a) Does not exist **(b)** $\begin{bmatrix} 4 & 2 & 9 \\ -1 & -2 & 11 \end{bmatrix}$

2. $\begin{bmatrix} 2 & 6 & 1 \\ 3 & 6 & -5 \end{bmatrix}$

2.4 Multiplication of Matrices

APPLY IT What is a contractor's total cost for materials required for various types of model homes?
Matrix multiplication will be used to answer this question in Example 6.

We begin by defining the product of a real number and a matrix. In work with matrices, a real number is called a **scalar**.

Product of a Matrix and a Scalar
The product of a scalar k and a matrix X is the matrix kX, each of whose elements is k times the corresponding element of X.

EXAMPLE 1 Scalar Product of a Matrix

Calculate $-5A$, where $A = \begin{bmatrix} 3 & 4 \\ 0 & -1 \end{bmatrix}$.

SOLUTION

$$(-5)\begin{bmatrix} 3 & 4 \\ 0 & -1 \end{bmatrix} = \begin{bmatrix} -15 & -20 \\ 0 & 5 \end{bmatrix}.$$

Finding the product of two matrices is more involved, but such multiplication is important in solving practical problems. To understand the reasoning behind matrix multiplication, it may be helpful to consider another example concerning EZ Life Company discussed in the previous section. Suppose sofas and chairs of the same model are often sold as sets. Matrix W shows the number of sets of each model in each warehouse.

$$\begin{array}{c} \\ \text{New York} \\ \text{Chicago} \\ \text{San Francisco} \end{array} \begin{array}{ccc} A & B & C \\ \begin{bmatrix} 10 & 7 & 3 \\ 5 & 9 & 6 \\ 4 & 8 & 2 \end{bmatrix} \end{array} = W$$

If the selling price of a model-A set is \$1000, of a model-B set \$1200, and of a model-C set \$1400, the total value of the sets in the New York warehouse is found as follows.

Value of Furniture				
Type	Number of Sets		Price of Set	Total
A	10	×	\$1000	= \$10,000
B	7	×	\$1200	= \$8400
C	3	×	\$1400	= \$4200
	(Total for New York)			\$22,600

The total value of the three kinds of sets in New York is \$22,600.

The work done in the table above is summarized as follows:

$$10(\$1000) + 7(\$1200) + 3(\$1400) = \$22,600.$$

In the same way, we find that the Chicago sets have a total value of

$$5(\$1000) + 9(\$1200) + 6(\$1400) = \$24,200,$$

and in San Francisco, the total value of the sets is

$$4(\$1000) + 8(\$1200) + 2(\$1400) = \$16,400.$$

The selling prices can be written as a column matrix P, and the total value in each location as another column matrix, V.

$$\begin{bmatrix} 1000 \\ 1200 \\ 1400 \end{bmatrix} = P \qquad \begin{bmatrix} 22{,}600 \\ 24{,}200 \\ 16{,}400 \end{bmatrix} = V$$

Look at the elements of W and P below; multiplying the first, second, and third elements of the first row of W by the first, second, and third elements, respectively, of the column matrix P and then adding these products gives the first element in V. Doing the same thing with the second row of W gives the second element of V; the third row of W leads to the third element of V, suggesting that it is reasonable to write the product of matrices

$$W = \begin{bmatrix} 10 & 7 & 3 \\ 5 & 9 & 6 \\ 4 & 8 & 2 \end{bmatrix} \qquad \text{and} \qquad P = \begin{bmatrix} 1000 \\ 1200 \\ 1400 \end{bmatrix}$$

as

$$WP = \begin{bmatrix} 10 & 7 & 3 \\ 5 & 9 & 6 \\ 4 & 8 & 2 \end{bmatrix} \begin{bmatrix} 1000 \\ 1200 \\ 1400 \end{bmatrix} = \begin{bmatrix} 22{,}600 \\ 24{,}200 \\ 16{,}400 \end{bmatrix} = V.$$

The product was found by multiplying the elements of *rows* of the matrix on the left and the corresponding elements of the *column* of the matrix on the right, and then finding the sum of these separate products. Notice that the product of a 3×3 matrix and a 3×1 matrix is a 3×1 matrix. Notice also that each element of the product of two matrices is a sum of products. This is exactly what you do when you go to the store and buy 8 candy bars at \$0.80 each, 4 bottles of water at \$1.25 each, and so forth, and calculate the total as $8 \times 0.80 + 4 \times 1.25 + \cdots$. ▬

The product AB of an $m \times n$ matrix A and an $n \times k$ matrix B is found as follows. Multiply each element of the first row of A by the corresponding element of the *first column* of B. The sum of these n products is the *first-row, first-column* element of AB. Similarly, the sum of the products found by multiplying the elements of the *first row* of A by the corresponding elements of the *second column* of B gives the *first-row, second-column* element of AB, and so on.

Product of Two Matrices

Let A be an $m \times n$ matrix and let B be an $n \times k$ matrix. To find the element in the ith row and jth column of the **product matrix** AB, multiply each element in the ith row of A by the corresponding element in the jth column of B, and then add these products. The product matrix AB is an $m \times k$ matrix.

EXAMPLE 2   Matrix Product

Find the product AB of matrices

$$A = \begin{bmatrix} 2 & 3 & -1 \\ 4 & 2 & 2 \end{bmatrix} \qquad \text{and} \qquad B = \begin{bmatrix} 1 \\ 8 \\ 6 \end{bmatrix}.$$

SOLUTION   Since A is 2×3 and B is 3×1, we can find the product matrix AB.

Step 1 Multiply the elements of the first row of A and the corresponding elements of the column of B.

$$\begin{bmatrix} \mathbf{2} & \mathbf{3} & \mathbf{-1} \\ 4 & 2 & 2 \end{bmatrix} \begin{bmatrix} \mathbf{1} \\ \mathbf{8} \\ \mathbf{6} \end{bmatrix} \qquad \mathbf{2 \cdot 1 + 3 \cdot 8 + (-1) \cdot 6} = 20$$

Thus, 20 is the first-row entry of the product matrix AB.

Step 2 Multiply the elements of the second row of A and the corresponding elements of B.

$$\begin{bmatrix} 2 & 3 & -1 \\ \mathbf{4} & \mathbf{2} & \mathbf{2} \end{bmatrix} \begin{bmatrix} \mathbf{1} \\ \mathbf{8} \\ \mathbf{6} \end{bmatrix} \qquad \mathbf{4 \cdot 1 + 2 \cdot 8 + 2 \cdot 6} = 32$$

The second-row entry of the product matrix AB is 32.

Step 3 Write the product as a column matrix using the two entries found above.

$$AB = \begin{bmatrix} 2 & 3 & -1 \\ 4 & 2 & 2 \end{bmatrix} \begin{bmatrix} 1 \\ 8 \\ 6 \end{bmatrix} = \begin{bmatrix} 20 \\ 32 \end{bmatrix}$$

Note that the product of a 2×3 matrix and a 3×1 matrix is a 2×1 matrix.

EXAMPLE 3 **Matrix Product**

Find the product CD of matrices

$$C = \begin{bmatrix} -3 & 4 & 2 \\ 5 & 0 & 4 \end{bmatrix} \qquad \text{and} \qquad D = \begin{bmatrix} -6 & 4 \\ 2 & 3 \\ 3 & -2 \end{bmatrix}.$$

SOLUTION Since C is 2×3 and D is 3×2, we can find the product matrix CD.

Step 1 $\begin{bmatrix} \mathbf{-3} & \mathbf{4} & \mathbf{2} \\ 5 & 0 & 4 \end{bmatrix} \begin{bmatrix} \mathbf{-6} & 4 \\ \mathbf{2} & 3 \\ \mathbf{3} & -2 \end{bmatrix}$ $\mathbf{(-3) \cdot (-6) + 4 \cdot 2 + 2 \cdot 3} = 32$

Step 2 $\begin{bmatrix} \mathbf{-3} & \mathbf{4} & \mathbf{2} \\ 5 & 0 & 4 \end{bmatrix} \begin{bmatrix} -6 & \mathbf{4} \\ 2 & \mathbf{3} \\ 3 & \mathbf{-2} \end{bmatrix}$ $\mathbf{(-3) \cdot 4 + 4 \cdot 3 + 2 \cdot (-2)} = -4$

Step 3 $\begin{bmatrix} -3 & 4 & 2 \\ \mathbf{5} & \mathbf{0} & \mathbf{4} \end{bmatrix} \begin{bmatrix} \mathbf{-6} & 4 \\ \mathbf{2} & 3 \\ \mathbf{3} & -2 \end{bmatrix}$ $\mathbf{5 \cdot (-6) + 0 \cdot 2 + 4 \cdot 3} = -18$

Step 4 $\begin{bmatrix} -3 & 4 & 2 \\ \mathbf{5} & \mathbf{0} & \mathbf{4} \end{bmatrix} \begin{bmatrix} -6 & \mathbf{4} \\ 2 & \mathbf{3} \\ 3 & \mathbf{-2} \end{bmatrix}$ $\mathbf{5 \cdot 4 + 0 \cdot 3 + 4 \cdot (-2)} = 12$

Step 5 The product is

$$CD = \begin{bmatrix} -3 & 4 & 2 \\ 5 & 0 & 4 \end{bmatrix} \begin{bmatrix} -6 & 4 \\ 2 & 3 \\ 3 & -2 \end{bmatrix} = \begin{bmatrix} 32 & -4 \\ -18 & 12 \end{bmatrix}.$$

Here the product of a 2×3 matrix and a 3×2 matrix is a 2×2 matrix.

TRY YOUR TURN 1

YOUR TURN 1 Calculate the product AB where $A = \begin{bmatrix} 3 & 4 \\ 1 & 2 \end{bmatrix}$ and $B = \begin{bmatrix} 1 & -2 \\ -2 & -4 \end{bmatrix}$.

NOTE One way to avoid errors in matrix multiplication is to lower the first matrix so it is below and to the left of the second matrix, and then write the product in the space between the two matrices. For example, to multiply the matrices in Example 2, we could rewrite the product as shown on the following page.

$$\downarrow$$

$$\begin{bmatrix} -6 & 4 \\ 2 & 3 \\ 3 & -2 \end{bmatrix}$$

$$\rightarrow \begin{bmatrix} -3 & 4 & 2 \\ 5 & 0 & 4 \end{bmatrix} \begin{bmatrix} & & \\ * & & \end{bmatrix}$$

To find the entry where the * is, for example, multiply the row and the column indicated by the arrows: $5 \cdot (-6) + 0 \cdot 2 + 4 \cdot 3 = -18$.

As the definition of matrix multiplication shows,

> the product AB of two matrices A and B can be found only if the number of columns of A is the same as the number of rows of B.

The final product will have as many rows as A and as many columns as B.

EXAMPLE 4 **Matrix Product**

Suppose matrix A is 2×2 and matrix B is 2×4. Can the products AB and BA be calculated? If so, what is the size of each product?

SOLUTION The following diagram helps decide the answers to these questions.

The product of A and B can be found because A has two columns and B has two rows. The size of the product is 2×4.

Matrix B Matrix A
size   size
2×4 2×2

do not match

The product BA cannot be found because B has 4 columns and A has 2 rows.

EXAMPLE 5 **Comparing Matrix Products *AB* and *BA***

Find AB and BA, given

$$A = \begin{bmatrix} 1 & -3 \\ 7 & 2 \\ -2 & 5 \end{bmatrix} \quad \text{and} \quad B = \begin{bmatrix} 1 & 0 & -1 \\ 3 & 1 & 4 \end{bmatrix}.$$

SOLUTION

Method 1
Calculating by Hand

$$AB = \begin{bmatrix} 1 & -3 \\ 7 & 2 \\ -2 & 5 \end{bmatrix} \begin{bmatrix} 1 & 0 & -1 \\ 3 & 1 & 4 \end{bmatrix}$$

$$= \begin{bmatrix} -8 & -3 & -13 \\ 13 & 2 & 1 \\ 13 & 5 & 22 \end{bmatrix}$$

YOUR TURN 2 Calculate each product AB and BA, if possible, where $A = \begin{bmatrix} 3 & 5 & -1 \\ 2 & 4 & -2 \end{bmatrix}$ and $B = \begin{bmatrix} 3 & -4 \\ -5 & -3 \end{bmatrix}$.

$$BA = \begin{bmatrix} 1 & 0 & -1 \\ 3 & 1 & 4 \end{bmatrix} \begin{bmatrix} 1 & -3 \\ 7 & 2 \\ -2 & 5 \end{bmatrix}$$

$$= \begin{bmatrix} 3 & -8 \\ 2 & 13 \end{bmatrix}$$

Method 2
Graphing Calculator

Matrix multiplication is easily performed on a graphing calculator. Figure 13 in the margin below shows the results. The matrices A and B were already entered into the calculator.

TRY YOUR TURN 2

TECHNOLOGY NOTE

Matrix multiplication can also be easily done with a spreadsheet. See the *Graphing Calculator and Excel Spreadsheet Manual* available with this textbook for details.

```
[A]*[B]
    [-8   -3  -13]
    [13    2    1]
    [13    5   22]
[B]*[A]
         [3   -8]
         [2   13]
```

FIGURE 13

Notice in Example 5 that $AB \neq BA$; matrices AB and BA aren't even the same size. In Example 4, we showed that they may not both exist. This means that matrix multiplication is *not* commutative. Even if both A and B are square matrices, in general, matrices AB and BA are not equal. (See Exercise 31.) Of course, there may be special cases in which they are equal, but this is not true in general.

CAUTION Since matrix multiplication is not commutative, always be careful to multiply matrices in the correct order.

Matrix multiplication *is* associative, however. For example, if

$$C = \begin{bmatrix} 3 & 2 \\ 0 & -4 \\ -1 & 1 \end{bmatrix},$$

then $(AB)C = A(BC)$, where A and B are the matrices given in Example 5. (Verify this.) Also, there is a distributive property of matrices such that, for appropriate matrices A, B, and C,

$$A(B + C) = AB + AC.$$

(See Exercises 32 and 33.) Other properties of matrix multiplication involving scalars are included in the exercises. Multiplicative inverses and multiplicative identities are defined in the next section.

EXAMPLE 6 Home Construction

A contractor builds three kinds of houses, models A, B, and C, with a choice of two styles, Spanish and contemporary. Matrix P shows the number of each kind of house planned for a new 100-home subdivision. The amounts for each of the exterior materials depend primarily on the style of the house. These amounts are shown in matrix Q. (Concrete is in cubic yards, lumber in units of 1000 board feet, brick in 1000s, and shingles in units of 100 ft^2.) Matrix R gives the cost in dollars for each kind of material.

$$\begin{array}{c} \\ \text{Model A} \\ \text{Model B} \\ \text{Model C} \end{array} \begin{array}{cc} \overset{\text{Spanish}}{} & \overset{\text{Contemporary}}{} \\ \left[\begin{array}{cc} 0 & 30 \\ 10 & 20 \\ 20 & 20 \end{array} \right] \end{array} = P$$

$$\begin{array}{c} \\ \text{Spanish} \\ \text{Contemporary} \end{array} \begin{array}{cccc} \overset{\text{Concrete}}{} & \overset{\text{Lumber}}{} & \overset{\text{Brick}}{} & \overset{\text{Shingles}}{} \\ \left[\begin{array}{cccc} 10 & 2 & 0 & 2 \\ 50 & 1 & 20 & 2 \end{array} \right] \end{array} = Q$$

$$\begin{array}{c} \\ \text{Concrete} \\ \text{Lumber} \\ \text{Brick} \\ \text{Shingles} \end{array} \begin{array}{c} \overset{\text{Cost per Unit}}{} \\ \left[\begin{array}{c} 20 \\ 180 \\ 60 \\ 25 \end{array} \right] \end{array} = R$$

(a) What is the total cost of these materials for each model?

SOLUTION To find the cost for each model, first find PQ, which shows the amount of each material needed for each model.

$$PQ = \begin{bmatrix} 0 & 30 \\ 10 & 20 \\ 20 & 20 \end{bmatrix} \begin{bmatrix} 10 & 2 & 0 & 2 \\ 50 & 1 & 20 & 2 \end{bmatrix}$$

$$= \begin{array}{c} \begin{array}{cccc} \overset{\text{Concrete}}{} & \overset{\text{Lumber}}{} & \overset{\text{Brick}}{} & \overset{\text{Shingles}}{} \end{array} \\ \begin{bmatrix} 1500 & 30 & 600 & 60 \\ 1100 & 40 & 400 & 60 \\ 1200 & 60 & 400 & 80 \end{bmatrix} \begin{array}{c} \text{Model A} \\ \text{Model B} \\ \text{Model C} \end{array} \end{array}$$

Now multiply PQ and R, the cost matrix, to get the total cost of the exterior materials for each model.

$$\begin{bmatrix} 1500 & 30 & 600 & 60 \\ 1100 & 40 & 400 & 60 \\ 1200 & 60 & 400 & 80 \end{bmatrix} \begin{bmatrix} 20 \\ 180 \\ 60 \\ 25 \end{bmatrix} = \begin{array}{c} \overset{\text{Cost}}{} \\ \begin{bmatrix} 72{,}900 \\ 54{,}700 \\ 60{,}800 \end{bmatrix} \begin{array}{c} \text{Model A} \\ \text{Model B} \\ \text{Model C} \end{array} \end{array}$$

The total cost of materials is \$72,900 for model A, \$54,700 for model B, and \$60,800 for model C.

(b) How much of each of the four kinds of material must be ordered?

SOLUTION The totals of the columns of matrix PQ will give a matrix whose elements represent the total amounts of each material needed for the subdivision. Call this matrix T, and write it as a row matrix.

$$T = \begin{bmatrix} 3800 & 130 & 1400 & 200 \end{bmatrix}$$

Thus, 3800 yd^3 of concrete, 130,000 board feet of lumber, 1,400,000 bricks, and 20,000 ft^2 of shingles are needed.

(c) What is the total cost for exterior materials?

SOLUTION For the total cost of all the exterior materials, find the product of matrix T, the matrix showing the total amount of each material, and matrix R, the cost matrix. (To multiply these and get a 1×1 matrix representing total cost, we need a 1×4 matrix multiplied by a 4×1 matrix. This is why T was written as a row matrix in (b) above.)

$$TR = \begin{bmatrix} 3800 & 130 & 1400 & 200 \end{bmatrix} \begin{bmatrix} 20 \\ 180 \\ 60 \\ 25 \end{bmatrix} = [188{,}400]$$

The total cost for exterior materials is $188,400.

(d) Suppose the contractor builds the same number of homes in five subdivisions. Calculate the total amount of each exterior material for each model for all five subdivisions.

SOLUTION   Multiply PQ by the scalar 5, as follows.

$$5(PQ) = 5 \begin{bmatrix} 1500 & 30 & 600 & 60 \\ 1100 & 40 & 400 & 60 \\ 1200 & 60 & 400 & 80 \end{bmatrix} = \begin{bmatrix} 7500 & 150 & 3000 & 300 \\ 5500 & 200 & 2000 & 300 \\ 6000 & 300 & 2000 & 400 \end{bmatrix}$$

The total amount of concrete needed for model A homes, for example, is 7500 yd³.

Meaning of a Matrix Product

It is helpful to use a notation that keeps track of the quantities a matrix represents. We will use the notation

meaning of the rows/meaning of the columns,

that is, writing the meaning of the rows first, followed by the meaning of the columns. In Example 6, we would use the notation models/styles for matrix P, styles/materials for matrix Q, and materials/cost for matrix R. In multiplying PQ, we are multiplying models/styles by styles/materials. The result is models/materials. Notice that styles, the common quantity in both P and Q, was eliminated in the product PQ. By this method, the product $(PQ)R$ represents models/cost.

In practical problems this notation helps us decide in which order to multiply matrices so that the results are meaningful. In Example 6(c) either RT or TR can be calculated. Since T represents subdivisions/materials and R represents materials/cost, the product TR gives subdivisions/cost, while the product RT is meaningless.

2.4   EXERCISES

Let $A = \begin{bmatrix} -2 & 4 \\ 0 & 3 \end{bmatrix}$ and $B = \begin{bmatrix} -6 & 2 \\ 4 & 0 \end{bmatrix}$. Find each value.

1. $2A$

2. $-3B$

3. $-6A$

4. $5B$

5. $-4A + 5B$

6. $7B - 3A$

In Exercises 7–12, the sizes of two matrices A and B are given. Find the sizes of the product AB and the product BA, whenever these products exist.

7. A is 2×2, and B is 2×2.

8. A is 3×3, and B is 3×3.

9. A is 3×4, and B is 4×4.

10. A is 4×3, and B is 3×6.

11. A is 4×2, and B is 3×4.

12. A is 3×2, and B is 1×3.

13. To find the product matrix AB, the number of _____ of A must be the same as the number of _____ of B.

14. The product matrix AB has the same number of _____ as A and the same number of _____ as B.

Find each matrix product, if possible.

15. $\begin{bmatrix} 2 & -1 \\ 5 & 8 \end{bmatrix} \begin{bmatrix} 3 \\ -2 \end{bmatrix}$

16. $\begin{bmatrix} -1 & 5 \\ 7 & 0 \end{bmatrix} \begin{bmatrix} 6 \\ 2 \end{bmatrix}$

17. $\begin{bmatrix} 2 & -1 & 7 \\ -3 & 0 & -4 \end{bmatrix} \begin{bmatrix} 5 \\ 10 \\ 2 \end{bmatrix}$

18. $\begin{bmatrix} 5 & 2 \\ 7 & 6 \\ 1 & 0 \end{bmatrix} \begin{bmatrix} 1 & 4 & 0 \\ 2 & -1 & 2 \end{bmatrix}$

19. $\begin{bmatrix} 2 & -1 \\ 3 & 6 \end{bmatrix} \begin{bmatrix} -1 & 0 & 4 \\ 5 & -2 & 0 \end{bmatrix}$

20. $\begin{bmatrix} 6 & 0 & -4 \\ 1 & 2 & 5 \\ 10 & -1 & 3 \end{bmatrix} \begin{bmatrix} 1 \\ 2 \\ 0 \end{bmatrix}$

21. $\begin{bmatrix} 2 & 2 & -1 \\ 3 & 0 & 1 \end{bmatrix} \begin{bmatrix} 0 & 2 \\ -1 & 4 \\ 0 & 2 \end{bmatrix}$

22. $\begin{bmatrix} -3 & 1 & 0 \\ 6 & 0 & 8 \end{bmatrix} \begin{bmatrix} 3 \\ -1 \\ -2 \end{bmatrix}$

23. $\begin{bmatrix} 1 & 2 \\ 3 & 4 \end{bmatrix} \begin{bmatrix} -1 & 5 \\ 7 & 0 \end{bmatrix}$

24. $\begin{bmatrix} 2 & 8 \\ -7 & 5 \end{bmatrix} \begin{bmatrix} 1 & 0 \\ 0 & 1 \end{bmatrix}$

25. $\begin{bmatrix} -2 & -3 & 7 \\ 1 & 5 & 6 \end{bmatrix} \begin{bmatrix} 1 \\ 2 \\ 3 \end{bmatrix}$

26. $\begin{bmatrix} 2 \\ -9 \\ 12 \end{bmatrix} \begin{bmatrix} 1 & 0 & -1 \end{bmatrix}$

27. $\left(\begin{bmatrix} 2 & 1 \\ -3 & -6 \\ 4 & 0 \end{bmatrix} \begin{bmatrix} 1 & -2 \\ 2 & -1 \end{bmatrix} \right) \begin{bmatrix} 3 \\ 1 \end{bmatrix}$

28. $\begin{bmatrix} 2 & 1 \\ -3 & -6 \\ 4 & 0 \end{bmatrix} \left(\begin{bmatrix} 1 & -2 \\ 2 & -1 \end{bmatrix} \begin{bmatrix} 3 \\ 1 \end{bmatrix} \right)$

29. $\begin{bmatrix} 2 & -2 \\ 1 & -1 \end{bmatrix} \left(\begin{bmatrix} 4 & 3 \\ 1 & 2 \end{bmatrix} + \begin{bmatrix} 7 & 0 \\ -1 & 5 \end{bmatrix} \right)$

30. $\begin{bmatrix} 2 & -2 \\ 1 & -1 \end{bmatrix} \begin{bmatrix} 4 & 3 \\ 1 & 2 \end{bmatrix} + \begin{bmatrix} 2 & -2 \\ 1 & -1 \end{bmatrix} \begin{bmatrix} 7 & 0 \\ -1 & 5 \end{bmatrix}$

31. Let $A = \begin{bmatrix} -2 & 4 \\ 1 & 3 \end{bmatrix}$ and $B = \begin{bmatrix} -2 & 1 \\ 3 & 6 \end{bmatrix}$.

    a. Find AB.

    b. Find BA.

    c. Did you get the same answer in parts a and b?

    d. In general, for matrices A and B such that AB and BA both exist, does AB always equal BA?

Given matrices $P = \begin{bmatrix} m & n \\ p & q \end{bmatrix}$, $X = \begin{bmatrix} x & y \\ z & w \end{bmatrix}$, and $T = \begin{bmatrix} r & s \\ t & u \end{bmatrix}$, verify that the statements in Exercises 32–35 are true. The statements are valid for any matrices whenever matrix multiplication and addition can be carried out. This, of course, depends on the size of the matrices.

32. $(PX)T = P(XT)$ (associative property: see Exercises 27 and 28)

33. $P(X + T) = PX + PT$ (distributive property: see Exercises 29 and 30)

34. $k(X + T) = kX + kT$ for any real number k.

35. $(k + h)P = kP + hP$ for any real numbers k and h.

36. Let I be the matrix $I = \begin{bmatrix} 1 & 0 \\ 0 & 1 \end{bmatrix}$, and let matrices P, X, and T be defined as for Exercises 32–35.

    a. Find IP, PI, and IX.

    b. Without calculating, guess what the matrix IT might be.

    c. Suggest a reason for naming a matrix such as I an *identity matrix*.

37. Show that the system of linear equations

$$2x_1 + 3x_2 + x_3 = 5$$
$$x_1 - 4x_2 + 5x_3 = 8$$

can be written as the matrix equation

$$\begin{bmatrix} 2 & 3 & 1 \\ 1 & -4 & 5 \end{bmatrix} \begin{bmatrix} x_1 \\ x_2 \\ x_3 \end{bmatrix} = \begin{bmatrix} 5 \\ 8 \end{bmatrix}.$$

38. Let $A = \begin{bmatrix} 1 & 2 \\ -3 & 5 \end{bmatrix}$, $X = \begin{bmatrix} x_1 \\ x_2 \end{bmatrix}$, and $B = \begin{bmatrix} -4 \\ 12 \end{bmatrix}$. Show that the equation $AX = B$ represents a linear system of two equations in two unknowns. Solve the system and substitute into the matrix equation to check your results.

Use a computer or graphing calculator and the following matrices to find the matrix products and sums in Exercises 39–41.

$$A = \begin{bmatrix} 2 & 3 & -1 & 5 & 10 \\ 2 & 8 & 7 & 4 & 3 \\ -1 & -4 & -12 & 6 & 8 \\ 2 & 5 & 7 & 1 & 4 \end{bmatrix}$$

$$B = \begin{bmatrix} 9 & 3 & 7 & -6 \\ -1 & 0 & 4 & 2 \\ -10 & -7 & 6 & 9 \\ 8 & 4 & 2 & -1 \\ 2 & -5 & 3 & 7 \end{bmatrix}$$

$$C = \begin{bmatrix} -6 & 8 & 2 & 4 & -3 \\ 1 & 9 & 7 & -12 & 5 \\ 15 & 2 & -8 & 10 & 11 \\ 4 & 7 & 9 & 6 & -2 \\ 1 & 3 & 8 & 23 & 4 \end{bmatrix}$$

$$D = \begin{bmatrix} 5 & -3 & 7 & 9 & 2 \\ 6 & 8 & -5 & 2 & 1 \\ 3 & 7 & -4 & 2 & 11 \\ 5 & -3 & 9 & 4 & -1 \\ 0 & 3 & 2 & 5 & 1 \end{bmatrix}$$

39. a. Find AC.   **b.** Find CA.   **c.** Does $AC = CA$?

40. a. Find CD.   **b.** Find DC.   **c.** Does $CD = DC$?

41. a. Find $C + D$.   **b.** Find $(C + D)B$.   **c.** Find CB.

    d. Find DB.   **e.** Find $CB + DB$.

    f. Does $(C + D)B = CB + DB$?

42. Which property of matrices does Exercise 41 illustrate?

APPLICATIONS

Business and Economics

43. Cost Analysis The four departments of Spangler Enterprises need to order the following amounts of the same products.

	Paper	Tape	Binders	Memo Pads	Pens
Department 1	10	4	3	5	6
Department 2	7	2	2	3	8
Department 3	4	5	1	0	10
Department 4	0	3	4	5	5

The unit price (in dollars) of each product is given below for two suppliers.

	Supplier A	Supplier B
Paper	2	3
Tape	1	1
Binders	4	3
Memo Pads	3	3
Pens	1	2

a. Use matrix multiplication to get a matrix showing the comparative costs for each department for the products from the two suppliers.

b. Find the total cost over all departments to buy products from each supplier. From which supplier should the company make the purchase?

44. Cost Analysis The Mundo Candy Company makes three types of chocolate candy: Cheery Cherry, Mucho Mocha, and Almond Delight. The company produces its products in San Diego, Mexico City, and Managua using two main ingredients: chocolate and sugar.

a. Each kilogram of Cheery Cherry requires 0.5 kg of sugar and 0.2 kg of chocolate; each kilogram of Mucho Mocha requires 0.4 kg of sugar and 0.3 kg of chocolate; and each kilogram of Almond Delight requires 0.3 kg of sugar and 0.3 kg of chocolate. Put this information into a 2 × 3 matrix called A, labeling the rows and columns.

b. The cost of 1 kg of sugar is $4 in San Diego, $2 in Mexico City, and $1 in Managua. The cost of 1 kg of chocolate is $3 in San Diego, $5 in Mexico City, and $7 in Managua. Put this information into a matrix called C in such a way that when you multiply it with your matrix from part a, you get a matrix representing the ingredient cost of producing each type of candy in each city.

c. Only one of the two products AC and CA is meaningful. Determine which one it is, calculate the product, and describe what the entries represent.

d. From your answer to part c, what is the combined sugar-and-chocolate cost to produce 1 kg of Mucho Mocha in Managua?

e. Mundo Candy needs to quickly produce a special shipment of 100 kg of Cheery Cherry, 200 kg of Mucho Mocha, and 500 kg of Almond Delight, and it decides to select one factory to fill the entire order. Use matrix multiplication to determine in which city the total sugar-and-chocolate cost to produce the order is the smallest.

45. Management In Exercise 39 from Section 2.3, consider the matrices $\begin{bmatrix} 4.27 & 6.94 \\ 3.45 & 3.65 \end{bmatrix}$, $\begin{bmatrix} 4.05 & 7.01 \\ 3.27 & 3.51 \end{bmatrix}$, and $\begin{bmatrix} 4.40 & 6.90 \\ 3.54 & 3.76 \end{bmatrix}$ for the production costs at the Boston, Chicago, and Seattle plants, respectively.

a. Assume each plant makes the same number of each item. Write a matrix that expresses the average production costs for all three plants.

b. In part b of Exercise 39 in Section 2.3, cost increases for the Chicago plant resulted in a new production cost matrix $\begin{bmatrix} 4.42 & 7.43 \\ 3.38 & 3.62 \end{bmatrix}$. Following those cost increases the Boston plant was closed and production divided evenly between the Chicago and Seattle plants. What is the matrix that now expresses the average production cost for the entire country?

46. House Construction Consider the matrices P, Q, and R given in Example 6.

a. Find and interpret the matrix product QR.

b. Verify that $P(QR)$ is equal to $(PQ)R$ calculated in Example 5.

47. Shoe Sales Sal's Shoes and Fred's Footwear both have outlets in California and Arizona. Sal's sells shoes for $80, sandals for $40, and boots for $120. Fred's prices are $60, $30, and $150 for shoes, sandals, and boots, respectively. Half of all sales in California stores are shoes, 1/4 are sandals, and 1/4 are boots. In Arizona the fractions are 1/5 shoes, 1/5 sandals, and 3/5 boots.

a. Write a 2 × 3 matrix called P representing prices for the two stores and three types of footwear.

b. Write a 3 × 2 matrix called F representing the fraction of each type of footwear sold in each state.

c. Only one of the two products PF and FP is meaningful. Determine which one it is, calculate the product, and describe what the entries represent.

d. From your answer to part c, what is the average price for a pair of footwear at an outlet of Fred's in Arizona?

48. Management In Exercise 40 from Section 2.3, consider the matrix

$$\begin{bmatrix} 88 & 105 & 60 \\ 48 & 72 & 40 \\ 16 & 21 & 0 \\ 112 & 147 & 50 \end{bmatrix}$$

expressing the sales information for the three stores.

a. Write a 3 × 1 matrix expressing the factors by which sales in each store should be multiplied to reflect the fact that sales increased during the following week by 25%, 1/3, and 10% in stores I, II, and III, respectively, as described in part b of Exercise 40 from Section 2.3.

b. Multiply the matrix expressing sales information by the matrix found in part a of this exercise to find the sales for all three stores in the second week.

Life Sciences

49. Dietetics In Exercise 41 from Section 2.3, label the matrices

$$\begin{bmatrix} 2 & 1 & 2 & 1 \\ 3 & 2 & 2 & 1 \\ 4 & 3 & 2 & 1 \end{bmatrix}, \begin{bmatrix} 5 & 0 & 7 \\ 0 & 10 & 1 \\ 0 & 15 & 2 \\ 10 & 12 & 8 \end{bmatrix}, \text{ and } \begin{bmatrix} 8 \\ 4 \\ 5 \end{bmatrix}$$

found in parts a, b, and c, respectively, X, Y, and Z.

a. Find the product matrix XY. What do the entries of this matrix represent?

b. Find the product matrix YZ. What do the entries represent?

c. Find the products $(XY)Z$ and $X(YZ)$ and verify that they are equal. What do the entries represent?

50. Motorcycle Helmets In Exercise 44 from Section 2.3, you constructed matrices that represented usage of motorcycle helmets for 2008 and 2009. Use matrix operations to combine these two matrices to form one matrix that represents the average of the two years.

51. Life Expectancy In Exercise 45 from Section 2.3, you constructed matrices that represent the life expectancy of African American and white American males and females. Use matrix operations to combine these two matrices to form one matrix that represents the combined life expectancy of both races at the beginning of each decade since 1970. Use the fact that of the combined African and white American population, African Americans are about one-sixth of the total and white Americans about five-sixths. (*Hint:* Multiply the matrix for African Americans by 1/6 and the matrix for the white Americans by 5/6, and then add the results.)

52. Northern Spotted Owl Population In an attempt to save the endangered northern spotted owl, the U.S. Fish and Wildlife Service imposed strict guidelines for the use of 12 million acres of Pacific Northwest forest. This decision led to a national debate between the logging industry and environmentalists. Mathematical ecologists have created a mathematical model to analyze population dynamics of the northern spotted owl by dividing the female owl population into three categories: juvenile (up to 1 year old), subadult (1 to 2 years), and adult (over 2 years old). By analyzing these three subgroups, it is possible to use the number of females in each subgroup at time n to estimate the number of females in each group at any time $n + 1$ with the following matrix equation:

$$\begin{bmatrix} j_{n+1} \\ s_{n+1} \\ a_{n+1} \end{bmatrix} = \begin{bmatrix} 0 & 0 & 0.33 \\ 0.18 & 0 & 0 \\ 0 & 0.71 & 0.94 \end{bmatrix} \begin{bmatrix} j_n \\ s_n \\ a_n \end{bmatrix},$$

where j_n is the number of juveniles, s_n is the number of subadults, and a_n is the number of adults at time n. *Source: Conservation Biology.*

a. If there are currently 4000 female northern spotted owls made up of 900 juveniles, 500 subadults, and 2600 adults, use a graphing calculator or spreadsheet and matrix operations to determine the total number of female owls for each of the next 5 years. (*Hint:* Round each answer to the nearest whole number after each matrix multiplication.)

b. With advanced techniques from linear algebra, it is possible to show that in the long run, the following holds.

$$\begin{bmatrix} j_{n+1} \\ s_{n+1} \\ a_{n+1} \end{bmatrix} \approx 0.98359 \begin{bmatrix} j_n \\ s_n \\ a_n \end{bmatrix}$$

What can we conclude about the long-term survival of the northern spotted owl?

c. Notice that only 18 percent of the juveniles become subadults. Assuming that, through better habitat management, this number could be increased to 40 percent, rework part a. Discuss possible reasons why only 18 percent of the juveniles become subadults. Under the new assumption, what can you conclude about the long-term survival of the northern spotted owl?

Social Sciences

53. World Population The 2010 birth and death rates per million for several regions and the world population (in millions) by region are given in the following tables. *Source: U. S. Census Bureau.*

	Births	Deaths
Africa	0.0346	0.0118
Asia	0.0174	0.0073
Latin America	0.0189	0.0059
North America	0.0135	0.0083
Europe	0.0099	0.0103

			Population (millions)		
Year	Africa	Asia	Latin America	North America	Europe
1970	361	2038	286	227	460
1980	473	2494	362	252	484
1990	627	2978	443	278	499
2000	803	3435	524	314	511
2010	1013	3824	591	344	522

a. Write the information in each table as a matrix.

b. Use the matrices from part a to find the total number (in millions) of births and deaths in each year (assuming birth and death rates for all years are close to these in 2010).

c. Using the results of part b, compare the number of births in 1970 and in 2010. Also compare the birth rates from part a. Which gives better information?

d. Using the results of part b, compare the number of deaths in 1980 and in 2010. Discuss how this comparison differs from a comparison of death rates from part a.

YOUR TURN ANSWERS

1. $\begin{bmatrix} -5 & -22 \\ -3 & -10 \end{bmatrix}$ **2.** AB does not exist; $BA = \begin{bmatrix} 1 & -1 & 5 \\ -21 & -37 & 11 \end{bmatrix}$

2.5 Matrix Inverses

APPLY IT   One top leader needs to get an important message to one of her agents. How can she encrypt the message to ensure secrecy?
This question is answered in Example 7.

In this section, we introduce the idea of a matrix inverse, which is comparable to the reciprocal of a real number. This will allow us to solve a matrix equation.

The real number 1 is the *multiplicative* identity for real numbers: for any real number a, we have $a \cdot 1 = 1 \cdot a = a$. In this section, we define a *multiplicative identity matrix I* that has properties similar to those of the number 1. We then use the definition of matrix I to find the *multiplicative inverse* of any square matrix that has an inverse.

If I is to be the identity matrix, both of the products AI and IA must equal A. This means that an identity matrix exists only for square matrices. The 2×2 **identity matrix** that satisfies these conditions is

$$I = \begin{bmatrix} 1 & 0 \\ 0 & 1 \end{bmatrix}.$$

To check that I, as defined above, is really the 2×2 identity, let

$$A = \begin{bmatrix} a & b \\ c & d \end{bmatrix}.$$

Then AI and IA should both equal A.

$$AI = \begin{bmatrix} a & b \\ c & d \end{bmatrix} \begin{bmatrix} 1 & 0 \\ 0 & 1 \end{bmatrix} = \begin{bmatrix} a(1) + b(0) & a(0) + b(1) \\ c(1) + d(0) & c(0) + d(1) \end{bmatrix} = \begin{bmatrix} a & b \\ c & d \end{bmatrix} = A$$

$$IA = \begin{bmatrix} 1 & 0 \\ 0 & 1 \end{bmatrix} \begin{bmatrix} a & b \\ c & d \end{bmatrix} = \begin{bmatrix} 1(a) + 0(c) & 1(b) + 0(d) \\ 0(a) + 1(c) & 0(b) + 1(d) \end{bmatrix} = \begin{bmatrix} a & b \\ c & d \end{bmatrix} = A$$

This verifies that I has been defined correctly.

It is easy to verify that the identity matrix I is unique. Suppose there is another identity; call it J. Then IJ must equal I, because J is an identity, and IJ must also equal J, because I is an identity. Thus $I = J$.

The identity matrices for 3×3 matrices and 4×4 matrices, respectively, are

$$I = \begin{bmatrix} 1 & 0 & 0 \\ 0 & 1 & 0 \\ 0 & 0 & 1 \end{bmatrix} \quad \text{and} \quad I = \begin{bmatrix} 1 & 0 & 0 & 0 \\ 0 & 1 & 0 & 0 \\ 0 & 0 & 1 & 0 \\ 0 & 0 & 0 & 1 \end{bmatrix}.$$

By generalizing, we can find an $n \times n$ identity matrix for any value of n.

Recall that the multiplicative inverse of the nonzero real number a is $1/a$. The product of a and its multiplicative inverse $1/a$ is 1. Given a matrix A, can a **multiplicative inverse matrix A^{-1}** (read "A-inverse") that will satisfy both

$$AA^{-1} = I \quad \text{and} \quad A^{-1}A = I$$

be found? For a given matrix, we often can find an inverse matrix by using the row operations of Section 2.2.

NOTE A^{-1} does not mean $1/A$; here, A^{-1} is just the notation for the multiplicative inverse of matrix A. Also, only square matrices can have inverses because both $A^{-1}A$ and AA^{-1} must exist and be equal to an identity matrix of the same size.

EXAMPLE 1 Inverse Matrices

Verify that the matrices $A = \begin{bmatrix} 1 & 3 \\ 2 & 5 \end{bmatrix}$ and $B = \begin{bmatrix} -5 & 3 \\ 2 & -1 \end{bmatrix}$ are inverses of each other.

SOLUTION Multiply A times B as in the previous section:

$$AB = \begin{bmatrix} 1 & 3 \\ 2 & 5 \end{bmatrix}\begin{bmatrix} -5 & 3 \\ 2 & -1 \end{bmatrix} = \begin{bmatrix} 1 & 0 \\ 0 & 1 \end{bmatrix}.$$

Similarly,

$$BA = \begin{bmatrix} -5 & 3 \\ 2 & -1 \end{bmatrix}\begin{bmatrix} 1 & 3 \\ 2 & 5 \end{bmatrix} = \begin{bmatrix} 1 & 0 \\ 0 & 1 \end{bmatrix}.$$

Since $AB = BA = I$, A and B are inverses of each other.

If an inverse exists, it is unique. That is, any given square matrix has no more than one inverse. The proof of this is left to Exercise 50 in this section.

As an example, let us find the inverse of

$$A = \begin{bmatrix} 1 & 3 \\ -1 & 2 \end{bmatrix}.$$

Let the unknown inverse matrix be

$$A^{-1} = \begin{bmatrix} x & y \\ z & w \end{bmatrix}.$$

By the definition of matrix inverse, $AA^{-1} = I$, or

$$AA^{-1} = \begin{bmatrix} 1 & 3 \\ -1 & 2 \end{bmatrix}\begin{bmatrix} x & y \\ z & w \end{bmatrix} = \begin{bmatrix} 1 & 0 \\ 0 & 1 \end{bmatrix}.$$

By matrix multiplication,

$$\begin{bmatrix} x + 3z & y + 3w \\ -x + 2z & -y + 2w \end{bmatrix} = \begin{bmatrix} 1 & 0 \\ 0 & 1 \end{bmatrix}.$$

Setting corresponding elements equal gives the system of equations

$$x \qquad\quad + 3z \qquad\quad = 1 \tag{1}$$
$$\qquad y \qquad\quad + 3w = 0 \tag{2}$$
$$-x \qquad + 2z \qquad\quad = 0 \tag{3}$$
$$\qquad - y \qquad\quad + 2w = 1. \tag{4}$$

Since equations (1) and (3) involve only x and z, while equations (2) and (4) involve only y and w, these four equations lead to two systems of equations,

$$\begin{array}{c} x + 3z = 1 \\ -x + 2z = 0 \end{array} \quad \text{and} \quad \begin{array}{c} y + 3w = 0 \\ -y + 2w = 1. \end{array}$$

Writing the two systems as augmented matrices gives

$$\begin{bmatrix} 1 & 3 & | & 1 \\ -1 & 2 & | & 0 \end{bmatrix} \quad \text{and} \quad \begin{bmatrix} 1 & 3 & | & 0 \\ -1 & 2 & | & 1 \end{bmatrix}.$$

Each of these systems can be solved by the Gauss-Jordan method. Notice, however, that the elements to the left of the vertical bar are identical. The two systems can be combined into the single matrix

$$\left[\begin{array}{cc|cc} 1 & 3 & 1 & 0 \\ -1 & 2 & 0 & 1 \end{array}\right].$$

This is of the form $[A\,|\,I]$. It is solved simultaneously as follows.

$$R_1 + R_2 \rightarrow R_2 \quad \left[\begin{array}{cc|cc} 1 & 3 & 1 & 0 \\ 0 & 5 & 1 & 1 \end{array}\right] \quad \begin{array}{l}\text{Get 0 in the second-row,} \\ \text{first-column position.}\end{array}$$

$$-3R_2 + 5R_1 \rightarrow R_1 \quad \left[\begin{array}{cc|cc} 5 & 0 & 2 & -3 \\ 0 & 5 & 1 & 1 \end{array}\right] \quad \begin{array}{l}\text{Get 0 in the first-row,} \\ \text{second-column position.}\end{array}$$

$$\begin{array}{l}\frac{1}{5}R_1 \rightarrow R_1 \\ \frac{1}{5}R_2 \rightarrow R_2\end{array} \quad \left[\begin{array}{cc|cc} 1 & 0 & \frac{2}{5} & -\frac{3}{5} \\ 0 & 1 & \frac{1}{5} & \frac{1}{5} \end{array}\right] \quad \begin{array}{l}\text{Get 1's down the} \\ \text{diagonal.}\end{array}$$

The numbers in the first column to the right of the vertical bar give the values of x and z. The second column gives the values of y and w. That is,

$$\left[\begin{array}{cc|cc} 1 & 0 & x & y \\ 0 & 1 & z & w \end{array}\right] = \left[\begin{array}{cc|cc} 1 & 0 & \frac{2}{5} & -\frac{3}{5} \\ 0 & 1 & \frac{1}{5} & \frac{1}{5} \end{array}\right]$$

so that

$$A^{-1} = \left[\begin{array}{cc} x & y \\ z & w \end{array}\right] = \left[\begin{array}{cc} \frac{2}{5} & -\frac{3}{5} \\ \frac{1}{5} & \frac{1}{5} \end{array}\right].$$

To check, multiply A by A^{-1}. The result should be I.

$$AA^{-1} = \left[\begin{array}{cc} 1 & 3 \\ -1 & 2 \end{array}\right]\left[\begin{array}{cc} \frac{2}{5} & -\frac{3}{5} \\ \frac{1}{5} & \frac{1}{5} \end{array}\right] = \left[\begin{array}{cc} \frac{2}{5}+\frac{3}{5} & -\frac{3}{5}+\frac{3}{5} \\ -\frac{2}{5}+\frac{2}{5} & \frac{3}{5}+\frac{2}{5} \end{array}\right] = \left[\begin{array}{cc} 1 & 0 \\ 0 & 1 \end{array}\right] = I$$

Verify that $A^{-1}A = I$, also.

Finding a Multiplicative Inverse Matrix

To obtain A^{-1} for any $n \times n$ matrix A for which A^{-1} exists, follow these steps.

1. Form the augmented matrix $[A\,|\,I]$, where I is the $n \times n$ identity matrix.
2. Perform row operations on $[A\,|\,I]$ to get a matrix of the form $[I\,|\,B]$, if this is possible.
3. Matrix B is A^{-1}.

EXAMPLE 2 Inverse Matrix

Find A^{-1} if $A = \left[\begin{array}{ccc} 1 & 0 & 1 \\ 2 & -2 & -1 \\ 3 & 0 & 0 \end{array}\right]$.

Method 1
Calculating by Hand

SOLUTION Write the augmented matrix $[A \mid I]$.

$$[A|I] = \left[\begin{array}{ccc|ccc} 1 & 0 & 1 & 1 & 0 & 0 \\ 2 & -2 & -1 & 0 & 1 & 0 \\ 3 & 0 & 0 & 0 & 0 & 1 \end{array}\right]$$

Begin by selecting the row operation that produces a zero for the first element in row 2.

$$\begin{array}{l}-2R_1 + R_2 \rightarrow R_2 \\ -3R_1 + R_3 \rightarrow R_3\end{array} \quad \left[\begin{array}{ccc|ccc} 1 & 0 & 1 & 1 & 0 & 0 \\ 0 & -2 & -3 & -2 & 1 & 0 \\ 0 & 0 & -3 & -3 & 0 & 1 \end{array}\right] \quad \text{Get 0's in the first column.}$$

Column 2 already has zeros in the required positions, so work on column 3.

$$\begin{array}{c} R_3 + 3R_1 \rightarrow R_1 \\ R_3 + (-1)R_2 \rightarrow R_2 \end{array} \left[\begin{array}{ccc|ccc} 3 & 0 & 0 & 0 & 0 & 1 \\ 0 & 2 & 0 & -1 & -1 & 1 \\ 0 & 0 & -3 & -3 & 0 & 1 \end{array}\right]$$ Get 0's in the third column.

Now get 1's down the main diagonal.

$$\begin{array}{c} \frac{1}{3}R_1 \rightarrow R_1 \\ \frac{1}{2}R_2 \rightarrow R_2 \\ -\frac{1}{3}R_3 \rightarrow R_3 \end{array} \left[\begin{array}{ccc|ccc} 1 & 0 & 0 & 0 & 0 & \frac{1}{3} \\ 0 & 1 & 0 & -\frac{1}{2} & -\frac{1}{2} & \frac{1}{2} \\ 0 & 0 & 1 & 1 & 0 & -\frac{1}{3} \end{array}\right]$$ Get 1's down the diagonal.

From the last transformation, the desired inverse is

YOUR TURN 1 Find A^{-1} if

$$A = \begin{bmatrix} 2 & 3 & 1 \\ 1 & -2 & -1 \\ 3 & 3 & 2 \end{bmatrix}.$$

$$A^{-1} = \begin{bmatrix} 0 & 0 & \frac{1}{3} \\ -\frac{1}{2} & -\frac{1}{2} & \frac{1}{2} \\ 1 & 0 & -\frac{1}{3} \end{bmatrix}.$$

Confirm this by forming the products $A^{-1}A$ and AA^{-1}, both of which should equal I.

Method 2
Graphing Calculator

The inverse of A can also be found with a graphing calculator, as shown in Figure 14 in the margin below. (The matrix A had previously been entered into the calculator.) The entire answer can be viewed by pressing the right and left arrow keys on the calculator.

TRY YOUR TURN 1

TECHNOLOGY NOTE

Spreadsheets also have the capability of calculating the inverse of a matrix with a simple command. See the *Graphing Calculator and Excel Spreadsheet Manual* available with this book for details.

FIGURE 14

EXAMPLE 3 Inverse Matrix

Find A^{-1} if $A = \begin{bmatrix} 2 & -4 \\ 1 & -2 \end{bmatrix}$.

SOLUTION Using row operations to transform the first column of the augmented matrix

$$\begin{bmatrix} 2 & -4 & 1 & 0 \\ 1 & -2 & 0 & 1 \end{bmatrix}$$

gives the following results.

$$R_1 + (-2)R_2 \rightarrow R_2 \begin{bmatrix} 2 & -4 & 1 & 0 \\ 0 & 0 & 1 & -2 \end{bmatrix}$$

Because the last row has all zeros to the left of the vertical bar, there is no way to complete the process of finding the inverse matrix. What is wrong? Just as the real number 0 has no multiplicative inverse, some matrices do not have inverses. Matrix A is an example of a matrix that has no inverse: there is no matrix A^{-1} such that $AA^{-1} = A^{-1}A = I$.

Solving Systems of Equations with Inverses

We used matrices to solve systems of linear equations by the Gauss-Jordan method in Section 2.2. Another way to use matrices to solve linear systems is to write the system as a matrix equation $AX = B$, where A is the matrix of the coefficients of the variables of the system, X is the matrix of the variables, and B is the matrix of the constants. Matrix A is called the **coefficient matrix**.

To solve the matrix equation $AX = B$, first see if A^{-1} exists. Assuming A^{-1} exists and using the facts that $A^{-1}A = I$ and $IX = X$ gives

$$AX = B$$
$$A^{-1}(AX) = A^{-1}B \qquad \text{Multiply both sides by } A^{-1}.$$
$$(A^{-1}A)X = A^{-1}B \qquad \text{Associative property}$$
$$IX = A^{-1}B \qquad \text{Multiplicative inverse property}$$
$$X = A^{-1}B. \qquad \text{Identity property}$$

CAUTION When multiplying by matrices on both sides of a matrix equation, be careful to multiply in the same order on both sides of the equation, since multiplication of matrices is not commutative (unlike multiplication of real numbers).

The work thus far leads to the following method of solving a system of equations written as a matrix equation.

Solving a System $AX = B$ Using Matrix Inverses

To solve a system of equations $AX = B$, where A is the square matrix of coefficients and A^{-1} exists, X is the matrix of variables, and B is the matrix of constants, first find A^{-1}. Then $X = A^{-1}B$.

This method is most practical in solving several systems that have the same coefficient matrix but different constants, as in Example 5 in this section. Then just one inverse matrix must be found.

EXAMPLE 4 Inverse Matrices and Systems of Equations

Use the inverse of the coefficient matrix to solve the linear system

$$2x - 3y = 4$$
$$x + 5y = 2.$$

SOLUTION To represent the system as a matrix equation, use the coefficient matrix of the system together with the matrix of variables and the matrix of constants:

$$A = \begin{bmatrix} 2 & -3 \\ 1 & 5 \end{bmatrix}, \quad X = \begin{bmatrix} x \\ y \end{bmatrix}, \quad \text{and} \quad B = \begin{bmatrix} 4 \\ 2 \end{bmatrix}.$$

The system can now be written in matrix form as the equation $AX = B$ since

$$AX = \begin{bmatrix} 2 & -3 \\ 1 & 5 \end{bmatrix} \begin{bmatrix} x \\ y \end{bmatrix} = \begin{bmatrix} 2x - 3y \\ x + 5y \end{bmatrix} = \begin{bmatrix} 4 \\ 2 \end{bmatrix} = B.$$

To solve the system, first find A^{-1}. Do this by using row operations on matrix $[A|I]$ to get

$$\begin{bmatrix} 1 & 0 & \frac{5}{13} & \frac{3}{13} \\ 0 & 1 & -\frac{1}{13} & \frac{2}{13} \end{bmatrix}.$$

From this result,

$$A^{-1} = \begin{bmatrix} \frac{5}{13} & \frac{3}{13} \\ -\frac{1}{13} & \frac{2}{13} \end{bmatrix}.$$

Next, find the product $A^{-1}B$.

$$A^{-1}B = \begin{bmatrix} \frac{5}{13} & \frac{3}{13} \\ -\frac{1}{13} & \frac{2}{13} \end{bmatrix} \begin{bmatrix} 4 \\ 2 \end{bmatrix} = \begin{bmatrix} 2 \\ 0 \end{bmatrix}.$$

Since $X = A^{-1}B$,

$$X = \begin{bmatrix} x \\ y \end{bmatrix} = \begin{bmatrix} 2 \\ 0 \end{bmatrix}.$$

The solution of the system is $(2, 0)$. TRY YOUR TURN 2

YOUR TURN 2 Use the inverse of the coefficient matrix to solve the linear system
$$5x + 4y = 23$$
$$4x - 3y = 6.$$

EXAMPLE 5 Fertilizer

Three brands of fertilizer are available that provide nitrogen, phosphoric acid, and soluble potash to the soil. One bag of each brand provides the following units of each nutrient.

		Brand		
		Fertifun	Big Grow	Soakem
Nutrient	*Nitrogen*	1	2	3
	Phosphoric Acid	3	1	2
	Potash	2	0	1

For ideal growth, the soil on a Michigan farm needs 18 units of nitrogen, 23 units of phosphoric acid, and 13 units of potash per acre. The corresponding numbers for a California farm are 31, 24, and 11, and for a Kansas farm are 20, 19, and 15. How many bags of each brand of fertilizer should be used per acre for ideal growth on each farm?

SOLUTION   Rather than solve three separate systems, we consider the single system

$$x + 2y + 3z = a$$
$$3x + y + 2z = b$$
$$2x + z = c,$$

where a, b, and c represent the units of nitrogen, phosphoric acid, and potash needed for the different farms. The system of equations is then of the form $AX = B$, where

$$A = \begin{bmatrix} 1 & 2 & 3 \\ 3 & 1 & 2 \\ 2 & 0 & 1 \end{bmatrix} \quad \text{and} \quad X = \begin{bmatrix} x \\ y \\ z \end{bmatrix}.$$

B has different values for the different farms. We find A^{-1} first, then use it to solve all three systems.

To find A^{-1}, we start with the matrix

$$[A|I] = \begin{bmatrix} 1 & 2 & 3 & | & 1 & 0 & 0 \\ 3 & 1 & 2 & | & 0 & 1 & 0 \\ 2 & 0 & 1 & | & 0 & 0 & 1 \end{bmatrix}$$

and use row operations to get $[I|A^{-1}]$. The result is

$$A^{-1} = \begin{bmatrix} -\frac{1}{3} & \frac{2}{3} & -\frac{1}{3} \\ -\frac{1}{3} & \frac{5}{3} & -\frac{7}{3} \\ \frac{2}{3} & -\frac{4}{3} & \frac{5}{3} \end{bmatrix}.$$

Now we can solve each of the three systems by using $X = A^{-1}B$.

For the Michigan farm, $B = \begin{bmatrix} 18 \\ 23 \\ 13 \end{bmatrix}$, and

$$X = \begin{bmatrix} -\frac{1}{3} & \frac{2}{3} & -\frac{1}{3} \\ -\frac{1}{3} & \frac{5}{3} & -\frac{7}{3} \\ \frac{2}{3} & -\frac{4}{3} & \frac{5}{3} \end{bmatrix} \begin{bmatrix} 18 \\ 23 \\ 13 \end{bmatrix} = \begin{bmatrix} 5 \\ 2 \\ 3 \end{bmatrix}.$$

Therefore, $x = 5$, $y = 2$, and $z = 3$. Buy 5 bags of Fertifun, 2 bags of Big Grow, and 3 bags of Soakem.

For the California farm, $B = \begin{bmatrix} 31 \\ 24 \\ 11 \end{bmatrix}$, and

$$X = \begin{bmatrix} -\frac{1}{3} & \frac{2}{3} & -\frac{1}{3} \\ -\frac{1}{3} & \frac{5}{3} & -\frac{7}{3} \\ \frac{2}{3} & -\frac{4}{3} & \frac{5}{3} \end{bmatrix} \begin{bmatrix} 31 \\ 24 \\ 11 \end{bmatrix} = \begin{bmatrix} 2 \\ 4 \\ 7 \end{bmatrix}.$$

Buy 2 bags of Fertifun, 4 bags of Big Grow, and 7 bags of Soakem.

For the Kansas farm, $B = \begin{bmatrix} 20 \\ 19 \\ 15 \end{bmatrix}$. Verify that this leads to $x = 1$, $y = -10$, and

$z = 13$. We cannot have a negative number of bags, so this solution is impossible. In buying enough bags to meet all of the nutrient requirements, the farmer must purchase an excess of some nutrients. In the next two chapters, we will study a method of solving such problems at a minimum cost.

In Example 5, using the matrix inverse method of solving the systems involved considerably less work than using row operations for each of the three systems.

EXAMPLE 6 Solving an Inconsistent System of Equations

Use the inverse of the coefficient matrix to solve the system

$$2x - 4y = 13$$
$$x - 2y = 1.$$

SOLUTION We saw in Example 3 that the coefficient matrix $\begin{bmatrix} 2 & -4 \\ 1 & -2 \end{bmatrix}$ does not have an inverse. This means that the given system either has no solution or has an infinite number of solutions. Verify that this system is inconsistent and has no solution.

NOTE If a matrix has no inverse, then a corresponding system of equations might have either no solutions or an infinite number of solutions, and we instead use the echelon or Gauss-Jordan method. In Example 3, we saw that the matrix $\begin{bmatrix} 2 & -4 \\ 1 & -2 \end{bmatrix}$ had no inverse. The reason is that the first row of this matrix is double the second row. The system

$$2x - 4y = 2$$
$$x - 2y = 1$$

has an infinite number of solutions because the first equation is double the second equation. The system

$$2x - 4y = 13$$
$$x - 2y = 1$$

has no solutions because the left side of the first equation is double the left side of the second equation, but the right side is not.

EXAMPLE 7 Cryptography

Throughout the Cold War and as the Internet has grown and developed, the need for sophisticated methods of coding and decoding messages has increased. Although there are many methods of encrypting messages, one fairly sophisticated method uses matrix operations. This method first assigns a number to each letter of the alphabet. The simplest way to do this is to assign the number 1 to A, 2 to B, and so on, with the number 27 used to represent a space between words.

APPLY IT

For example, the message *math is cool* can be divided into groups of three letters and spaces each and then converted into numbers as follows

$$\begin{bmatrix} m \\ a \\ t \end{bmatrix} = \begin{bmatrix} 13 \\ 1 \\ 20 \end{bmatrix}.$$

The entire message would then consist of four 3×1 columns of numbers:

$$\begin{bmatrix} 13 \\ 1 \\ 20 \end{bmatrix}, \quad \begin{bmatrix} 8 \\ 27 \\ 9 \end{bmatrix}, \quad \begin{bmatrix} 19 \\ 27 \\ 3 \end{bmatrix}, \quad \begin{bmatrix} 15 \\ 15 \\ 12 \end{bmatrix}.$$

This code is easy to break, so we further complicate the code by choosing a matrix that has an inverse (in this case a 3×3 matrix) and calculate the products of the matrix and each of the column vectors above.

If we choose the coding matrix

$$A = \begin{bmatrix} 1 & 3 & 4 \\ 2 & 1 & 3 \\ 4 & 2 & 1 \end{bmatrix},$$

then the products of A with each of the column vectors above produce a new set of vectors

$$\begin{bmatrix} 96 \\ 87 \\ 74 \end{bmatrix}, \quad \begin{bmatrix} 125 \\ 70 \\ 95 \end{bmatrix}, \quad \begin{bmatrix} 112 \\ 74 \\ 133 \end{bmatrix}, \quad \begin{bmatrix} 108 \\ 81 \\ 102 \end{bmatrix}.$$

This set of vectors represents our coded message, and it will be transmitted as 96, 87, 74, 125 and so on.

When the intended person receives the message, it is divided into groups of three numbers, and each group is formed into a column matrix. The message is easily decoded if the receiver knows the inverse of the original matrix. The inverse of matrix A is

$$A^{-1} = \begin{bmatrix} -0.2 & 0.2 & 0.2 \\ 0.4 & -0.6 & 0.2 \\ 0 & 0.4 & -0.2 \end{bmatrix}.$$

Thus, the message is decoded by taking the product of the inverse matrix with each column vector of the received message. For example,

$$A^{-1} \begin{bmatrix} 96 \\ 87 \\ 74 \end{bmatrix} = \begin{bmatrix} 13 \\ 1 \\ 20 \end{bmatrix}.$$

YOUR TURN 3 Use the matrix A and its inverse A^{-1} in Example 7 to do the following.

a) Encode the message "Behold".
b) Decode the message 96, 87, 74, 141, 117, 114.

Unless the original matrix or its inverse is known, this type of code can be difficult to break. In fact, very large matrices can be used to encrypt data. It is interesting to note that many mathematicians are employed by the National Security Agency to develop encryption methods that are virtually unbreakable. **TRY YOUR TURN 3**

2.5 EXERCISES

Decide whether the given matrices are inverses of each other. (Check to see if their product is the identity matrix I.)

1. $\begin{bmatrix} 2 & 1 \\ 5 & 3 \end{bmatrix}$ and $\begin{bmatrix} 3 & -1 \\ -5 & 2 \end{bmatrix}$ **2.** $\begin{bmatrix} 1 & -4 \\ 2 & -7 \end{bmatrix}$ and $\begin{bmatrix} -7 & 4 \\ -2 & 1 \end{bmatrix}$

3. $\begin{bmatrix} 2 & 6 \\ 2 & 4 \end{bmatrix}$ and $\begin{bmatrix} -1 & 2 \\ 2 & -4 \end{bmatrix}$ **4.** $\begin{bmatrix} -1 & 2 \\ 3 & -5 \end{bmatrix}$ and $\begin{bmatrix} -5 & -2 \\ -3 & -1 \end{bmatrix}$

5. $\begin{bmatrix} 2 & 0 & 1 \\ 1 & 1 & 2 \\ 0 & 1 & 0 \end{bmatrix}$ and $\begin{bmatrix} 1 & 1 & -1 \\ 0 & 1 & 0 \\ -1 & -2 & 2 \end{bmatrix}$

6. $\begin{bmatrix} 0 & 1 & 0 \\ 0 & 0 & -2 \\ 1 & -1 & 0 \end{bmatrix}$ and $\begin{bmatrix} 1 & 0 & 1 \\ 1 & 0 & 0 \\ 0 & -1 & 0 \end{bmatrix}$

7. $\begin{bmatrix} 1 & 3 & 3 \\ 1 & 4 & 3 \\ 1 & 3 & 4 \end{bmatrix}$ and $\begin{bmatrix} 7 & -3 & -3 \\ -1 & 1 & 0 \\ -1 & 0 & 1 \end{bmatrix}$

8. $\begin{bmatrix} 1 & 0 & 0 \\ -1 & -2 & 3 \\ 0 & 1 & 0 \end{bmatrix}$ and $\begin{bmatrix} 1 & 0 & 0 \\ 0 & 0 & 1 \\ \frac{1}{3} & \frac{1}{3} & \frac{2}{3} \end{bmatrix}$

9. Does a matrix with a row of all zeros have an inverse? Why?

 10. Matrix A has A^{-1} as its inverse. What does $(A^{-1})^{-1}$ equal? (*Hint:* Experiment with a few matrices to see what you get.)

Find the inverse, if it exists, for each matrix.

11. $\begin{bmatrix} 1 & -1 \\ 2 & 0 \end{bmatrix}$

12. $\begin{bmatrix} 1 & 1 \\ 2 & 3 \end{bmatrix}$

13. $\begin{bmatrix} 3 & -1 \\ -5 & 2 \end{bmatrix}$

14. $\begin{bmatrix} -3 & -8 \\ 1 & 3 \end{bmatrix}$

15. $\begin{bmatrix} 1 & -3 \\ -2 & 6 \end{bmatrix}$

16. $\begin{bmatrix} 5 & 10 \\ -3 & -6 \end{bmatrix}$

17. $\begin{bmatrix} 1 & 0 & 0 \\ 0 & -1 & 0 \\ 1 & 0 & 1 \end{bmatrix}$

18. $\begin{bmatrix} 1 & 3 & 0 \\ 0 & 2 & -1 \\ 1 & 0 & 2 \end{bmatrix}$

19. $\begin{bmatrix} -1 & -1 & -1 \\ 4 & 5 & 0 \\ 0 & 1 & -3 \end{bmatrix}$

20. $\begin{bmatrix} 2 & 1 & 0 \\ 0 & 3 & 1 \\ 4 & -1 & -3 \end{bmatrix}$

21. $\begin{bmatrix} 1 & 2 & 3 \\ -3 & -2 & -1 \\ -1 & 0 & 1 \end{bmatrix}$

22. $\begin{bmatrix} 2 & 0 & 4 \\ 1 & 0 & -1 \\ 3 & 0 & -2 \end{bmatrix}$

23. $\begin{bmatrix} 1 & 3 & -2 \\ 2 & 7 & -3 \\ 3 & 8 & -5 \end{bmatrix}$

24. $\begin{bmatrix} 4 & 1 & -4 \\ 2 & 1 & -1 \\ -2 & -4 & 5 \end{bmatrix}$

25. $\begin{bmatrix} 1 & -2 & 3 & 0 \\ 0 & 1 & -1 & 1 \\ -2 & 2 & -2 & 4 \\ 0 & 2 & -3 & 1 \end{bmatrix}$

26. $\begin{bmatrix} 1 & 1 & 0 & 2 \\ 2 & -1 & 1 & -1 \\ 3 & 3 & 2 & -2 \\ 1 & 2 & 1 & 0 \end{bmatrix}$

Solve each system of equations by using the inverse of the coefficient matrix if it exists and by the echelon method if the inverse doesn't exist.

27. $2x + 5y = 15$
$x + 4y = 9$

28. $-x + 2y = 15$
$-2x - y = 20$

29. $2x + y = 5$
$5x + 3y = 13$

30. $-x - 2y = 8$
$3x + 4y = 24$

31. $3x - 2y = 3$
$7x - 5y = 0$

32. $3x - 6y = 1$
$-5x + 9y = -1$

33. $-x - 8y = 12$
$3x + 24y = -36$

34. $2x + 7y = 14$
$4x + 14y = 28$

Solve each system of equations by using the inverse of the coefficient matrix if it exists and by the Gauss-Jordan method if the inverse doesn't exist. (The inverses for the first four problems were found in Exercises 19, 20, 23, and 24.)

35. $-x - y - z = 1$
$4x + 5y = -2$
$y - 3z = 3$

36. $2x + y = 1$
$3y + z = 8$
$4x - y - 3z = 8$

37. $x + 3y - 2z = 4$
$2x + 7y - 3z = 8$
$3x + 8y - 5z = -4$

38. $4x + y - 4z = 17$
$2x + y - z = 12$
$-2x - 4y + 5z = 17$

39. $2x - 2y = 5$
$4y + 8z = 7$
$x + 2z = 1$

40. $x + 2z = -1$
$y - z = 5$
$x + 2y = 7$

Solve each system of equations by using the inverse of the coefficient matrix. (The inverses were found in Exercises 25 and 26.)

41. $x - 2y + 3z = 4$
$y - z + w = -8$
$-2x + 2y - 2z + 4w = 12$
$2y - 3z + w = -4$

42. $x + y + 2w = 3$
$2x - y + z - w = 3$
$3x + 3y + 2z - 2w = 5$
$x + 2y + z = 3$

Let $A = \begin{bmatrix} a & b \\ c & d \end{bmatrix}$ and $0 = \begin{bmatrix} 0 & 0 \\ 0 & 0 \end{bmatrix}$ in Exercises 43–48.

43. Show that $IA = A$.

44. Show that $AI = A$.

45. Show that $A \cdot O = O$.

46. Find A^{-1}. (Assume $ad - bc \neq 0$.)

47. Show that $A^{-1}A = I$.

48. Show that $AA^{-1} = I$.

49. Using the definition and properties listed in this section, show that for square matrices A and B of the same size, if $AB = O$ and if A^{-1} exists, then $B = O$, where O is a matrix whose elements are all zeros.

50. Prove that, if it exists, the inverse of a matrix is unique. (*Hint:* Assume there are two inverses B and C for some matrix A, so that $AB = BA = I$ and $AC = CA = I$. Multiply the first equation by C and the second by B.)

 Use matrices C and D in Exercises 51–55.

$$C = \begin{bmatrix} -6 & 8 & 2 & 4 & -3 \\ 1 & 9 & 7 & -12 & 5 \\ 15 & 2 & -8 & 10 & 11 \\ 4 & 7 & 9 & 6 & -2 \\ 1 & 3 & 8 & 23 & 4 \end{bmatrix}, \quad D = \begin{bmatrix} 5 & -3 & 7 & 9 & 2 \\ 6 & 8 & -5 & 2 & 1 \\ 3 & 7 & -4 & 2 & 11 \\ 5 & -3 & 9 & 4 & -1 \\ 0 & 3 & 2 & 5 & 1 \end{bmatrix}$$

51. Find C^{-1}.

52. Find $(CD)^{-1}$.

53. Find D^{-1}.

54. Is $C^{-1}D^{-1} = (CD)^{-1}$?

55. Is $D^{-1}C^{-1} = (CD)^{-1}$?

Solve the matrix equation $AX = B$ for X by finding A^{-1}, given A and B as follows.

56. $A = \begin{bmatrix} 2 & -5 & 7 \\ 4 & -3 & 2 \\ 15 & 2 & 6 \end{bmatrix}$, $B = \begin{bmatrix} -2 \\ 5 \\ 8 \end{bmatrix}$

57. $A = \begin{bmatrix} 2 & 5 & 7 & 9 \\ 1 & 3 & -4 & 6 \\ -1 & 0 & 5 & 8 \\ 2 & -2 & 4 & 10 \end{bmatrix}$, $B = \begin{bmatrix} 3 \\ 7 \\ -1 \\ 5 \end{bmatrix}$

58. $A = \begin{bmatrix} 3 & 2 & -1 & -2 & 6 \\ -5 & 17 & 4 & 3 & 15 \\ 7 & 9 & -3 & -7 & 12 \\ 9 & -2 & 1 & 4 & 8 \\ 1 & 21 & 9 & -7 & 25 \end{bmatrix}$, $B = \begin{bmatrix} -2 \\ 5 \\ 3 \\ -8 \\ 25 \end{bmatrix}$

APPLICATIONS

Business and Economics

Solve each exercise by using the inverse of the coefficient matrix to solve a system of equations.

59. Analysis of Orders   The Bread Box Bakery sells three types of cakes, each requiring the amounts of the basic ingredients shown in the following matrix.

$$\begin{array}{c} \\ \text{Ingredient} \end{array} \begin{array}{c} \\ \text{Flour (in cups)} \\ \text{Sugar (in cups)} \\ \text{Eggs} \end{array} \begin{array}{c} \text{Type of Cake} \\ \begin{array}{ccc} \text{I} & \text{II} & \text{III} \end{array} \\ \begin{bmatrix} 2 & 4 & 2 \\ 2 & 1 & 2 \\ 2 & 1 & 3 \end{bmatrix} \end{array}$$

To fill its daily orders for these three kinds of cake, the bakery uses 72 cups of flour, 48 cups of sugar, and 60 eggs.

a. Write a 3 × 1 matrix for the amounts used daily.

b. Let the number of daily orders for cakes be a 3 × 1 matrix X with entries x_1, x_2, and x_3. Write a matrix equation that can be solved for X, using the given matrix and the matrix from part a.

c. Solve the equation from part b to find the number of daily orders for each type of cake.

60. Production Requirements   An electronics company produces transistors, resistors, and computer chips. Each transistor requires 3 units of copper, 1 unit of zinc, and 2 units of glass. Each resistor requires 3, 2, and 1 units of the three materials, and each computer chip requires 2, 1, and 2 units of these materials, respectively. How many of each product can be made with the following amounts of materials?

a. 810 units of copper, 410 units of zinc, and 490 units of glass

b. 765 units of copper, 385 units of zinc, and 470 units of glass

c. 1010 units of copper, 500 units of zinc, and 610 units of glass

61. Investments   An investment firm recommends that a client invest in AAA-, A-, and B-rated bonds. The average yield on AAA bonds is 6%, on A bonds 6.5%, and on B bonds 8%. The client wants to invest twice as much in AAA bonds as in B bonds. How much should be invested in each type of bond under the following conditions?

a. The total investment is $25,000, and the investor wants an annual return of $1650 on the three investments.

b. The values in part a are changed to $30,000 and $1985, respectively.

c. The values in part a are changed to $40,000 and $2660, respectively.

62. Production   Pretzels cost $4 per lb, dried fruit $5 per lb, and nuts $9 per lb. The three ingredients are to be combined in a trail mix containing twice the weight of pretzels as dried fruit. How many pounds of each should be used to produce the following amounts at the given cost?

a. 140 lb at $6 per lb

b. 100 lb at $7.60 per lb

c. 125 lb at $6.20 per lb

Life Sciences

63. Vitamins   Greg Tobin mixes together three types of vitamin tablets. Each Super Vim tablet contains, among other things,

15 mg of niacin and 12 I.U. of vitamin E. The figures for a Multitab tablet are 20 mg and 15 I.U., and for a Mighty Mix are 25 mg and 35 I.U. How many of each tablet are there if the total number of tablets, total amount of niacin, and total amount of vitamin E are as follows?

a. 225 tablets, 4750 mg of niacin, and 5225 I.U. of vitamin E

b. 185 tablets, 3625 mg of niacin, and 3750 I.U. of vitamin E

c. 230 tablets, 4450 mg of niacin, and 4210 I.U. of vitamin E

General Interest

64. Encryption   Use the matrices presented in Example 7 of this section to do the following:

a. Encode the message, "All is fair in love and war."

b. Decode the message 138, 81, 102, 101, 67, 109, 162, 124, 173, 210, 150, 165.

65. Encryption   Use the methods presented in Example 7 along with the given matrix B to do the following.

$$B = \begin{bmatrix} 2 & 4 & 6 \\ -1 & -4 & -3 \\ 0 & 1 & -1 \end{bmatrix}$$

a. Encode the message, "To be or not to be."

b. Find the inverse of B.

c. Use the inverse of B to decode the message 116, −60, −15, 294, −197, −2, 148, −92, −9, 96, −64, 4, 264, −182, −2.

66. Music   During a marching band's half-time show, the band members generally line up in such a way that a common shape is recognized by the fans. For example, as illustrated in the figure, a band might form a letter T, where an **x** represents a member of the band. As the music is played, the band will either create a new shape or rotate the original shape. In doing this, each member of the band will need to move from one point on the field to another. For larger bands, keeping track of who goes where can be a daunting task. However, it is possible to use matrix inverses to make the process a bit easier. The entire process is calculated by knowing how three band members, all of whom cannot be in a straight line, will move from the current position to a new position. For example, in the figure, we can see that there are band members at $(50, 0)$, $(50, 15)$, and $(45, 20)$. We will assume that these three band members move to $(40, 10)$, $(55, 10)$, and $(60, 15)$, respectively. *Source: The College Mathematics Journal.*

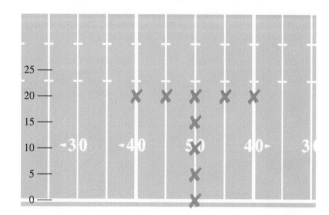

a. Find the inverse of $B = \begin{bmatrix} 50 & 50 & 45 \\ 0 & 15 & 20 \\ 1 & 1 & 1 \end{bmatrix}$.

b. Find $A = \begin{bmatrix} 40 & 55 & 60 \\ 10 & 10 & 15 \\ 1 & 1 & 1 \end{bmatrix} B^{-1}$.

c. Use the result of part b to find the new position of the other band members. What is the shape of the new position? (*Hint:* Multiply the matrix A by a 3×1 column vector with the first two components equal to the original position of each band member and the third component equal to 1. The new position of the band member is in the first two components of the product.)

YOUR TURN ANSWERS

1. $\begin{bmatrix} 1/8 & 3/8 & 1/8 \\ 5/8 & -1/8 & -3/8 \\ -9/8 & -3/8 & 7/8 \end{bmatrix}$ **2.** $(3, 2)$ **3. a.** 49, 33, 26, 67, 54, 88 **b.** matrix

2.6 Input-Output Models

APPLY IT What production levels are needed to keep an economy going and to supply demands from outside the economy?

A method for solving such questions is developed in this section and applied in Examples 3 and 4.

Wassily Leontief (1906–1999) developed an interesting and powerful application of matrix theory to economics and was recognized for this contribution with the Nobel prize in economics in 1973. His matrix models for studying the interdependencies in an economy are called *input-output* models. In practice these models are very complicated, with many variables. Only simple examples with a few variables are discussed here.

Input-output models are concerned with the production and flow of goods (and perhaps services). In an economy with n basic commodities, or sectors, the production of each commodity uses some (perhaps all) of the commodities in the economy as inputs. For example, oil is needed to run the machinery that plants and harvests the wheat, and wheat is used to feed the people who drill and refine the oil. The amounts of each commodity used in the production of one unit of each commodity can be written as an $n \times n$ matrix A, called the **technological matrix** or **input-output matrix** of the economy.

EXAMPLE 1 Input-Output Matrix

Suppose a simplified economy involves just three commodity categories: agriculture, manufacturing, and transportation, all in appropriate units. Production of 1 unit of agriculture requires 1/2 unit of manufacturing and 1/4 unit of transportation; production of 1 unit of manufacturing requires 1/4 unit of agriculture and 1/4 unit of transportation; and production of 1 unit of transportation requires 1/3 unit of agriculture and 1/4 unit of manufacturing. Give the input-output matrix for this economy.

SOLUTION

$$\begin{array}{c} \\ \text{Agriculture} \\ \text{Manufacturing} \\ \text{Transportation} \end{array} \begin{array}{ccc} \text{Agriculture} & \text{Manufacturing} & \text{Transportation} \end{array} \\ \begin{bmatrix} 0 & \frac{1}{4} & \frac{1}{3} \\ \frac{1}{2} & 0 & \frac{1}{4} \\ \frac{1}{4} & \frac{1}{4} & 0 \end{bmatrix} = A$$

The first column of the input-output matrix represents the amount of each of the three commodities consumed in the production of 1 unit of agriculture. The second column gives the amounts required to produce 1 unit of manufacturing, and the last column gives the amounts required to produce 1 unit of transportation. (Although it is perhaps unrealistic that production of a unit of each commodity requires none of that commodity, the simpler matrix involved is useful for our purposes.)

NOTE Notice that for each commodity produced, the various units needed are put in a column. Each column corresponds to a commodity produced, and the rows correspond to what is needed to produce the commodity.

Another matrix used with the input-output matrix is the matrix giving the amount of each commodity produced, called the **production matrix**, or the matrix of gross output. In an economy producing n commodities, the production matrix can be represented by a column matrix X with entries $x_1, x_2, x_3, \ldots, x_n$.

EXAMPLE 2 Production Matrix

In Example 1, suppose the production matrix is

$$X = \begin{bmatrix} 60 \\ 52 \\ 48 \end{bmatrix}.$$

Then 60 units of agriculture, 52 units of manufacturing, and 48 units of transportation are produced. Because 1/4 unit of agriculture is used for each unit of manufacturing produced, $1/4 \times 52 = 13$ units of agriculture must be used in the "production" of manufacturing. Similarly, $1/3 \times 48 = 16$ units of agriculture will be used in the "production" of transportation. Thus, $13 + 16 = 29$ units of agriculture are used for production in the economy. Look again at the matrices A and X. Since X gives the number of units of each commodity produced and A gives the amount (in units) of each commodity used to produce 1 unit of each of the various commodities, the matrix product AX gives the amount of each commodity used in the production process.

$$AX = \begin{bmatrix} 0 & \frac{1}{4} & \frac{1}{3} \\ \frac{1}{2} & 0 & \frac{1}{4} \\ \frac{1}{4} & \frac{1}{4} & 0 \end{bmatrix} \begin{bmatrix} 60 \\ 52 \\ 48 \end{bmatrix} = \begin{bmatrix} 29 \\ 42 \\ 28 \end{bmatrix}$$

From this result, 29 units of agriculture, 42 units of manufacturing, and 28 units of transportation are used to produce 60 units of agriculture, 52 units of manufacturing, and 48 units of transportation.

The matrix product AX represents the amount of each commodity used in the production process. The remainder (if any) must be enough to satisfy the demand for the various commodities from outside the production system. In an n-commodity economy, this demand can be represented by a **demand matrix** D with entries $d_1, d_2, \ldots, d_n$. If no production is to remain unused, the difference between the production matrix X and the amount AX used in the production process must equal the demand D, or

$$D = X - AX.$$

In Example 2,

$$D = \begin{bmatrix} 60 \\ 52 \\ 48 \end{bmatrix} - \begin{bmatrix} 29 \\ 42 \\ 28 \end{bmatrix} = \begin{bmatrix} 31 \\ 10 \\ 20 \end{bmatrix},$$

so production of 60 units of agriculture, 52 units of manufacturing, and 48 units of transportation would satisfy a demand of 31, 10, and 20 units of each commodity, respectively.

In practice, A and D usually are known and X must be found. That is, we need to decide what amounts of production are needed to satisfy the required demands. Matrix algebra can be used to solve the equation $D = X - AX$ for X.

$$D = X - AX$$
$$D = IX - AX \qquad \text{Identity property}$$
$$D = (I - A)X \qquad \text{Distributive property}$$

If the matrix $I - A$ has an inverse, then

$$X = (I - A)^{-1}D.$$

---FOR REVIEW---

Recall that I is the identity matrix, a square matrix in which each element on the main diagonal is 1 and all other elements are 0.

⊞ **TECHNOLOGY NOTE** | If the production matrix is large or complicated, we could use a graphing calculator. On the TI-84 Plus, for example, we would enter the command `(identity(3) - [A])`$^{-1}$`*[D]` for a 3 × 3 matrix A.

⊞ **TECHNOLOGY NOTE** | It is also practical to do these calculations on a spreadsheet. For more details, see the *Graphing Calculator and Excel Spreadsheet Manual* available with this book.

EXAMPLE 3 Demand Matrix

Suppose, in the three-commodity economy from Examples 1 and 2, there is a demand for 516 units of agriculture, 258 units of manufacturing, and 129 units of transportation. What should production of each commodity be?

APPLY IT **SOLUTION** The demand matrix is

$$D = \begin{bmatrix} 516 \\ 258 \\ 129 \end{bmatrix}.$$

To find the production matrix X, first calculate $I - A$.

$$I - A = \begin{bmatrix} 1 & 0 & 0 \\ 0 & 1 & 0 \\ 0 & 0 & 1 \end{bmatrix} - \begin{bmatrix} 0 & \frac{1}{4} & \frac{1}{3} \\ \frac{1}{2} & 0 & \frac{1}{4} \\ \frac{1}{4} & \frac{1}{4} & 0 \end{bmatrix} = \begin{bmatrix} 1 & -\frac{1}{4} & -\frac{1}{3} \\ -\frac{1}{2} & 1 & -\frac{1}{4} \\ -\frac{1}{4} & -\frac{1}{4} & 1 \end{bmatrix}$$

Use row operations to find the inverse of $I - A$ (the entries are rounded to three decimal places).

$$(I - A)^{-1} = \begin{bmatrix} 1.395 & 0.496 & 0.589 \\ 0.837 & 1.364 & 0.620 \\ 0.558 & 0.465 & 1.302 \end{bmatrix}$$

Since $X = (I - A)^{-1}D$,

$$X = \begin{bmatrix} 1.395 & 0.496 & 0.589 \\ 0.837 & 1.364 & 0.620 \\ 0.558 & 0.465 & 1.302 \end{bmatrix} \begin{bmatrix} 516 \\ 258 \\ 129 \end{bmatrix} = \begin{bmatrix} 924 \\ 864 \\ 576 \end{bmatrix}.$$

(Each entry in X has been rounded to the nearest whole number.)

The last result shows that production of 924 units of agriculture, 864 units of manufacturing, and 576 units of transportation are required to satisfy demands of 516, 258, and 129 units, respectively.

The entries in the matrix $(I - A)^{-1}$ are often called *multipliers*, and they have important economic interpretations. For example, every \$1 increase in total agricultural demand will result in an increase in agricultural production by about \$1.40, an increase in manufacturing production by about \$0.84, and an increase in transportation production by about \$0.56. Similarly, every \$3 increase in total manufacturing demand will result in an increase of about $3(0.50) = 1.50$, $3(1.36) = 4.08$, and $3(0.47) = 1.41$ dollars in agricultural production, manufacturing production, and transportation production, respectively.

YOUR TURN 1 Find the production of each commodity for the economy in Example 3 if there is a demand for 322 units of agriculture, 447 units of manufacturing, and 133 units of transportation.

TRY YOUR TURN 1

EXAMPLE 4 Wheat and Oil Production

An economy depends on two basic products, wheat and oil. To produce 1 metric ton of wheat requires 0.25 metric tons of wheat and 0.33 metric tons of oil. Production of 1 metric ton of oil consumes 0.08 metric tons of wheat and 0.11 metric tons of oil.

(a) Find the production that will satisfy a demand for 500 metric tons of wheat and 1000 metric tons of oil.

APPLY IT

SOLUTION The input-output matrix is

$$A = \begin{bmatrix} 0.25 & 0.08 \\ 0.33 & 0.11 \end{bmatrix}.$$

Also,

$$I - A = \begin{bmatrix} 0.75 & -0.08 \\ -0.33 & 0.89 \end{bmatrix}.$$

Next, calculate $(I - A)^{-1}$.

$$(I - A)^{-1} = \begin{bmatrix} 1.3882 & 0.1248 \\ 0.5147 & 1.1699 \end{bmatrix} \quad \text{(rounded)}$$

To find the production matrix X, use the equation $X = (I - A)^{-1}D$, with

$$D = \begin{bmatrix} 500 \\ 1000 \end{bmatrix}.$$

The production matrix is

$$X = \begin{bmatrix} 1.3882 & 0.1248 \\ 0.5147 & 1.1699 \end{bmatrix} \begin{bmatrix} 500 \\ 1000 \end{bmatrix} \approx \begin{bmatrix} 819 \\ 1427 \end{bmatrix}.$$

Production of 819 metric tons of wheat and 1427 metric tons of oil is required to satisfy the indicated demand.

(b) Suppose the demand for wheat goes up from 500 to 600 metric tons. Find the increased production in wheat and oil that will be required to meet the new demand.

SOLUTION One way to solve this problem is using the multipliers for wheat, found in the first column of $(I - A)^{-1}$ from part (a). The element in the first row, 1.3882, is used to find the increased production in wheat, while the item in the second row, 0.5147, is used to find the increased production in oil. Since the increase in demand for wheat is 100 metric tons, the increased production in wheat must be $100(1.3882) \approx 139$ metric tons. Similarly, the increased production in oil is $100(0.5147) \approx 51$ metric tons.

Alternatively, we could have found the new production in wheat and oil with the equation $X = (I - A)^{-1}D$, giving

$$X = \begin{bmatrix} 1.3882 & 0.1248 \\ 0.5147 & 1.1699 \end{bmatrix} \begin{bmatrix} 600 \\ 1000 \end{bmatrix} \approx \begin{bmatrix} 958 \\ 1479 \end{bmatrix}.$$

We find the increased production by subtracting the answers found in part (a) from these answers. The increased production in wheat is $958 - 819 = 139$ metric tons, and the increased production in oil is $1479 - 1427 = 52$ metric tons. The slight difference here from the previous answer of 51 metric tons is due to rounding.

Closed Models

The input-output model discussed above is referred to as an **open model**, since it allows for a surplus from the production equal to D. In the **closed model**, all the production is consumed internally in the production process, so that $X = AX$. There is nothing left over to satisfy any outside demands from other parts of the economy or from other economies. In this case, the sum of each column in the input-output matrix equals 1.

To solve the closed model, set $D = O$ in the equation derived earlier, where O is a **zero matrix,** a matrix whose elements are all zeros.

$$(I - A)X = D = O$$

─FOR REVIEW─
Parameters were discussed in the first section of this chapter. As mentioned there, parameters are required when a system has infinitely many solutions.

The system of equations that corresponds to $(I - A)X = O$ does not have a single unique solution, but it can be solved in terms of a parameter. (It can be shown that if the columns of a matrix A sum to 1, then the equation $(I - A)X = O$ has an infinite number of solutions.)

EXAMPLE 5 Closed Input-Output Model

Use matrix A below to find the production of each commodity in a closed model.

$$A = \begin{bmatrix} \frac{1}{2} & \frac{1}{4} & \frac{1}{3} \\ 0 & \frac{1}{4} & \frac{1}{3} \\ \frac{1}{2} & \frac{1}{2} & \frac{1}{3} \end{bmatrix}$$

SOLUTION Find the value of $I - A$, then set $(I - A)X = O$ to find X.

$$I - A = \begin{bmatrix} \frac{1}{2} & -\frac{1}{4} & -\frac{1}{3} \\ 0 & \frac{3}{4} & -\frac{1}{3} \\ -\frac{1}{2} & -\frac{1}{2} & \frac{2}{3} \end{bmatrix}$$

$$(I - A)X = \begin{bmatrix} \frac{1}{2} & -\frac{1}{4} & -\frac{1}{3} \\ 0 & \frac{3}{4} & -\frac{1}{3} \\ -\frac{1}{2} & -\frac{1}{2} & \frac{2}{3} \end{bmatrix} \begin{bmatrix} x_1 \\ x_2 \\ x_3 \end{bmatrix} = \begin{bmatrix} 0 \\ 0 \\ 0 \end{bmatrix}$$

Multiply to get

$$\begin{bmatrix} \frac{1}{2}x_1 - \frac{1}{4}x_2 - \frac{1}{3}x_3 \\ 0x_1 + \frac{3}{4}x_2 - \frac{1}{3}x_3 \\ -\frac{1}{2}x_1 - \frac{1}{2}x_2 + \frac{2}{3}x_3 \end{bmatrix} = \begin{bmatrix} 0 \\ 0 \\ 0 \end{bmatrix}.$$

The last matrix equation corresponds to the following system.

$$\frac{1}{2}x_1 - \frac{1}{4}x_2 - \frac{1}{3}x_3 = 0$$
$$\frac{3}{4}x_2 - \frac{1}{3}x_3 = 0$$
$$-\frac{1}{2}x_1 - \frac{1}{2}x_2 + \frac{2}{3}x_3 = 0$$

YOUR TURN 2 Change the last column of matrix A in Example 5 to $\begin{bmatrix} \frac{1}{6} \\ \frac{1}{6} \\ \frac{2}{3} \end{bmatrix}$ and find the solution corresponding to $x_3 = 9$.

Solving the system with x_3 as the parameter gives the solution of the system

$$\left(\frac{8}{9}x_3, \frac{4}{9}x_3, x_3\right).$$

For example, if $x_3 = 9$ (a choice that eliminates fractions in the answer), then $x_1 = 8$ and $x_2 = 4$, so the production of the three commodities should be in the ratio 8:4:9.

TRY YOUR TURN 2

Finding a Production Matrix
To obtain the production matrix, X, for an open input-output model, follow these steps:

1. Form the $n \times n$ input-output matrix, A, by placing in each column the amount of the various commodities required to produce 1 unit of a particular commodity.
2. Calculate $I - A$, where I is the $n \times n$ identity matrix.
3. Find the inverse, $(I - A)^{-1}$.
4. Multiply the inverse on the right by the demand matrix, D, to obtain $X = (I - A)^{-1}D$.

To obtain a production matrix, X, for a closed input-output model, solve the system $(I - A)X = O$.

Production matrices for actual economies are much larger than those shown in this section. An analysis of the U.S. economy in 1997 has close to 500 commodity categories. *Source: U.S. Bureau of Economic Analysis.* Such matrices require large human and computer resources for their analysis. Some of the exercises at the end of this section use actual data in which categories have been combined to simplify the work.

2.6 EXERCISES

Find the production matrix for the following input-output and demand matrices using the open model.

1. $A = \begin{bmatrix} 0.8 & 0.2 \\ 0.2 & 0.7 \end{bmatrix}$, $D = \begin{bmatrix} 2 \\ 3 \end{bmatrix}$

2. $A = \begin{bmatrix} 0.2 & 0.04 \\ 0.6 & 0.05 \end{bmatrix}$, $D = \begin{bmatrix} 3 \\ 10 \end{bmatrix}$

3. $A = \begin{bmatrix} 0.1 & 0.03 \\ 0.07 & 0.6 \end{bmatrix}$, $D = \begin{bmatrix} 5 \\ 10 \end{bmatrix}$

4. $A = \begin{bmatrix} 0.02 & 0.03 \\ 0.06 & 0.08 \end{bmatrix}$, $D = \begin{bmatrix} 100 \\ 200 \end{bmatrix}$

5. $A = \begin{bmatrix} 0.8 & 0 & 0.1 \\ 0.1 & 0.5 & 0.2 \\ 0 & 0 & 0.7 \end{bmatrix}$, $D = \begin{bmatrix} 1 \\ 6 \\ 3 \end{bmatrix}$

6. $A = \begin{bmatrix} 0.1 & 0.5 & 0 \\ 0 & 0.3 & 0.4 \\ 0.1 & 0.2 & 0.1 \end{bmatrix}$, $D = \begin{bmatrix} 10 \\ 4 \\ 2 \end{bmatrix}$

Find the ratios of products A, B, and C using a closed model.

7.
$$\begin{array}{cc} & \begin{array}{ccc} A & B & C \end{array} \\ \begin{array}{c} A \\ B \\ C \end{array} & \begin{bmatrix} 0.3 & 0.1 & 0.8 \\ 0.5 & 0.6 & 0.1 \\ 0.2 & 0.3 & 0.1 \end{bmatrix} \end{array}$$

8.
$$\begin{array}{cc} & \begin{array}{ccc} A & B & C \end{array} \\ \begin{array}{c} A \\ B \\ C \end{array} & \begin{bmatrix} 0.3 & 0.2 & 0.3 \\ 0.1 & 0.5 & 0.4 \\ 0.6 & 0.3 & 0.3 \end{bmatrix} \end{array}$$

Use a graphing calculator or computer to find the production matrix X, given the following input-output and demand matrices.

9. $A = \begin{bmatrix} 0.25 & 0.25 & 0.25 & 0.05 \\ 0.01 & 0.02 & 0.01 & 0.1 \\ 0.3 & 0.3 & 0.01 & 0.1 \\ 0.2 & 0.01 & 0.3 & 0.01 \end{bmatrix}$, $D = \begin{bmatrix} 2930 \\ 3570 \\ 2300 \\ 580 \end{bmatrix}$

10. $A = \begin{bmatrix} 0.01 & 0.2 & 0.01 & 0.2 \\ 0.5 & 0.02 & 0.03 & 0.02 \\ 0.09 & 0.05 & 0.02 & 0.03 \\ 0.3 & 0.2 & 0.2 & 0.01 \end{bmatrix}$, $D = \begin{bmatrix} 5000 \\ 1000 \\ 4000 \\ 500 \end{bmatrix}$

APPLICATIONS

Business and Economics

Input-Output Open Model In Exercises 11 and 12, refer to Example 4.

11. If the demand is changed to 925 metric tons of wheat and 1250 metric tons of oil, how many units of each commodity should be produced?

12. Change the technological matrix so that production of 1 metric ton of wheat requires 1/5 metric ton of oil (and no wheat), and production of 1 metric ton of oil requires 1/3 metric ton of wheat (and no oil). To satisfy the same demand matrix, how many units of each commodity should be produced?

Input-Output Open Model In Exercises 13–16, refer to Example 3.

13. If the demand is changed to 607 units of each commodity, how many units of each commodity should be produced?

14. Suppose 1/3 unit of manufacturing (no agriculture or transportation) is required to produce 1 unit of agriculture, 1/4 unit of transportation is required to produce 1 unit of manufacturing, and 1/2 unit of agriculture is required to produce 1 unit of transportation. How many units of each commodity should be produced to satisfy a demand of 1000 units of each commodity?

15. Suppose 1/4 unit of manufacturing and 1/2 unit of transportation are required to produce 1 unit of agriculture, 1/2 unit of agriculture and 1/4 unit of transportation to produce 1 unit of manufacturing, and 1/4 unit of agriculture and 1/4 unit of manufacturing to produce 1 unit of transportation. How many units of each commodity should be produced to satisfy a demand of 1000 units for each commodity?

16. If the input-output matrix is changed so that 1/4 unit of manufacturing and 1/2 unit of transportation are required to produce 1 unit of agriculture, 1/2 unit of agriculture and 1/4 unit of transportation are required to produce 1 unit of manufacturing, and 1/4 unit each of agriculture and manufacturing are required to produce 1 unit of transportation, find the number of units of each commodity that should be produced to satisfy a demand for 500 units of each commodity.

Input-Output Open Model

17. A primitive economy depends on two basic goods, yams and pork. Production of 1 bushel of yams requires 1/4 bushel of yams and 1/2 of a pig. To produce 1 pig requires 1/6 bushel of yams. Find the amount of each commodity that should be produced to get the following.

a. 1 bushel of yams and 1 pig

b. 100 bushels of yams and 70 pigs

18. A simple economy depends on three commodities: oil, corn, and coffee. Production of 1 unit of oil requires 0.2 unit of oil, 0.4 unit of corn, and no units of coffee. To produce 1 unit of corn requires 0.4 unit of oil, 0.2 unit of corn, and 0.1 unit of coffee. To produce 1 unit of coffee requires 0.2 unit of oil, 0.1 unit of corn, and 0.2 unit of coffee. Find the production required to meet a demand of 1000 units each of oil, corn, and coffee.

19. In his work *Input-Output Economics*, Leontief provides an example of a simplified economy with just three sectors: agriculture, manufacturing, and households (i.e., the sector of the economy that produces labor). It has the following input-output matrix: ***Source: Input-Output Economics.***

	Agriculture	Manufacturing	Households
Agriculture	0.25	0.40	0.133
Manufacturing	0.14	0.12	0.100
Households	0.80	3.60	0.133

He also gives the demand matrix

$$D = \begin{bmatrix} 35 \\ 38 \\ 40 \end{bmatrix}.$$

Find the amount of each commodity that should be produced.

20. A much-simplified version of Leontief's 42-sector analysis of the 1947 American economy has the following input-output matrix. ***Source: Input-Output Economics.***

	Agriculture	Manufacturing	Households
Agriculture	0.245	0.102	0.051
Manufacturing	0.099	0.291	0.279
Households	0.433	0.372	0.011

The demand matrix (in billions of dollars) is

$$D = \begin{bmatrix} 2.88 \\ 31.45 \\ 30.91 \end{bmatrix}.$$

Find the amount of each commodity that should be produced.

21. An analysis of the 1958 Israeli economy is simplified here by grouping the economy into three sectors, with the following input-output matrix. ***Source: Input-Output Economics.***

	Agriculture	Manufacturing	Energy
Agriculture	0.293	0	0
Manufacturing	0.014	0.207	0.017
Energy	0.044	0.010	0.216

The demand (in thousands of Israeli pounds) as measured by exports is

$$D = \begin{bmatrix} 138,213 \\ 17,597 \\ 1786 \end{bmatrix}.$$

Find the amount of each commodity that should be produced.

22. The 1981 Chinese economy can be simplified to three sectors: agriculture, industry and construction, and transportation and commerce. The input-output matrix is given below. ***Source: Input-Output Tables of China, 1981.***

	Agriculture	Industry/ Constr.	Trans./ Commerce
Agriculture	0.158	0.156	0.009
Industry/Constr.	0.136	0.432	0.071
Trans./Commerce	0.013	0.041	0.011

The demand (in 100,000 RMB, the unit of money in China) is

$$D = \begin{bmatrix} 106,674 \\ 144,739 \\ 26,725 \end{bmatrix}.$$

a. Find the amount of each commodity that should be produced.

b. Interpret the economic value of an increase in demand of 1 RMB in agricultural exports.

23. **Washington** The 1987 economy of the state of Washington has been simplified to four sectors: natural resources, manufacturing, trade and services, and personal consumption. The input-output matrix is given below. ***Source: University of Washington.***

	Natural Resources	Manufacturing	Trade & Services	Personal Consumption
Natural Resources	0.1045	0.0428	0.0029	0.0031
Manufacturing	0.0826	0.1087	0.0584	0.0321
Trade & Services	0.0867	0.1019	0.2032	0.3555
Personal Consumption	0.6253	0.3448	0.6106	0.0798

Suppose the demand (in millions of dollars) is

$$D = \begin{bmatrix} 450 \\ 300 \\ 125 \\ 100 \end{bmatrix}.$$

Find the amount of each commodity that should be produced.

24. **Washington** In addition to solving the previous input-output model, most models of this nature also include an employment equation. For the previous model, the employment equation is added and a new system of equations is obtained as follows. ***Source: University of Washington.***

$$\begin{bmatrix} x_1 \\ x_2 \\ x_3 \\ x_4 \\ N \end{bmatrix} = (I - B)^{-1}C,$$

where x_1, x_2, x_3, x_4 represent the amount, in millions of dollars, that must be produced to satisfy internal and external demands of the four sectors; N is the total workforce required for a particular set of demands; and

$$B = \begin{bmatrix} 0.1045 & 0.0428 & 0.0029 & 0.0031 & 0 \\ 0.0826 & 0.1087 & 0.0584 & 0.0321 & 0 \\ 0.0867 & 0.1019 & 0.2032 & 0.3555 & 0 \\ 0.6253 & 0.3448 & 0.6106 & 0.0798 & 0 \\ 21.6 & 6.6 & 20.2 & 0 & 0 \end{bmatrix}.$$

a. Suppose that a \$50 million change in manufacturing occurs. How will this increase in demand affect the economy?

$$(\textit{Hint: Find } (I - B)^{-1}C, \text{ where } C = \begin{bmatrix} 0 \\ 50 \\ 0 \\ 0 \\ 0 \end{bmatrix}.)$$

b. Interpret the meaning of the bottom row in the matrix $(I - B)^{-1}$.

25. Community Links The use of input-output analysis can also be used to model how changes in one city can affect cities that are connected with it in some way. For example, if a large manufacturing company shuts down in one city, it is very likely that the economic welfare of all of the cities around it will suffer. Consider three Pennsylvania communities: Sharon, Farrell, and Hermitage. Due to their proximity to each other, residents of these three communities regularly spend time and money in the other communities. Suppose that we have gathered information in the form of an input-output matrix. *Source: Thayer Watkins.*

$$A = \begin{matrix} & \begin{matrix} S & F & H \end{matrix} \\ \begin{matrix} S \\ F \\ H \end{matrix} & \begin{bmatrix} 0.2 & 0.1 & 0.1 \\ 0.1 & 0.1 & 0 \\ 0.5 & 0.6 & 0.7 \end{bmatrix} \end{matrix}$$

This matrix can be thought of as the likelihood that a person from a particular community will spend money in each of the communities.

a. Treat this matrix like an input-output matrix and calculate $(I - A)^{-1}$.

b. Interpret the entries of this inverse matrix.

Input-Output Closed Model

26. Use the input-output matrix

$$\begin{matrix} & \begin{matrix} \text{Yams} & \text{Pigs} \end{matrix} \\ \begin{matrix} \text{Yams} \\ \text{Pigs} \end{matrix} & \begin{bmatrix} \frac{1}{4} & \frac{1}{2} \\ \frac{3}{4} & \frac{1}{2} \end{bmatrix} \end{matrix}$$

and the closed model to find the ratio of yams to pigs produced.

27. Use the input-output matrix

$$\begin{matrix} & \begin{matrix} \text{Steel} & \text{Coal} \end{matrix} \\ \begin{matrix} \text{Steel} \\ \text{Coal} \end{matrix} & \begin{bmatrix} \frac{3}{4} & \frac{1}{3} \\ \frac{1}{4} & \frac{2}{3} \end{bmatrix} \end{matrix}$$

and the closed model to find the ratio of coal to steel produced.

28. Suppose that production of 1 unit of agriculture requires 1/3 unit of agriculture, 1/3 unit of manufacturing, and 1/3 unit of transportation. To produce 1 unit of manufacturing requires 1/2 unit of agriculture, 1/4 unit of manufacturing, and 1/4 unit of transportation. To produce 1 unit of transportation requires 0 units of agriculture, 1/4 unit of manufacturing, and 3/4 unit of transportation. Find the ratio of the three commodities in the closed model.

29. Suppose that production of 1 unit of mining requires 1/5 unit of mining, 2/5 unit of manufacturing, and 2/5 unit of communication. To produce 1 unit of manufacturing requires 3/5 unit of mining, 1/5 unit of manufacturing, and 1/5 unit of communication. To produce 1 unit of communication requires 0 units of mining, 4/5 unit of manufacturing, and 1/5 unit of communication. Find the ratio of the three commodities in the closed model.

YOUR TURN ANSWERS

1. 749 units of agriculture, 962 units of manufacturing, and 561 units of transportation

2. (4, 2, 9)

2 CHAPTER REVIEW

SUMMARY

In this chapter we extended our study of linear functions to include finding solutions of systems of linear equations. Techniques such as the echelon method and the Gauss-Jordan method were developed and used to solve systems of linear equations. We introduced matrices, which are used to store mathematical information. We saw that matrices can be combined using addition, subtraction, scalar multiplication, and matrix multiplication. Two special matrices, the zero matrix and the identity matrix, were also introduced.

- The zero matrix O is a matrix whose elements are all zero.
- The identity matrix I is an $n \times n$ matrix consisting of 1's along the diagonal and 0's elsewhere.

We then developed the concept of a multiplicative inverse of a matrix and used such inverses to solve systems of equations. We concluded the chapter by introducing the Leontief input-output models, which are used to study interdependencies in an economy.

Row Operations   For any augmented matrix of a system of equations, the following operations produce the augmented matrix of an equivalent system:

1. interchanging any two rows;
2. multiplying the elements of a row by a nonzero real number;
3. adding a nonzero multiple of the elements of one row to the corresponding elements of a nonzero multiple of some other row.

The Gauss-Jordan Method

1. Write each equation so that variable terms are in the same order on the left side of the equal sign and constants are on the right.
2. Write the augmented matrix that corresponds to the system.
3. Use row operations to transform the first column so that all elements except the element in the first row are zero.
4. Use row operations to transform the second column so that all elements except the element in the second row are zero.
5. Use row operations to transform the third column so that all elements except the element in the third row are zero.
6. Continue in this way, when possible, until the last row is written in the form

$$[0\ 0\ 0\ \cdots\ 0\,j\,|\,k],$$

where j and k are constants with $j \neq 0$. When this is not possible, continue until every row has more zeros on the left than the previous row (except possibly for any rows of all zero at the bottom of the matrix), and the first nonzero entry in each row is the only nonzero entry in its column.
7. Multiply each row by the reciprocal of the nonzero element in that row.

Adding Matrices   The sum of two $m \times n$ matrices X and Y is the $m \times n$ matrix $X + Y$ in which each element is the sum of the corresponding elements of X and Y.

Subtracting Matrices   The difference of two $m \times n$ matrices X and Y is the $m \times n$ matrix $X - Y$ in which each element is found by subtracting the corresponding elements of X and Y.

Product of a Matrix and a Scalar   The product of a scalar k and a matrix X is the matrix kX, each of whose elements is k times the corresponding element of X.

Product of Two Matrices   Let A be an $m \times n$ matrix and let B be an $n \times k$ matrix. To find the element in the ith row and jth column of the product AB, multiply each element in the ith row of A by the corresponding element in the jth column of B, and then add these products. The product matrix AB is an $m \times k$ matrix.

Solving a System $AX = B$ Using Matrix Inverses   To solve a system of equations $AX = B$, where A is a square matrix of coefficients, X is the matrix of variables, and B is the matrix of constants, first find A^{-1}. Then, $X = A^{-1}B$.

Finding a Production Matrix

1. Form the input-output matrix, A.
2. Calculate $I - A$, where I is the $n \times n$ identity matrix.
3. Find the inverse, $(I - A)^{-1}$.
4. Multiply the inverse on the right by the demand matrix, D, to obtain $X = (I - A)^{-1}D$.

To obtain a production matrix, X, for a closed input-output model, solve the system $(I - A)X = O$.

KEY TERMS

To understand the concepts presented in this chapter, you should know the meaning and use of the following terms.
For easy reference, the section in the chapter where a word (or expression) was first used is provided.

system of equations	unique solution	echelon method	**2.2**
2.1	inconsistent system	back-substitution	matrix (matrices)
first-degree equation in n	dependent equations	parameter	element (entry)
unknowns	equivalent system		augmented matrix

row operations
Gauss-Jordan method

2.3
size
square matrix
row matrix (row vector)

column matrix (column vector)
2.4
scalar
product matrix
2.5
identity matrix

multiplicative inverse matrix
coefficient matrix
2.6
input-output (technological)
  matrix
production matrix

demand matrix
open model
closed model
zero matrix

REVIEW EXERCISES

CONCEPT CHECK

Determine whether each of the following statements is true or false, and explain why.

1. If a system of equations has three equations and four unknowns, then it could have a unique solution.

2. If $A = \begin{bmatrix} 2 & 3 \\ 1 & -1 \end{bmatrix}$ and $B = \begin{bmatrix} 3 & 4 \\ 7 & 4 \\ 1 & 0 \end{bmatrix}$, then $A + B = \begin{bmatrix} 5 & 7 \\ 8 & 3 \\ 1 & 0 \end{bmatrix}$.

3. If a system of equations has three equations and three unknowns, then it may have a unique solution, an infinite number of solutions, or no solutions.

4. The only solution to the system of equations

$$2x + 3y = 7$$
$$5x - 4y = 6$$

is $x = 2$ and $y = 1$.

5. If A is a 2×3 matrix and B is a 3×4 matrix, then $A + B$ is a 2×4 matrix.

6. If A is an $n \times k$ matrix and B is a $k \times m$ matrix, then AB is an $n \times m$ matrix.

7. If A is a 4×4 matrix and B is a 4×4 matrix, then $AB = BA$.

8. A 3×4 matrix could have an inverse.

9. It is not possible to find a matrix A such that $OA = AO = I$, where O is a 5×5 zero matrix and I is a 5×5 identity matrix.

10. When solving a system of equations by the Gauss-Jordan method, we can add a nonzero multiple of the elements of one column to the corresponding elements of some nonzero multiple of some other column.

11. Every square matrix has an inverse.

12. If A, B, and C are matrices such that $AB = C$, then $B = \dfrac{C}{A}$.

13. A system of three equations in three unknowns might have exactly five positive integer solutions.

14. If A and B are matrices such that $A = B^{-1}$, then $AB = BA$.

15. If A, B, and C are matrices such that $AB = CB$, then $A = C$.

16. The difference between an open and a closed input-output model is that in a closed model, the demand matrix D is a zero matrix.

PRACTICE AND EXPLORATIONS

17. What is true about the number of solutions to a system of m linear equations in n unknowns if $m = n$? If $m < n$? If $m > n$?

18. Suppose someone says that a more reasonable way to multiply two matrices than the method presented in the text is to multiply corresponding elements. For example, the result of

$$\begin{bmatrix} 1 & 2 \\ 3 & 4 \end{bmatrix} \cdot \begin{bmatrix} 3 & 5 \\ 7 & 11 \end{bmatrix} \text{ should be } \begin{bmatrix} 3 & 10 \\ 21 & 44 \end{bmatrix},$$

according to this person. How would you respond?

Solve each system by the echelon method.

19. $2x - 3y = 14$
    $3x + 2y = -5$

20. $\dfrac{x}{2} + \dfrac{y}{4} = 3$
    $\dfrac{x}{4} - \dfrac{y}{2} = 4$

21. $2x - 3y + z = -5$
    $5x + 5y + 3z = 14$

22. $2x + 3y + 4z = 5$
    $3x + 4y + 5z = 6$

Solve each system by the Gauss-Jordan method.

23. $2x + 4y = -6$
    $-3x - 5y = 12$

24. $x - 4y = 10$
    $5x + 3y = 119$

25. $x - y + 3z = 13$
    $4x + y + 2z = 17$
    $3x + 2y + 2z = 1$

26. $x + 2y + 3z = 9$
    $x - 2y = 4$
    $3x + 2z = 12$

27. $3x - 6y + 9z = 12$
    $-x + 2y - 3z = -4$
    $x + y + 2z = 7$

28. $x - 2z = 5$
    $3x + 2y = 8$
    $-x + 2z = 10$

Find the size of each matrix, find the values of any variables, and identify any square, row, or column matrices.

29. $\begin{bmatrix} 2 & 3 \\ 5 & q \end{bmatrix} = \begin{bmatrix} a & b \\ c & 9 \end{bmatrix}$

30. $\begin{bmatrix} 2 & x \\ y & 6 \\ 5 & z \end{bmatrix} = \begin{bmatrix} a & -1 \\ 4 & 6 \\ p & 7 \end{bmatrix}$

31. $\begin{bmatrix} 2m & 4 & 3z & -12 \end{bmatrix} = \begin{bmatrix} 12 & k+1 & -9 & r-3 \end{bmatrix}$

32. $\begin{bmatrix} a+5 & 3b & 6 \\ 4c & 2+d & -3 \\ -1 & 4p & q-1 \end{bmatrix} = \begin{bmatrix} -7 & b+2 & 2k-3 \\ 3 & 2d-1 & 4l \\ m & 12 & 8 \end{bmatrix}$

Given the matrices

$$A = \begin{bmatrix} 4 & 10 \\ -2 & -3 \\ 6 & 9 \end{bmatrix}, \quad B = \begin{bmatrix} 2 & 3 & -2 \\ 2 & 4 & 0 \\ 0 & 1 & 2 \end{bmatrix}, \quad C = \begin{bmatrix} 5 & 0 \\ -1 & 3 \\ 4 & 7 \end{bmatrix},$$

$$D = \begin{bmatrix} 6 \\ 1 \\ 0 \end{bmatrix}, \quad E = \begin{bmatrix} 1 & 3 & -4 \end{bmatrix},$$

$$F = \begin{bmatrix} -1 & 4 \\ 3 & 7 \end{bmatrix}, \quad G = \begin{bmatrix} -2 & 0 \\ 1 & 5 \end{bmatrix},$$

find each of the following, if it exists.

33. $A + C$ **34.** $2G - 4F$ **35.** $3C + 2A$

36. $B - C$ **37.** $2A - 5C$ **38.** AG

39. AC **40.** DE **41.** ED

42. BD **43.** EC **44.** F^{-1}

45. B^{-1} **46.** $(A + C)^{-1}$

Find the inverse of each matrix that has an inverse.

47. $\begin{bmatrix} 1 & 3 \\ 2 & 7 \end{bmatrix}$ **48.** $\begin{bmatrix} -4 & 2 \\ 0 & 3 \end{bmatrix}$

49. $\begin{bmatrix} 3 & -6 \\ -4 & 8 \end{bmatrix}$ **50.** $\begin{bmatrix} 6 & 4 \\ 3 & 2 \end{bmatrix}$

51. $\begin{bmatrix} 2 & -1 & 0 \\ 1 & 0 & 1 \\ 1 & -2 & 0 \end{bmatrix}$ **52.** $\begin{bmatrix} 2 & 0 & 4 \\ 1 & -1 & 0 \\ 0 & 1 & -2 \end{bmatrix}$

53. $\begin{bmatrix} 1 & 3 & 6 \\ 4 & 0 & 9 \\ 5 & 15 & 30 \end{bmatrix}$ **54.** $\begin{bmatrix} 2 & -3 & 4 \\ 1 & 5 & 7 \\ -4 & 6 & -8 \end{bmatrix}$

Solve the matrix equation $AX = B$ for **X** using the given matrices.

55. $A = \begin{bmatrix} 5 & 1 \\ -2 & -2 \end{bmatrix}, \quad B = \begin{bmatrix} -8 \\ 24 \end{bmatrix}$

56. $A = \begin{bmatrix} 1 & 2 \\ 2 & 4 \end{bmatrix}, \quad B = \begin{bmatrix} 5 \\ 10 \end{bmatrix}$

57. $A = \begin{bmatrix} 1 & 0 & 2 \\ -1 & 1 & 0 \\ 3 & 0 & 4 \end{bmatrix}, \quad B = \begin{bmatrix} 8 \\ 4 \\ -6 \end{bmatrix}$

58. $A = \begin{bmatrix} 2 & 4 & 0 \\ 1 & -2 & 0 \\ 0 & 0 & 3 \end{bmatrix}, \quad B = \begin{bmatrix} 72 \\ -24 \\ 48 \end{bmatrix}$

Solve each system of equations by inverses.

59. $x + 2y = 4$
$2x - 3y = 1$

60. $5x + 10y = 80$
$3x - 2y = 120$

61. $x + y + z = 1$
$2x + y \phantom{{}+ z} = -2$
$\phantom{2x + {}} 3y + z = 2$

62. $x - 4y + 2z = -1$
$-2x + y - 3z = -9$
$3x + 5y - 2z = 7$

Find each production matrix, given the following input-output and demand matrices.

63. $A = \begin{bmatrix} 0.01 & 0.05 \\ 0.04 & 0.03 \end{bmatrix}, \quad D = \begin{bmatrix} 200 \\ 300 \end{bmatrix}$

64. $A = \begin{bmatrix} 0.2 & 0.1 & 0.3 \\ 0.1 & 0 & 0.2 \\ 0 & 0 & 0.4 \end{bmatrix}, \quad D = \begin{bmatrix} 500 \\ 200 \\ 100 \end{bmatrix}$

65. The following system of equations is given.

$$x + 2y + z = 7$$
$$2x - y - z = 2$$
$$3x - 3y + 2z = -5$$

a. Solve by the echelon method.

b. Solve by the Gauss-Jordan method. Compare with the echelon method.

c. Write the system as a matrix equation, $AX = B$.

d. Find the inverse of matrix A from part c.

e. Solve the system using A^{-1} from part d.

APPLICATIONS

Business and Economics

In Exercises 66–69, write a system of equations and solve.

66. Scheduling Production   An office supply manufacturer makes two kinds of paper clips, standard and extra large. To make 1000 standard paper clips requires 1/4 hour on a cutting machine and 1/2 hour on a machine that shapes the clips. One thousand extra large paper clips require 1/3 hour on each machine. The manager of paper clip production has 4 hours per day available on the cutting machine and 6 hours per day on the shaping machine. How many of each kind of clip can he make?

67. Production Requirements   The Waputi Indians make woven blankets, rugs, and skirts. Each blanket requires 24 hours for spinning the yarn, 4 hours for dyeing the yarn, and 15 hours for weaving. Rugs require 30, 5, and 18 hours and skirts 12, 3, and 9 hours, respectively. If there are 306, 59, and 201 hours available for spinning, dyeing, and weaving, respectively, how many of each item can be made? (*Hint:* Simplify the equations you write, if possible, before solving the system.)

68. Distribution   An oil refinery in Tulsa sells 50% of its production to a Chicago distributor, 20% to a Dallas distributor, and 30% to an Atlanta distributor. Another refinery in New Orleans sells 40% of its production to the Chicago distributor, 40% to the Dallas distributor, and 20% to the Atlanta distributor. A third refinery in Ardmore sells the same distributors 30%, 40%, and 30% of its production. The three distributors received 219,000, 192,000, and 144,000 gal of oil, respectively. How many gallons of oil were produced at each of the three plants?

69. Stock Reports   The New York Stock Exchange reports in daily newspapers give the dividend, price-to-earnings ratio, sales (in hundreds of shares), last price, and change in price for each company. Write the following stock reports as a 4×5 matrix: American Telephone & Telegraph: 1.33, 17.6, 152,000, 26.75,

+1.88; General Electric: 1.00, 20.0, 238,200, 32.36, −1.50; Sara Lee: 0.79, 25.4, 39,110, 16.51, −0.89; Walt Disney Company: 0.27, 21.2, 122,500, 28.60, +0.75.

70. Filling Orders A printer has three orders for pamphlets that require three kinds of paper, as shown in the following matrix.

$$
\begin{array}{cc}
& \text{Order} \\
& \begin{array}{ccc} \text{I} & \text{II} & \text{III} \end{array} \\
\text{Paper} \begin{array}{l} \text{High-grade} \\ \text{Medium-grade} \\ \text{Coated} \end{array} &
\begin{bmatrix} 10 & 5 & 8 \\ 12 & 0 & 4 \\ 0 & 10 & 5 \end{bmatrix}
\end{array}
$$

The printer has on hand 3170 sheets of high-grade paper, 2360 sheets of medium-grade paper, and 1800 sheets of coated paper. All the paper must be used in preparing the order.

a. Write a 3 × 1 matrix for the amounts of paper on hand.

b. Write a matrix of variables to represent the number of pamphlets that must be printed in each of the three orders.

c. Write a matrix equation using the given matrix and your matrices from parts a and b.

d. Solve the equation from part c.

71. Input-Output An economy depends on two commodities, goats and cheese. It takes 2/3 of a unit of goats to produce 1 unit of cheese and 1/2 unit of cheese to produce 1 unit of goats.

a. Write the input-output matrix for this economy.

b. Find the production required to satisfy a demand of 400 units of cheese and 800 units of goats.

72. Nebraska The 1970 economy of the state of Nebraska has been condensed to six sectors: livestock, crops, food products, mining and manufacturing, households, and other. The input-output matrix is given below. *Source: University of Nebraska Lincoln.*

$$
\begin{bmatrix}
0.178 & 0.018 & 0.411 & 0 & 0.005 & 0 \\
0.143 & 0.018 & 0.088 & 0 & 0.001 & 0 \\
0.089 & 0 & 0.035 & 0 & 0.060 & 0.003 \\
0.001 & 0.010 & 0.012 & 0.063 & 0.007 & 0.014 \\
0.141 & 0.252 & 0.088 & 0.089 & 0.402 & 0.124 \\
0.188 & 0.156 & 0.103 & 0.255 & 0.008 & 0.474
\end{bmatrix}
$$

a. Find the matrix $(I - A)^{-1}$ and interpret the value in row 2, column 1 of this matrix.

b. Suppose the demand (in millions of dollars) is

$$
D = \begin{bmatrix} 1980 \\ 650 \\ 1750 \\ 1000 \\ 2500 \\ 3750 \end{bmatrix}.
$$

Find the dollar amount of each commodity that should be produced.

Life Sciences

73. Animal Activity The activities of a grazing animal can be classified roughly into three categories: grazing, moving, and resting. Suppose horses spend 8 hours grazing, 8 moving, and 8 resting; cattle spend 10 grazing, 5 moving, and 9 resting; sheep spend 7 grazing, 10 moving, and 7 resting; and goats spend 8 grazing, 9 moving, and 7 resting. Write this information as a 4 × 3 matrix.

74. CAT Scans Computer Aided Tomography (CAT) scanners take X-rays of a part of the body from different directions, and put the information together to create a picture of a cross section of the body. The amount by which the energy of the X-ray decreases, measured in linear-attenuation units, tells whether the X-ray has passed through healthy tissue, tumorous tissue, or bone, based on the following table. *Source: The Mathematics Teacher.*

Type of Tissue	Linear-Attenuation Values
Healthy tissue	0.1625–0.2977
Tumorous tissue	0.2679–0.3930
Bone	0.3857–0.5108

The part of the body to be scanned is divided into cells. If an X-ray passes through more than one cell, the total linear-attenuation value is the sum of the values for the cells. For example, in the figure, let a, b, and c be the values for cells A, B, and C. The attenuation value for beam 1 is $a + b$ and for beam 2 is $a + c$.

a. Find the attenuation value for beam 3.

b. Suppose that the attenuation values are 0.8, 0.55, and 0.65 for beams 1, 2, and 3, respectively. Set up and solve the system of three equations for a, b, and c. What can you conclude about cells A, B, and C?

c. Find the inverse of the coefficient matrix from part b to find a, b, and c for the following three cases, and make conclusions about cells A, B, and C for each.

Patient	Linear-Attenuation Values		
	Beam 1	Beam 2	Beam 3
X	0.54	0.40	0.52
Y	0.65	0.80	0.75
Z	0.51	0.49	0.44

75. CAT Scans (Refer to Exercise 74.) Four X-ray beams are aimed at four cells, as shown in the following figure. *Source: The Mathematics Teacher.*

Beam 1 Beam 2

a. Suppose the attenuation values for beams 1, 2, 3, and 4 are 0.60, 0.75, 0.65, and 0.70, respectively. Do we have enough information to determine the values of a, b, c, and d? Explain.

b. Suppose we have the data from part a, as well as the following values for d. Find the values for a, b, and c, and draw conclusions about cells A, B, C, and D in each case.

(i) 0.33   **(ii)** 0.43

c. Two X-ray beams are added, as shown in the figure. In addition to the data in part a, we now have attenuation values for beams 5 and 6 of 0.85 and 0.50. Find the values for a, b, c, and d, and make conclusions about cells A, B, C, and D. 109

Beam 1 Beam 2

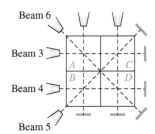

d. Six X-ray beams are not necessary because four appropriately chosen beams are sufficient. Give two examples of four beams (chosen from beams 1–6 in part c) that will give the solution. (*Note:* There are 12 possible solutions.)

e. Discuss what properties the four beams selected in part d must have in order to provide a unique solution.

76. Hockey In a recent study, the number of head and neck injuries among hockey players wearing full face shields and half face shields were compared. The following table provides the rates per 1000 athlete-exposures for specific injuries that caused a player wearing either shield to miss one or more events. *Source: JAMA.*

	Half Shield	Full Shield
Head and Face Injuries (excluding Concussions)	3.54	1.41
Concussions	1.53	1.57
Neck Injuries	0.34	0.29
Other	7.53	6.21

If an equal number of players in a large league wear each type of shield and the total number of athlete-exposures for the league in a season is 8000, use matrix operations to estimate the total number of injuries of each type.

Physical Sciences

77. Roof Trusses Linear systems occur in the design of roof trusses for new homes and buildings. The simplest type of roof truss is a triangle. The truss shown in the figure below is used to frame roofs of small buildings. If a 100-lb force is applied at the peak of the truss, then the forces or weights W_1 and W_2 exerted parallel to each rafter of the truss are determined by the following linear system of equations.

$$\frac{\sqrt{3}}{2}(W_1 + W_2) = 100$$

$$W_1 - W_2 = 0$$

Solve the system to find W_1 and W_2. *Source: Structural Analysis.*

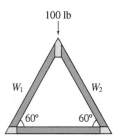

78. Roof Trusses (Refer to Exercise 77.) Use the following system of equations to determine the force or weights W_1 and W_2 exerted on each rafter for the truss shown in the figure.

$$\frac{1}{2}W_1 + \frac{\sqrt{2}}{2}W_2 = 150$$

$$\frac{\sqrt{3}}{2}W_1 - \frac{\sqrt{2}}{2}W_2 = 0$$

79. Carbon Dioxide   Determining the amount of carbon dioxide in the atmosphere is important because carbon dioxide is known to be a greenhouse gas. Carbon dioxide concentrations (in parts per million) have been measured at Mauna Loa, Hawaii, for more than 40 years. The concentrations have increased quadratically. The table lists readings for 3 years. *Source: Scripps Institution of Oceanography.*

Year	CO_2
1960	317
1980	339
2004	377

a. If the relationship between the carbon dioxide concentration C and the year t is expressed as $C = at^2 + bt + c$, where $t = 0$ corresponds to 1960, use a linear system of equations to determine the constants a, b, and c.

b. Predict the year when the amount of carbon dioxide in the atmosphere will double from its 1960 level. (*Hint:* This requires solving a quadratic equation. For review on how to do this, see Section R.4.)

80. Chemistry   When carbon monoxide (CO) reacts with oxygen (O_2), carbon dioxide (CO_2) is formed. This can be written as $CO + (1/2)O_2 = CO_2$ and as a matrix equation. If we form a 2×1 column matrix by letting the first element be the number of carbon atoms and the second element be the number of oxygen atoms, then CO would have the column matrix *Source: Journal of Chemical Education.*

$$\begin{bmatrix} 1 \\ 1 \end{bmatrix}.$$

Similarly, O_2 and CO_2 would have the column matrices $\begin{bmatrix} 0 \\ 2 \end{bmatrix}$ and $\begin{bmatrix} 1 \\ 2 \end{bmatrix}$, respectively.

a. Use the Gauss-Jordan method to find numbers x and y (known as *stoichiometric numbers*) that solve the system of equations

$$\begin{bmatrix} 1 \\ 1 \end{bmatrix} x + \begin{bmatrix} 0 \\ 2 \end{bmatrix} y = \begin{bmatrix} 1 \\ 2 \end{bmatrix}.$$

Compare your answers to the equation written above.

b. Repeat the process for $xCO_2 + yH_2 + zCO = H_2O$, where H_2 is hydrogen, and H_2O is water. In words, what does this mean?

General Interest

81. Students   Suppose 20% of the boys and 30% of the girls in a high school like tennis, and 60% of the boys and 90% of the girls like math. If 500 students like tennis and 1500 like math, how many boys and girls are in the school? Find all possible solutions.

82. Baseball   In the 2009 Major League Baseball season, slugger Ichiro Suzuki had a total of 225 hits. The number of singles he hit was 11 more than four times the combined total of doubles and home runs. The number of doubles he hit was 1 more than twice the combined total of triples and home runs. The number of singles and home runs together was 15 more than five times the combined total of doubles and triples. Find the number of singles, doubles, triples, and home runs that Suzuki hit during the season. *Source: Baseball-Reference.com.*

83. Cookies   Regular Nabisco Oreo cookies are made of two chocolate cookie wafers surrounding a single layer of vanilla cream. The claim on the package states that a single serving is 34 g, which is three cookies. Nabisco Double Stuf cookies are made of the same two chocolate cookie wafers surrounding a double layer of vanilla cream. The claim on this package states that a single serving is 29 g, which is two Double Stuf cookies. If the Double Stuf cookies truly have a double layer of vanilla cream, find the weight of a single chocolate wafer and the weight of a single layer of vanilla cream.

EXTENDED APPLICATION

CONTAGION

Suppose that three people have contracted a contagious disease. *Source: Finite Mathematics with Applications to Business, Life Sciences, and Social Sciences.* A second group of five people may have been in contact with the three infected persons. A third group of six people may have been in contact with the

second group. We can form a 3×5 matrix P with rows representing the first group of three and columns representing the second group of five. We enter a one in the corresponding position if a person in the first group has contact with a person in the second group. These direct contacts are called *first-order contacts*. Similarly, we form a 5×6 matrix Q representing the first-order contacts between the second and third group. For example, suppose

$$P = \begin{bmatrix} 1 & 0 & 0 & 1 & 0 \\ 0 & 0 & 1 & 1 & 0 \\ 1 & 1 & 0 & 0 & 0 \end{bmatrix} \text{ and}$$

$$Q = \begin{bmatrix} 1 & 1 & 0 & 1 & 1 & 1 \\ 0 & 0 & 0 & 0 & 1 & 0 \\ 0 & 0 & 0 & 0 & 0 & 0 \\ 0 & 1 & 0 & 1 & 0 & 0 \\ 1 & 0 & 0 & 0 & 1 & 0 \end{bmatrix}.$$

From matrix P we see that the first person in the first group had contact with the first and fourth persons in the second group. Also, none of the first group had contact with the last person in the second group.

A *second-order contact* is an indirect contact between persons in the first and third groups through some person in the second group. The product matrix PQ indicates these contacts. Verify that the second-row, fourth-column entry of PQ is 1. That is, there is one second-order contact between the second person in group one and the fourth person in group three. Let a_{ij} denote the element in the ith row and jth column of the matrix PQ. By looking at the products that form a_{24} below, we see that the common contact was with the fourth individual in group two. (The p_{ij} are entries in P, and the q_{ij} are entries in Q.)

$$a_{24} = p_{21}q_{14} + p_{22}q_{24} + p_{23}q_{34} + p_{24}q_{44} + p_{25}q_{54}$$
$$= 0 \cdot 1 + 0 \cdot 0 + 1 \cdot 0 + 1 \cdot 1 + 0 \cdot 0$$
$$= 1$$

The second person in group 1 and the fourth person in group 3 both had contact with the fourth person in group 2.

This idea could be extended to third-, fourth-, and larger-order contacts. It indicates a way to use matrices to trace the spread of a contagious disease. It could also pertain to the dispersal of ideas or anything that might pass from one individual to another.

EXERCISES

1. Find the second-order contact matrix PQ mentioned in the text.

2. How many second-order contacts were there between the second contagious person and the third person in the third group?

3. Is there anyone in the third group who has had no contacts at all with the first group?

4. The totals of the columns in PQ give the total number of second-order contacts per person, while the column totals in P and Q give the total number of first-order contacts per person. Which person(s) in the third group had the most contacts, counting first- and second-order contacts?

5. Go to the website WolframAlpha.com and enter: "multiply matrices." Study how matrix multiplication can be performed by Wolfram|Alpha. Try Exercise 1 with Wolfram|Alpha and discuss how it compares with Microsoft Excel and with your graphing calculator.

DIRECTIONS FOR GROUP PROJECT

Assume that your group (3–5 students) is trying to map the spread of a new disease. Suppose also that the information given above has been obtained from interviews with the first three people that were hospitalized with symptoms of the disease and their contacts. Using the questions above as a guide, prepare a presentation for a public meeting that describes the method of obtaining the data, the data itself, and addresses the spirit of each question. Formulate a strategy for how to handle the spread of this disease to other people. The presentation should be mathematically sound, grammatically correct, and professionally crafted. Use presentation software, such as Microsoft PowerPoint, to present your findings.

3

Linear Programming: The Graphical Method

An oil refinery turns crude oil into many different products, including gasoline and fuel oil. Efficient management requires matching the output of each product to the demand and the available shipping capacity. In an exercise in Section 3, we explore the use of linear programming to allocate refinery production for maximum profit.

Many realistic problems involve inequalities—a factory can manufacture *no more* than 12 items on a shift, or a medical researcher must interview *at least* a hundred patients to be sure that a new treatment for a disease is better than the old treatment. *Linear inequalities* of the form $ax + by \leq c$ (or with $\geq$, $<$, or $>$ instead of $\leq$) can be used in a process called *linear programming* to *optimize* (find the maximum or minimum value of a quantity) for a given situation.

In this chapter we introduce some *linear programming* problems that can be solved by graphical methods. Then, in Chapter 4, we discuss the simplex method, a general method for solving linear programming problems with many variables.

3.1 Graphing Linear Inequalities

APPLY IT How can a company determine the feasible number of units of each product to manufacture in order to meet all production requirements? *We will answer this question in Example 6 by graphing a set of inequalities.*

As mentioned earlier, a linear inequality is defined as follows.

Linear Inequality
A **linear inequality** in two variables has the form

$$ax + by \leq c$$
$$ax + by < c,$$
$$ax + by \geq c,$$
$$\text{or} \quad ax + by > c,$$

for real numbers a, b, and c, with a and b not both 0.

EXAMPLE 1 Graphing an Inequality

Graph the linear inequality $2x - 3y \leq 12$.

SOLUTION Because of the "=" portion of $\leq$, the points of the line $2x - 3y = 12$ satisfy the linear inequality $2x - 3y \leq 12$ and are part of its graph. As in Chapter 1, find the intercepts by first letting $x = 0$ and then letting $y = 0$; use these points to get the graph of $2x - 3y = 12$ shown in Figure 1.

FOR REVIEW

Recall from Chapter 1 that one way to sketch a line is to first let $x = 0$ to find the y-intercept, then let $y = 0$ to find the x-intercept. For example, given $2x - 3y = 12$, letting $x = 0$ yields $-3y = 12$, so $y = -4$, and the corresponding point is $(0, -4)$. Letting $y = 0$ yields $2x = 12$, so $x = 6$ and the point is $(6, 0)$. Plot these two points, as in Figure 1, then use a straightedge to draw a line through them.

FIGURE 1

FIGURE 2

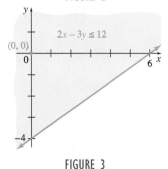

FIGURE 3

The points on the line satisfy "$2x - 3y$ *equals* 12." To locate the points satisfying "$2x - 3y$ *is less than* or equal to 12," first solve $2x - 3y \leq 12$ for y.

$$2x - 3y \leq 12$$

$$-3y \leq -2x + 12 \qquad \text{Subtract } 2x.$$

$$y \geq \frac{2}{3}x - 4 \qquad \text{Multiply by } -\frac{1}{3}.$$

(Recall that multiplying both sides of an inequality by a negative number reverses the direction of the inequality symbol.)

As shown in Figure 2, the points *above* the line $2x - 3y = 12$ satisfy

$$y > \frac{2}{3}x - 4,$$

while those below the line satisfy

$$y < \frac{2}{3}x - 4.$$

In summary, the inequality $2x - 3y \leq 12$ is satisfied by all points *on or above* the line $2x - 3y = 12$. Indicate the points above the line by shading, as in Figure 3. The line and shaded region in Figure 3 make up the graph of the linear inequality $2x - 3y \leq 12$.

CAUTION In this chapter, be sure to use a straightedge to draw lines and to plot the points with care. A sloppily drawn line could give a deceptive picture of the region being considered.

In Example 1, the line $2x - 3y = 12$, which separates the points in the solution from the points that are not in the solution, is called the **boundary**.

There is an alternative way to find the correct region to shade or to check the method shown above. Choose as a test point any point not on the boundary line. For example, in Example 1 we could choose the point $(0, 0)$, which is not on the line $2x - 3y = 12$. Substitute 0 for x and 0 for y in the given inequality.

$$2x - 3y \leq 12$$

$$2(0) - 3(0) \leq 12$$

$$0 \leq 12 \qquad \text{True}$$

Since the result $0 \leq 12$ is true, the test point $(0, 0)$ belongs on the side of the boundary where all points satisfy $2x - 3y < 12$. For this reason, we shade the side containing $(0, 0)$, as in Figure 3. Choosing a point on the other side of the line, such as $(4, -3)$, would produce a false result when the values $x = 4$ and $y = -3$ were substituted into the given inequality. In such a case, we would shade the side of the line *not including* the test point.

NOTE Many of the inequalities in this chapter are of the form $ax + by \leq c$ or $ax + by \geq c$. These are most easily graphed by changing the $\leq$ or $\geq$ to = and then plotting the two intercepts by letting $x = 0$ and $y = 0$, as in Example 1. Shade the appropriate side of the line as described above. If both $a > 0$ and $b > 0$ the shaded region for $ax + by \leq c$ is *below* the line, while the shaded region for $ax + by \geq c$ is *above* the line.

FIGURE 4

EXAMPLE 2 Graphing an Inequality

Graph $x - 4y > 4$.

SOLUTION The boundary here is the line $x - 4y = 4$. Since the points on this line do not satisfy $x - 4y > 4$, the line is drawn dashed, as in Figure 4. To decide whether to shade the region above the line or the region below the line, we will choose a test point not on the boundary line. Choosing $(0, 0)$, we replace x with 0 and y with 0:

$$x - 4y > 4$$
$$0 - 4(0) > 4$$
$$0 > 4. \quad \text{False}$$

YOUR TURN 1

Graph $3x + 2y \leq 18$.

The correct half-plane is the one that does *not* contain $(0, 0)$; the region below the boundary line is shaded, as shown in Figure 4.   **TRY YOUR TURN 1**

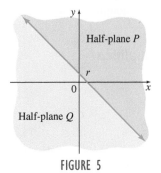

FIGURE 5

> **CAUTION** Be careful. If the point $(0, 0)$ is on the boundary line, it cannot be used as a test point.

As the examples above suggest, the graph of a linear inequality is represented by a shaded region in the plane, perhaps including the line that is the boundary of the region. Each shaded region is an example of a **half-plane**, a region on one side of a line. For example, in Figure 5 line r divides the plane into half-planes P and Q. The points on r belong neither to P nor to Q. Line r is the boundary of each half-plane.

TECHNOLOGY NOTE

Graphing calculators can shade regions on the plane. TI calculators have a DRAW menu that includes an option to shade above or below a line. For instance, to graph the inequality in Example 2, first solve the equation for y, then use your calculator to graph the line $y = (1/4)x - 1$. Then the command Shade(-10, (1/4)X - 1) produces Figure 6(a).

The TI-84 Plus calculator offers another way to graph the region above or below a line. Press the Y= key. Note the slanted line to the left of Y_1, Y_2, and so on. Use the left arrow key to move the cursor to that position for Y_1. Press ENTER until you see the symbol ◣. This indicates that the calculator will shade below the line whose equation is entered in Y_1. (The symbol ◤ operates similarly to shade above a line.) We used this method to get the graph in Figure 6(b). For more details, see the *Graphing Calculator and Excel Spreadsheet Manual* available with this book.

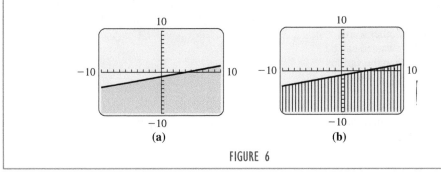

FIGURE 6

The steps in graphing a linear inequality are summarized below.

Graphing a Linear Inequality

1. Draw the graph of the boundary line. Make the line solid if the inequality involves $\leq$ or $\geq$; make the line dashed if the inequality involves $<$ or $>$.

2. Decide which half-plane to shade. Use either of the following methods.

   a. Solve the inequality for y; shade the region above the line if the inequality is of the form $y >$ or $y \geq$; shade the region below the line if the inequality is of the form $y <$ or $y \leq$.

   b. Choose any point not on the line as a test point. Shade the half-plane that includes the test point if the test point satisfies the original inequality; otherwise, shade the half-plane on the other side of the boundary line.

Systems of Inequalities

Realistic problems often involve many inequalities. For example, a manufacturing problem might produce inequalities resulting from production requirements as well as inequalities about cost requirements. A collection of at least two inequalities is called a **system of inequalities**. The solution of a system of inequalities is made up of all those points that satisfy all the inequalities of the system at the same time. To graph the solution of a system of inequalities, graph all the inequalities on the same axes and identify, by heavy shading or direction arrows, the region common to all graphs. The next example shows how this is done.

EXAMPLE 3 **Graphing a System of Inequalities**

Graph the system

$$y < -3x + 12$$
$$x < 2y.$$

SOLUTION The graph of the first inequality has the line $y = -3x + 12$ as its boundary. Because of the $<$ symbol, we use a dotted line and shade *below* the line. The second inequality should first be solved for y to get $y > (1/2)x$ to see that the graph is the region *above* the dotted boundary line $y = (1/2)x$.

The heavily shaded region in Figure 7(a) shows all the points that satisfy both inequalities of the system. Since the points on the boundary lines are not in the solution, the boundary lines are dashed.

NOTE
When shading regions by hand, it may be difficult to tell what is shaded heavily and what is shaded only lightly, particularly when more than two inequalities are involved. In such cases, an alternative technique, called *reverse shading,* is to shade the region *opposite* that of the inequality. In other words, the region that is *not* wanted can be shaded. Then, when the various regions are shaded, whatever is not shaded is the desired region. We will not use this technique in this text, but you may wish to try it on your own.

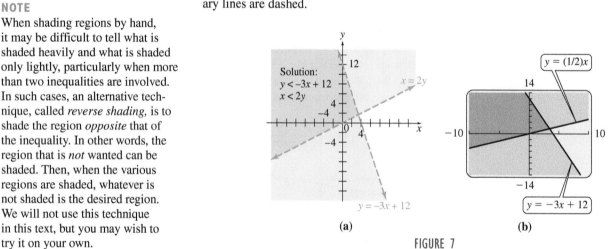

(a)   (b)

FIGURE 7

⊞ **TECHNOLOGY NOTE** A calculator graph of the system in Example 3 is shown in Figure 7(b). You can graph this system on a TI-84 Plus using `Shade(Y₂,Y₁)`.

A region consisting of the overlapping parts of two or more graphs of inequalities in a system, such as the heavily shaded region in Figure 7, is sometimes called the **region of feasible solutions** or the **feasible region**, since it is made up of all the points that satisfy (are feasible for) all inequalities of the system.

EXAMPLE 4 **Graphing a Feasible Region**

Graph the feasible region for the system

$$y \leq -2x + 8$$
$$-2 \leq x \leq 1.$$

SOLUTION The boundary line of the first inequality is $y = -2x + 8$. Because of the $\leq$ symbol, we use a solid line and shade *below* the line.

YOUR TURN 2 Graph the feasible region for the system

$$3x - 4y \geq 12$$
$$x + y \geq 0.$$

The second inequality is a compound inequality, indicating $-2 \leq x \ and \ x \leq 1$. Recall that the graph $x = -2$ is the vertical line through $(-2, 0)$ and that the graph $x = 1$ is the vertical line through $(1, 0)$. For $-2 \leq x$, we draw a vertical line and shade the region to the right. For $x \leq 1$, we draw a vertical line and shade the region to the left.

The shaded region in Figure 8 shows all the points that satisfy the system of inequalities. **TRY YOUR TURN 2**

EXAMPLE 5 Graphing a Feasible Region

Graph the feasible region for the system

$$2x - 5y \leq 10$$
$$x + 2y \leq 8$$
$$x \geq 0$$
$$y \geq 0.$$

SOLUTION On the same axes, graph each inequality by graphing the boundary and choosing the appropriate half-plane. Then find the feasible region by locating the overlap of all the half-planes. This feasible region is shaded in Figure 9. The inequalities $x \geq 0$ and $y \geq 0$ restrict the feasible region to the first quadrant.

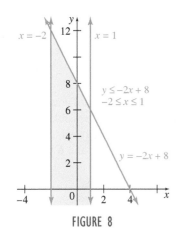

FIGURE 8

The feasible region in Example 5 is **bounded**, since the region is enclosed by boundary lines on all sides. On the other hand, the feasible regions in Examples 3 and 4 are **unbounded.**

Applications
As shown in Section 3 of this chapter, many realistic problems lead to systems of linear inequalities. The next example is typical of such problems.

EXAMPLE 6 Manufacturing

Happy Ice Cream Cone Company makes cake cones and sugar cones, both of which must be processed in the mixing department and the baking department. Manufacturing one batch of cake cones requires 1 hour in the mixing department and 2 hours in the baking department, and producing one batch of sugar cones requires 2 hours in the mixing department and 1 hour in the baking department. Each department is operated for at most 12 hours per day.

FIGURE 9

APPLY IT

(a) Write a system of inequalities that expresses these restrictions.

SOLUTION Let x represent the number of batches of cake cones made and y represent the number of batches of sugar cones made. Then, make a table that summarizes the given information.

Production Requirements for Ice Cream Cones				
	Cake	Sugar		Total
Number of Units Made	x	y		
Hours in Mixing Dept.	1	2	$\leq$	12
Hours in Baking Dept.	2	1	$\leq$	12

Since the departments operate at most 12 hours per day, we put the total number of hours as ≤ 12. Putting the inequality ($\leq$ or $\geq$) next to the number in the chart may help you remember which way to write the inequality.

In the mixing department, x batches of cake cones require a total of $1 \cdot x = x$ hours, and y batches of sugar cones require $2 \cdot y = 2y$ hours. Since the mixing department can operate no more than 12 hours per day,

$$x + 2y \leq 12. \quad \text{Mixing department}$$

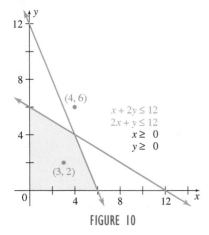

FIGURE 10

We translated "no more than" as "less than or equal to." Notice how this inequality corresponds to the row in the table for the mixing department. Similarly, the row corresponding to the baking department gives

$$2x + y \leq 12. \quad \text{Baking department}$$

Since it is not possible to produce a negative number of cake cones or sugar cones,

$$x \geq 0 \quad \text{and} \quad y \geq 0.$$

(b) Graph the feasible region.

   SOLUTION   The feasible region for this system of inequalities is shown in Figure 10.

(c) Using the graph from part (b), can 3 batches of cake cones and 2 batches of sugar cones be manufactured in one day? Can 4 batches of cake cones and 6 batches of sugar cones be manufactured in one day?

   SOLUTION   Three batches of cake cones and two batches of sugar cones correspond to the point $(3, 2)$. Since $(3, 2)$ is in the feasible region in Figure 10, it is possible to manufacture these quantities in one day. However, since $(4, 6)$ is *not* in the feasible region in Figure 10, it is *not* possible to manufacture 4 batches of cake cones and 6 batches of sugar cones in one day.

The following steps summarize the process of finding the feasible region.

1. Form a table that summarizes the information.

2. Convert the table into a set of linear inequalities.

3. Graph each linear inequality.

4. Graph the region that is common to all the regions graphed in step 3.

3.1   EXERCISES

Graph each linear inequality.

1. $x + y \leq 2$

2. $y \leq x + 1$

3. $x \geq 2 - y$

4. $y \geq x - 3$

5. $4x - y < 6$

6. $4y + x > 6$

7. $4x + y < 8$

8. $2x - y > 2$

9. $x + 3y \geq -2$

10. $2x + 3y \leq 6$

11. $x \leq 3y$

12. $2x \geq y$

13. $x + y \leq 0$

14. $3x + 2y \geq 0$

15. $y < x$

16. $y > 5x$

17. $x < 4$

18. $y > 5$

19. $y \leq -2$

20. $x \geq -4$

Graph the feasible region for each system of inequalities. Tell whether each region is bounded or unbounded.

21. $x + y \leq 1$
      $x - y \geq 2$

22. $4x - y < 6$
      $3x + y < 9$

23. $x + 3y \leq 6$
      $2x + 4y \geq 7$

24. $-x - y < 5$
      $2x - y < 4$

25. $x + y \leq 7$
      $x - y \leq -4$
      $4x + y \geq 0$

26. $3x - 2y \geq 6$
      $x + y \leq -5$
      $y \leq -6$

27. $-2 < x < 3$
      $-1 \leq y \leq 5$
      $2x + y < 6$

28. $1 < x < 4$
      $y > 2$
      $x > y$

29. $y - 2x \leq 4$
      $y \geq 2 - x$
      $x \geq 0$
      $y \geq 0$

30. $2x + 3y \leq 12$
      $2x + 3y > 3$
      $3x + y < 4$
      $x \geq 0$
      $y \geq 0$

31. $3x + 4y > 12$
      $2x - 3y < 6$
      $0 \leq y \leq 2$
      $x \geq 0$

32. $0 \leq x \leq 9$
      $x - 2y \geq 4$
      $3x + 5y \leq 30$
      $y \geq 0$

Use a graphing calculator to graph the following.

33. $2x - 6y > 12$

34. $4x - 3y < 12$

35. $3x - 4y < 6$
      $2x + 5y > 15$

36. $6x - 4y > 8$
      $2x + 5y < 5$

37. The regions A through G in the figure can be described by the inequalities

$$x + 3y \ ? \ 6$$
$$x + y \ ? \ 3$$
$$x - 2y \ ? \ 2$$
$$x \geq 0$$
$$y \geq 0,$$

where ? can be either $\leq$ or $\geq$. For each region, tell what the ? should be in the three inequalities. For example, for region A, the ? should be $\geq$, $\leq$, and $\leq$, because region A is described by the inequalities

$$x + 3y \geq 6$$
$$x + y \leq 3$$
$$x - 2y \leq 2$$
$$x \geq 0$$
$$y \geq 0.$$

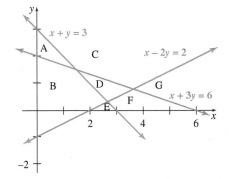

APPLICATIONS

Business and Economics

38. Production Scheduling A small pottery shop makes two kinds of planters, glazed and unglazed. The glazed type requires 1/2 hour to throw on the wheel and 1 hour in the kiln. The unglazed type takes 1 hour to throw on the wheel and 6 hours in the kiln. The wheel is available for at most 8 hours per day, and the kiln for at most 20 hours per day.

a. Complete the following table.

	Glazed	Unglazed	Total
Number Made	x	y	
Time on Wheel			
Time in Kiln			

b. Set up a system of inequalities and graph the feasible region.

c. Using your graph from part b, can 5 glazed and 2 unglazed planters be made? Can 10 glazed and 2 unglazed planters be made?

39. Time Management Carmella and Walt produce handmade shawls and afghans. They spin the yarn, dye it, and then weave it. A shawl requires 1 hour of spinning, 1 hour of dyeing, and 1 hour of weaving. An afghan needs 2 hours of spinning, 1 hour of dyeing, and 4 hours of weaving. Together, they spend at most 8 hours spinning, 6 hours dyeing, and 14 hours weaving.

a. Complete the following table.

	Shawls	Afghans	Total
Number Made	x	y	
Spinning Time			
Dyeing Time			
Weaving Time			

b. Set up a system of inequalities and graph the feasible region.

c. Using your graph from part b, can 3 shawls and 2 afghans be made? Can 4 shawls and 3 afghans be made?

For Exercises 40–45, perform the following steps.

a. Write a system of inequalities to express the conditions of the problem.

b. Graph the feasible region of the system.

40. Transportation Southwestern Oil supplies two distributors located in the Northwest. One distributor needs at least 3000 barrels of oil, and the other needs at least 5000 barrels. Southwestern can send out at most 10,000 barrels. Let $x =$ the number of barrels of oil sent to distributor 1 and $y =$ the number sent to distributor 2.

41. Finance The loan department in a bank will use at most $30 million for commercial and home loans. The bank's policy is to allocate at least four times as much money to home loans as to commercial loans. The bank's return is 6% on a home loan and 8% on a commercial loan. The manager of the loan department wants to earn a return of at least $1.6 million on these loans. Let $x =$ the amount (in millions) for home loans and $y =$ the amount (in millions) for commercial loans.

42. Transportation The California Almond Growers have at most 2400 boxes of almonds to be shipped from their plant in Sacramento to Des Moines and San Antonio. The Des Moines market needs at least 1000 boxes, while the San Antonio market must have at least 800 boxes. Let $x =$ the number of boxes to be shipped to Des Moines and $y =$ the number of boxes to be shipped to San Antonio.

43. Management The Gillette Company produces two popular battery-operated razors, the M3Power™ and the Fusion Power™. Because of demand, the number of M3Power™ razors is never more than one-half the number of Fusion Power™ razors. The factory's production cannot exceed 800 razors per day. Let $x =$ the number of M3Power™ razors and $y =$ the number of Fusion Power™ razors produced per day.

44. Production Scheduling A cement manufacturer produces at least 3.2 million barrels of cement annually. He is told by the Environmental Protection Agency (EPA) that his operation emits 2.5 lb of dust for each barrel produced. The EPA has ruled that annual emissions must be reduced to no more than 1.8 million lb. To do this, the manufacturer plans to replace the present dust collectors with two types of electronic precipitators. One type would reduce emissions to 0.5 lb per barrel and operating costs would be 16¢ per barrel. The other would reduce the dust to 0.3 lb per barrel and operating costs would be 20¢ per barrel. The manufacturer does not want to spend more than 0.8 million dollars in operating costs on the precipitators. He needs to know how many barrels he could produce with each type. Let x = the number of barrels (in millions) produced with the first type and y = the number of barrels (in millions) produced with the second type.

Life Sciences

45. **Nutrition** A dietician is planning a snack package of fruit and nuts. Each ounce of fruit will supply 1 unit of protein, 2 units

of carbohydrates, and 1 unit of fat. Each ounce of nuts will supply 1 unit of protein, 1 unit of carbohydrates, and 1 unit of fat. Every package must provide at least 7 units of protein, at least 10 units of carbohydrates, and no more than 9 units of fat. Let x = the ounces of fruit and y = the ounces of nuts to be used in each package.

YOUR TURN ANSWERS

1.

2.

3.2 Solving Linear Programming Problems Graphically

Many mathematical models designed to solve problems in business, biology, and economics involve finding an optimum value (maximum or minimum) of a function, subject to certain restrictions. In a **linear programming** problem, we must find the maximum or minimum value of a function, called the **objective function**, and satisfy a set of restrictions, or **constraints**, given by linear inequalities. When only two variables are involved, the solution to a linear programming problem can be found by first graphing the set of constraints, then finding the feasible region as discussed in the previous section. This method is explained in the following example.

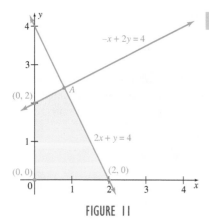

FIGURE 11

EXAMPLE 1 **Maximization**

Find the maximum value of the objective function $z = 3x + 4y$, subject to the following constraints.

$$2x + y \leq 4$$
$$-x + 2y \leq 4$$
$$x \geq 0$$
$$y \geq 0$$

SOLUTION The feasible region is graphed in Figure 11. We can find the coordinates of point A, $(4/5, 12/5)$, by solving the system

$$2x + y = 4$$
$$-x + 2y = 4.$$

Every point in the feasible region satisfies all the constraints; however, we want to find those points that produce the maximum possible value of the objective function. To see how to find this maximum value, change the graph of Figure 11 by adding lines that represent the objective function $z = 3x + 4y$ for various sample values of z. By choosing the values 0, 5, 10, and 15 for z, the objective function becomes (in turn)

$$0 = 3x + 4y, \quad 5 = 3x + 4y, \quad 10 = 3x + 4y, \quad \text{and} \quad 15 = 3x + 4y.$$

─ FOR REVIEW ─

Recall from Chapter 2 that two equations in two unknowns can be solved by using row operations to eliminate one variable. For example, to solve the system

$$2x + y = 4$$
$$-x + 2y = 4,$$

we could take the first equation plus 2 times the second to eliminate x. (This is equivalent to $R_1 + 2R_2 \rightarrow R_2$ in the Gauss-Jordan method.) The result is $5y = 12$, so $y = 12/5$. We can then substitute this value of y into either equation and solve for x. For example, substitution into the first equation yields

$$2x + \frac{12}{5} = 4$$

$$2x = \frac{8}{5}$$

$$x = \frac{4}{5}.$$

We instead could have subtracted the original second equation from twice the first equation to eliminate y, yielding $5x = 4$, or $x = 4/5$, and then substitute into either equation and solve for y.

These four lines (known as **isoprofit lines**) are graphed in Figure 12. (Why are the lines parallel?) The figure shows that z cannot take on the value 15 because the graph for $z = 15$ is entirely outside the feasible region. The maximum possible value of z will be obtained from a line parallel to the others and between the lines representing the objective function when $z = 10$ and $z = 15$. The value of z will be as large as possible and all constraints will be satisfied if this line just touches the feasible region. This occurs at point A. We find that A has coordinates $(4/5, 12/5)$. (See the review in the margin.) The value of z at this point is

$$z = 3x + 4y = 3\left(\frac{4}{5}\right) + 4\left(\frac{12}{5}\right) = \frac{60}{5} = 12.$$

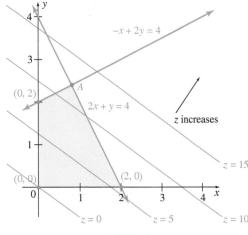

FIGURE 12

The maximum possible value of z is 12. Of all the points in the feasible region, A leads to the largest possible value of z.

TECHNOLOGY NOTE A graphing calculator can be useful for finding the coordinates of intersection points such as point A. We do this by solving each equation for y, graphing each line, and then using the capability of the calculator to find the coordinates of the point of intersection.

Points such as A in Example 1 are called corner points. A **corner point** is a point in the feasible region where the boundary lines of two constraints cross. Since corner points occur where two straight lines cross, the coordinates of a corner point are the solution of a system of two linear equations. As we saw in Example 1, corner points play a key role in the solution of linear programming problems. We will make this explicit after the following example.

EXAMPLE 2 **Minimization**

Solve the following linear programming problem.

$$\text{Minimize} \quad z = 2x + 4y$$
$$\text{subject to:} \quad x + 2y \geq 10$$
$$3x + y \geq 10$$
$$x \geq 0$$
$$y \geq 0.$$

SOLUTION Figure 13 on the next page shows the feasible region and the lines that result when z in the objective function is replaced by 0, 10, 20, 40, and 50. The line representing the objective function touches the region of feasible solutions when $z = 20$. Two corner points, $(2, 4)$ and $(10, 0)$, lie on this line; both $(2, 4)$ and $(10, 0)$, as well as all the points on the boundary line between them, give the same optimum value of z. There are infinitely many equally good values of x and y that will give the same minimum value of the objective function $z = 2x + 4y$. This minimum value is 20.

FIGURE 13

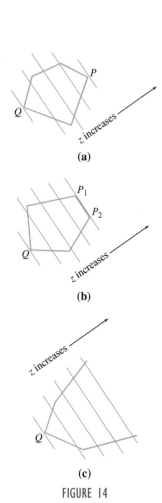

As long as the feasible region is not empty, linear programming problems with bounded regions always have solutions. On the other hand, the feasible region in Example 2 is unbounded, and no solution will *maximize* the value of the objective function because z can be made as large as you like.

Some general conclusions can be drawn from the method of solution used in Examples 1 and 2. Imagine a line sliding across a region. Figure 14 shows various feasible regions and the position of the line $ax + by = z$ for various values of z. We assume here that as the line slides from the lower left to the upper right, the value of z increases. In Figure 14(a), the objective function takes on its minimum value at corner point Q and its maximum value at P. The minimum is again at Q in part (b), but the maximum occurs at P_1 or P_2, or any point on the line segment connecting them. Finally, in part (c), the minimum value occurs at Q, but the objective function has no maximum value because the feasible region is unbounded. As long as the objective function increases as x and y increase, the objective function will have no maximum over an unbounded region.

The preceding discussion suggests the truth of the **corner point theorem**.

Corner Point Theorem

If an optimum value (either a maximum or a minimum) of the objective function exists, it will occur at one or more of the corner points of the feasible region.

This theorem simplifies the job of finding an optimum value. First, we graph the feasible region and find all corner points. Then we test each corner point in the objective function. Finally, we identify the corner point producing the optimum solution. For unbounded regions, we must decide whether the required optimum can be found (see Example 2).

With the theorem, we can solve the problem in Example 1 by first identifying the four corner points in Figure 11: $(0, 0)$, $(0, 2)$, $(4/5, 12/5)$, and $(2, 0)$. Then we substitute each of the four points into the objective function $z = 3x + 4y$ to identify the corner point that produces the maximum value of z.

Values of the Objective Function at Corner Points	
Corner Point	Value of $z = 3x + 4y$
$(0, 0)$	$3(0) + 4(0) = 0$
$(0, 2)$	$3(0) + 4(2) = 8$
$\left(\frac{4}{5}, \frac{12}{5}\right)$	$3\left(\frac{4}{5}\right) + 4\left(\frac{12}{5}\right) = 12$ Maximum
$(2, 0)$	$3(2) + 4(0) = 6$

From these results, the corner point $(4/5, 12/5)$ yields the maximum value of 12. This is the same as the result found earlier.

The following summary gives the steps to use in solving a linear programming problem by the graphical method.

NOTE
As the corner point theorem states and Example 2 illustrates, the optimal value of a linear programming problem may occur at more than one corner point. When the optimal solution occurs at two corner points, every point on the line segment between the two points is also an optimal solution.

Solving a Linear Programming Problem

1. Write the objective function and all necessary constraints.
2. Graph the feasible region.
3. Identify all corner points.
4. Find the value of the objective function at each corner point.
5. For a bounded region, the solution is given by the corner point producing the optimum value of the objective function.
6. For an unbounded region, check that a solution actually exists. If it does, it will occur at a corner point.

When asked to solve a linear programming problem, give the maximum or minimum value, as well any points where that value occurs.

EXAMPLE 3   Maximization and Minimization

Sketch the feasible region for the following set of constraints, and then find the maximum and minimum values of the objective function $z = x + 10y$.

$$x + 4y \geq 12$$
$$x - 2y \leq 0$$
$$2y - x \leq 6$$
$$x \leq 6$$

SOLUTION   The graph in Figure 15 shows that the feasible region is bounded. Use the corner points from the graph to find the maximum and minimum values of the objective function.

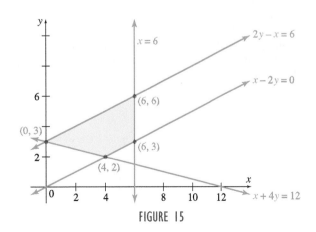

FIGURE 15

Values of the Objective Function at Corner Points	
Corner Point	Value of $z = x + 10y$
$(0, 3)$	$0 + 10(3) = 30$
$(4, 2)$	$4 + 10(2) = 24$ Minimum
$(6, 3)$	$6 + 10(3) = 36$
$(6, 6)$	$6 + 10(6) = 66$ Maximum

YOUR TURN 1 Find the maximum and minimum values of the objective function $z = 3x + 4y$ on the region bounded by

$$2x + y \geq 5$$
$$x + 5y \geq 16$$
$$2x + y \leq 14$$
$$-x + 4y \leq 20$$

The minimum value of $z = x + 10y$ is 24 at the corner point $(4, 2)$. The maximum value is 66 at $(6, 6)$.   TRY YOUR TURN 1

To verify that the minimum or maximum is correct in a linear programming problem, you might want to add the graph of the line $z = 0$ to the graph of the feasible region. For instance, in Example 3, the result of adding the line $x + 10y = 0$ is shown in Figure 16. Now imagine moving a straightedge through the feasible region parallel to this line. It appears that the first place the line touches the feasible region is at $(4, 2)$, where we found the minimum. Similarly, the last place the line touches is at $(6, 6)$, where we found the maximum. In Figure 16, these parallel lines, labeled $z = 24$ and $z = 66$, are also shown.

NOTE
The graphical method is very difficult for a problem with three variables (where the feasible region is three dimensional) and impossible with four or more variables. A method for solving such problems will be shown in the next chapter.

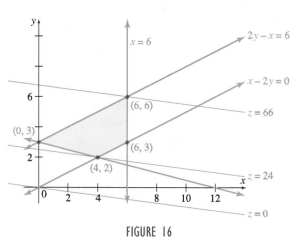

FIGURE 16

3.2   EXERCISES

The following graphs show regions of feasible solutions. Use these regions to find maximum and minimum values of the given objective functions.

1. a. $z = 3x + 2y$

  b. $z = x + 4y$

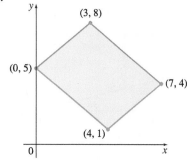

2. a. $z = x + 4y$

  b. $z = 5x + 2y$

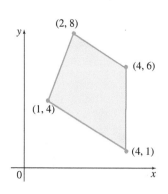

3. a. $z = 0.40x + 0.75y$

  b. $z = 1.50x + 0.25y$

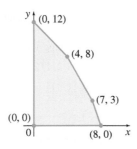

4. a. $z = 0.35x + 1.25y$

  b. $z = 1.5x + 0.5y$

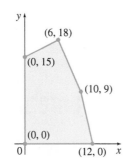

5. a. $z = 4x + 2y$

  b. $z = 2x + 3y$

  c. $z = 2x + 4y$

  d. $z = x + 4y$

6. a. $z = 4x + y$

  b. $z = 5x + 6y$

  c. $z = x + 2y$

  d. $z = x + 6y$

Use graphical methods to solve each linear programming problem.

7. Minimize $z = 4x + 7y$

  subject to: $x - y \geq 1$

  $3x + 2y \geq 18$

  $x \geq 0$

  $y \geq 0.$

8. Minimize $z = x + 3y$

  subject to: $x + y \leq 10$

  $5x + 2y \geq 20$

  $-x + 2y \geq 0$

  $x \geq 0$

  $y \geq 0.$

9. Maximize $z = 5x + 2y$

  subject to: $4x - y \leq 16$

  $2x + y \geq 11$

  $x \geq 3$

  $y \leq 8.$

10. Maximize $z = 10x + 8y$

  subject to: $2x + 3y \leq 100$

  $5x + 4y \leq 200$

  $x \geq 10$

  $0 \leq y \leq 20.$

11. Maximize $z = 10x + 10y$

  subject to: $5x + 8y \geq 200$

  $25x - 10y \geq 250$

  $x + y \leq 150$

  $x \geq 0$

  $y \geq 0.$

12. Maximize $z = 4x + 5y$

  subject to: $10x - 5y \leq 100$

  $20x + 10y \geq 150$

  $x + y \geq 12$

  $x \geq 0$

  $y \geq 0.$

13. Maximize $z = 3x + 6y$

  subject to: $2x - 3y \leq 12$

  $x + y \leq 5$

  $3x + 4y \geq 24$

  $x \geq 0$

  $y \geq 0.$

14. Maximize $z = 4x + 6y$

  subject to: $3 \leq x + y \leq 10$

  $x - y \geq 3$

  $x \geq 0$

  $y \geq 0.$

15. Find values of $x \geq 0$ and $y \geq 0$ that maximize $z = 10x + 12y$ subject to each set of constraints.

  a. $x + y \leq 20$ **b.** $3x + y \leq 15$ **c.** $2x + 5y \geq 22$

  $x + 3y \leq 24$ $x + 2y \leq 18$ $4x + 3y \leq 28$

  $2x + 2y \leq 17$

16. Find values of $x \geq 0$ and $y \geq 0$ that minimize $z = 3x + 2y$ subject to each set of constraints.

  a. $10x + 7y \leq 42$ **b.** $6x + 5y \geq 25$ **c.** $x + 2y \geq 10$

  $4x + 10y \geq 35$ $2x + 6y \geq 15$ $2x + y \geq 12$

  $x - y \leq 8$

17. You are given the following linear programming problem:*

Maximize $\quad z = c_1 x_1 + c_2 x_2$

subject to: $\quad 2x_1 + x_2 \le 11$

$ -x_1 + 2x_2 \le 2$

$ x_1 \ge 0, x_2 \ge 0.$

If $c_2 > 0$, determine the range of c_1/c_2 for which $(x_1, x_2) = (4, 3)$ is an optimal solution. (Choose one of the following.) *Source: Society of Actuaries.*

a. $[-2, 1/2]$ **b.** $[-1/2, 2]$ **c.** $[-11, -1]$

d. $[1, 11]$ **e.** $[-11, 11]$

*The notation x_1 and x_2 used in this exercise is the same as x and y.

YOUR TURN ANSWERS

1. Maximum of 36 at (4,6); minimum of 15 at (1,3)

3.3 Applications of Linear Programming

APPLY IT   How many canoes and kayaks should a business purchase, given a limited budget and limited storage?
We will use linear programming to answer this question in Example 1.

EXAMPLE 1   Canoe Rentals

Andrew Crowley plans to start a new business called River Explorers, which will rent canoes and kayaks to people to travel 10 miles down the Clarion River in Cook Forest State Park. He has $45,000 to purchase new boats. He can buy the canoes for $600 each and the kayaks for $750 each. His facility can hold up to 65 boats. The canoes will rent for $25 a day, and the kayaks will rent for $30 a day. How many canoes and how many kayaks should he buy to earn the most revenue if all boats can be rented each day?

APPLY IT   **SOLUTION**   Let x represent the number of canoes and let y represent the number of kayaks. Summarize the given information in a table.

Rental Information				
	Canoes	**Kayaks**		**Total**
Number of Boats	x	y	$\le$	65
Cost of Each	$600	$750	$\le$	$45,000
Revenue	$25	$30		

The constraints, imposed by the number of boats and the cost, correspond to the rows in the table as follows.

$$x + y \le 65$$

$$600x + 750y \le 45{,}000$$

Dividing both sides of the second constraint by 150 gives the equivalent inequality

$$4x + 5y \le 300.$$

Since the number of boats cannot be negative, $x \ge 0$ and $y \ge 0$. The objective function to be maximized gives the amount of revenue. If the variable z represents the total revenue, the objective function is

$$z = 25x + 30y.$$

In summary, the mathematical model for the given linear programming problem is as follows:

$$\text{Maximize} \qquad z = 25x + 30y \tag{1}$$
$$\text{subject to:} \qquad x + y \le 65 \tag{2}$$
$$4x + 5y \le 300 \tag{3}$$
$$x \ge 0 \tag{4}$$
$$y \ge 0. \tag{5}$$

Using the methods described in the previous section, graph the feasible region for the system of inequalities (2)–(5), as in Figure 17. Three of the corner points can be identified from the graph as (0, 0), (65, 0), and (0, 60). The fourth corner point, labeled Q in the figure, can be found by solving the system of equations

$$x + y = 65$$
$$4x + 5y = 300.$$

Solve this system to find that Q is the point (25, 40). Now test these four points in the objective function to determine the maximum value of z. The results are shown in the table.

Values of the Objective Function at Corner Points	
Corner Point	Value of $z = 25x + 30y$
$(0, 0)$	$25(0) + 30(0) = 0$
$(65, 0)$	$25(65) + 30(0) = 1625$
$(0, 60)$	$25(0) + 30(60) = 1800$
$(25, 40)$	$25(25) + 30(40) = 1825$ Maximum

The objective function, which represents revenue, is maximized when $x = 25$ and $y = 40$. He should buy 25 canoes and 40 kayaks for a maximum revenue of \$1825 a day.

TRY YOUR TURN 1 AND 2

YOUR TURN 1 Solve Example 1 with everything the same except the revenue for a kayak changed to \$35 a day.

YOUR TURN 2 Suppose that in Example 6 in Sec. 3.1, the company earns \$20 in profit for each batch of cake cones and \$30 for each batch of sugar cones. How many batches of each should the company make to maximize profit?

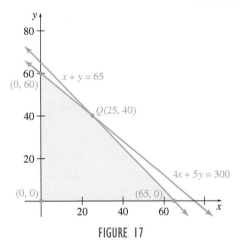

FIGURE 17

Fortunately, the answer to the linear programming problem in Example 1 is a point with integer coordinates, as the number of each type of boat must be an integer. Unfortunately, there is no guarantee that this will always happen at a corner point. When the solution to a linear programming problem is restricted to integers, it is an *integer programming* problem, which is more difficult to solve than a linear programming problem. The feasible region for an integer programming problem consists only of those points with integer coordinates that satisfy the constraints. In this text, all problems in which fractional solutions are meaningless are contrived to have integer solutions.

EXAMPLE 2 **Farm Animals**

A 4-H member raises only goats and pigs. She wants to raise no more than 16 animals, including no more than 10 goats. She spends $25 to raise a goat and $75 to raise a pig, and she has $900 available for this project. Each goat produces $12 in profit and each pig $40 in profit. How many goats and how many pigs should she raise to maximize total profit?

SOLUTION   First, set up a table that shows the information given in the problem.

4-H Animal Information				
	Goats	Pigs		Total
Number Raised	x	y	$\leq$	16
Goat Limit	x		$\leq$	10
Cost to Raise	$25	$75	$\leq$	$900
Profit (each)	$12	$40		

Use the table to write the necessary constraints. Since the total number of animals cannot exceed 16, the first constraint is

$$x + y \leq 16.$$

"No more than 10 goats" means

$$x \leq 10.$$

The cost to raise x goats at $25 per goat is $25x$ dollars, while the cost for y pigs at $75 each is $75y$ dollars. Since only $900 is available,

$$25x + 75y \leq 900.$$

Dividing both sides by 25 gives the equivalent inequality

$$x + 3y \leq 36.$$

The number of goats and pigs cannot be negative, so

$$x \geq 0 \quad \text{and} \quad y \geq 0.$$

The 4-H member wants to know how many goats and pigs to raise in order to produce maximum profit. Each goat yields $12 profit and each pig $40. If z represents total profit, then

$$z = 12x + 40y.$$

In summary, we have the following linear programming problem:

$$\begin{aligned} \text{Maximize} \quad & z = 12x + 40y \\ \text{subject to:} \quad & x + y \leq 16 \\ & x + 3y \leq 36 \\ & x \leq 10 \\ & x \geq 0 \\ & y \geq 0. \end{aligned}$$

A graph of the feasible region is shown in Figure 18. The corner points $(0, 12)$, $(0, 0)$, and $(10, 0)$ can be read directly from the graph. The coordinates of each of the other corner points can be found by solving a system of linear equations.

Test each corner point in the objective function to find the maximum profit.

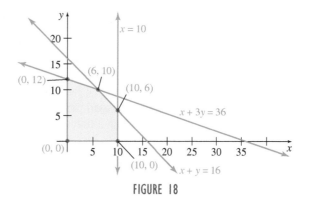

FIGURE 18

YOUR TURN 3 Solve Example 2 with everything the same except the total amount available for the project changed to $1050.

FIGURE 19

FIGURE 20

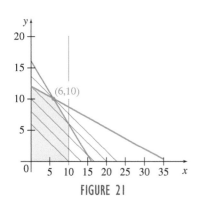

FIGURE 21

Values of the Objective Function at Corner Points		
Corner Point	**Value of $z = 12x + 40y$**	
$(0, 12)$	$12(0) + 40(12) = 480$	Maximum
$(6, 10)$	$12(6) + 40(10) = 472$	
$(10, 6)$	$12(10) + 40(6) = 360$	
$(10, 0)$	$12(10) + 40(0) = 120$	
$(0, 0)$	$12(0) + 40(0) = 0$	

The maximum of 480 occurs at $(0, 12)$. Thus, 12 pigs and no goats will produce a maximum profit of $480.   **TRY YOUR TURN 3**

In the maximization problem in Example 2, since the profit for a single pig is $40 and the profit for a single goat is only $12, it is more profitable to raise only pigs and no goats. However, if the profit from raising pigs begins to decrease (or the profit from goats begins to increase), it will eventually be more profitable to raise both goats and pigs. In fact, if the profit from raising pigs decreases to a number below $36, then the previous solution is no longer optimal.

To see why this is true, in Figure 19 we have graphed the original objective function ($z = 12x + 40y$) for various values of z, as we did in Example 1 of the previous section. Notice that each of these objective lines has slope $m = -12/40 = -3/10$. When $z = 480$, the line touches only one feasible point, $(0, 12)$, which is where the maximum profit occurs.

If the profit from raising pigs decreases from $40 to p, where p is a value slightly below 40, the objective function lines will have the equation $z = 12x + py$ for various values of z, and the slope of the lines becomes $m = -12/p$. Eventually, as p becomes smaller, the slope of these objective lines will be equal to the slope of the line $x + 3y = 36$ (that is, $-1/3$), corresponding to the second constraint. This occurs when $-12/p = -1/3$, or $p = 36$, as illustrated by the overlapping blue and dotted lines in Figure 20. In this case, the optimal solution occurs at every point on the line segment that joins $(0, 12)$ and $(6, 10)$.

Once the profit from raising pigs decreases to below $36, the slopes of the sample objective function lines become more negative (steeper) and the optimal solution changes, as indicated in Figure 21. As z increases, the last feasible point that the lines touch is $(6, 10)$. For profits from raising pigs that are slightly below $36, the optimal solution will occur when $x = 6$ and $y = 10$. In other words, the maximum profit will occur when she raises both goats and pigs.

EXAMPLE 3 Nutrition

Certain animals in a rescue shelter must have at least 30 g of protein and at least 20 g of fat per feeding period. These nutrients come from food A, which costs 18 cents per unit and supplies 2 g of protein and 4 g of fat; and food B, which costs 12 cents per unit and has 6 g of protein and 2 g of fat. Food B is bought under a long-term contract requiring that at least 2 units of B be used per serving. Another contract requires that the amount of food B used be no more than 3 times the amount of food A used.

(a) How much of each food must be bought to produce the minimum cost per serving?

SOLUTION Let x represent the required amount of food A and y the amount of food B. Use the given information to prepare the following table.

Rescue Animal Nutrition Information				
	Food A	Food B		Total
Number of Units	x	y		
Grams of Protein	2	6	$\geq$	30
Grams of Fat	4	2	$\geq$	20
Long-Term Contract		y	$\geq$	2
Cost	18¢	12¢		

Since the animals must have *at least* 30 g of protein and 20 g of fat, we use $\geq$ in the inequality. If the animals needed *at most* a certain amount of some nutrient, we would use $\leq$. The long-term contract requires that $y \geq 2$.

In addition to the information in the table, we also have the requirement that the amount of food B used be no more than 3 times the amount of food A used. We can write this as $y \leq 3x$.

The linear programming problem can be stated as follows.

$$\text{Minimize} \quad z = 0.18x + 0.12y$$
$$\text{subject to:} \quad 2x + 6y \geq 30 \quad \text{Protein}$$
$$4x + 2y \geq 20 \quad \text{Fat}$$
$$2 \leq y \leq 3x \quad \text{Contracts}$$
$$x \geq 0.$$

(The usual constraint $y \geq 0$ is redundant because of the constraint $y \geq 2$.) A graph of the feasible region is shown in Figure 22. The corner points are $(2, 6)$, $(3, 4)$, and $(9, 2)$. Test each corner point in the objective function to find the minimum cost.

FIGURE 22

Values of the Objective Function at Corner Points	
Corner Point	**Value of $z = 0.18x + 0.12y$**
$(2, 6)$	$0.18(2) + 0.12(6) = 1.08$
$(3, 4)$	$0.18(3) + 0.12(4) = 1.02$ Minimum
$(9, 2)$	$0.18(9) + 0.12(2) = 1.86$

The minimum of 1.02 occurs at $(3, 4)$. Thus, 3 units of food A and 4 units of food B will produce a minimum cost of $1.02 per serving.

(b) The rescue shelter manager notices that although the long-term contract states that at least 2 units of food B be used per serving, the solution uses 4 units of food B, which is 2 units more than the minimum amount required. Can a more economical solution be found that only uses 2 units of food B?

SOLUTION The solution found in part (a) is the most economical solution, even though it exceeds the requirement for using at least 2 units of food B. Notice from Figure 22 that the four lines representing the four constraints do not meet at a single point, so any solution in the feasible region will have to exceed at least one constraint. The rescue shelter manager might use this information to negotiate a better deal with the distributor of food B by making a guarantee to use at least 4 units of food B per serving in the future.

The notion that some constraints are not met exactly is related to the concepts of *surplus* and *slack variables*, which will be explored in the next chapter.

The feasible region in Figure 22 is an *unbounded* feasible region—the region extends indefinitely to the upper right. With this region it would not be possible to *maximize* the objective function, because the total cost of the food could always be increased by encouraging the animals to eat more.

3.3 EXERCISES

Write Exercises 1–6 as linear inequalities. Identify all variables used. (Note: Not all of the given information is used in Exercises 5 and 6.)

1. Product A requires 3 hours on a machine, while product B needs 5 hours on the same machine. The machine is available for at most 60 hours per week.

2. A cow requires a third of an acre of pasture and a sheep needs a quarter acre. A rancher wants to use at least 120 acres of pasture.

3. Jessica Corpo needs at least 1500 units of calcium supplements per day. Her calcium carbonate supplement provides 600 units, and her calcium citrate supplement supplies 250 units.

4. Pauline Wong spends 3 hours selling a small computer and 5 hours selling a larger model. She works no more than 45 hours per week.

5. Coffee costing $8 per lb is to be mixed with coffee costing $10 per lb to get at least 40 lb of a blended coffee.

6. A tank in an oil refinery holds 120 gal. The tank contains a mixture of light oil worth $1.25 per gal and heavy oil worth $0.80 per gal.

APPLICATIONS

Business and Economics

7. Transportation The Miers Company produces small engines for several manufacturers. The company receives orders from two assembly plants for their Top-flight engine. Plant I needs at least 45 engines, and plant II needs at least 32 engines. The company can send at most 120 engines to these two assembly plants. It costs $30 per engine to ship to plant I and $40 per engine to ship to plant II. Plant I gives Miers $20 in rebates toward its products for each engine they buy, while plant II gives similar $15 rebates. Miers estimates that they need at least $1500 in rebates to cover products they plan to buy from the two plants. How many engines should be shipped to each plant to minimize shipping costs? What is the minimum cost?

8. Transportation A manufacturer of refrigerators must ship at least 100 refrigerators to its two West Coast warehouses. Each warehouse holds a maximum of 100 refrigerators. Warehouse A holds 25 refrigerators already, and warehouse B has 20 on hand. It costs $12 to ship a refrigerator to warehouse A and $10 to ship one to warehouse B. Union rules require that at least 300 workers be hired. Shipping a refrigerator to warehouse A requires 4 workers, while shipping a refrigerator to warehouse B requires 2 workers. How many refrigerators should be shipped to each warehouse to minimize costs? What is the minimum cost?

9. Insurance Premiums A company is considering two insurance plans with the types of coverage and premiums shown in the following table.

	Policy A	Policy B
Fire/Theft	$10,000	$15,000
Liability	$180,000	$120,000
Premium	$50	$40

(For example, this means that $50 buys one unit of plan A, consisting of $10,000 fire and theft insurance and $180,000 of liability insurance.)

a. The company wants at least $300,000 fire/theft insurance and at least $3,000,000 liability insurance from these plans. How many units should be purchased from each plan to minimize the cost of the premiums? What is the minimum premium?

b. Suppose the premium for policy A is reduced to $25. Now how many units should be purchased from each plan to minimize the cost of the premiums? What is the minimum premium?

10. **Profit** The Muro Manufacturing Company makes two kinds of plasma screen television sets. It produces the Flexscan set that sells for $350 profit and the Panoramic I that sells for $500 profit. On the assembly line, the Flexscan requires 5 hours, and the Panoramic I takes 7 hours. The cabinet shop spends 1 hour on the cabinet for the Flexscan and 2 hours on the cabinet for the Panoramic I. Both sets require 4 hours for testing and packing. On a particular production run, the Muro Company has available 3600 work-hours on the assembly line, 900 work-hours in the cabinet shop, and 2600 work-hours in the testing and packing department.

a. How many sets of each type should it produce to make a maximum profit? What is the maximum profit?

b. Suppose the profit on the Flexscan goes up to $450. Now how many sets of each type should it produce to make a maximum profit? What is the maximum profit?

c. The solutions from parts a and b leave some unused time in either the assembly line, the cabinet shop, or the testing and packing department. Identify any unused time in each solution. Is it possible to have a solution that leaves no excess time? Explain.

11. **Revenue** A machine shop manufactures two types of bolts. The bolts require time on each of the three groups of machines, but the time required on each group differs, as shown in the table below.

	Type I	Type II
Machine 1	0.2 min	0.2 min
Machine 2	0.6 min	0.2 min
Machine 3	0.04 min	0.08 min

Production schedules are made up one day at a time. In a day, 300, 720, and 100 minutes are available, respectively, on these machines. Type I bolts sell for 15¢ and type II bolts for 20¢.

a. How many of each type of bolt should be manufactured per day to maximize revenue?

b. What is the maximum revenue?

c. Suppose the selling price of type I bolts began to increase. Beyond what amount would this price have to increase before a different number of each type of bolts should be produced to maximize revenue?

12. **Revenue** The manufacturing process requires that oil refineries must manufacture at least 2 gal of gasoline for every gallon of fuel oil. To meet the winter demand for fuel oil, at least 3 million gal a day must be produced. The demand for gasoline is no more than 6.4 million gal per day. It takes 15 minutes to ship each million gal of gasoline and 1 hour to ship each million gal of fuel oil out of the warehouse. No more than 4 hours and 39 minutes are available for shipping.

a. If the refinery sells gasoline for $2.50 per gal and fuel oil for $2 per gal, how much of each should be produced to maximize revenue?

b. Find the maximum revenue.

c. Suppose the price for fuel oil begins to increase. Beyond what amount would this price have to increase before a different amount of gasoline and fuel oil should be produced to maximize revenue?

13. **Revenue** A candy company has 150 kg of chocolate-covered nuts and 90 kg of chocolate-covered raisins to be sold as two different mixes. One mix will contain half nuts and half raisins and will sell for $7 per kg. The other mix will contain 3/4 nuts and 1/4 raisins and will sell for $9.50 per kg.

a. How many kilograms of each mix should the company prepare for the maximum revenue? Find the maximum revenue.

b. The company raises the price of the second mix to $11 per kg. Now how many kilograms of each mix should the company prepare for the maximum revenue? Find the maximum revenue.

14. **Profit** A small country can grow only two crops for export, coffee and cocoa. The country has 500,000 hectares of land available for the crops. Long-term contracts require that at least 100,000 hectares be devoted to coffee and at least 200,000 hectares to cocoa. Cocoa must be processed locally, and production bottlenecks limit cocoa to 270,000 hectares. Coffee requires two workers per hectare, with cocoa requiring five. No more than 1,750,000 people are available for working with these crops. Coffee produces a profit of $220 per hectare and cocoa a profit of $550 per hectare. How many hectares should the country devote to each crop in order to maximize profit? Find the maximum profit.

15. **Blending** The Mostpure Milk Company gets milk from two dairies and then blends the milk to get the desired amount of butterfat for the company's premier product. Milk from dairy I costs $2.40 per gal, and milk from dairy II costs $0.80 per gal. At most $144 is available for purchasing milk. Dairy I can supply at most 50 gal of milk averaging 3.7% butterfat. Dairy II can supply at most 80 gal of milk averaging 3.2% butterfat.

a. How much milk from each dairy should Mostpure use to get at most 100 gal of milk with the maximum total amount of butterfat? What is the maximum amount of butterfat?

b. The solution from part a leaves both dairy I and dairy II with excess capacity. Calculate the amount of additional milk each dairy could produce. Is there any way all this capacity could be used while still meeting the other constraints? Explain.

16. **Transportation** A flash drive manufacturer has 370 boxes of a particular drive in warehouse I and 290 boxes of the same drive in warehouse II. A computer store in San Jose orders 350 boxes of the drive, and another store in Memphis orders 300 boxes. The shipping costs per box to these stores from the two warehouses are shown in the following table.

		Destination	
		San Jose	Memphis
Warehouse	I	$2.50	$2.20
	II	$2.30	$2.10

How many boxes should be shipped to each city from each warehouse to minimize shipping costs? What is the minimum cost? (*Hint:* Use x, $350 - x$, y, and $300 - y$ as the variables.)

17. **Finance** A pension fund manager decides to invest a total of at most $30 million in U.S. Treasury bonds paying 4% annual interest and in mutual funds paying 8% annual interest. He plans to invest at least $5 million in bonds and at least $10 million in mutual funds. Bonds have an initial fee of $100 per million dollars, while the fee for mutual funds is $200 per million. The fund manager is allowed to spend no more than $5000 on fees. How much should be invested in each to maximize annual interest? What is the maximum annual interest?

Manufacturing (Note: Exercises 18–20 are from qualification examinations for Certified Public Accountants.) *Source: American Institute of Certified Public Accountants.* The Random Company manufactures two products, Zeta and Beta. Each product must pass through two processing operations. All materials are introduced at the start of Process No. 1. There are no work-in-process inventories. Random may produce either one product exclusively or various combinations of both products subject to the following constraints:

	Process No. 1	Process No. 2	Contribution Margin (per unit)
Hours Required to Produce One Unit:			
Zeta	1 hr	1 hr	$4.00
Beta	2 hr	3 hr	$5.25
Total Capacity (in hours per day)	1000 hr	1275 hr	

A shortage of technical labor has limited Beta production to 400 units per day. There are no constraints on the production of Zeta other than the hour constraints in the above schedule. Assume that all relationships between capacity and production are linear.

18. Given the objective to maximize total contribution margin, what is the production constraint for Process No. 1? (Choose one of the following.)

  a. Zeta + Beta ≤ 1000   **b.** Zeta + 2 Beta ≤ 1000

  c. Zeta + Beta ≥ 1000   **d.** Zeta + 2 Beta ≥ 1000

19. Given the objective to maximize total contribution margin, what is the labor constraint for production of Beta? (Choose one of the following.)

  a. Beta ≤ 400   **b.** Beta ≥ 400

  c. Beta ≤ 425   **d.** Beta ≥ 425

20. What is the objective function of the data presented? (Choose one of the following.)

  a. Zeta + 2 Beta = $9.25

  b. $4.00 Zeta + 3($5.25)Beta = Total Contribution Margin

  c. $4.00 Zeta + $5.25 Beta = Total Contribution Margin

  d. 2($4.00) Zeta + 3($5.25) Beta = Total Contribution Margin

Life Sciences

21. **Health Care** Glen Spencer takes vitamin pills. Each day he must have at least 480 IU of vitamin A, 5 mg of vitamin B_1, and 100 mg of vitamin C. He can choose between pill 1, which contains 240 IU of vitamin A, 1 mg of vitamin B_1, and 10 mg of vitamin C, and pill 2, which contains 60 IU of vitamin A, 1 mg of vitamin B_1, and 35 mg of vitamin C. Pill 1 costs 15¢, and pill 2 costs 30¢.

  a. How many of each pill should he buy in order to minimize his cost? What is the minimum cost?

  b. For the solution in part a, Glen is receiving more than he needs of at least one vitamin. Identify that vitamin, and tell how much surplus he is receiving. Is there any way he can avoid receiving that surplus while still meeting the other constraints and minimizing the cost? Explain.

22. **Predator Food Requirements** A certain predator requires at least 10 units of protein and 8 units of fat per day. One prey of species I provides 5 units of protein and 2 units of fat; one prey of species II provides 3 units of protein and 4 units of fat. Capturing and digesting each species-II prey requires 3 units of energy, and capturing and digesting each species-I prey requires 2 units of energy. How many of each prey would meet the predator's daily food requirements with the least expenditure of energy? Are the answers reasonable? How could they be interpreted?

23. **Nutrition** A dietician is planning a snack package of fruit and nuts. Each ounce of fruit will supply zero units of protein, 2 units of carbohydrates, and 1 unit of fat, and will contain 20 calories. Each ounce of nuts will supply 3 units of protein, 1 unit of carbohydrate, and 2 units of fat, and will contain 30 calories. Every package must provide at least 6 units of protein, at least 10 units of carbohydrates, and no more than 9 units of fat. Find the number of ounces of fruit and number of ounces of nuts that will meet the requirement with the least number of calories. What is the least number of calories?

24. **Health Care** Ms. Oliveras was given the following advice. She should supplement her daily diet with at least 6000 USP units of vitamin A, at least 195 mg of vitamin C, and at least 600 USP units of vitamin D. Ms. Oliveras finds that Mason's Pharmacy carries Brand X vitamin pills at 5¢ each and Brand Y vitamins at 4¢ each. Each Brand X pill contains 3000 USP units of A, 45 mg of C, and 75 USP units of D, while Brand Y pills contain 1000 USP units of A, 50 mg of C, and 200 USP units of D.

  a. What combination of vitamin pills should she buy to obtain the least possible cost? What is the least possible cost per day?

  b. For the solution in part a, Ms. Oliveras is receiving more than she needs of at least one vitamin. Identify that vitamin, and tell how much surplus she is receiving. Is there any way she can avoid receiving that surplus while still meeting the other constraints and minimizing the cost? Explain.

Social Sciences

25. **Anthropology** An anthropology article presents a hypothetical situation that could be described by a linear programming model. Suppose a population gathers plants and animals for

survival. They need at least 360 units of energy, 300 units of protein, and 8 hides during some time period. One unit of plants provides 30 units of energy, 10 units of protein, and no hides. One animal provides 20 units of energy, 25 units of protein, and 1 hide. Only 25 units of plants and 25 animals are available. It costs the population 30 hours of labor to gather one unit of a plant and 15 hours for an animal. Find how many units of plants and how many animals should be gathered to meet the requirements with a minimum number of hours of labor. *Source: Annual Review of Anthropology.*

General Interest

 26. Construction In a small town in South Carolina, zoning rules require that the window space (in square feet) in a house be at least one-sixth of the space used up by solid walls. The cost to build windows is $10 per ft^2, while the cost to build solid walls is $20 per ft^2. The total amount available for building walls and windows is no more than $12,000. The estimated

monthly cost to heat the house is $0.32 for each square foot of windows and $0.20 for each square foot of solid walls. Find the maximum total area (windows plus walls) if no more than $160 per month is available to pay for heat.

27. Farming An agricultural advisor looks at the results of Example 2 and claims that it cannot possibly be correct. After all, the 4-H member is able to raise 16 animals, and she is only raising 12 animals. Surely she can earn more profit by raising all 16 animals. How would you respond?

YOUR TURN ANSWERS

1. He should buy 60 kayaks and no canoes for a maximum revenue of $2100 a day.

2. Make 4 batches of each for a maximum profit of $200.

3. 14 pigs and no goats produces a maximum profit of $560.

3 CHAPTER REVIEW

SUMMARY

In this chapter, we introduced linear programming, which attempts to solve maximization and minimization problems with linear constraints. Linear programming models can be used to analyze a wide range of applications from many disciplines. The corner point theorem assures us that the optimal solution to a linear program, if it exists, must occur at one or more of the corner points of the feasible region. Linear programs can be solved using the graphical method, which graphs the region described by the linear constraints and then locates the corner point corresponding to the optimal solution value. The graphical method, however, is restricted to problems with two or three variables. In the next chapter, we will study a method that does not have this restriction.

Graphing a Linear Inequality

1. Draw the graph of the boundary line. Make the line solid if the inequality involves $\leq$ or $\geq$; make the line dashed if the inequality involves $<$ or $>$.

2. Decide which half-plane to shade. Use either of the following methods.

   a. Solve the inequality for y; shade the region above the line if the inequality is of the form of $y >$ or $y \geq$; shade the region below the line if the inequality is of the form of $y <$ or $y \leq$.

   b. Choose any point not on the line as a test point. Shade the half-plane that includes the test point if the test point satisfies the original inequality; otherwise, shade the half-plane on the other side of the boundary line.

Corner Point Theorem

If an optimum value (either a maximum or a minimum) of the objective function exists, it will occur at one or more of the corner points of the feasible region.

Solving a Linear Programming Problem

1. Write the objective function and all necessary constraints.

2. Graph the feasible region.

3. Identify all corner points.

4. Find the value of the objective function at each corner point.

5. For a bounded region, the solution is given by the corner point(s) producing the optimum value of the objective function.

6. For an unbounded region, check that a solution actually exists. If it does, it will occur at one or more corner points.

KEY TERMS

To understand the concepts presented in this chapter, you should know the meaning and use of the following terms.

3.1
linear inequality
boundary
half-plane
system of inequalities

region of feasible solutions
feasible region
bounded
unbounded

3.2
linear programming
objective function
constraints

isoprofit line
corner point

REVIEW EXERCISES

CONCEPT CHECK

Determine whether each of the following statements is true or false, and explain why.

 1. The graphical method can be used to solve a linear programming problem with four variables.

 2. For the inequality $5x + 4y \geq 20$, the test point $(3, 4)$ suggests that the correct half-plane to shade includes this point.

 3. Let x represent the number of acres of wheat planted and y represent the number of acres of corn planted. The inequality $x \leq 2y$ implies that the number of acres of wheat planted will be at least twice the number of acres of corn planted.

 4. For the variables in Exercise 3, assume that we have a total of 60 hours to plant the wheat and corn and that it takes 2 hours per acre to prepare a wheat field and 1 hour per acre to prepare a corn field. The inequality $2x + y \geq 60$ represents the constraint on the amount of time available for planting.

 5. For the variables in Exercise 3, assume that we make a profit of $14 for each acre of corn and $10 for each acre of wheat. The objective function that can be used to maximize profit is $14x + 10y$.

6. The point $(2, 3)$ is a corner point of the linear programming problem

$$\begin{aligned} \text{Maximize} \quad & z = 7x + 4y \\ \text{subject to:} \quad & 3x + 8y \leq 30 \\ & 4x + 2y \leq 15 \\ & x \geq 0, y \geq 0. \end{aligned}$$

 7. The point $(2, 3)$ is in the feasible region of the linear programming problem in Exercise 6.

 8. The optimal solution to the linear programming problem in Exercise 6 occurs at point $(2, 3)$.

 9. It is possible to find a point that lies on both sides of a linear inequality.

 10. Every linear programming problem with a feasible region that is not empty either has a solution or is unbounded.

 11. Solutions to linear programming problems may include fractions.

12. The inequality $4^2x + 5^2y \leq 7^2$ is a linear constraint.

13. The optimal solution to a linear programming problem can occur at a point that is not a corner point.

PRACTICE AND EXPLORATIONS

14. How many constraints are we limited to in the graphical method?

Graph each linear inequality.

15. $y \geq 2x + 3$

16. $5x - 2y \leq 10$

17. $2x + 6y \leq 8$

18. $2x - 6y \geq 18$

19. $y \geq x$

20. $y \geq -2$

Graph the solution of each system of inequalities. Find all corner points and tell whether each region is bounded or unbounded.

21. $\begin{aligned} x + y &\leq 6 \\ 2x - y &\geq 3 \end{aligned}$

22. $\begin{aligned} 3x + 2y &\geq 12 \\ 4x - 5y &\leq 20 \end{aligned}$

23. $\begin{aligned} -4 &\leq x \leq 2 \\ -1 &\leq y \leq 3 \\ x + y &\leq 4 \end{aligned}$

24. $\begin{aligned} 2 &\leq x \leq 5 \\ 1 &\leq y \leq 7 \\ x - y &\leq 3 \end{aligned}$

25. $\begin{aligned} x + 2y &\leq 4 \\ 5x - 6y &\leq 12 \\ x &\geq 0 \\ y &\geq 0 \end{aligned}$

26. $\begin{aligned} x + 2y &\leq 4 \\ 2x - 3y &\leq 6 \\ x &\geq 0 \\ y &\geq 0 \end{aligned}$

Use the given regions to find the maximum and minimum values of the objective function $z = 2x + 4y$.

27.

28.

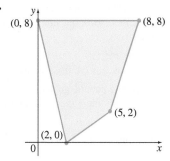

Use the graphical method to solve each linear programming problem.

29. Maximize $z = 2x + 4y$

subject to: $3x + 2y \leq 12$

$5x + y \geq 5$

$x \geq 0$

$y \geq 0.$

30. Minimize $z = 5x + 3y$

subject to: $8x + 5y \geq 40$

$4x + 10y \geq 40$

$x \geq 0$

$y \geq 0.$

31. Minimize $z = 4x + 2y$

subject to: $x + y \leq 50$

$2x + y \geq 20$

$x + 2y \geq 30$

$x \geq 0$

$y \geq 0.$

32. Maximize $z = 8x + 4y$

subject to: $3x + 12y \leq 36$

$x + y \leq 4$

$x \geq 0$

$y \geq 0.$

33. Why must the solution to a linear programming problem always occur at a corner point of the feasible region?

34. Is there necessarily a unique point in the feasible region where the maximum or minimum occurs? Why or why not?

35. It is not necessary to check all corner points in a linear programming problem. This exercise illustrates an alternative procedure, which is essentially an expansion of the ideas illustrated in Example 1 of Section 3.2.

Maximize $z = 3x + 4y$

subject to: $2x + y \leq 4$

$-x + 2y \leq 4$

$x \geq 0$

$y \geq 0.$

a. Sketch the feasible region, and add the line $z = 8$. (*Note:* 8 is chosen because the numbers work out simply, but the chosen value of z is arbitrary.)

b. Draw a line parallel to the line $z = 8$ that is as far from the origin as possible but still touches the feasible region.

c. The line you drew in part b should go through the point $(4/5, 12/5)$. Explain how you know the maximum must be located at this point.

36. Use the method described in the previous exercise to solve Exercise 32.

APPLICATIONS

Business and Economics

37. Time Management   A bakery makes both cakes and cookies. Each batch of cakes requires 2 hours in the oven and 3 hours in the decorating room. Each batch of cookies needs $1\frac{1}{2}$ hours in the oven and $\frac{2}{3}$ hour in the decorating room. The oven is available no more than 15 hours per day, and the decorating room can be used no more than 13 hours per day. Set up a system of inequalities, and then graph the solution of the system.

38. Cost Analysis   DeMarco's pizza shop makes two specialty pizzas, the Mighty Meaty and the Very Veggie. The Mighty Meaty is topped with 5 different meat toppings and 2 different cheeses. The Very Veggie has 6 different vegetable toppings and 4 different cheeses. The shop sells at least 4 Mighty Meaty and 6 Very Veggie pizzas every day. The cost of the toppings for each Mighty Meaty is $3, and the cost of the vegetable toppings is $2 for each Very Veggie. No more than $60 per day can be spent on these toppings. The cheese used for the Mighty Meaty is $2 per pizza, and the cheese for the Very Veggie is $4 per pizza. No more than $80 per day can be spent on cheese. Set up a system of inequalities, and then graph the solution of the system.

39. Profit   Refer to Exercise 37.

a. How many batches of cakes and cookies should the bakery in Exercise 37 make in order to maximize profits if cookies produce a profit of $20 per batch and cakes produce a profit of $30 per batch?

b. How much would the profit from selling cookies have to increase before it becomes more profitable to sell only cookies?

40. Revenue   How many pizzas of each kind should the pizza shop in Exercise 38 make in order to maximize revenue if the Mighty Meaty sells for $15 and the Very Veggie sells for $12?

41. Planting   In Karla's garden shop, she makes two kinds of mixtures for planting. A package of gardening mixture requires 2 lb of soil, 1 lb of peat moss, and 1 lb of fertilizer. A package of potting mixture requires 1 lb of soil, 2 lb of peat moss, and 3 lb of fertilizer. She has 16 lb of soil, 11 lb of peat moss, and 15 lb of fertilizer. If a package of gardening mixture sells for $3 and a package of potting mixture for $5, how many of each should she make in order to maximize her income? What is the maximum income?

42. Construction   A contractor builds boathouses in two basic models, the Atlantic and the Pacific. Each Atlantic model requires 1000 ft of framing lumber, 3000 ft^3 of concrete, and $2000 for advertising. Each Pacific model requires 2000 ft of framing lumber, 3000 ft^3 of concrete, and $3000 for advertising. Contracts call for using at least 8000 ft of framing lumber, 18,000 ft^3 of concrete, and $15,000 worth of advertising. If the construction cost for each Atlantic model is $30,000 and the construction cost for each Pacific model is $40,000, how many of each model should be built to minimize construction costs?

43. Steel   A steel company produces two types of alloys. A run of type I requires 3000 lb of molybdenum and 2000 tons of iron ore pellets as well as $2000 in advertising. A run of type II requires 3000 lb of molybdenum and 1000 tons of iron ore pellets as well as $3000 in advertising. Total costs are $15,000 on a run of type I and $6000 on a run of type II. Because of various contracts, the company must use at least 18,000 lb of molybdenum and 7000 tons of iron ore pellets and spend at least $14,000 on advertising. How much of each type should be produced to minimize costs?

Life Sciences

44. Nutrition A dietician in a hospital is to arrange a special diet containing two foods, Health Trough and Power Gunk. Each ounce of Health Trough contains 30 mg of calcium, 10 mg of iron, 10 IU of vitamin A, and 8 mg of cholesterol. Each ounce of Power Gunk contains 10 mg of calcium, 10 mg of iron, 30 IU of vitamin A, and 4 mg of cholesterol. If the minimum daily requirements are 360 mg of calcium, 160 mg of iron, and 240 IU of vitamin A, how many ounces of each food should be used to meet the minimum requirements and at the same time minimize the cholesterol intake? Also, what is the minimum cholesterol intake?

Social Sciences

45. Anthropology A simplified model of the Mountain Fur economy of central Africa has been proposed. In this model, two crops can be grown, millet and wheat, which produce 400 lb and 800 lb per acre, respectively. Millet requires 36 days to harvest one acre, while wheat requires only 8 days. There are 2 acres of land and 48 days of harvest labor available. How many acres should be devoted to each crop to maximize the pounds of grain harvested? *Source: Themes in Economic Anthropology.*

General Interest

46. Studying Jim Pringle is trying to allocate his study time this weekend. He can spend time working with either his math tutor or his accounting tutor to prepare for exams in both classes the following Monday. His math tutor charges $20 per hour, and his accounting tutor charges $40 per hour. He has $220 to spend on tutoring. Each hour that he spends working with his math tutor requires 1 aspirin and 1 hour of sleep to recover, while each hour he spends with his accounting tutor requires 1/2 aspirin and 3 hours of sleep. The maximum dosage of aspirin that he can safely take during his study time is 8 tablets, and he can only afford 15 hours of sleep this weekend. He expects that each hour with his math tutor will increase his score on the math exam by 3 points, while each hour with his accounting tutor will increase his score on the accounting exam by 5 points. How many hours should he spend with each tutor in order to maximize the number of points he will get on the two tests combined?

EXTENDED APPLICATION

SENSITIVITY ANALYSIS

In Section 3 of this chapter we used the graphical method to solve linear programming problems. A quick analysis of the strengths and weaknesses of the process of modeling real-life problems using these techniques reveals two apparent problems. First, most real-life problems require far more than two variables to adequately capture the essence of the problem. Second, our world is so dynamic that the values used to model a problem today can quickly change, leaving the current solution irrelevant or even infeasible.

In Chapter 4, we show how the simplex method can be used to solve linear programming problems with thousands or even millions of variables and constraints. In this extended application, we introduce the idea of *sensitivity analysis*, which provides a way to efficiently handle the constantly changing inputs to a linear programming problem, often without having to resolve the problem from scratch. We will limit our study to linear programs with only two variables and begin by analyzing changes in objective function coefficients.

Recall that in Example 2 of Section 3.3, a linear programming problem was developed to determine the optimal number of goats and pigs to raise for a 4-H project. The linear program was written as

$$\text{Maximize} \quad z = 12x + 40y$$
$$\text{Subject to:} \quad x + y \le 16$$
$$x + 3y \le 36$$
$$x \le 10$$
$$x \ge 0, y \ge 0,$$

where x is the number of goats and y is the number of pigs.

A graph of the feasible region, with corner points illustrated, is shown in Figure 23 on the next page. We determined that a maximum profit of $480 occurs when 12 pigs and no goats are raised. This is no surprise given that the profit from a pig is $40 and the profit for a goat is just $12. In fact, we saw in that example that if the profit from raising a pig decreases to $36, then it would become profitable to raise goats, too.

FIGURE 23

FIGURE 24

CHANGES IN OBJECTIVE FUNCTION COEFFICIENTS

Suppose that the 4-H member, whom we will call Sarah, now wonders what the profit from raising a goat would have to become so that it would become profitable for her to raise both pigs and goats.

Mathematically, we replace the $12 in the objective function with the variable $12 + c$, where c is the change in profit for raising a goat. That is, $z = (12 + c)x + 40y$. Now, for any particular profit z, we can think of this equation as a line, which we called an *isoprofit line* in Section 3.2. With $c = 0$ and $z = 480$, the isoprofit line is $480 = 12x + 40y$, which is plotted in green in Figure 23. Solving for y helps us to see that the line represented by this equation has slope $-\dfrac{12 + c}{40}$. That is,

$$z = (12 + c)x + 40y,$$

or

$$40y = -(12 + c)x + z,$$

which simplifies to

$$y = -\frac{12 + c}{40}x + \frac{z}{40}.$$

The line that represents the boundary of the constraint $x + 3y = 36$ has slope $-\frac{1}{3}$. If c begins to increase, forcing the slope of the isoprofit line to become more negative, eventually the slope of the isoprofit line corresponding to the optimal profit of $480 will have slope $-\frac{1}{3}$. If c continues to increase beyond this level, the optimal profit will occur at the corner point $(6, 10)$. That is, as long as the slope of the isoprofit line exceeds $-\frac{1}{3}$, the optimal solution will continue to be to raise 12 pigs and no goats. If, however, the slope of the isoprofit line becomes less than $-\frac{1}{3}$, then it will become profitable to raise goats as well. That is, if c increases to the point at which

$$-\frac{12 + c}{40} < -\frac{1}{3},$$

which simplifies to,

$$\frac{12 + c}{40} > \frac{1}{3},$$

or

$$c > \frac{40}{3} - 12 = \frac{4}{3},$$

the optimal solution changes from the corner point $(0, 12)$ to $(6, 10)$. Further analysis, as illustrated by Figure 24, shows that the optimal solution will remain at the corner point $(6, 10)$ as long as the slope of the isoprofit line stays between

$$-1 \le -\frac{12 + c}{40} \le -\frac{1}{3},$$

or when

$$\frac{4}{3} \le c \le 28.$$

Then the optimal solution will be to raise 6 goats and 10 pigs.

Beyond $c = \$28$ or a profit of $40 per goat, it will be optimal to raise 10 goats and 6 pigs. Note that this analysis can be used to completely determine the optimal solution for changes in a single cost coefficient for any two variable linear programming problem, without having to resolve the linear program.

CHANGES IN THE RIGHT HAND SIDE OF A CONSTRAINT

Sarah begins to wonder if the right-hand sides of any of the constraints might be changed so that the profit would increase. For example, the easiest thing to do would be for Sarah to increase the third constraint, corresponding to the restriction that no more than 10 goats are raised. Sarah considers the possibility of lifting this constraint. Notice, however, that if we increase the right-hand side of the third constraint, it has no affect on the optimal corner point. As you can see graphically with the red lines in Figure 25, increasing the right-hand side will not change the optimal solution. In fact, decreasing the third constraint even to zero will not change the optimal solution.

Now suppose that Sarah realizes that she has overestimated the total number of animals she can raise by 3 and wants to see how this will affect the optimal solution. The boundary of the first

FIGURE 25

FIGURE 27

constraint can be written as the line $y = -x + 16$, which has y-intercept at the point $(0,16)$. Since Sarah has overestimated the total number of animals by three, the boundary line becomes $y = -x + 13$, which has y-intercept at the point $(0,13)$, as illustrated in Figure 26.

This change will not have an effect on the solution because raising 13 pigs is not feasible for the second constraint. That is, $(0, 13)$ is not a feasible corner point and cannot be a solution to the problem. In fact, as long as the total number of animals is at least 12 in the first constraint, the optimal solution is for Sarah to raise 12 pigs and no goats. In this case, we would say that the right-hand side of the first constraint is not sensitive to small changes. If, on the other hand, Sarah has overestimated the total number of animals she can raise and that, in fact, the total number is actually 11, then the optimal solution changes. As you can see in Figure 27, the feasible region has diminished to the point that the second constraint is now redundant and has no influence on the optimal solution. In fact, the optimal solution is to raise 11 pigs and no goats. This makes sense since the profit from raising pigs is so high that it does not become profitable to raise goats when a smaller total number of animals are raised. The same type of analysis can be performed on the right-hand side of the second constraint.

SHADOW PROFITS

Changes in the resources available in a linear programming problem usually result in a change in the value of the objective function in the optimal solution. For example, if an optimal solution uses all of the material available, then a sudden increase/decrease in the amount of that material available can change the objective function value. In the analysis above, decreasing the right-hand side of the first constraint from 16 to 12 did not change the optimal solution. In this case, we would say that the shadow profit, or the increase in the profit for changing the right-hand side of the first constraint by one unit is $0. On the other hand, if we increase the amount of money available for the project by $75, the optimal solution would change from raising 12 pigs to raising 13 pigs and thereby increase profit by $40. This implies that for each dollar increase in the amount of money available, the profit will increase by $40/75 or by about $0.53. In this case, the shadow profit would be $0.53.

CHANGES IN CONSTRAINT COEFFICIENTS

Sarah continues to explore reasons why the optimal policy is to only raise pigs. She wonders if any of the coefficients in the constraints are having an effect on the optimal solution. In the process, she realizes that it may cost more than $75 to raise a pig. In the original statement of the problem, Sarah had up to $900 to spend on her project, with each goat costing $25 to raise and each pig costing $75 to raise. This information was translated into the constraint $25x + 75y \leq 900$, which was then simplified by dividing the inequality by 25. Sarah wonders how much the $75 would have to increase before the optimal solution would include raising goats. Letting b represent the change in the cost of raising a pig, the constraint becomes $25x + (75 + b)y \leq 900$, and the corresponding boundary line can then be simplified and written as

$$y = -\frac{25}{75 + b}x + \frac{900}{75 + b}.$$

FIGURE 26

To be consistent, every dollar increase in the cost of raising a pig also forces the profit to decrease by a dollar. That is, the 40 in the objective function is replaced with $40 - b$, becoming

$$z = 12x + (40 - b)y.$$

The isoprofit lines for this objective function will each have slope of $-\dfrac{12}{40 - b}$.

When the slope of the boundary line corresponding to the altered second constraint increases to the point that it is larger than the slope of the isoprofit lines, the optimal solution will change and move to the intersection point of the first and second constraints. This occurs when

$$-\frac{25}{75 + b} > -\frac{12}{40 - b},$$

which simplifies to

$$b > \frac{100}{37} \approx 2.70.$$

In other words, as long as the cost of raising a pig is at or below $75 + 2.70 = \$77.70$, the optimal policy is to only raise pigs. When the cost exceeds this amount the optimal solution will change, and it may become profitable to raise goats, too. For example, suppose the cost of raising a pig increases to $100. The new feasible region has corner points at (0, 0), (0, 9), (10, 0), (10, 6), and (28/3, 20/3), as indicated by Figure 28. It can be easily verified that the optimal

FIGURE 28

solution now occurs at (28/3, 20/3), with objective function value of $z = 12(\frac{28}{3}) + 15(\frac{20}{3}) = 212$. Of course, it is impossible to raise a fractional number of animals so some additional work is required to determine the optimal solution. Unfortunately, simply rounding the fractional solution downward to obtain $x = 9$ and $y = 6$ does not give the optimal solution. In fact, it can be shown that the optimal integer solution is $x = 10$ and $y = 6$ with an objective function value of $210. Thus, if the cost of raising a pig is $100 then the optimal policy is to raise 6 pigs and 10 goats.

EXERCISES

1. Use sensitivity analysis to find the optimal solution to the original 4-H problem, if the profit from raising a goat increases from $12 to $25.

2. Use sensitivity analysis to find the optimal solution to the original 4-H problem, if the profit from raising a pig decreases from $40 to $35.

3. Use sensitivity analysis to determine the smallest decrease in the cost of raising a goat, so that the optimal policy of raising 12 pigs and no goats changes. Note that changing this cost also changes the profit level for goats.

4. Katie's Landscaping Services weeds flower beds and mows lawns. Katie makes a profit of $8 for every hour she weeds and $25 for every hour she mows. Because Katie is also in college, she can only take on 18 jobs each week for her business. Katie has found that the flower beds in her neighborhood are very poorly maintained and that weeding a flower bed must be considered as two jobs. Each week, Katie sets aside $72 for her brother Nate to help her and feels that a fair price to pay Nate is $3 per hour for weeding and $9 per hour for mowing a lawn.

a. Show that this problem can be set up as follows:

$$\begin{aligned} \text{Maximize} \quad & z = 8x + 25y \\ \text{Subject to:} \quad & 2x + y \leq 18 \\ & 3x + 9y \leq 72 \\ & x \geq 0, y \geq 0 \end{aligned}$$

b. Use the graphical method to solve this linear program.

c. Alter the graph from part b to determine the new optimal solution if the right hand side of the second constraint increases to 81. (*Hint:* You shouldn't have to completely resolve this problem. Simply change the intercepts of one of the constraints and use isoprofit lines to identify the corner point where the new optimal solution occurs.)

d. What is the shadow profit associated with the change from 72 to 81 in part c?

e. Using the original problem, determine the smallest increase (to the nearest penny) in the objective function coefficient for variable x that will cause the value of x to increase in the optimal solution. In this case, we would say that the cost coefficient associated with variable x is sensitive to change.

f. If the y-coefficient in the second constraint of the original problem begins to increase, forcing an equal decrease in the y-coefficient in the objective function, determine the smallest amount (to the nearest penny) that this coefficient can increase before it becomes optimal to produce positive quantities of variable x. For simplicity, assume that it is possible to have fractional amounts of each variable.

5. Go to the website WolframAlpha.com, and enter "minimize $8x + 25y$ with $2x + y <= 18$, $3x + 9y <= 72$, $x >= 0$, $y >= 0$".

Study the solution provided by Wolfram|Alpha. Notice that the solution given is the same as the solution you found in Exercise 4b. Use Wolfram|Alpha to verify your answers to Exercises 4c–4f.

DIRECTIONS FOR GROUP PROJECT

Suppose that you are the manager of a company that manufactures two types of products. Develop a simple linear program with a solution that gives how many of each type of product the company should produce. Then perform sensitivity analysis on various aspects of the model. Use presentation software to report your model and your findings to the class.

5

Mathematics of Finance

Buying a car usually requires both some savings for a down payment and a loan for the balance. An exercise in Section 2 calculates the regular deposits that would be needed to save up the full purchase price, and other exercises and examples in this chapter compute the payments required to amortize a loan.

Everybody uses money. Sometimes you work for your money and other times your money works for you. For example, unless you are attending college on a full scholarship, it is very likely that you and your family have either saved money or borrowed money, or both, to pay for your education. When we borrow money, we normally have to pay interest for that privilege. When we save money, for a future purchase or retirement, we are lending money to a financial institution and we expect to earn interest on our investment. We will develop the mathematics in this chapter to understand better the principles of borrowing and saving. These ideas will then be used to compare different financial opportunities and make informed decisions.

5.1 Simple and Compound Interest

APPLY IT If you can borrow money at 8% interest compounded annually or at 7.9% compounded monthly, which loan would cost less?

In this section we will learn how to compare different interest rates with different compounding periods. The question above will be answered in Example 8.

Simple Interest

Interest on loans of a year or less is frequently calculated as **simple interest**, a type of interest that is charged (or paid) only on the amount borrowed (or invested) and not on past interest. The amount borrowed is called the **principal**. The **rate** of interest is given as a percentage per year, expressed as a decimal. For example, $6\% = 0.06$ and $11\frac{1}{2}\% = 0.115$. The **time** the money is earning interest is calculated in years. One year's interest is calculated by multiplying the principal times the interest rate, or Pr. If the time that the money earns interest is other than one year, we multiply the interest for one year by the number of years, or Prt.

Simple Interest

$$I = Prt$$

where

P is the principal;

r is the annual interest rate;

t is the time in years.

EXAMPLE 1 **Simple Interest**

To buy furniture for a new apartment, Candace Cooney borrowed $5000 at 8% simple interest for 11 months. How much interest will she pay?

SOLUTION Use the formula $I = Prt$, with $P = 5000$, $r = 0.08$, and $t = 11/12$ (in years). The total interest she will pay is

$$I = 5000(0.08)(11/12) \approx 366.67,$$

or $366.67.

A deposit of P dollars today at a rate of interest r for t years produces interest of $I = Prt$. The interest, added to the original principal P, gives

$$P + Prt = P(1 + rt).$$

This amount is called the *future value* of P dollars at an interest rate r for time t in years. When loans are involved, the future value is often called the *maturity value* of the loan. This idea is summarized as follows.

Future or Maturity Value for Simple Interest

The **future** or **maturity value** A of P dollars at a simple interest rate r for t years is

$$A = P(1 + rt).$$

EXAMPLE 2 **Maturity Values**

Find the maturity value for each loan at simple interest.

(a) A loan of $2500 to be repaid in 8 months with interest of 4.3%

SOLUTION The loan is for 8 months, or $8/12 = 2/3$ of a year. The maturity value is

$$A = P(1 + rt)$$

$$A = 2500\left[1 + 0.043\left(\frac{2}{3}\right)\right]$$

$$A \approx 2500(1 + 0.028667) = 2571.67,$$

or $2571.67. (The answer is rounded to the nearest cent, as is customary in financial problems.) Of this maturity value,

$$\$2571.67 - \$2500 = \$71.67$$

represents interest.

(b) A loan of $11,280 for 85 days at 7% interest

SOLUTION It is common to assume 360 days in a year when working with simple interest. We shall usually make such an assumption in this book. The maturity value in this example is

$$A = 11,280\left[1 + 0.07\left(\frac{85}{360}\right)\right] \approx 11,466.43,$$

or $11,466.43.

YOUR TURN 1 Find the maturity value for a $3000 loan at 5.8% interest for 100 days.

TRY YOUR TURN 1

CAUTION When using the formula for future value, as well as all other formulas in this chapter, we often neglect the fact that in real life, money amounts are rounded to the nearest penny. As a consequence, when the amounts are rounded, their values may differ by a few cents from the amounts given by these formulas. For instance, in Example 2(a), the interest in each monthly payment would be $2500(0.043/12) \approx$ $8.96, rounded to the nearest penny. After 8 months, the total is $8(\$8.96) =$ $71.68, which is 1¢ more than we computed in the example.

In part (b) of Example 2 we assumed 360 days in a year. Historically, to simplify calculations, it was often assumed that each year had twelve 30-day months, making a year 360 days long. Treasury bills sold by the U.S. government assume a 360-day year in calculating interest. Interest found using a 360-day year is called *ordinary interest* and interest found using a 365-day year is called *exact interest*.

The formula for future value has four variables, P, r, t, and A. We can use the formula to find any of the quantities that these variables represent, as illustrated in the next example.

EXAMPLE 3 Simple Interest

Theresa Cortesini wants to borrow $8000 from Christine O'Brien. She is willing to pay back $8180 in 6 months. What interest rate will she pay?

SOLUTION Use the formula for future value, with $A = 8180$, $P = 8000$, $t = 6/12 = 0.5$, and solve for r.

$$A = P(1 + rt)$$
$$8180 = 8000(1 + 0.5r)$$
$$8180 = 8000 + 4000r \quad \text{Distributive property}$$
$$180 = 4000r \quad \text{Subtract 8000.}$$
$$r = 0.045 \quad \text{Divide by 4000.}$$

YOUR TURN 2 Find the interest rate if $5000 is borrowed, and $5243.75 is paid back 9 months later.

Thus, the interest rate is 4.5%. **TRY YOUR TURN 2**

When you deposit money in the bank and earn interest, it is as if the bank borrowed the money from you. Reversing the scenario in Example 3, if you put $8000 in a bank account that pays simple interest at a rate of 4.5% annually, you will have accumulated $8180 after 6 months.

Compound Interest
As mentioned earlier, simple interest is normally used for loans or investments of a year or less. For longer periods compound interest is used. With **compound interest**, interest is charged (or paid) on interest as well as on principal. For example, if $1000 is deposited at 5% interest for 1 year, at the end of the year the interest is $1000(0.05)(1) = $50. The balance in the account is $1000 + $50 = $1050. If this amount is left at 5% interest for another year, the interest is calculated on $1050 instead of the original $1000, so the amount in the account at the end of the second year is $1050 + $1050(0.05)(1) = $1102.50. Note that simple interest would produce a total amount of only

$$\$1000[1 + (0.05)(2)] = \$1100.$$

The additional $2.50 is the interest on $50 at 5% for one year.

To find a formula for compound interest, first suppose that P dollars is deposited at a rate of interest r per year. The amount on deposit at the end of the first year is found by the simple interest formula, with $t = 1$.

$$A = P(1 + r \cdot 1) = P(1 + r)$$

If the deposit earns compound interest, the interest earned during the second year is paid on the total amount on deposit at the end of the first year. Using the formula $A = P(1 + rt)$ again, with P replaced by $P(1 + r)$ and $t = 1$, gives the total amount on deposit at the end of the second year.

$$A = [P(1 + r)](1 + r \cdot 1) = P(1 + r)^2$$

In the same way, the total amount on deposit at the end of the third year is

$$P(1 + r)^3.$$

Generalizing, in t years the total amount on deposit is

$$A = P(1 + r)^t,$$

called the **compound amount**.

NOTE Compare this formula for compound interest with the formula for simple interest.

Compound interest $\quad A = P(1 + r)^t$

Simple interest $\quad\quad\; A = P(1 + rt)$

The important distinction between the two formulas is that in the compound interest formula, the number of years, t, is an *exponent*, so that money grows much more rapidly when interest is compounded.

Interest can be compounded more than once per year. Common compounding periods include *semiannually* (two periods per year), *quarterly* (four periods per year), *monthly* (twelve periods per year), or *daily* (usually 365 periods per year). The *interest rate per period*, i, is found by dividing the annual interest rate, r, by the number of compounding periods, m, per year. To find the total number of compounding periods, n, we multiply the number of years, t, by the number of compounding periods per year, m. The following formula can be derived in the same way as the previous formula.

Compound Amount

$$A = P(1 + i)^n$$

where $i = \dfrac{r}{m}$ and $n = mt$,

A is the future (maturity) value;
P is the principal;
r is the annual interest rate;
m is the number of compounding periods per year;
t is the number of years;
n is the number of compounding periods;
i is the interest rate per period.

EXAMPLE 4   Compound Interest

Suppose \$1000 is deposited for 6 years in an account paying 4.25% per year compounded annually.

(a) Find the compound amount.

SOLUTION   In the formula for the compound amount, $P = 1000$, $i = 0.0425/1$, and $n = 6(1) = 6$. The compound amount is

$$A = P(1 + i)^n$$
$$A = 1000(1.0425)^6.$$

Using a calculator, we get

$$A \approx \$1283.68,$$

the compound amount.

(b) Find the amount of interest earned.

SOLUTION   Subtract the initial deposit from the compound amount.

$$\text{Amount of interest} = \$1283.68 - \$1000 = \$283.68$$

EXAMPLE 5   Compound Interest

Find the amount of interest earned by a deposit of \$2450 for 6.5 years at 5.25% compounded quarterly.

SOLUTION   Interest compounded quarterly is compounded 4 times a year. In 6.5 years, there are $6.5(4) = 26$ periods. Thus, $n = 26$. Interest of 5.25% per year is 5.25%/4 per quarter, so $i = 0.0525/4$. Now use the formula for compound amount.

YOUR TURN 3   Find the amount of interest earned by a deposit of \$1600 for 7 years at 4.2% compounded monthly.

$$A = P(1 + i)^n$$
$$A = 2450(1 + 0.0525/4)^{26} \approx 3438.78$$

Rounded to the nearest cent, the compound amount is \$3438.78, so the interest is \$3438.78 - \$2450 = \$988.78.   TRY YOUR TURN 3

CAUTION   As shown in Example 5, compound interest problems involve two rates—the annual rate r and the rate per compounding period i. Be sure you understand the distinction between them. When interest is compounded annually, these rates are the same. In all other cases, $i \neq r$. Similarly, there are two quantities for time: the number of years t and the number of compounding periods n. When interest is compounded annually, these variables have the same value. In all other cases, $n \neq t$.

It is interesting to compare loans at the same rate when simple or compound interest is used. Figure 1 shows the graphs of the simple interest and compound interest formulas with $P = 1000$ at an annual rate of 10% from 0 to 20 years. The future value after 15 years is shown for each graph. After 15 years of compound interest, $1000 grows to $4177.25, whereas with simple interest, it amounts to $2500.00, a difference of $1677.25.

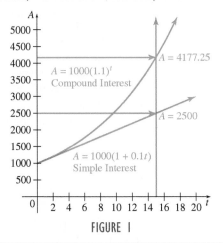

FIGURE 1

TECHNOLOGY NOTE   Spreadsheets are ideal for performing financial calculations. Figure 2 shows a Microsoft Excel spreadsheet with the formulas for compound and simple interest used to create columns B and C, respectively, when $1000 is invested at an annual rate of 10%. Compare row 16 with Figure 1. For more details on the use of spreadsheets in the mathematics of finance, see the *Graphing Calculator and Excel Spreadsheet Manual* available with this book.

	A	B	C
1	period	compound	simple
2	1	1100	1100
3	2	1210	1200
4	3	1331	1300
5	4	1464.1	1400
6	5	1610.51	1500
7	6	1771.561	1600
8	7	1948.7171	1700
9	8	2143.58881	1800
10	9	2357.947691	1900
11	10	2593.74246	2000
12	11	2853.116706	2100
13	12	3138.428377	2200
14	13	3452.27124	2300
15	14	3797.498336	2400
16	15	4177.248169	2500
17	16	4594.972986	2600
18	17	5054.470285	2700
19	18	5559.917313	2800
20	19	6115.909045	2900
21	20	6727.499949	3000

FIGURE 2

We can also solve the compound amount formula for the interest rate, as in the following example.

EXAMPLE 6 Compound Interest Rate

Suppose Carol Merrigan invested $5000 in a savings account that paid quarterly interest. After 6 years the money had accumulated to $6539.96. What was the annual interest rate?

SOLUTION Because $m = 4$ and $t = 6$, the number of compounding periods is $n = 4 \times 6 = 24$. Using this value along with $P = 5000$ and $A = 6539.96$ in the formula for compound amount, we have

YOUR TURN 4 Find the annual interest rate if $6500 is worth $8665.69 after being invested for 8 years in an account that compounded interest monthly.

$$5000(1 + r/4)^{24} = 6539.96$$
$$(1 + r/4)^{24} = 1.30799 \qquad \text{Divide both sides by 5000.}$$
$$1 + r/4 = 1.30799^{1/24} \approx 1.01125 \qquad \text{Take both sides to the 1/24 power.}$$
$$r/4 = 0.01125 \qquad \text{Subtract 1 from both sides.}$$
$$r = 0.045 \qquad \text{Multiply both sides by 4.}$$

The annual interest rate was 4.5%. **TRY YOUR TURN 4**

Effective Rate
If $1 is deposited at 4% compounded quarterly, a calculator can be used to find that at the end of one year, the compound amount is $1.0406, an increase of 4.06% over the original $1. The actual increase of 4.06% in the money is somewhat higher than the stated increase of 4%. To differentiate between these two numbers, 4% is called the **nominal** or **stated rate** of interest, while 4.06% is called the *effective rate*.* To avoid confusion between stated rates and effective rates, we shall continue to use r for the stated rate and we will use r_E for the effective rate.

EXAMPLE 7 Effective Rate

Find the effective rate corresponding to a stated rate of 6% compounded semiannually.

SOLUTION Here, $i = r/m = 0.06/2 = 0.03$ for $m = 2$ periods. Use a calculator to find that $(1.03)^2 \approx 1.06090$, which shows that $1 will increase to $1.06090, an actual increase of 6.09%. The effective rate is $r_E = 6.09\%$.

Generalizing from this example, the effective rate of interest is given by the following formula.

Effective Rate
The **effective rate** corresponding to a stated rate of interest r compounded m times per year is

$$r_E = \left(1 + \frac{r}{m}\right)^m - 1.$$

EXAMPLE 8 Effective Rate

Joe Vetere needs to borrow money. His neighborhood bank charges 8% interest compounded semiannually. A downtown bank charges 7.9% interest compounded monthly. At which bank will Joe pay the lesser amount of interest?

*When applied to consumer finance, the effective rate is called the annual percentage rate, APR, or annual percentage yield, APY.

APPLY IT

SOLUTION Compare the effective rates.

$$\text{Neighborhood bank:} \quad r_E = \left(1 + \frac{0.08}{2}\right)^2 - 1 = 0.0816 = 8.16\%$$

$$\text{Downtown bank:} \quad r_E = \left(1 + \frac{0.079}{12}\right)^{12} - 1 \approx 0.081924 \approx 8.19\%$$

YOUR TURN 5 Find the effective rate for an account that pays 2.7% compounded monthly.

The neighborhood bank has the lower effective rate, although it has a higher stated rate.

TRY YOUR TURN 5

Present Value The formula for compound interest, $A = P(1 + i)^n$, has four variables: A, P, i, and n. Given the values of any three of these variables, the value of the fourth can be found. In particular, if A (the future amount), i, and n are known, then P can be found. Here P is the amount that should be deposited today to produce A dollars in n periods.

EXAMPLE 9 **Present Value**

Rachel Reeve must pay a lump sum of $6000 in 5 years. What amount deposited today at 6.2% compounded annually will amount to $6000 in 5 years?

SOLUTION Here $A = 6000$, $i = 0.062$, $n = 5$, and P is unknown. Substituting these values into the formula for the compound amount gives

$$6000 = P(1.062)^5$$

$$P = \frac{6000}{(1.062)^5} \approx 4441.49,$$

or $4441.49. If Rachel leaves $4441.49 for 5 years in an account paying 6.2% compounded annually, she will have $6000 when she needs it. To check your work, use the compound interest formula with $P = \$4441.49$, $i = 0.062$, and $n = 5$. You should get $A = \$6000.00$.

As Example 9 shows, $6000 in 5 years is approximately the same as $4441.49 today (if money can be deposited at 6.2% compounded annually). An amount that can be deposited today to yield a given sum in the future is called the *present value* of the future sum. Generalizing from Example 9, by solving $A = P(1 + i)^n$ for P, we get the following formula for present value.

> **Present Value for Compound Interest**
> The **present value** of A dollars compounded at an interest rate i per period for n periods is
> $$P = \frac{A}{(1 + i)^n} \quad \text{or} \quad P = A(1 + i)^{-n}.$$

EXAMPLE 10 **Present Value**

Find the present value of $16,000 in 9 years if money can be deposited at 6% compounded semiannually.

SOLUTION In 9 years there are $2 \cdot 9 = 18$ semiannual periods. A rate of 6% per year is 3% in each semiannual period. Apply the formula with $A = 16,000$, $i = 0.03$, and $n = 18$.

YOUR TURN 6 Find the present value of $10,000 in 7 years if money can be deposited at 4.25% compounded quarterly.

$$P = \frac{A}{(1 + i)^n} = \frac{16,000}{(1.03)^{18}} \approx 9398.31$$

A deposit of $9398.31 today, at 6% compounded semiannually, will produce a total of $16,000 in 9 years.

TRY YOUR TURN 6

We can solve the compound amount formula for n also, as the following example shows.

EXAMPLE 11   Compounding Time

Suppose the $2450 from Example 5 is deposited at 5.25% compounded quarterly until it reaches at least $10,000. How much time is required?

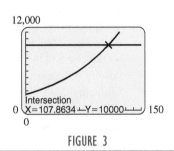 **Method 1**
Graphing Calculator

SOLUTION   Graph the functions $y = 2450(1 + 0.0525/4)^x$ and $y = 10,000$ in the same window, and then find the point of intersection. As Figure 3 shows, the functions intersect at $x = 107.8634$. Note, however, that interest is only added to the account every quarter, so we must wait 108 quarters, or $108/4 = 27$ years, for the money to be worth at least $10,000.

FIGURE 3

Method 2
Using Logarithms
(Optional)

The goal is to solve the equation

$$2450(1 + 0.0525/4)^n = 10,000.$$

Divide both sides by 2450, and simplify the expression in parentheses to get

$$1.013125^n = \frac{10,000}{2450}.$$

Now take the logarithm (either base 10 or base e) of both sides to get

$$\log(1.013125^n) = \log(10,000/2450)$$
$$n \log(1.013125) = \log(10,000/2450) \qquad \text{Use logarithm property } \log x^r = r \log x.$$
$$n = \frac{\log(10,000/2450)}{\log(1.013125)} \qquad \text{Divide both sides by } \log(1.013125).$$
$$\approx 107.86.$$

As in Method 1, this means that we must wait 108 quarters, or $108/4 = 27$ years, for the money to be worth at least $10,000.

-FOR REVIEW-

For a review of logarithmic functions, please refer to Appendix B if you are using *Finite Mathematics*, or to Section 10.5 if you are using *Finite Mathematics and Calculus with Applications*. The only property of logarithms that is needed to find the compounding time is $\log x^r = r \log x$. Logarithms may be used in base 10, using the LOG button on a calculator, or in base e, using the LN button.

EXAMPLE 12   Price Doubling

Suppose the general level of inflation in the economy averages 8% per year. Find the number of years it would take for the overall level of prices to double.

SOLUTION   To find the number of years it will take for $1 worth of goods or services to cost $2, find n in the equation

$$2 = 1(1 + 0.08)^n,$$

where $A = 2$, $P = 1$, and $i = 0.08$. This equation simplifies to

$$2 = (1.08)^n.$$

YOUR TURN 7   Find the time needed for $3800 deposited at 3.5% compounded semiannually to be worth at least $7000.

Solving this equation using either a graphing calculator or logarithms, as in Example 11, shows that $n = 9.00647$. Thus, the overall level of prices will double in about 9 years.

TRY YOUR TURN 7

You can quickly estimate how long it takes a sum of money to double, when compounded annually, by using either the **rule of 70** or the **rule of 72**. The rule of 70 (used for small rates of growth) says that for $0.001 \leq r < 0.05$, the value of $70/100r$ gives a good approximation of the doubling time. The rule of 72 (used for larger rates of growth) says that for $0.05 \leq r \leq 0.12$, the value of $72/100r$ approximates the doubling time well. In Example 12, the inflation rate is 8%, so the doubling time is approximately $72/8 = 9$ years.*

Continuous Compounding

Suppose that a bank, in order to attract more business, offers to not just compound interest every quarter, or every month, or every day, or even every hour, but constantly? This type of compound interest, in which the number of times a year that the interest is compounded becomes infinite, is known as **continuous compounding.** To see how it works, look back at Example 5, where we found that $2450, when deposited for 6.5 years at 5.25% compounded quarterly, resulted in a compound amount of $3438.78. We can find the compound amount if we compound more often by putting different values of n in the formula $A = 2450(1 + 0.0525/n)^{6.5n}$, as shown in the following table.

	Compounding n Times Annually	
n	Type of Compounding	Compound Amount
4	quarterly	$3438.78
12	monthly	$3443.86
360	daily	$3446.34
8640	every hour	$3446.42

Notice that as n becomes larger, the compound amount also becomes larger, but by a smaller and smaller amount. In this example, increasing the number of compounding periods a year from 360 to 8640 only earns 8¢ more. It is shown in calculus that as n becomes infinitely large, $P(1 + r/n)^{nt}$ gets closer and closer to Pe^{rt}, where e is a very important irrational number whose approximate value is 2.718281828. To calculate interest with continuous compounding, use the e^x button on your calculator. You will learn more about the number e if you study calculus, where e plays as important a role as π does in geometry.

Continuous Compounding

If a deposit of P dollars is invested at a rate of interest r compounded continuously for t years, the compound amount is

$$A = Pe^{rt} \text{ dollars.}$$

EXAMPLE 13 Continuous Compounding

Suppose that $2450 is deposited at 5.25% compounded continuously.

(a) Find the compound amount and the interest earned after 6.5 years.

> **SOLUTION** Using the formula for continuous compounding with $P = 2450$, $r = 0.0525$, and $t = 6.5$, the compound amount is
>
> $$A = 2450e^{0.0525(6.5)} \approx 3446.43.$$
>
> The compound amount is $3446.43, which is just a penny more than if it had been compounded hourly, or 9¢ more than daily compounding. Because it makes so little difference, continuous compounding has dropped in popularity in recent years. The interest in this case is $3446.43 − 2450 = 996.43, or $7.65 more than if it were compounded quarterly, as in Example 5.

*To see where the rule of 70 and the rule of 72 come from, see the section on Taylor Series in *Calculus with Applications* by Margaret L. Lial, Raymond N. Greenwell, and Nathan P. Ritchey, Pearson, 2012.

(b) Find the effective rate.

SOLUTION As in Example 7, the effective rate is just the amount of interest that $1 would earn in one year, or

$$e^{0.0525} - 1 \approx 0.0539,$$

or 5.39%. In general, the effective rate for interest compounded continuously at a rate r is just $e^r - 1$.

(c) Find the time required for the original $2450 to grow to $10,000.

SOLUTION Similar to the process in Example 11, we must solve the equation

$$10,000 = 2450e^{0.0525t}.$$

Divide both sides by 2450, and solve the resulting equation as in Example 11, either by taking logarithms of both sides or by using a graphing calculator to find the intersection of the graphs of $y = 2450e^{0.0525t}$ and $y = 10,000$. If you use logarithms, you can take advantage of the fact that $\ln(e^x) = x$, where $\ln x$ represents the logarithm in base e. In either case, the answer is 26.79 years.

Notice that unlike in Example 11, you don't need to wait until the next compounding period to reach this amount, because interest is being added to the account continuously.

YOUR TURN 8 Find the interest earned on $5000 deposited at 3.8% compounded continuously for 9 years.

TRY YOUR TURN 8

At this point, it seems helpful to summarize the notation and the most important formulas for simple and compound interest. We use the following variables.

P = principal or present value

A = future or maturity value

r = annual (stated or nominal) interest rate

t = number of years

m = number of compounding periods per year

i = interest rate per period $i = r/m$

n = total number of compounding periods $n = tm$

r_E = effective rate

Simple Interest	Compound Interest	Continuous Compounding
$A = P(1 + rt)$	$A = P(1 + i)^n$	$A = Pe^{rt}$
$P = \dfrac{A}{1 + rt}$	$P = \dfrac{A}{(1 + i)^n} = A(1 + i)^{-n}$	$P = Ae^{-rt}$
	$r_E = \left(1 + \dfrac{r}{m}\right)^m - 1$	$r_E = e^r - 1$

5.1 EXERCISES

1. What factors determine the amount of interest earned on a fixed principal?

2. In your own words, describe the *maturity value* of a loan.

3. What is meant by the *present value* of money?

4. We calculated the loan in Example 2(b) assuming 360 days in a year. Find the maturity value using 365 days in a year. Which is more advantageous to the borrower?

Find the simple interest.

5. $25,000 at 3% for 9 months

6. $4289 at 4.5% for 35 weeks

7. $1974 at 6.3% for 25 weeks

8. $6125 at 1.25% for 6 months

Find the simple interest. Assume a 360-day year.

9. $8192.17 at 3.1% for 72 days

10. $7236.15 at 4.25% for 30 days

Find the maturity value and the amount of simple interest earned.

11. $3125 at 2.85% for 7 months

12. $12,000 at 5.3% for 11 months

13. If $1500 earned simple interest of $56.25 in 6 months, what was the simple interest rate?

14. If $23,500 earned simple interest of $1057.50 in 9 months, what was the simple interest rate?

15. Explain the difference between simple interest and compound interest.

16. What is the difference between r and i?

17. What is the difference between t and n?

18. In Figure 1, one line is straight and the other is curved. Explain why this is, and which represents each type of interest.

Find the compound amount for each deposit and the amount of interest earned.

19. $1000 at 6% compounded annually for 8 years

20. $1000 at 4.5% compounded annually for 6 years

21. $470 at 5.4% compounded semiannually for 12 years

22. $15,000 at 6% compounded monthly for 10 years

23. $8500 at 8% compounded quarterly for 5 years

24. $9100 at 6.4% compounded quarterly for 9 years

Find the interest rate for each deposit and compound amount.

25. $8000 accumulating to $11,672.12, compounded quarterly for 8 years

26. $12,500 accumulating to $20,077.43, compounded quarterly for 9 years

27. $4500 accumulating to $5994.79, compounded monthly for 5 years

28. $6725 accumulating to $10,353.47, compounded monthly for 7 years

Find the effective rate corresponding to each nominal rate.

29. 4% compounded quarterly

30. 6% compounded quarterly

31. 7.25% compounded semiannually

32. 6.25% compounded semiannually

Find the present value (the amount that should be invested now to accumulate the following amount) if the money is compounded as indicated.

33. $12,820.77 at 4.8% compounded annually for 6 years

34. $36,527.13 at 5.3% compounded annually for 10 years

35. $2000 at 6% compounded semiannually for 8 years

36. $2000 at 7% compounded semiannually for 8 years

37. $8800 at 5% compounded quarterly for 5 years

38. $7500 at 5.5% compounded quarterly for 9 years

39. How do the nominal or stated interest rate and the effective interest rate differ?

40. If interest is compounded more than once per year, which rate is higher, the stated rate or the effective rate?

Using either logarithms or a graphing calculator, find the time required for each initial amount to be at least equal to the final amount.

41. $5000, deposited at 4% compounded quarterly, to reach at least $9000

42. $8000, deposited at 3% compounded quarterly, to reach at least $23,000

43. $4500, deposited at 3.6% compounded monthly, to reach at least $11,000

44. $6800, deposited at 5.4% compounded monthly, to reach at least $15,000

Find the doubling time for each of the following levels of inflation using (a) logarithms or a graphing calculator, and (b) the rule of 70 or 72, whichever is appropriate.

45. 3.3%   46. 6.25%

For each of the following amounts at the given interest rate compounded continuously, find (a) the future value after 9 years, (b) the effective rate, and (c) the time to reach $10,000.

47. $5500 at 3.1%   48. $4700 at 4.65%

APPLICATIONS

Business and Economics

49. **Loan Repayment** Tanya Kerchner borrowed $7200 from her father to buy a used car. She repaid him after 9 months, at an annual interest rate of 6.2%. Find the total amount she repaid. How much of this amount is interest?

50. **Delinquent Taxes** An accountant for a corporation forgot to pay the firm's income tax of $321,812.85 on time. The government charged a penalty based on an annual interest rate of 13.4% for the 29 days the money was late. Find the total amount (tax and penalty) that was paid. (Use a 365-day year.)

51. **Savings** A $1500 certificate of deposit held for 75 days was worth $1521.25. To the nearest tenth of a percent, what interest rate was earned? Assume a 360-day year.

52. **Bond Interest** A bond with a face value of $10,000 in 10 years can be purchased now for $5988.02. What is the simple interest rate?

53. **Stock Growth** A stock that sold for $22 at the beginning of the year was selling for $24 at the end of the year. If the stock paid a dividend of $0.50 per share, what is the simple interest rate on an investment in this stock? (*Hint:* Consider the interest to be the increase in value plus the dividend.)

54. **Wealth** A 1997 article in *The New York Times* discussed how long it would take for Bill Gates, the world's second richest person at the time (behind the Sultan of Brunei), to become the world's first trillionaire. His birthday is October 28, 1955, and on

July 16, 1997, he was worth $42 billion. (*Note:* A trillion dollars is 1000 billion dollars.) *Source: The New York Times.*

a. Assume that Bill Gates's fortune grows at an annual rate of 58%, the historical growth rate through 1997 of Microsoft stock, which made up most of his wealth in 1997. Find the age at which he becomes a trillionaire. (*Hint:* Use the formula for interest compounded annually, $A = P(1 + i)^n$, with $P = 42$. Graph the future value as a function of n on a graphing calculator, and find where the graph crosses the line $y = 1000$.)

b. Repeat part a using 10.5% growth, the average return on all stocks since 1926. *Source: CNN.*

c. What rate of growth would be necessary for Bill Gates to become a trillionaire by the time he is eligible for Social Security on January 1, 2022, after he has turned 66?

d. *Forbes* magazine's listings of billionaires for 2006 and 2010 have given Bill Gates's worth as roughly $50.0 billion and $53.0 billion, respectively. What was the rate of growth of his wealth between 2006 and 2010? *Source: Forbes.*

55. Student Loan Upon graduation from college, Kelly was able to defer payment on his $40,000 subsidized Stafford student loan for 6 months. Since the interest will no longer be paid on his behalf, it will be added to the principal until payments begin. If the interest is 6.54% compounded monthly, what will the principal amount be when he must begin repaying his loan? *Source: SallieMae.*

56. Comparing Investments Two partners agree to invest equal amounts in their business. One will contribute $10,000 immediately. The other plans to contribute an equivalent amount in 3 years, when she expects to acquire a large sum of money. How much should she contribute at that time to match her partner's investment now, assuming an interest rate of 6% compounded semiannually?

57. Comparing Investments As the prize in a contest, you are offered $1000 now or $1210 in 5 years. If money can be invested at 6% compounded annually, which is larger?

58. Retirement Savings The pie graph below shows the percent of baby boomers aged 46–49 who said they had investments with a total value as shown in each category. *Source: The New York Times.*

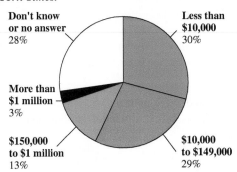

Figures add to more than 100% because of rounding.

Note that 30% have saved less than $10,000. Assume the money is invested at an average rate of 8% compounded quarterly. What will the top numbers in each category amount to in 20 years, when this age group will be ready for retirement?

Negative Interest Under certain conditions, Swiss banks pay negative interest: they charge you. (You didn't think all that secrecy was free?) Suppose a bank "pays" −2.4% interest compounded annually. Find the compound amount for a deposit of $150,000 after each period.

59. 4 years   **60.** 8 years

61. Investment In the New Testament, Jesus commends a widow who contributed 2 mites to the temple treasury (Mark 12: 42–44). A mite was worth roughly 1/8 of a cent. Suppose the temple invested those 2 mites at 4% interest compounded quarterly. How much would the money be worth 2000 years later?

62. Investments Eric Cobbe borrowed $5200 from his friend Frank Cronin to pay for remodeling work on his house. He repaid the loan 10 months later with simple interest at 7%. Frank then invested the proceeds in a 5-year certificate of deposit paying 6.3% compounded quarterly. How much will he have at the end of 5 years? (*Hint:* You need to use both simple and compound interest.)

63. Investments Suppose $10,000 is invested at an annual rate of 5% for 10 years. Find the future value if interest is compounded as follows.

a. Annually   **b.** Quarterly   **c.** Monthly

d. Daily (365 days)   **e.** Continuously

64. Investments In Exercise 63, notice that as the money is compounded more often, the compound amount becomes larger and larger. Is it possible to compound often enough so that the compound amount is $17,000 after 10 years? Explain.

The following exercise is from an actuarial examination. *Source: The Society of Actuaries.*

65. Savings On January 1, 2000, Jack deposited $1000 into bank X to earn interest at a rate of j per annum compounded semiannually. On January 1, 2005, he transferred his account to bank Y to earn interest at the rate of k per annum compounded quarterly. On January 1, 2008, the balance of bank Y is $1990.76. If Jack could have earned interest at the rate of k per annum compounded quarterly from January 1, 2000, through January 1, 2008, his balance would have been $2203.76. Calculate the ratio k/j.

66. Interest Rate In 1995, O. G. McClain of Houston, Texas, mailed a $100 check to a descendant of Texas independence hero Sam Houston to repay a $100 debt of McClain's great-great-grandfather, who died in 1835, to Sam Houston. A bank estimated the interest on the loan to be $420 million for the 160 years it was due. Find the interest rate the bank was using, assuming interest is compounded annually. *Source: The New York Times.*

67. Comparing CD Rates Marine Bank offered the following CD (Certificates of Deposit) rates. The rates are annual percentage yields, or effective rates, which are higher than the corresponding nominal rates. Assume quarterly compounding. Solve for r to approximate the corresponding nominal rates to the nearest hundredth. *Source: Marine Bank.*

Term	6 mo	Special! 9 mo	1 yr	2 yr	3 yr
APY%	2.50	5.10	4.25	4.50	5.25

68. Effective Rate   A Web site for E*TRADE Financial claims that they have "one of the highest yields in the nation" on a 6-month CD. The stated yield was 5.46%; the actual rate was not stated. Assuming monthly compounding, find the actual rate. *Source: E*TRADE.*

69. Effective Rate   On August 18, 2006, Centennial Bank of Fountain Valley, California, paid 5.5% interest, compounded monthly, on a 1-year CD, while First Source Bank of South Bend, Indiana, paid 5.63% compounded annually. What are the effective rates for the two CDs, and which bank pays a higher effective rate? *Source: Bankrate.com.*

70. Savings   A department has ordered 8 new Dell computers at a cost of $2309 each. The order will not be delivered for 6 months. What amount could the department deposit in a special 6-month CD paying 4.79% compounded monthly to have enough to pay for the machines at time of delivery?

71. Buying a House   Steve May wants to have $30,000 available in 5 years for a down payment on a house. He has inherited $25,000. How much of the inheritance should he invest now to accumulate $30,000, if he can get an interest rate of 5.5% compounded quarterly?

72. Rule of 70   On the day of their first grandchild's birth, a new set of grandparents invested $10,000 in a trust fund earning 4.5% compounded monthly.

   a. Use the rule of 70 to estimate how old the grandchild will be when the trust fund is worth $20,000.

   b. Use your answer to part a to determine the actual amount that will be in the trust fund at that time. How close was your estimate in part a?

Doubling Time   Use the ideas from Example 12 to find the time it would take for the general level of prices in the economy to double at each average annual inflation rate.

73. 4%   **74.** 5%

75. Doubling Time   The consumption of electricity has increased historically at 6% per year. If it continues to increase at this rate indefinitely, find the number of years before the electric utilities will need to double their generating capacity.

76. Doubling Time   Suppose a conservation campaign coupled with higher rates causes the demand for electricity to increase at only 2% per year, as it has recently. Find the number of years before the utilities will need to double generating capacity.

77. Mitt Romney   According to *The New York Times*, "During the fourteen years [Mitt Romney] ran it, Bain Capital's investments reportedly earned an annual rate of return of over 100 percent, potentially turning an initial investment of $1 million into more than $14 million by the time he left in 1998." *Source: The New York Times.*

   a. What rate of return, compounded annually, would turn $1 million into $14 million by 1998?

   b. The actual rate of return of Bain Capital during the 14 years that Romney ran it was 113%. *Source: The American.* How much would $1 million, compounded annually at this rate, be worth after 14 years?

YOUR TURN ANSWERS

1. $3048.33	**2.** 6.5%	**3.** $545.75
4. 3.6%	**5.** 2.73%	**6.** $7438.39
7. 18 years	**8.** $2038.80	

5.2 Future Value of an Annuity

APPLY IT   If you deposit $1500 each year for 6 years in an account paying 8% interest compounded annually, how much will be in your account at the end of this period?

In this section and the next, we develop future value and present value formulas for such periodic payments. To develop these formulas, we must first discuss sequences.

Geometric Sequences

If a and r are nonzero real numbers, the infinite list of numbers $a, ar, ar^2, ar^3, ar^4, \ldots, ar^n, \ldots$ is called a **geometric sequence**. For example, if $a = 3$ and $r = -2$, we have the sequence

$$3, 3(-2), 3(-2)^2, 3(-2)^3, 3(-2)^4, \ldots,$$

or

$$3, -6, 12, -24, 48, \ldots.$$

In the sequence $a, ar, ar^2, ar^3, ar^4, \ldots$, the number a is called the **first term** of the sequence, ar is the **second term**, ar^2 is the **third term**, and so on. Thus, for any $n \geq 1$,

ar^{n-1} is the nth term of the sequence.

Each term in the sequence is r times the preceding term. The number r is called the **common ratio** of the sequence.

> **CAUTION** Do not confuse r, the ratio of two successive terms in a geometric series, with r, the annual interest rate. Different letters might have been helpful, but the usage in both cases is almost universal.

EXAMPLE 1 Geometric Sequence

Find the seventh term of the geometric sequence 5, 20, 80, 320, ...

SOLUTION The first term in the sequence is 5, so $a = 5$. The common ratio, found by dividing the second term by the first, is $r = 20/5 = 4$. We want the seventh term, so $n = 7$. Use ar^{n-1}, with $a = 5$, $r = 4$, and $n = 7$.

$$ar^{n-1} = (5)(4)^{7-1} = 5(4)^6 = 20{,}480$$

Next, we need to find the sum S_n of the first n terms of a geometric sequence, where

$$S_n = a + ar + ar^2 + ar^3 + ar^4 + \cdots + ar^{n-1}. \tag{1}$$

If $r = 1$, then

$$S_n = \underbrace{a + a + a + a + \cdots + a}_{n \text{ terms}} = na.$$

If $r \neq 1$, multiply both sides of equation (1) by r to get

$$rS_n = ar + ar^2 + ar^3 + ar^4 + \cdots + ar^n. \tag{2}$$

Now subtract corresponding sides of equation (1) from equation (2).

$$
\begin{aligned}
rS_n &= ar + ar^2 + ar^3 + ar^4 + \cdots + ar^{n-1} + ar^n \\
-S_n &= -(a + ar + ar^2 + ar^3 + ar^4 + \cdots + ar^{n-1}) \\
\hline
rS_n - S_n &= -a + ar^n \\
S_n(r - 1) &= a(r^n - 1) \qquad \text{Factor.} \\
S_n &= \frac{a(r^n - 1)}{r - 1} \qquad \text{Divide both sides by } r - 1.
\end{aligned}
$$

This result is summarized below.

Sum of Terms

If a geometric sequence has first term a and common ratio r, then the sum S_n of the first n terms is given by

$$S_n = \frac{a(r^n - 1)}{r - 1}, \quad r \neq 1.$$

EXAMPLE 2 Sum of a Geometric Sequence

Find the sum of the first six terms of the geometric sequence 3, 12, 48, ...

SOLUTION Here $a = 3$, $r = 4$, and $n = 6$. Find S_6 by the formula above.

$$
\begin{aligned}
S_6 &= \frac{3(4^6 - 1)}{4 - 1} \qquad n = 6, a = 3, r = 4. \\
&= \frac{3(4096 - 1)}{3} \\
&= 4095
\end{aligned}
$$

YOUR TURN 1 Find the sum of the first 9 terms of the geometric series 4, 12, 36, ...

TRY YOUR TURN 1

Ordinary Annuities

A sequence of equal payments made at equal periods of time is called an **annuity**. If the payments are made at the end of the time period, and if the frequency of payments is the same as the frequency of compounding, the annuity is called an **ordinary annuity**. The time between payments is the **payment period**, and the time from the beginning of the first payment period to the end of the last period is called the **term** of the annuity. The **future value of the annuity**, the final sum on deposit, is defined as the sum of the compound amounts of all the payments, compounded to the end of the term.

Two common uses of annuities are to accumulate funds for some goal or to withdraw funds from an account. For example, an annuity may be used to save money for a large purchase, such as an automobile, a college education, or a down payment on a home. An annuity also may be used to provide monthly payments for retirement. We explore these options in this and the next section.

APPLY IT

For example, suppose $1500 is deposited at the end of each year for the next 6 years in an account paying 8% per year compounded annually. Figure 4 shows this annuity. To find the future value of the annuity, look separately at each of the $1500 payments. The first of these payments will produce a compound amount of

$$1500(1 + 0.08)^5 = 1500(1.08)^5.$$

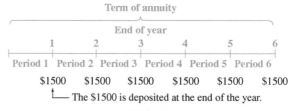

FIGURE 4

Use 5 as the exponent instead of 6, since the money is deposited at the *end* of the first year and earns interest for only 5 years. The second payment of $1500 will produce a compound amount of $1500(1.08)^4$. As shown in Figure 5, the future value of the annuity is

$$1500(1.08)^5 + 1500(1.08)^4 + 1500(1.08)^3 + 1500(1.08)^2$$
$$+ 1500(1.08)^1 + 1500.$$

(The last payment earns no interest at all.)

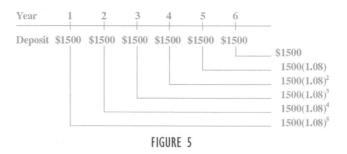

FIGURE 5

Reading this sum in reverse order, we see that it is the sum of the first six terms of a geometric sequence, with $a = 1500$, $r = 1.08$, and $n = 6$. Thus, the sum equals

$$\frac{a(r^n - 1)}{r - 1} = \frac{1500[(1.08)^6 - 1]}{1.08 - 1} \approx \$11,003.89.$$

To generalize this result, suppose that payments of R dollars each are deposited into an account at the end of each period for n periods, at a rate of interest i per period. The first payment of R dollars will produce a compound amount of $R(1 + i)^{n-1}$ dollars, the second payment will produce $R(1 + i)^{n-2}$ dollars, and so on; the final payment earns no interest and contributes just R dollars to the total. If S represents the future value (or sum) of the annuity, then (as shown in Figure 6),

$$S = R(1 + i)^{n-1} + R(1 + i)^{n-2} + R(1 + i)^{n-3} + \cdots + R(1 + i) + R,$$

or, written in reverse order,

$$S = R + R(1 + i)^1 + R(1 + i)^2 + \cdots + R(1 + i)^{n-1}.$$

FIGURE 6

This result is the sum of the first n terms of the geometric sequence having first term R and common ratio $1 + i$. Using the formula for the sum of the first n terms of a geometric sequence,

$$S = \frac{R[(1 + i)^n - 1]}{(1 + i) - 1} = \frac{R[(1 + i)^n - 1]}{i} = R\left[\frac{(1 + i)^n - 1}{i}\right].$$

The quantity in brackets is commonly written $s_{\overline{n}|i}$ (read "s-angle-n at i"), so that

$$S = R \cdot s_{\overline{n}|i}.$$

Values of $s_{\overline{n}|i}$ can be found with a calculator.

A formula for the future value of an annuity S of n payments of R dollars each at the end of each consecutive interest period, with interest compounded at a rate i per period, follows.* Recall that this type of annuity, with payments at the *end* of each time period, is called an ordinary annuity.

Future Value of an Ordinary Annuity

$$S = R\left[\frac{(1 + i)^n - 1}{i}\right] \qquad \text{or} \qquad S = Rs_{\overline{n}|i}$$

where

S is the future value;

R is the periodic payment;

i is the interest rate per period;

n is the number of periods.

TECHNOLOGY NOTE   A calculator will be very helpful in computations with annuities. The TI-84 Plus graphing calculator has a special FINANCE menu that is designed to give any desired result after entering the basic information. If your calculator does not have this feature, many calculators can easily be programmed to evaluate the formulas introduced in this section and the next. We include these programs in the *Graphing Calculator and Excel Spreadsheet Manual* available for this text.

*We use S for the future value here, instead of A as in the compound interest formula, to help avoid confusing the two formulas.

EXAMPLE 3 Ordinary Annuity

Bethany Ward is an athlete who believes that her playing career will last 7 years. To prepare for her future, she deposits $22,000 at the end of each year for 7 years in an account paying 6% compounded annually. How much will she have on deposit after 7 years?

SOLUTION Her payments form an ordinary annuity, with $R = 22,000$, $n = 7$, and $i = 0.06$. Using the formula for future value of an annuity,

$$S = 22,000\left[\frac{(1.06)^7 - 1}{0.06}\right] \approx 184,664.43,$$

YOUR TURN 2 Find the accumulated amount after 11 years if $250 is deposited every month in an account paying 3.3% interest compounded monthly.

or $184,664.43. Note that she made 7 payments of $22,000, or $154,000. The interest that she earned is $184,664.43 − $154,000 = $30,664.43.　　　TRY YOUR TURN 2

Sinking Funds
A fund set up to receive periodic payments as in Example 3 is called a **sinking fund**. The periodic payments, together with the interest earned by the payments, are designed to produce a given sum at some time in the future. For example, a sinking fund might be set up to receive money that will be needed to pay off the principal on a loan at some future time. If the payments are all the same amount and are made at the end of a regular time period, they form an ordinary annuity.

EXAMPLE 4 Sinking Fund

Experts say that the baby boom generation (Americans born between 1946 and 1960) cannot count on a company pension or Social Security to provide a comfortable retirement, as their parents did. It is recommended that they start to save early and regularly. Nancy Hart, a baby boomer, has decided to deposit $200 each month for 20 years in an account that pays interest of 7.2% compounded monthly.

(a) How much will be in the account at the end of 20 years?

SOLUTION This savings plan is an annuity with $R = 200$, $i = 0.072/12$, and $n = 12(20)$. The future value is

$$S = 200\left[\frac{(1 + (0.072/12))^{12(20)} - 1}{0.072/12}\right] \approx 106,752.47,$$

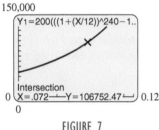

150,000

Y1=200(((1+(X/12))^240−1..

Intersection
0 X=.072 Y=106752.47 0.12
0

FIGURE 7

or $106,752.47. Figure 7 shows a calculator graph of the function

$$S = 200\left[\frac{(1 + (x/12))^{12(20)} - 1}{x/12}\right]$$

where r, the annual interest rate, is designated x. The value of the function at $x = 0.072$, shown at the bottom of the window, agrees with our result above.

(b) Nancy believes she needs to accumulate $130,000 in the 20-year period to have enough for retirement. What interest rate would provide that amount?

SOLUTION

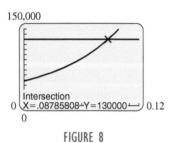

150,000

Intersection
0 X=.08785808 Y=130000 0.12
0

FIGURE 8

Method I
Graphing Calculator

One way to answer this question is to solve the equation for S in terms of x with $S = 130,000$. This is a difficult equation to solve. Although trial and error could be used, it would be easier to use the graphing calculator graph in Figure 7. Adding the line $y = 130,000$ to the graph and then using the capability of the calculator to find the intersection point with the curve shows the annual interest rate must be at least 8.79% to the nearest hundredth. See Figure 8.

Method 2
TVM Solver

Using the TVM Solver under the FINANCE menu on the TI-84 Plus calculator, enter 240 for N (the number of periods), 0 for PV (present value), −200 for PMT (negative because the money is being paid out), 130000 for FV (future value), and 12 for P/Y (payments per year). Put the cursor next to I% (payment) and press SOLVE. The result, shown in Figure 9, indicates that an interest rate of 8.79% is needed.

```
N=240
∎I%=8.785807706
PV=0∎
PMT=-200
FV=130000
P/Y=12
C/Y=12
PMT: END BEGIN
```

FIGURE 9

In Example 4 we used sinking fund calculations to determine the amount of money that accumulates over time through monthly payments and interest. We can also use this formula to determine the amount of money necessary to periodically invest at a given interest rate to reach a particular goal. Start with the annuity formula

$$S = R\left[\frac{(1 + i)^n - 1}{i}\right],$$

and multiply both sides by $i/[(1 + i)^n - 1]$ to derive the following formula.

Sinking Fund Payment

$$R = \frac{Si}{(1 + i)^n - 1} \quad \text{or} \quad R = \frac{S}{s_{\overline{n}|i}}$$

where

R is the periodic payment;

S is the future value;

i is the interest rate per period;

n is the number of periods.

EXAMPLE 5 Sinking Fund Payment

Suppose Nancy, in Example 4, cannot get the higher interest rate to produce $130,000 in 20 years. To meet that goal, she must increase her monthly payment. What payment should she make each month?

SOLUTION   Nancy's goal is to accumulate $130,000 in 20 years at 7.2% compounded monthly. Therefore, the future value is $S = 130,000$, the monthly interest rate is $i = 0.072/12$, and the number of periods is $n = 12(20)$. Use the sinking fund payment formula to find the payment R.

$$R = \frac{(130,000)(0.072/12)}{(1 + (0.072/12))^{12(20)} - 1} \approx 243.5540887$$

Nancy will need payments of $243.56 each month for 20 years to accumulate at least $130,000. Notice that $243.55 is not quite enough, so round up here. Figure 10(a) shows the point of intersection of the graphs of

$$Y_1 = X\left[\frac{(1 + 0.072/12)^{12(20)} - 1}{0.072/12}\right]$$

YOUR TURN 3 Find the quarterly payment needed to produce $13,500 in 14 years at 3.75% interest compounded quarterly.

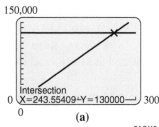

(a)

X	Y₁
241	128637
242	129170
243	129704
244	130238
245	130772
246	131306
247	131839

X=244

(b)

FIGURE 10

and $Y_2 = 130,000$. The result agrees with the answer we found analytically. The table shown in Figure 10(b) confirms that the payment should be between \$243 and \$244.

TRY YOUR TURN 3

TECHNOLOGY NOTE

We can also use a graphing calculator or spreadsheet to make a table of the amount in a sinking fund. In the formula for future value of an annuity, simply let n be a variable with values from 1 to the total number of payments. Figure 11(a) shows the beginning of such a table generated on a TI-84 Plus for Example 5. Figure 11(b) shows the beginning of the same table using Microsoft Excel.

X	Y₁
1	243.55
2	488.56
3	735.04
4	983
5	1232.5
6	1483.4
7	1735.8

X=1

(a)

n	Amount in Fund
1	243.55
2	488.56
3	735.04
4	983.00
5	1232.45
6	1483.40
7	1735.85
8	1989.81
9	2245.30
10	2502.32
11	2760.89
12	3021.00

(b)

FIGURE 11

Annuities Due The formula developed above is for *ordinary annuities*—those with payments made at the *end* of each time period. These results can be modified slightly to apply to **annuities due**—annuities in which payments are made at the *beginning* of each time period. To find the future value of an annuity due, treat each payment as if it were made at the *end* of the *preceding* period. That is, find $s_{\overline{n}|i}$ for *one additional period*; to compensate for this, subtract the amount of one payment.

Thus, the **future value of an annuity due** of n payments of R dollars each at the beginning of consecutive interest periods, with interest compounded at the rate of i per period, is

$$S = R\left[\frac{(1+i)^{n+1} - 1}{i}\right] - R \quad \text{or} \quad S = Rs_{\overline{n+1}|i} - R.$$

TECHNOLOGY NOTE

The finance feature of the TI-84 Plus can be used to find the future value of an annuity due as well as an ordinary annuity. If this feature is not built in, you may wish to program your calculator to evaluate this formula, too.

EXAMPLE 6 Future Value of an Annuity Due

Find the future value of an annuity due if payments of \$500 are made at the beginning of each quarter for 7 years, in an account paying 6% compounded quarterly.

SOLUTION In 7 years, there are $n = 28$ quarterly periods. Add one period to get $n + 1 = 29$, and use the formula with $i = 0.06/4 = 0.015$.

$$S = 500\left[\frac{(1.015)^{29} - 1}{0.015}\right] - 500 \approx 17,499.35$$

The account will have a total of \$17,499.35 after 7 years.

TRY YOUR TURN 4

YOUR TURN 4 Find the future value of an annuity due with \$325 made at the beginning of each month for 5 years in an account paying 3.3% compounded monthly.

5.2 EXERCISES

Find the fifth term of each geometric sequence.

1. $a = 3$; $r = 2$

2. $a = 7$; $r = 5$

3. $a = -8$; $r = 3$

4. $a = -6$; $r = 2$

5. $a = 1$; $r = -3$

6. $a = 12$; $r = -2$

7. $a = 256$; $r = \dfrac{1}{4}$

8. $a = 729$; $r = \dfrac{1}{3}$

Find the sum of the first four terms for each geometric sequence.

9. $a = 1$; $r = 2$

10. $a = 4$; $r = 4$

11. $a = 5$; $r = \dfrac{1}{5}$

12. $a = 6$; $r = \dfrac{1}{2}$

13. $a = 128$; $r = -\dfrac{3}{2}$

14. $a = 64$; $r = -\dfrac{3}{4}$

15. Explain how a geometric sequence is related to an ordinary annuity.

16. Explain the difference between an ordinary annuity and an annuity due.

Find the future value of each ordinary annuity. Interest is compounded annually.

17. $R = 100$; $i = 0.06$; $n = 4$

18. $R = 1000$; $i = 0.06$; $n = 5$

19. $R = 25,000$; $i = 0.045$; $n = 36$

20. $R = 29,500$; $i = 0.058$; $n = 15$

Find the future value of each ordinary annuity, if payments are made and interest is compounded as given. Then determine how much of this value is from contributions and how much is from interest.

21. $R = 9200$; 10% interest compounded semiannually for 7 years

22. $R = 1250$; 5% interest compounded semiannually for 18 years

23. $R = 800$; 6.51% interest compounded semiannually for 12 years

24. $R = 4600$; 8.73% interest compounded quarterly for 9 years

25. $R = 12,000$; 4.8% interest compounded quarterly for 16 years

26. $R = 42,000$; 10.05% interest compounded semiannually for 12 years

27. What is meant by a sinking fund? Give an example of a sinking fund.

28. List some reasons for establishing a sinking fund.

Determine the interest rate needed to accumulate the following amounts in a sinking fund, with monthly payments as given.

29. Accumulate $56,000, monthly payments of $300 over 12 years

30. Accumulate $120,000, monthly payments of $500 over 15 years

Find the periodic payment that will amount to each given sum under the given conditions.

31. $S = \$10,000$; interest is 5% compounded annually; payments are made at the end of each year for 12 years.

32. $S = \$150,000$; interest is 6% compounded semiannually; payments are made at the end of each semiannual period for 11 years.

Find the amount of each payment to be made into a sinking fund so that enough will be present to accumulate the following amounts. Payments are made at the end of each period.

33. $8500; money earns 8% compounded annually; there are 7 annual payments.

34. $2750; money earns 5% compounded annually; there are 5 annual payments.

35. $75,000; money earns 6% compounded semiannually for $4\frac{1}{2}$ years.

36. $25,000; money earns 5.7% compounded quarterly for $3\frac{1}{2}$ years.

37. $65,000; money earns 7.5% compounded quarterly for $2\frac{1}{2}$ years.

38. $9000; money earns 4.8% compounded monthly for $2\frac{1}{2}$ years.

Find the future value of each annuity due. Assume that interest is compounded annually.

39. $R = 600$; $i = 0.06$; $n = 8$

40. $R = 1700$; $i = 0.04$; $n = 15$

41. $R = 16,000$; $i = 0.05$; $n = 7$

42. $R = 4000$; $i = 0.06$; $n = 11$

Find the future value of each annuity due. Then determine how much of this value is from contributions and how much is from interest.

43. Payments of $1000 made at the beginning of each semiannual period for 9 years at 8.15% compounded semiannually

44. $750 deposited at the beginning of each month for 15 years at 5.9% compounded monthly

45. $250 deposited at the beginning of each quarter for 12 years at 4.2% compounded quarterly

46. $1500 deposited at the beginning of each semiannual period for 11 years at 5.6% compounded semiannually

APPLICATIONS

Business and Economics

47. Comparing Accounts Laurie Campbell deposits $12,000 at the end of each year for 9 years in an account paying 8% interest compounded annually.

  a. Find the final amount she will have on deposit.

  b. Laurie's brother-in-law works in a bank that pays 6% compounded annually. If she deposits money in this bank instead of the one above, how much will she have in her account?

c. How much would Laurie lose over 9 years by using her brother-in-law's bank?

48. Savings Matthew Pastier is saving for a Plasma HDTV. At the end of each month he puts $100 in a savings account that pays 2.25% interest compounded monthly. How much is in the account after 2 years? How much did Matthew deposit? How much interest did he earn?

49. Savings A typical pack-a-day smoker spends about $136.50 per month on cigarettes. Suppose the smoker invests that amount each month in a savings account at 4.8% interest compounded monthly. What would the account be worth after 40 years? *Source: MSN.*

50. Retirement Planning A 45-year-old man puts $2500 in a retirement account at the end of each quarter until he reaches the age of 60, then makes no further deposits. If the account pays 6% interest compounded quarterly, how much will be in the account when the man retires at age 65?

51. Retirement Planning At the end of each quarter, a 50-year-old woman puts $3000 in a retirement account that pays 5% interest compounded quarterly. When she reaches 60, she withdraws the entire amount and places it in a mutual fund that pays 6.9% interest compounded monthly. From then on she deposits $300 in the mutual fund at the end of each month. How much is in the account when she reaches age 65?

Individual Retirement Accounts **Suppose a 40-year-old person deposits $4000 per year in an Individual Retirement Account until age 65. Find the total in the account with the following assumptions of interest rates. (Assume quarterly compounding, with payments of $1000 made at the end of each quarter period.) Find the total amount of interest earned.**

52. 6%   **53.** 8%   **54.** 4%   **55.** 10%

56. Savings Greg Tobin needs $10,000 in 8 years.

a. What amount should he deposit at the end of each quarter at 8% compounded quarterly so that he will have his $10,000?

b. Find Greg's quarterly deposit if the money is deposited at 6% compounded quarterly.

57. Buying Equipment Harv, the owner of Harv's Meats, knows that he must buy a new deboner machine in 4 years. The machine costs $12,000. In order to accumulate enough money to pay for the machine, Harv decides to deposit a sum of money at the end of each 6 months in an account paying 6% compounded semiannually. How much should each payment be?

58. Buying a Car Amanda Perdaris wants to have a $20,000 down payment when she buys a new car in 6 years. How much money must she deposit at the end of each quarter in an account paying 3.2% compounded quarterly so that she will have the down payment she desires?

59. Savings Stacy Schrank is paid on the first day of the month and $80 is automatically deducted from her pay and deposited in a savings account. If the account pays 2.5% interest compounded monthly, how much will be in the account after 3 years and 9 months?

60. Savings A father opened a savings account for his daughter on the day she was born, depositing $1000. Each year on her birthday he deposits another $1000, making the last deposit on her 21st birthday. If the account pays 5.25% interest compounded annually, how much is in the account at the end of the day on his daughter's 21st birthday? How much interest has been earned?

61. Savings Beth Dahlke deposits $2435 at the beginning of each semiannual period for 8 years in an account paying 6% compounded semiannually. She then leaves that money alone, with no further deposits, for an additional 5 years. Find the final amount on deposit after the entire 13-year period.

62. Savings David Kurzawa deposits $10,000 at the beginning of each year for 12 years in an account paying 5% compounded annually. He then puts the total amount on deposit in another account paying 6% compounded semiannually for another 9 years. Find the final amount on deposit after the entire 21-year period.

In Exercises 63 and 64, use a graphing calculator to find the value of *i* that produces the given value of *S*. (See Example 4(b).)

63. Retirement To save for retirement, Karla Harby put $300 each month into an ordinary annuity for 20 years. Interest was compounded monthly. At the end of the 20 years, the annuity was worth $147,126. What annual interest rate did she receive?

64. Rate of Return Caroline DiTullio made payments of $250 per month at the end of each month to purchase a piece of property. At the end of 30 years, she completely owned the property, which she sold for $330,000. What annual interest rate would she need to earn on an annuity for a comparable rate of return?

65. Lottery In a 1992 Virginia lottery, the jackpot was $27 million. An Australian investment firm tried to buy all possible combinations of numbers, which would have cost $7 million. In fact, the firm ran out of time and was unable to buy all combinations but ended up with the only winning ticket anyway. The firm received the jackpot in 20 equal annual payments of $1.35 million. Assume these payments meet the conditions of an ordinary annuity. *Source: The Washington Post.*

a. Suppose the firm can invest money at 8% interest compounded annually. How many years would it take until the investors would be further ahead than if they had simply invested the $7 million at the same rate? (*Hint:* Experiment with different values of *n*, the number of years, or use a graphing calculator to plot the value of both investments as a function of the number of years.)

b. How many years would it take in part a at an interest rate of 12%?

66. Buying Real Estate Vicki Kakounis sells some land in Nevada. She will be paid a lump sum of $60,000 in 7 years. Until then, the buyer pays 8% simple interest quarterly.

a. Find the amount of each quarterly interest payment on the $60,000.

b. The buyer sets up a sinking fund so that enough money will be present to pay off the $60,000. The buyer will make semiannual payments into the sinking fund; the account pays 6% compounded semiannually. Find the amount of each payment into the fund.

67. Buying Rare Stamps Phil Weaver bought a rare stamp for his collection. He agreed to pay a lump sum of $4000 after 5 years. Until then, he pays 6% simple interest semiannually on the $4000.

a. Find the amount of each semiannual interest payment.

b. Paul sets up a sinking fund so that enough money will be present to pay off the $4000. He will make annual payments into the fund. The account pays 8% compounded annually. Find the amount of each payment.

68. Down Payment A conventional loan, such as for a car or a house, is similar to an annuity but usually includes a down payment. Show that if a down payment of D dollars is made at the beginning of the loan period, the future value of all the payments, including the down payment, is

$$S = D(1 + i)^n + R\left[\frac{(1 + i)^n - 1}{i}\right].$$

YOUR TURN ANSWERS

1. 39,364
2. $39,719.98
3. $184.41
4. $21,227.66

5.3 Present Value of an Annuity; Amortization

APPLY IT   What monthly payment will pay off a $17,000 car loan in 36 monthly payments at 6% annual interest?

The answer to this question is given in Example 2 in this section. We shall see that it involves finding the present value of an annuity.

Suppose that at the end of each year, for the next 10 years, $500 is deposited in a savings account paying 7% interest compounded annually. This is an example of an ordinary annuity. The **present value of an annuity** is the amount that would have to be deposited in one lump sum today (at the same compound interest rate) in order to produce exactly the same balance at the end of 10 years. We can find a formula for the present value of an annuity as follows.

Suppose deposits of R dollars are made at the end of each period for n periods at interest rate i per period. Then the amount in the account after n periods is the future value of this annuity:

$$S = R \cdot s_{\overline{n}|i} = R\left[\frac{(1 + i)^n - 1}{i}\right].$$

On the other hand, if P dollars are deposited today at the same compound interest rate i, then at the end of n periods, the amount in the account is $P(1 + i)^n$. If P is the present value of the annuity, this amount must be the same as the amount S in the formula above; that is,

$$P(1 + i)^n = R\left[\frac{(1 + i)^n - 1}{i}\right].$$

To solve this equation for P, multiply both sides by $(1 + i)^{-n}$.

$$P = R(1 + i)^{-n}\left[\frac{(1 + i)^n - 1}{i}\right]$$

Use the distributive property; also recall that $(1 + i)^{-n}(1 + i)^n = 1$.

$$P = R\left[\frac{(1 + i)^{-n}(1 + i)^n - (1 + i)^{-n}}{i}\right] = R\left[\frac{1 - (1 + i)^{-n}}{i}\right]$$

The amount P is the *present value of the annuity*. The quantity in brackets is abbreviated as $a_{\overline{n}|i}$, so

$$a_{\overline{n}|i} = \frac{1 - (1 + i)^{-n}}{i}.$$

(The symbol $a_{\overline{n}|i}$ is read "*a*-angle-*n* at *i*." Compare this quantity with $s_{\overline{n}|i}$ in the previous section.) The formula for the present value of an annuity is summarized on the next page.

FOR REVIEW

Recall from Section R.6 that for any nonzero number a, $a^0 = 1$. Also, by the product rule for exponents, $a^x \cdot a^y = a^{x+y}$. In particular, if a is any nonzero number, $a^n \cdot a^{-n} = a^{n+(-n)} = a^0 = 1$.

Present Value of an Ordinary Annuity

The present value P of an annuity of n payments of R dollars each at the end of consecutive interest periods with interest compounded at a rate of interest i per period is

$$P = R\left[\frac{1 - (1 + i)^{-n}}{i}\right] \quad \text{or} \quad P = Ra_{\overline{n}|i}.$$

CAUTION Don't confuse the formula for the present value of an annuity with the one for the future value of an annuity. Notice the difference: the numerator of the fraction in the present value formula is $1 - (1 + i)^{-n}$, but in the future value formula, it is $(1 + i)^n - 1$.

TECHNOLOGY NOTE The financial feature of the TI-84 Plus calculator can be used to find the present value of an annuity by choosing that option from the menu and entering the required information. If your calculator does not have this built-in feature, it will be useful to store a program to calculate present value of an annuity in your calculator. A program is given in the *Graphing Calculator and Excel Spreadsheet Manual* available with this book.

EXAMPLE 1 Present Value of an Annuity

John Cross and Wendy Mears are both graduates of the Brisbane Institute of Technology (BIT). They both agree to contribute to the endowment fund of BIT. John says that he will give $500 at the end of each year for 9 years. Wendy prefers to give a lump sum today. What lump sum can she give that will equal the present value of John's annual gifts, if the endowment fund earns 7.5% compounded annually?

SOLUTION Here, $R = 500$, $n = 9$, and $i = 0.075$, and we have

$$P = R \cdot a_{\overline{9}|0.075} = 500\left[\frac{1 - (1.075)^{-9}}{0.075}\right] \approx 3189.44.$$

YOUR TURN 1 Find the present value of an annuity of $120 at the end of each month put into an account yielding 4.8% compounded monthly for 5 years.

Therefore, Wendy must donate a lump sum of $3189.44 today. **TRY YOUR TURN 1**

One of the most important uses of annuities is in determining the equal monthly payments needed to pay off a loan, as illustrated in the next example.

EXAMPLE 2 Car Payments

A car costs $19,000. After a down payment of $2000, the balance will be paid off in 36 equal monthly payments with interest of 6% per year on the unpaid balance. Find the amount of each payment.

APPLY IT

SOLUTION A single lump sum payment of $17,000 today would pay off the loan. So, $17,000 is the present value of an annuity of 36 monthly payments with interest of $6\%/12 = 0.5\%$ per month. Thus, $P = 17,000$, $n = 36$, $i = 0.005$, and we must find the monthly payment R in the formula

$$P = R\left[\frac{1 - (1 + i)^{-n}}{i}\right]$$

YOUR TURN 2 Find the car payment in Example 2 if there are 48 equal monthly payments and the interest rate is 5.4%.

$$17,000 = R\left[\frac{1 - (1.005)^{-36}}{0.005}\right]$$

$$R \approx 517.17.$$

A monthly payment of $517.17 will be needed. **TRY YOUR TURN 2**

Each payment in Example 2 includes interest on the unpaid balance, with the remainder going to reduce the loan. For example, the first payment of $517.17 includes interest of $0.005($17,000) = 85 and is divided as follows.

monthly   interest   to reduce
payment   due   the balance

$$\$517.17 - \$85 = \$432.17$$

At the end of this section, amortization schedules show that this procedure does reduce the loan to $0 after all payments are made (the final payment may be slightly different).

Amortization   A loan is **amortized** if both the principal and interest are paid by a sequence of equal periodic payments. In Example 2, a loan of $17,000 at 6% interest compounded monthly could be amortized by paying $517.17 per month for 36 months.

The periodic payment needed to amortize a loan may be found, as in Example 2, by solving the present value equation for R.

Amortization Payments
A loan of P dollars at interest rate i per period may be amortized in n equal periodic payments of R dollars made at the end of each period, where

$$R = \frac{P}{\left[\dfrac{1 - (1 + i)^{-n}}{i}\right]} = \frac{Pi}{1 - (1 + i)^{-n}} \quad \text{or} \quad R = \frac{P}{a_{\overline{n}|i}}.$$

EXAMPLE 3   Home Mortgage

The Perez family buys a house for $275,000, with a down payment of $55,000. They take out a 30-year mortgage for $220,000 at an annual interest rate of 6%.

(a) Find the amount of the monthly payment needed to amortize this loan.

   SOLUTION   Here $P = 220,000$ and the monthly interest rate is $i = 0.06/12 = 0.005$.* The number of monthly payments is $12(30) = 360$. Therefore,

$$R = \frac{220,000}{a_{\overline{360}|0.005}} = \frac{220,000}{\left[\dfrac{1 - (1.005)^{-360}}{0.005}\right]} = 1319.01.$$

   Monthly payments of $1319.01 are required to amortize the loan.

(b) Find the total amount of interest paid when the loan is amortized over 30 years.

   SOLUTION   The Perez family makes 360 payments of $1319.01 each, for a total of $474,843.60. Since the amount of the loan was $220,000, the total interest paid is

$$\$474,843.60 - \$220,000 = \$254,843.60.$$

   This large amount of interest is typical of what happens with a long mortgage. A 15-year mortgage would have higher payments but would involve significantly less interest.

(c) Find the part of the first payment that is interest and the part that is applied to reducing the debt.

   SOLUTION   During the first month, the entire $220,000 is owed. Interest on this amount for 1 month is found by the formula for simple interest, with $r = $ annual interest rate and $t = $ time in years.

$$I = Prt = 220,000(0.06)\frac{1}{12} = \$1100$$

*Mortgage rates are quoted in terms of annual interest, but it is always understood that the monthly rate is 1/12 of the annual rate and that interest is compounded monthly.

YOUR TURN 3 Find the monthly payment and total amount of interest paid in Example 3 if the mortgage is for 15 years and the interest rate is 7%.

At the end of the month, a payment of $1319.01 is made; since $1100 of this is interest, a total of

$$\$1319.01 - \$1100 = \$219.01$$

is applied to the reduction of the original debt. **TRY YOUR TURN 3**

It can be shown that the unpaid balance after x payments is given by the function

$$y = R\left[\frac{1 - (1 + i)^{-(n-x)}}{i}\right],$$

although this formula will only give an approximation if R is rounded to the nearest penny. For example, the unrounded value of R in Example 3 is 1319.011155. When this value is put into the above formula, the unpaid balance is found to be

$$y = 1319.011155\left[\frac{1 - (1.005)^{-359}}{0.005}\right] = 219{,}780.99,$$

while rounding R to 1319.01 in the above formula gives an approximate balance of $219,780.80. A graph of this function is shown in Figure 12.

We can find the unpaid balance after any number of payments, x, by finding the y-value that corresponds to x. For example, the remaining balance after 5 years or 60 payments is shown at the bottom of the graphing calculator screen in Figure 13(a). You may be surprised that the remaining balance on a $220,000 loan is as large as $204,719.41. This is because most of the early payments on a loan go toward interest, as we saw in Example 3(c).

By adding the graph of $y = (1/2)220{,}000 = 110{,}000$ to the figure, we can find when half the loan has been repaid. From Figure 13(b) we see that 252 payments are required. Note that only 108 payments remain at that point, which again emphasizes the fact that the earlier payments do little to reduce the loan.

The graph on the left shows $y = 1319.01\left[\frac{1 - (1.005)^{-(360-x)}}{0.005}\right]$

FIGURE 12

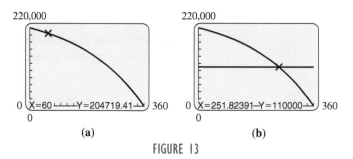

(a)   **(b)**

FIGURE 13

Amortization Schedules

In the preceding example, 360 payments are made to amortize a $220,000 loan. The loan balance after the first payment is reduced by only $219.01, which is much less than $(1/360)(220{,}000) \approx \$611.11$. Therefore, even though equal *payments* are made to amortize a loan, the loan *balance* does not decrease in equal steps. This fact is very important if a loan is paid off early.

EXAMPLE 4 **Early Payment**

Ami Aigen borrows $1000 for 1 year at 12% annual interest compounded monthly. Verify that her monthly loan payment is $88.8488, which is rounded to $88.85. After making three payments, she decides to pay off the remaining balance all at once. How much must she pay?

SOLUTION Since nine payments remain to be paid, they can be thought of as an annuity consisting of nine payments of $88.85 at 1% interest per period. The present value of this annuity is

$$88.8488\left[\frac{1 - (1.01)^{-9}}{0.01}\right] \approx 761.08.$$

So Ami's remaining balance, computed by this method, is $761.08.

An alternative method of figuring the balance is to consider the payments already made as an annuity of three payments. At the beginning, the present value of this annuity was

$$88.85\left[\frac{1 - (1.01)^{-3}}{0.01}\right] \approx 261.31.$$

So she still owes the difference $1000 - $261.31 = 738.69. Furthermore, she owes the interest on this amount for 3 months, for a total of

$$(738.69)(1.01)^3 \approx \$761.07.$$

YOUR TURN 4 Find the remaining balance in Example 4 if the balance was to be paid off after four months. Use the unrounded value for R of $88.8488.

This balance due differs from the one obtained by the first method by 1 cent because the monthly payment and the other calculations were rounded to the nearest penny. If we had used the more accurate value of $R = 88.8488$ and not rounded any intermediate answers, both methods would have given the same value of $761.08. **TRY YOUR TURN 4**

Although most people would not quibble about a difference of 1 cent in the balance due in Example 4, the difference in other cases (larger amounts or longer terms) might be more than that. A bank or business must keep its books accurately to the nearest penny, so it must determine the balance due in such cases unambiguously and exactly. This is done by means of an **amortization schedule**, which lists how much of each payment is interest and how much goes to reduce the balance, as well as how much is owed after *each* payment.

EXAMPLE 5 **Amortization Table**

Determine the exact amount Ami Aigen in Example 4 owes after three monthly payments.

SOLUTION An amortization table for the loan is shown below. It is obtained as follows. The annual interest rate is 12% compounded monthly, so the interest rate per month is $12\%/12 = 1\% = 0.01$. When the first payment is made, 1 month's interest—namely $0.01(1000) = 10—is owed. Subtracting this from the $88.85 payment leaves $78.85 to be applied to repayment. Hence, the principal at the end of the first payment period is $1000 - $78.85 = 921.15, as shown in the "payment 1" line of the chart.

When payment 2 is made, 1 month's interest on $921.15 is owed, namely $0.01(921.15) = 9.21. Subtracting this from the $88.85 payment leaves $79.64 to reduce the principal. Hence, the principal at the end of payment 2 is $921.15 - $79.64 = 841.51. The interest portion of payment 3 is based on this amount, and the remaining lines of the table are found in a similar fashion.

The schedule shows that after three payments, she still owes $761.08, an amount that agrees with the first method in Example 4.

		Amortization Table		
Payment Number	Amount of Payment	Interest for Period	Portion to Principal	Principal at End of Period
0	—	—	—	$1000.00
1	$88.85	$10.00	$78.85	$921.15
2	$88.85	$9.21	$79.64	$841.51
3	$88.85	$8.42	$80.43	$761.08
4	$88.85	$7.61	$81.24	$679.84
5	$88.85	$6.80	$82.05	$597.79
6	$88.85	$5.98	$82.87	$514.92
7	$88.85	$5.15	$83.70	$431.22
8	$88.85	$4.31	$84.54	$346.68
9	$88.85	$3.47	$85.38	$261.30
10	$88.85	$2.61	$86.24	$175.06
11	$88.85	$1.75	$87.10	$87.96
12	$88.84	$0.88	$87.96	$0.00

The amortization schedule in Example 5 is typical. In particular, note that all payments are the same except the last one. It is often necessary to adjust the amount of the final payment to account for rounding off earlier and to ensure that the final balance is exactly 0.

An amortization schedule also shows how the periodic payments are applied to interest and principal. The amount going to interest decreases with each payment, while the amount going to reduce the principal increases with each payment.

⊞ TECHNOLOGY NOTE

A graphing calculator program to produce an amortization schedule is available in the *Graphing Calculator and Excel Spreadsheet Manual* available with this book. The TI-84 Plus includes a built-in program to find the amortization payment. Spreadsheets are another useful tool for creating amortization tables. Microsoft Excel has a built-in feature for calculating monthly payments. Figure 14 shows an Excel amortization table for Example 5. For more details, see the *Graphing Calculator and Excel Spreadsheet Manual*, also available with this book.

	A	B	C	D	E	F
1	Pmt#	Payment	Interest	Principal	End Prncpl	
2	0				1000	
3	1	88.85	10.00	78.85	921.15	
4	2	88.85	9.21	79.64	841.51	
5	3	88.85	8.42	80.43	761.08	
6	4	88.85	7.61	81.24	679.84	
7	5	88.85	6.80	82.05	597.79	
8	6	88.85	5.98	82.87	514.92	
9	7	88.85	5.15	83.70	431.22	
10	8	88.85	4.31	84.54	346.68	
11	9	88.85	3.47	85.38	261.30	
12	10	88.85	2.61	86.24	175.06	
13	11	88.85	1.75	87.10	87.96	
14	12	88.85	0.88	87.97	-0.01	

FIGURE 14

EXAMPLE 6 **Paying Off a Loan Early**

Suppose that in Example 2, the car owner decides that she can afford to make payments of $700 rather than $517.17. How much earlier would she pay off the loan? How much interest would she save?

SOLUTION Putting $R = 700$, $P = 17,000$, and $i = 0.005$ into the formula for the present value of an annuity gives

$$17,000 = 700\left[\frac{1 - 1.005^{-n}}{0.005}\right].$$

Multiply both sides by 0.005 and divide by 700 to get

$$\frac{85}{700} = 1 - 1.005^{-n},$$

or

$$1.005^{-n} = 1 - \frac{85}{700}.$$

Solve this using either logarithms or a graphing calculator, as in Example 11 in Section 5.1, to get $n = 25.956$. This means that 25 payments of $700, plus a final, smaller payment, would be sufficient to pay off the loan. Create an amortization table to verify that the final payment would be $669.47 (the sum of the principal after the penultimate payment plus the interest on that principal for the final month). The loan would then be paid off after 26 months, or 10 months early.

The original loan required 36 payments of $517.17, or 36(517.17) = $18,618.12, although the amount is actually $18,618.24 because the final payment was $517.29, as an amortization table would show. With larger payments, the car owner paid 25(700) + 669.47 = $18,169.47. Therefore, the car owner saved $18,618.24 − $18,169.47 = $448.77 in interest by making larger payments each month.

5.3 EXERCISES

1. Explain the difference between the present value of an annuity and the future value of an annuity. For a given annuity, which is larger? Why?

2. What does it mean to amortize a loan?

Find the present value of each ordinary annuity.

3. Payments of $890 each year for 16 years at 6% compounded annually

4. Payments of $1400 each year for 8 years at 6% compounded annually

5. Payments of $10,000 semiannually for 15 years at 5% compounded semiannually

6. Payments of $50,000 quarterly for 10 years at 4% compounded quarterly

7. Payments of $15,806 quarterly for 3 years at 6.8% compounded quarterly

8. Payments of $18,579 every 6 months for 8 years at 5.4% compounded semiannually

Find the lump sum deposited today that will yield the same total amount as payments of $10,000 at the end of each year for 15 years at each of the given interest rates.

9. 4% compounded annually

10. 6% compounded annually

Find (a) the payment necessary to amortize each loan; (b) the total payments and the total amount of interest paid based on the calculated monthly payments, and (c) the total payments and total amount of interest paid based upon an amortization table.

11. $2500; 6% compounded quarterly; 6 quarterly payments

12. $41,000; 8% compounded semiannually; 10 semiannual payments

13. $90,000; 6% compounded annually; 12 annual payments

14. $140,000; 8% compounded quarterly; 15 quarterly payments

15. $7400; 6.2% compounded semiannually; 18 semiannual payments

16. $5500; 10% compounded monthly; 24 monthly payments

Suppose that in the loans described in Exercises 13–16, the borrower paid off the loan after the time indicated below. Calculate the amount needed to pay off the loan, using either of the two methods described in Example 4.

17. After 3 years in Exercise 13

18. After 5 quarters in Exercise 14

19. After 3 years in Exercise 15

20. After 7 months in Exercise 16

Use the amortization table in Example 5 to answer the questions in Exercises 21–24.

21. How much of the fourth payment is interest?

22. How much of the eleventh payment is used to reduce the debt?

23. How much interest is paid in the first 4 months of the loan?

24. How much interest is paid in the last 4 months of the loan?

25. What sum deposited today at 5% compounded annually for 8 years will provide the same amount as $1000 deposited at the end of each year for 8 years at 6% compounded annually?

26. What lump sum deposited today at 8% compounded quarterly for 10 years will yield the same final amount as deposits of $4000 at the end of each 6-month period for 10 years at 6% compounded semiannually?

Find the monthly house payments necessary to amortize each loan. Then calculate the total payments and the total amount of interest paid.

27. $199,000 at 7.01% for 25 years

28. $175,000 at 6.24% for 30 years

29. $253,000 at 6.45% for 30 years

30. $310,000 at 5.96% for 25 years

Suppose that in the loans described in Exercises 13–16, the borrower made a larger payment, as indicated below. Calculate (a) the time needed to pay off the loan, (b) the total amount of the payments, and (c) the amount of interest saved, compared with part c of Exercises 13–16.

31. $16,000 in Exercise 13

32. $18,000 in Exercise 14

33. $850 in Exercise 15

34. $400 in Exercise 16

APPLICATIONS

Business and Economics

35. **House Payments** Calculate the monthly payment and total amount of interest paid in Example 3 with a 15-year loan, and then compare with the results of Example 3.

36. **Installment Buying** Stereo Shack sells a stereo system for $600 down and monthly payments of $30 for the next 3 years. If the interest rate is 1.25% per month on the unpaid balance, find

   a. the cost of the stereo system.

   b. the total amount of interest paid.

37. **Car Payments** Hong Le buys a car costing $14,000. He agrees to make payments at the end of each monthly period for 4 years. He pays 7% interest, compounded monthly.

   a. What is the amount of each payment?

   b. Find the total amount of interest Le will pay.

38. **Credit Card Debt** Tom Shaffer charged $8430 on his credit card to relocate for his first job. When he realized that the interest rate for the unpaid balance was 27% compounded monthly, he decided not to charge any more on that account. He wants to have this account paid off by the end of 3 years,

so he arranges to have automatic payments sent at the end of each month.

a. What monthly payment must he make to have the account paid off by the end of 3 years?

b. How much total interest will he have paid?

39. New Car In Spring 2010, some dealers offered a cash-back allowance of $2250 or 0.9% financing for 36 months on an Acura TL. *Source: cars.com.*

a. Determine the payments on an Acura TL if a buyer chooses the 0.9% financing option and needs to finance $30,000 for 36 months, compounded monthly. Find the total amount the buyer will pay for this option.

b. Determine the payments on an Acura TL if a buyer chooses the cash-back option and now needs to finance only $27,750. At the time, it was possible to get a new car loan at 6.33% for 48 months, compounded monthly. Find the total amount the buyer will pay for this option.

c. Discuss which deal is best and why.

40. New Car In Spring 2010, some dealers offered a cash-back allowance of $1500 or 1.9% financing for 36 months on a Volkswagen Tiguan. *Source: cars.com.*

a. Determine the payments on a Volkswagen Tiguan if a buyer chooses the 1.9% financing option and needs to finance $25,000 for 36 months, compounded monthly. Find the total amount the buyer will pay for this option.

b. Determine the payments on a Volkswagen Tiguan if a buyer chooses the cash-back option and now needs to finance only $23,500. At the time, it was possible to get a new car loan at 6.33% for 48 months, compounded monthly. Find the total amount the buyer will pay for this option.

c. Discuss which deal is best and why.

41. Lottery Winnings In most states, the winnings of million-dollar lottery jackpots are divided into equal payments given annually for 20 years. (In Colorado, the results are distributed over 25 years.) This means that the present value of the jackpot is worth less than the stated prize, with the actual value determined by the interest rate at which the money could be invested. *Source: The New York Times Magazine.*

a. Find the present value of a $1 million lottery jackpot distributed in equal annual payments over 20 years, using an interest rate of 5%.

b. Find the present value of a $1 million lottery jackpot distributed in equal annual payments over 20 years, using an interest rate of 9%.

c. Calculate the answer for part a using the 25-year distribution time in Colorado.

d. Calculate the answer for part b using the 25-year distribution time in Colorado.

Student Loans Student borrowers now have more options to choose from when selecting repayment plans. The standard plan repays the loan in up to 10 years with equal monthly payments.

The extended plan allows up to 25 years to repay the loan. *Source: U.S. Department of Education.* **A student borrows $55,000 at 6.80% compounded monthly.**

42. Find the monthly payment and total interest paid under the standard plan over 10 years.

43. Find the monthly payment and total interest paid under the extended plan over 25 years.

Installment Buying In Exercises 44–46, prepare an amortization schedule showing the first four payments for each loan.

44. An insurance firm pays $4000 for a new printer for its computer. It amortizes the loan for the printer in 4 annual payments at 8% compounded annually.

45. Large semitrailer trucks cost $110,000 each. Ace Trucking buys such a truck and agrees to pay for it by a loan that will be amortized with 9 semiannual payments at 8% compounded semiannually.

46. One retailer charges $1048 for a laptop computer. A firm of tax accountants buys 8 of these laptops. They make a down payment of $1200 and agree to amortize the balance with monthly payments at 6% compounded monthly for 4 years.

47. Investment In 1995, Oseola McCarty donated $150,000 to the University of Southern Mississippi to establish a scholarship fund. What is unusual about her is that the entire amount came from what she was able to save each month from her work as a washer woman, a job she began in 1916 at the age of 8, when she dropped out of school. *Sources: The New York Times.*

a. How much would Ms. McCarty have to put into her savings account at the end of every 3 months to accumulate $150,000 over 79 years? Assume she received an interest rate of 5.25% compounded quarterly.

b. Answer part a using a 2% and a 7% interest rate.

48. Loan Payments   When Nancy Hart opened her law office, she bought $14,000 worth of law books and $7200 worth of office furniture. She paid $1200 down and agreed to amortize the balance with semiannual payments for 5 years, at 8% compounded semiannually.

a. Find the amount of each payment.

b. Refer to the text and Figure 13. When her loan had been reduced below $5000, Nancy received a large tax refund and decided to pay off the loan. How many payments were left at this time?

49. House Payments   Ian Desrosiers buys a house for $285,000. He pays $60,000 down and takes out a mortgage at 6.5% on the balance. Find his monthly payment and the total amount of interest he will pay if the length of the mortgage is

a. 15 years;

b. 20 years;

c. 25 years.

d. Refer to the text and Figure 13. When will half the 20-year loan in part b be paid off?

50. House Payments   The Chavara family buys a house for $225,000. They pay $50,000 down and take out a 30-year mortgage on the balance. Find their monthly payment and the total amount of interest they will pay if the interest rate is

a. 6%;

b. 6.5%;

c. 7%.

d. Refer to the text and Figure 13. When will half the 7% loan in part c be paid off?

51. Refinancing a Mortgage   Fifteen years ago, the Budai family bought a home and financed $150,000 with a 30-year mortgage at 8.2%.

a. Find their monthly payment, the total amount of their payments, and the total amount of interest they will pay over the life of this loan.

b. The Budais made payments for 15 years. Estimate the unpaid balance using the formula

$$y = R\left[\frac{1 - (1 + i)^{-(n-x)}}{i}\right],$$

and then calculate the total of their remaining payments.

c. Suppose interest rates have dropped since the Budai family took out their original loan. One local bank now offers a 30-year mortgage at 6.5%. The bank fees for refinancing are $3400. If the Budais pay this fee up front and refinance the balance of their loan, find their monthly payment. Including the refinancing fee, what is the total amount of their payments? Discuss whether or not the family should refinance with this option.

d. A different bank offers the same 6.5% rate but on a 15-year mortgage. Their fee for financing is $4500. If the Budais pay this fee up front and refinance the balance of their loan, find their monthly payment. Including the refinancing fee, what is the total amount of their payments? Discuss whether or not the family should refinance with this option.

52. Inheritance   Deborah Harden has inherited $25,000 from her grandfather's estate. She deposits the money in an account offering 6% interest compounded annually. She wants to make equal annual withdrawals from the account so that the money (principal and interest) lasts exactly 8 years.

a. Find the amount of each withdrawal.

b. Find the amount of each withdrawal if the money must last 12 years.

53. Charitable Trust   The trustees of a college have accepted a gift of $150,000. The donor has directed the trustees to deposit the money in an account paying 6% per year, compounded semiannually. The trustees may make equal withdrawals at the end of each 6-month period; the money must last 5 years.

a. Find the amount of each withdrawal.

b. Find the amount of each withdrawal if the money must last 6 years.

Amortization   **Prepare an amortization schedule for each loan.**

54. A loan of $37,948 with interest at 6.5% compounded annually, to be paid with equal annual payments over 10 years.

55. A loan of $4836 at 7.25% interest compounded semi-annually, to be repaid in 5 years in equal semiannual payments.

56. Perpetuity   A *perpetuity* is an annuity in which the payments go on forever. We can derive a formula for the present value of a perpetuity by taking the formula for the present value of an annuity and looking at what happens when n gets larger and larger. Explain why the present value of a perpetuity is given by

$$P = \frac{R}{i}.$$

57. Perpetuity   Using the result of Exercise 56, find the present value of perpetuities for each of the following.

a. Payments of $1000 a year with 4% interest compounded annually

b. Payments of $600 every 3 months with 6% interest compounded quarterly

YOUR TURN ANSWERS

1. $6389.86   **2.** $394.59
3. $1977.42, $135,935.60   **4.** $679.84

5 CHAPTER REVIEW

SUMMARY

In this chapter we introduced the mathematics of finance. We first extended simple interest calculations to compound interest, which is interest earned on interest previously earned. We then developed the mathematics associated with the following financial concepts.

- In an annuity, money continues to be deposited at regular intervals, and compound interest is earned on that money as well.
- In an ordinary annuity, payments are made at the end of each time period, and the compounding period is the same as the time between payments, which simplifies the calculations.

- An annuity due is slightly different, in that the payments are made at the beginning of each time period.
- A sinking fund is like an ordinary annuity; a fund is set up to receive periodic payments. The payments plus the compound interest will produce a desired sum by a certain date.
- The present value of an annuity is the amount that would have to be deposited today to produce the same amount as the annuity at the end of a specified time.
- An amortization table shows how a loan is paid back after a specified time. It shows the payments broken down into interest and principal.

We have presented a lot of new formulas in this chapter. By answering the following questions, you can decide which formula to use for a particular problem.

1. Is simple or compound interest involved?

   Simple interest is normally used for investments or loans of a year or less; compound interest is normally used in all other cases.

2. If simple interest is being used, what is being sought: interest amount, future value, present value, or interest rate?

3. If compound interest is being used, does it involve a lump sum (single payment) or an annuity (sequence of payments)?

   a. For a lump sum, what is being sought: present value, future value, number of periods at interest, or effective rate?

   b. For an annuity,

      i. Is it an ordinary annuity (payment at the end of each period) or an annuity due (payment at the beginning of each period)?

      ii. What is being sought: present value, future value, or payment amount?

Once you have answered these questions, choose the appropriate formula and work the problem. As a final step, consider whether the answer you get makes sense. For instance, present value should always be less than future value. The amount of interest or the payments in an annuity should be fairly small compared to the total future value.

List of Variables r is the annual interest rate.

i is the interest rate per period.

t is the number of years.

n is the number of periods.

m is the number of periods per year.

P is the principal or present value.

A is the future value of a lump sum.

S is the future value of an annuity.

R is the periodic payment in an annuity.

$$i = \frac{r}{m} \qquad n = tm$$

	Simple Interest	Compound Interest	Continuous Compounding
Interest	$I = Prt$	$I = A - P$	$I = A - P$
Future Value	$A = P(1 + rt)$	$A = P(1 + i)^n$	$A = Pe^{rt}$
Present Value	$P = \dfrac{A}{1 + rt}$	$P = \dfrac{A}{(1 + i)^n} = A(1 + i)^{-n}$	$P = Ae^{-rt}$
Effective Rate		$r_E = \left(1 + \dfrac{r}{m}\right)^m - 1$	$r_E = e^r - 1$

Ordinary Annuity   Future Value $S = R\left[\dfrac{(1 + i)^n - 1}{i}\right] = R \cdot s_{\overline{n}|i}$

Present Value $P = R\left[\dfrac{1 - (1 + i)^{-n}}{i}\right] = R \cdot a_{\overline{n}|i}$

Annuity Due   Future Value $S = R\left[\dfrac{(1 + i)^{n+1} - 1}{i}\right] - R$

Sinking Fund Payment $R = \dfrac{Si}{(1 + i)^n - 1} = \dfrac{S}{s_{\overline{n}|i}}$

Amortization Payments $R = \dfrac{Pi}{1 - (1 + i)^{-n}} = \dfrac{P}{a_{\overline{n}|i}}$

KEY TERMS

5.1
simple interest
principal
rate
time
future value
maturity value
compound interest
compound amount

nominal (stated) rate
effective rate
present value
rule of 70
rule of 72
continuous compounding

5.2
geometric sequence
terms

common ratio
annuity
ordinary annuity
payment period
future value of an annuity
term of an annuity
future value of an ordinary
  annuity
sinking fund

annuity due
future value of an annuity due

5.3
present value of an annuity
amortize a loan
amortization schedule

REVIEW EXERCISES

CONCEPT CHECK

Determine whether each of the following statements is true or false, and explain why.

  1. For a particular interest rate, compound interest is always better than simple interest.

 2. The sequence 1, 2, 4, 6, 8, . . . is a geometric sequence.

 3. If a geometric sequence has first term 3 and common ratio 2, then the sum of the first 5 terms is $S_5 = 93$.

 4. The value of a sinking fund should decrease over time.

5. For payments made on a mortgage, the (noninterest) portion of the payment applied on the principal increases over time.

 6. On a 30-year conventional home mortgage, at recent interest rates, it is common to pay more money on the interest on the loan than the actual loan itself.

7. One can use the amortization payments formula to calculate the monthly payment of a car loan.

 8. The effective rate formula can be used to calculate the present value of a loan.

9. The following calculation gives the monthly payment on a $25,000 loan, compounded monthly at a rate of 5% for a period of six years:

$$25{,}000\left[\dfrac{(1 + 0.05/12)^{72} - 1}{0.05/12}\right].$$

 10. The following calculation gives the present value of an annuity of $5,000 payments at the end of each year for 10 years. The fund earns 4.5% compounded annually.

$$5000\left[\dfrac{1 - (1.045)^{-10}}{0.045}\right]$$

PRACTICE AND EXPLORATION

Find the simple interest for each loan.

11. $15,903 at 6% for 8 months

12. $4902 at 5.4% for 11 months

13. $42,368 at 5.22% for 7 months

14. $3478 at 6.8% for 88 days (assume a 360-day year)

15. For a given amount of money at a given interest rate for a given time period, does simple interest or compound interest produce more interest?

Find the compound amount in each loan.

16. $2800 at 7% compounded annually for 10 years

17. $19,456.11 at 8% compounded semiannually for 7 years

18. $312.45 at 5.6% compounded semiannually for 16 years

19. $57,809.34 at 6% compounded quarterly for 5 years

Find the amount of interest earned by each deposit.

20. $3954 at 8% compounded annually for 10 years

21. $12,699.36 at 5% compounded semiannually for 7 years

22. $12,903.45 at 6.4% compounded quarterly for 29 quarters

23. $34,677.23 at 4.8% compounded monthly for 32 months

24. What is meant by the present value of an amount A?

Find the present value of each amount.

25. $42,000 in 7 years, 6% compounded monthly

26. $17,650 in 4 years, 4% compounded quarterly

27. $1347.89 in 3.5 years, 6.77% compounded semiannually

28. $2388.90 in 44 months, 5.93% compounded monthly

29. Write the first five terms of the geometric sequence with $a = 2$ and $r = 3$.

30. Write the first four terms of the geometric sequence with $a = 4$ and $r = 1/2$.

31. Find the sixth term of the geometric sequence with $a = -3$ and $r = 2$.

32. Find the fifth term of the geometric sequence with $a = -2$ and $r = -2$.

33. Find the sum of the first four terms of the geometric sequence with $a = -3$ and $r = 3$.

34. Find the sum of the first five terms of the geometric sequence with $a = 8000$ and $r = -1/2$.

35. Find $s_{\overline{30}|0.02}$.

36. Find $s_{\overline{20}|0.06}$.

37. What is meant by the future value of an annuity?

Find the future value of each annuity and the amount of interest earned.

38. $500 deposited at the end of each 6-month period for 10 years; money earns 6% compounded semiannually.

39. $1288 deposited at the end of each year for 14 years; money earns 4% compounded annually.

40. $4000 deposited at the end of each quarter for 7 years; money earns 5% compounded quarterly.

41. $233 deposited at the end of each month for 4 years; money earns 4.8% compounded monthly.

42. $672 deposited at the beginning of each quarter for 7 years; money earns 4.4% compounded quarterly.

43. $11,900 deposited at the beginning of each month for 13 months; money earns 6% compounded monthly.

44. What is the purpose of a sinking fund?

Find the amount of each payment that must be made into a sinking fund to accumulate each amount.

45. $6500; money earns 5% compounded annually for 6 years.

46. $57,000; money earns 4% compounded semiannually for $8\frac{1}{2}$ years.

47. $233,188; money earns 5.2% compounded quarterly for $7\frac{3}{4}$ years.

48. $1,056,788; money earns 7.2% compounded monthly for $4\frac{1}{2}$ years.

Find the present value of each ordinary annuity.

49. Deposits of $850 annually for 4 years at 6% compounded annually

50. Deposits of $1500 quarterly for 7 years at 5% compounded quarterly

51. Payments of $4210 semiannually for 8 years at 4.2% compounded semiannually

52. Payments of $877.34 monthly for 17 months at 6.4% compounded monthly

53. Give two examples of the types of loans that are commonly amortized.

Find the amount of the payment necessary to amortize each loan. Calculate the total interest paid.

54. $80,000; 5% compounded annually; 9 annual payments

55. $3200; 8% compounded quarterly; 12 quarterly payments

56. $32,000; 6.4% compounded quarterly; 17 quarterly payments

57. $51,607; 8% compounded monthly; 32 monthly payments

Find the monthly house payments for each mortgage. Calculate the total payments and interest.

58. $256,890 at 5.96% for 25 years

59. $177,110 at 6.68% for 30 years

A portion of an amortization table is given below for a $127,000 loan at 8.5% interest compounded monthly for 25 years.

Payment Number	Amount of Payment	Interest for Period	Portion to Principal	Principal at End of Period
1	$1022.64	$899.58	$123.06	$126,876.94
2	$1022.64	$898.71	$123.93	$126,753.01
3	$1022.64	$897.83	$124.81	$126,628.20
4	$1022.64	$896.95	$125.69	$126,502.51
5	$1022.64	$896.06	$126.58	$126,375.93
6	$1022.64	$895.16	$127.48	$126,248.45
7	$1022.64	$894.26	$128.38	$126,120.07
8	$1022.64	$893.35	$129.29	$125,990.78
9	$1022.64	$892.43	$130.21	$125,860.57
10	$1022.64	$891.51	$131.13	$125,729.44
11	$1022.64	$890.58	$132.06	$125,597.38
12	$1022.64	$889.65	$132.99	$125,464.39

Use the table to answer the following questions.

60. How much of the fifth payment is interest?

61. How much of the twelfth payment is used to reduce the debt?

62. How much interest is paid in the first 3 months of the loan?

63. How much has the debt been reduced at the end of the first year?

APPLICATIONS

Business and Economics

64. Personal Finance Jane Fleming owes $5800 to her mother. She has agreed to repay the money in 10 months at an interest rate of 5.3%. How much will she owe in 10 months? How much interest will she pay?

65. Business Financing Julie Ward needs to borrow $9820 to buy new equipment for her business. The bank charges her 6.7% simple interest for a 7-month loan. How much interest will she be charged? What amount must she pay in 7 months?

66. Business Financing An accountant loans $28,000 at simple interest to her business. The loan is at 6.5% and earns $1365 interest. Find the time of the loan in months.

67. Business Investment A developer deposits $84,720 for 7 months and earns $4055.46 in simple interest. Find the interest rate.

68. Personal Finance In 3 years Beth Rechsteiner must pay a pledge of $7500 to her college's building fund. What lump sum can she deposit today, at 5% compounded semiannually, so that she will have enough to pay the pledge?

69. Personal Finance Tom, a graduate student, is considering investing $500 now, when he is 23, or waiting until he is 40 to invest $500. How much more money will he have at the age of 65 if he invests now, given that he can earn 5% interest compounded quarterly?

70. Pensions Pension experts recommend that you start drawing at least 40% of your full pension as early as possible. Suppose you have built up a pension of $12,000-annual payments by working 10 years for a company. When you leave to accept a better job, the company gives you the option of collecting half of the full pension when you reach age 55 or the full pension at age 65. Assume an interest rate of 8% compounded annually. By age 75, how much will each plan produce? Which plan would produce the larger amount? *Source: Smart Money.*

71. Business Investment A firm of attorneys deposits $5000 of profit-sharing money at the end of each semiannual period for $7\frac{1}{2}$ years. Find the final amount in the account if the deposits earn 10% compounded semiannually. Find the amount of interest earned.

72. Business Financing A small resort must add a swimming pool to compete with a new resort built nearby. The pool will cost $28,000. The resort borrows the money and agrees to repay it with equal payments at the end of each quarter for $6\frac{1}{2}$ years at an interest rate of 8% compounded quarterly. Find the amount of each payment.

73. Business Financing The owner of Eastside Hallmark borrows $48,000 to expand the business. The money will be repaid in equal payments at the end of each year for 7 years. Interest is 6.5%. Find the amount of each payment and the total amount of interest paid.

74. Personal Finance To buy a new computer, Mark Nguyen borrows $3250 from a friend at 4.2% interest compounded annually for 4 years. Find the compound amount he must pay back at the end of the 4 years.

75. Effective Rate On May 21, 2010, Ascencia (a division of PBI Bank) paid 1.49% interest, compounded monthly, on a 1-year CD, while giantbank.com paid 1.45% compounded daily. What are the effective rates for the two CDs, and which bank paid a higher effective rate? *Source: Bankrate.com.*

76. Home Financing When the Lee family bought their home, they borrowed $315,700 at 7.5% compounded monthly for 25 years. If they make all 300 payments, repaying the loan on schedule, how much interest will they pay? (Assume the last payment is the same as the previous ones.)

77. New Car In Spring 2010, some dealers offered the following options on a Chevrolet HHR: a cash-back allowance of $4000, 0% financing for 60 months, or 3.9% financing for 72 months. *Source: cars.com.*

  a. Determine the payments on a Chevrolet HHR if a buyer chooses the 0% financing option and needs to finance $16,000 for 60 months. Find the total amount of the payments.

  b. Repeat part a for the 3.9% financing option for 72 months.

  c. Determine the payments on a Chevrolet HHR if a buyer chooses the cash-back option and now needs to finance only $12,000. At the time, it was possible to get a new car loan at 6.33% for 48 months, compounded monthly. Find the total amount of the payments.

  d. Discuss which deal is best and why.

78. New Car In Spring 2010, some dealers offered a cash-back allowance of $5000 or 0% financing for 72 months on a Chevrolet Silverado. *Source: cars.com.*

  a. Determine the payments on a Chevrolet Silverado if a buyer chooses the 0% financing option and needs to finance $30,000 for 72 months. Find the total amount of the payments.

  b. Determine the payments on a Chevrolet Silverado if a buyer chooses the cash-back option and now needs to finance only $25,000. At the time, it was possible to get a new car loan at 6.33% for 48 months, compounded monthly. Find the total amount of the payments.

  c. Discuss which deal is best and why.

  d. Find the interest rate at the bank that would make the total amount of payments for the two options equal.

79. Buying and Selling a House The Bahary family bought a house for $191,000. They paid $40,000 down and took out a 30-year mortgage for the balance at 6.5%.

  a. Find their monthly payment.

  b. How much of the first payment is interest?

After 180 payments, the family sells its house for $238,000. They must pay closing costs of $3700 plus 2.5% of the sale price.

c. Estimate the current mortgage balance at the time of the sale using one of the methods from Example 4 in Section 3.

d. Find the total closing costs.

e. Find the amount of money they receive from the sale after paying off the mortgage.

The following exercise is from an actuarial examination. *Source: The Society of Actuaries.*

80. Death Benefit The proceeds of a $10,000 death benefit are left on deposit with an insurance company for 7 years at an annual effective interest rate of 5%. The balance at the end of 7 years is paid to the beneficiary in 120 equal monthly payments of X, with the first payment made immediately. During the payout period, interest is credited at an annual effective interest rate of 3%. Calculate X. Choose one of the following.

    a. 117   **b.** 118   **c.** 129   **d.** 135   **e.** 158

81. Investment *The New York Times* posed a scenario with two individuals, Sue and Joe, who each have $1200 a month to spend on housing and investing. Each takes out a mortgage for $140,000. Sue gets a 30-year mortgage at a rate of 6.625%. Joe gets a 15-year mortgage at a rate of 6.25%. Whatever money is left after the mortgage payment is invested in a mutual fund with a return of 10% annually. *Source: The New york Times.*

a. What annual interest rate, when compounded monthly, gives an effective annual rate of 10%?

b. What is Sue's monthly payment?

c. If Sue invests the remainder of her $1200 each month, after the payment in part b, in a mutual fund with the interest rate in part a, how much money will she have in the fund at the end of 30 years?

d. What is Joe's monthly payment?

e. You found in part d that Joe has nothing left to invest until his mortgage is paid off. If he then invests the entire $1200 monthly in a mutual fund with the interest rate in part a, how much money will he have at the end of 30 years (that is, after 15 years of paying the mortgage and 15 years of investing)?

f. Who is ahead at the end of the 30 years and by how much?

g. Discuss to what extent the difference found in part f is due to the different interest rates or to the different amounts of time.

EXTENDED APPLICATION

TIME, MONEY, AND POLYNOMIALS

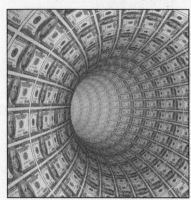

A *time line* is often helpful for evaluating complex investments. For example, suppose you buy a $1000 CD at time t_0. After one year $2500 is added to the CD at t_1. By time t_2, after another year, your money has grown to $3851 with interest. What rate of interest, called *yield to maturity* (YTM), did your money earn? A time line for this situation is shown in Figure 15.

FIGURE 15

Assuming interest is compounded annually at a rate i, and using the compound interest formula, gives the following description of the YTM.

$$1000(1 + i)^2 + 2500(1 + i) = 3851$$

Source: COMAP.

To determine the yield to maturity, we must solve this equation for i. Since the quantity $1 + i$ is repeated, let $x = 1 + i$ and first solve the second-degree (quadratic) polynomial equation for x.

$$1000x^2 + 2500x - 3851 = 0$$

We can use the quadratic formula with $a = 1000$, $b = 2500$, and $c = -3851$.

$$x = \frac{-2500 \pm \sqrt{2500^2 - 4(1000)(-3851)}}{2(1000)}$$

We get $x = 1.0767$ and $x = -3.5767$. Since $x = 1 + i$, the two values for i are $0.0767 = 7.67\%$ and $-4.5767 = -457.67\%$. We reject the negative value because the final accumulation is greater than the sum of the deposits. In some applications, however, negative rates may be meaningful. By checking in the first equation, we see that the yield to maturity for the CD is 7.67%.

Now let us consider a more complex but realistic problem. Suppose Austin Caperton has contributed for 4 years to a retirement fund. He contributed $6000 at the beginning of the first year. At the beginning of the next 3 years, he contributed $5840, $4000, and $5200, respectively. At the end of the fourth year, he had $29,912.38 in his fund. The interest rate earned by the fund varied between 21% and -3%, so Caperton would like to know the YTM $= i$ for his hard-earned retirement dollars. From a time line (see Figure 16), we set up the following equation in $1 + i$ for Caperton's savings program.

$$6000(1 + i)^4 + 5840(1 + i)^3 + 4000(1 + i)^2$$
$$+ 5200(1 + i) = 29{,}912.38$$

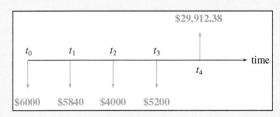

FIGURE 16

Let $x = 1 + i$. We need to solve the fourth-degree polynomial equation

$$f(x) = 6000x^4 + 5840x^3 + 4000x^2 + 5200x$$
$$-29{,}912.38 = 0.$$

There is no simple way to solve a fourth-degree polynomial equation, so we will use a graphing calculator.

We expect that $0 < i < 1$, so that $1 < x < 2$. Let us calculate $f(1)$ and $f(2)$. If there is a change of sign, we will know that there is a solution to $f(x) = 0$ between 1 and 2. We find that

$$f(1) = -8872.38 \quad \text{and} \quad f(2) = 139{,}207.62.$$

Using a graphing calculator, we find that there is one positive solution to this equation, $x = 1.14$, so $i = $ YTM $= 0.14 = 14\%$.

EXERCISES

1. Lorri Morgan received $50 on her 16th birthday, and $70 on her 17th birthday, both of which she immediately invested in the bank, with interest compounded annually. On her 18th birthday, she had $127.40 in her account. Draw a time line, set up a polynomial equation, and calculate the YTM.

2. At the beginning of the year, Blake Allvine invested $10,000 at 5% for the first year. At the beginning of the second year, he added $12,000 to the account. The total account earned 4.5% for the second year.

    a. Draw a time line for this investment.
    b. How much was in the fund at the end of the second year?
    c. Set up and solve a polynomial equation and determine the YTM. What do you notice about the YTM?

3. On January 2 each year for 3 years, Michael Bailey deposited bonuses of $1025, $2200, and $1850, respectively, in an account. He received no bonus the following year, so he made no deposit. At the end of the fourth year, there was $5864.17 in the account.

    a. Draw a time line for these investments.
    b. Write a polynomial equation in x ($x = 1 + i$) and use a graphing calculator to find the YTM for these investments.
    c. Go to the website WolframAlpha.com, and ask it to solve the polynomial from part b. Compare this method of solving the equation with using a graphing calculator.

4. Don Beville invested yearly in a fund for his children's college education. At the beginning of the first year, he invested $1000; at the beginning of the second year, $2000; at the third through the sixth, $2500 each year, and at the beginning of the seventh, he invested $5000. At the beginning of the eighth year, there was $21,259 in the fund.

    a. Draw a time line for this investment program.
    b. Write a seventh-degree polynomial equation in $1 + i$ that gives the YTM for this investment program.
    c. Use a graphing calculator to show that the YTM is less than 5.07% and greater than 5.05%.
    d. Use a graphing calculator to calculate the solution for $1 + i$ and find the YTM.
    e. Go to the website WolframAlpha.com, and ask it to solve the polynomial from part b. Compare this method of solving the equation with using a graphing calculator.

5. People often lose money on investments. Melissa Fischer invested $50 at the beginning of each of 2 years in a mutual fund, and at the end of 2 years her investment was worth $90.

    a. Draw a time line and set up a polynomial equation in $1 + i$. Solve for i.
    b. Examine each negative solution (rate of return on the investment) to see if it has a reasonable interpretation in the context of the problem. To do this, use the compound interest formula on each value of i to trace each $50 payment to maturity.

DIRECTIONS FOR GROUP PROJECT

Assume that you are in charge of a group of financial analysts and that you have been asked by the broker at your firm to develop a time line for each of the people listed in the exercises above. Prepare a report for each client that presents the YTM for each investment strategy. Make sure that you describe the methods used to determine the YTM in a manner that the average client should understand.

7

Sets and Probability

The study of probability begins with counting. An exercise in Section 2 of this chapter counts trucks carrying different combinations of early, late, and extra late peaches from the orchard to canning facilities. You'll see trees in another context in Section 5, where we use branching tree diagrams to calculate conditional probabilities.

O ur lives are bombarded by seemingly chance events — the chance of rain, the risk of an accident, the possibility the stock market increases, the likelihood of winning the lottery — all whose particular outcome may appear to be quite random. The field of probability attempts to quantify the likelihood of chance events and helps us to prepare for this uncertainty. In short, probability helps us to better understand the world in which we live. In this chapter and the next, we introduce the basic ideas of probability theory and give a sampling of some of its uses. Since the language of sets and set operations is used in the study of probability, we begin there.

7.1 Sets

APPLY IT   In how many ways can two candidates win the 50 states plus the District of Columbia in a U.S. presidential election?
Using knowledge of sets, we will answer this question in Exercise 69.

Think of a **set** as a well-defined collection of objects in which it is possible to determine if a given object is included in the collection. A set of coins might include one of each type of coin now put out by the U.S. government. Another set might be made up of all the students in your English class. By contrast, a collection of young adults does not constitute a set unless the designation "young adult" is clearly defined. For example, this set might be defined as those aged 18 to 29.

In mathematics, sets are often made up of numbers. The set consisting of the numbers 3, 4, and 5 is written

$$\{3, 4, 5\},$$

with set braces, $\{\ \}$, enclosing the numbers belonging to the set. The numbers 3, 4, and 5 are called the **elements** or **members** of this set. To show that 4 is an element of the set $\{3, 4, 5\}$, we use the symbol $\in$ and write

$$4 \in \{3, 4, 5\},$$

read "4 is an element of the set containing 3, 4, and 5." Also, $5 \in \{3, 4, 5\}$.

To show that 8 is *not* an element of this set, place a slash through the symbol:

$$8 \notin \{3, 4, 5\}.$$

Sets often are named with capital letters, so that if

$$B = \{5, 6, 7\},$$

then, for example, $6 \in B$ and $10 \notin B$.

It is possible to have a set with no elements. Some examples are the set of counting numbers less than one, the set of foreign-born presidents of the United States, and the set of men more than 10 feet tall. A set with no elements is called the **empty set** (or **null set**) and is written $\emptyset$.

CAUTION   Be careful to distinguish between the symbols 0, $\emptyset$, $\{0\}$, and $\{\emptyset\}$. The symbol 0 represents a *number*; $\emptyset$ represents a *set* with 0 elements; $\{0\}$ represents a set with one element, 0; and $\{\emptyset\}$ represents a set with one element, $\emptyset$.

We use the symbol $n(A)$ to indicate the *number* of elements in a finite set A. For example, if $A = \{a, b, c, d, e\}$, then $n(A) = 5$. Using this notation, we can write the information in the previous Caution as $n(\emptyset) = 0$ and $n(\{0\}) = n(\{\emptyset\}) = 1$.

Two sets are *equal* if they contain the same elements. The sets $\{5, 6, 7\}$, $\{7, 6, 5\}$, and $\{6, 5, 7\}$ all contain exactly the same elements and are equal. In symbols,

$$\{5, 6, 7\} = \{7, 6, 5\} = \{6, 5, 7\}.$$

This means that the ordering of the elements in a set is unimportant. Note that each element of the set is only listed once. Sets that do not contain exactly the same elements are *not equal*. For example, the sets $\{5, 6, 7\}$ and $\{7, 8, 9\}$ do not contain exactly the same elements and, thus, are not equal. To indicate that these sets are not equal, we write

$$\{5, 6, 7\} \neq \{7, 8, 9\}.$$

Sometimes we are interested in a common property of the elements in a set, rather than a list of the elements. This common property can be expressed by using **set-builder notation**, for example,

$$\{x \,|\, x \text{ has property } P\}$$

(read "the set of all elements x such that x has property P") represents the set of all elements x having some stated property P.

EXAMPLE 1 Sets

Write the elements belonging to each set.

(a) $\{x \,|\, x$ is a natural number less than 5$\}$

SOLUTION The natural numbers less than 5 make up the set $\{1, 2, 3, 4\}$.

(b) $\{x \,|\, x$ is a state that borders Florida$\}$

SOLUTION The states that border Florida make up the set $\{$Alabama, Georgia$\}$.

TRY YOUR TURN 1

YOUR TURN 1 Write the elements belonging to the set. $\{x \,|\, x$ is a state whose name begins with the letter O$\}$.

The **universal set** for a particular discussion is a set that includes all the objects being discussed. In elementary school arithmetic, for instance, the set of whole numbers might be the universal set, while in a college algebra class the universal set might be the set of real numbers. The universal set will be specified when necessary, or it will be clearly understandable from the context of the problem.

Subsets

Sometimes every element of one set also belongs to another set. For example, if

$$A = \{3, 4, 5, 6\}$$

and

$$B = \{2, 3, 4, 5, 6, 7, 8\},$$

then every element of A is also an element of B. This is an example of the following definition.

> **Subset**
>
> Set A is a **subset** of set B (written $A \subseteq B$) if every element of A is also an element of B. Set A is a *proper subset* (written $A \subset B$) if $A \subseteq B$ and $A \neq B$.

To indicate that A is *not* a subset of B, we write $A \nsubseteq B$.

EXAMPLE 2 Sets

Decide whether the following statements are *true* or *false*.

(a) $\{3, 4, 5, 6\} = \{4, 6, 3, 5\}$

SOLUTION Both sets contain exactly the same elements, so the sets are equal and the given statement is true. (The fact that the elements are listed in a different order does not matter.)

YOUR TURN 2 Decide if the following statement is *true* or *false*.
$\{2, 4, 6\} \subseteq \{6, 2, 4\}$

(b) $\{5, 6, 9, 12\} \subseteq \{5, 6, 7, 8, 9, 10, 11\}$

SOLUTION The first set is not a subset of the second because it contains an element, 12, that does not belong to the second set. Therefore, the statement is false.

TRY YOUR TURN 2

The empty set, $\emptyset$, by default, is a subset of every set A since it is impossible to find an element of the empty set (it has no elements) that is not an element of the set A. Similarly, A is a subset of itself, since every element of A is also an element of the set A.

> **Subset Properties**
> For any set A,
>
> $$\emptyset \subseteq A \quad \text{and} \quad A \subseteq A.$$

EXAMPLE 3 Subsets

List all possible subsets for each set.

(a) $\{7, 8\}$

SOLUTION There are 4 subsets of $\{7, 8\}$:

$$\emptyset, \quad \{7\}, \quad \{8\}, \quad \text{and} \quad \{7, 8\}.$$

(b) $\{a, b, c\}$

SOLUTION There are 8 subsets of $\{a, b, c\}$:

$$\emptyset, \quad \{a\}, \quad \{b\}, \quad \{c\}, \quad \{a, b\}, \quad \{a, c\}, \quad \{b, c\}, \quad \text{and} \quad \{a, b, c\}.$$

A good way to find the subsets of $\{7, 8\}$ and the subsets of $\{a, b, c\}$ in Example 3 is to use a **tree diagram**—a systematic way of listing all the subsets of a given set. Figure 1 shows tree diagrams for finding the subsets of $\{7, 8\}$ and $\{a, b, c\}$.

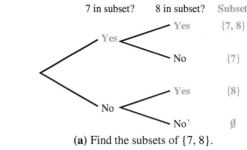

(a) Find the subsets of $\{7, 8\}$.

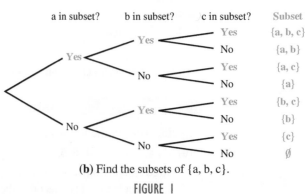

(b) Find the subsets of $\{a, b, c\}$.

FIGURE 1

As Figure 1 shows, there are two possibilities for each element (either it's in the subset or it's not), so a set with 2 elements has $2 \cdot 2 = 2^2 = 4$ subsets, and a set with 3 elements has $2^3 = 8$ subsets. This idea can be extended to a set with any finite number of elements, which leads to the following conclusion.

Number of Subsets

A set of k distinct elements has 2^k subsets.

In other words, if $n(A) = k$, then $n(\text{the set of all subsets of } A) = 2^k$.

EXAMPLE 4   Subsets

Find the number of subsets for each set.

(a) $\{3, 4, 5, 6, 7\}$

SOLUTION   This set has 5 elements; thus, it has 2^5 or 32 subsets.

(b) $\{x \mid x \text{ is a day of the week}\}$

SOLUTION   This set has 7 elements and therefore has $2^7 = 128$ subsets.

(c) $\emptyset$

SOLUTION   Since the empty set has 0 elements, it has $2^0 = 1$ subset—itself.

TRY YOUR TURN 3

YOUR TURN 3   Find the number of subsets for the set $\{x \mid x \text{ is a season of the year}\}$.

![Venn diagram showing set A inside set B, inside universal set U rectangle, labeled A ⊆ B]

$A \subseteq B$

FIGURE 2

Figure 2 shows a set A that is a subset of set B. The rectangle and everything inside it represents the universal set, U. Such diagrams, called **Venn diagrams**—after the English logician John Venn (1834–1923), who invented them in 1876—are used to help illustrate relationships among sets. Venn diagrams are very similar to Euler diagrams, described in Section 6.6. Euler diagrams are used in logic to denote variables having a certain property or not, while Venn diagrams are used in the context of sets to denote something being an element of a set or not.

Set Operations
It is possible to form new sets by combining or manipulating one or more existing sets. Given a set A and a universal set U, the set of all elements of U that do *not* belong to A is called the *complement* of set A. For example, if set A is the set of all the female students in a class, and U is the set of all students in the class, then the complement of A would be the set of all male students in the class. The complement of set A is written A', read "A-prime."

Complement of a Set

Let A be any set, with U representing the universal set. Then the **complement** of A, colored pink in the figure, is

$$A' = \{x \mid x \notin A \text{ and } x \in U\}.$$

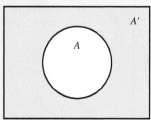

(Recall that the rectangle represents the universal set U.)

EXAMPLE 5   **Set Operations**

Let $U = \{1, 2, 3, 4, 5, 6, 7, 8, 9, 10, 11\}$, $A = \{1, 2, 4, 5, 7\}$, and $B = \{2, 4, 5, 7, 9, 11\}$. Find each set.

(a) A'

  SOLUTION   Set A' contains the elements of U that are not in A.

$$A' = \{3, 6, 8, 9, 10, 11\}$$

(b) $B' = \{1, 3, 6, 8, 10\}$

(c) $\emptyset' = U$ and $U' = \emptyset$

(d) $(A')' = A$

Given two sets A and B, the set of all elements belonging to *both* set A and set B is called the *intersection* of the two sets, written $A \cap B$. For example, the elements that belong to both set $A = \{1, 2, 4, 5, 7\}$ and set $B = \{2, 4, 5, 7, 9, 11\}$ are 2, 4, 5, and 7, so that

$$A \cap B = \{1, 2, 4, 5, 7\} \cap \{2, 4, 5, 7, 9, 11\} = \{2, 4, 5, 7\}.$$

Intersection of Two Sets

The **intersection** of sets A and B, shown in green in the figure, is

$$A \cap B = \{x \,|\, x \in A \text{ and } x \in B\}.$$

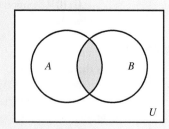

EXAMPLE 6   **Set Operations**

Let $A = \{3, 6, 9\}$, $B = \{2, 4, 6, 8\}$, and the universal set $U = \{0, 1, 2, \dots, 10\}$. Find each set.

(a) $A \cap B$

  SOLUTION

$$A \cap B = \{3, 6, 9\} \cap \{2, 4, 6, 8\} = \{6\}$$

(b) $A \cap B'$

  SOLUTION

$$A \cap B' = \{3, 6, 9\} \cap \{0, 1, 3, 5, 7, 9, 10\} = \{3, 9\}$$ TRY YOUR TURN 4

YOUR TURN 4   For the sets in Example 6, find $A' \cap B$.

Two sets that have no elements in common are called *disjoint sets*. For example, there are no elements common to both $\{50, 51, 54\}$ and $\{52, 53, 55, 56\}$, so these two sets are disjoint, and

$$\{50, 51, 54\} \cap \{52, 53, 55, 56\} = \emptyset.$$

This result can be generalized as follows.

Disjoint Sets

For any sets A and B, if A and B are **disjoint sets**, then $A \cap B = \emptyset$.

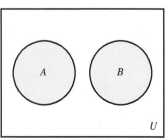

A and B are disjoint sets.

FIGURE 3

Figure 3 shows a pair of disjoint sets.

The set of all elements belonging to set A, to set B, or to both sets is called the *union* of the two sets, written $A \cup B$. For example,

$$\{1, 3, 5\} \cup \{3, 5, 7, 9\} = \{1, 3, 5, 7, 9\}.$$

Union of Two Sets

The **union** of sets A and B, shown in blue in the figure, is

$$A \cup B = \{x \mid x \in A \text{ or } x \in B \text{ (or both)}\}.$$

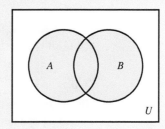

EXAMPLE 7   Union of Sets

Let $A = \{1, 3, 5, 7, 9, 11\}$, $B = \{3, 6, 9, 12\}$, $C = \{1, 2, 3, 4, 5\}$, and the universal set $U = \{0, 1, 2, \ldots, 12\}$. Find each set.

(a) $A \cup B$

   SOLUTION   Begin by listing the elements of the first set, $\{1, 3, 5, 7, 9, 11\}$. Then include any elements from the second set *that are not already listed*. Doing this gives

$$A \cup B = \{1, 3, 5, 7, 9, 11\} \cup \{3, 6, 9, 12\} = \{1, 3, 5, 7, 9, 11, 6, 12\}$$
$$= \{1, 3, 5, 6, 7, 9, 11, 12\}.$$

(b) $(A \cup B) \cap C'$

   SOLUTION   Begin with the expression in parentheses, which we calculated in part (a), and then intersect this with C'.

$$(A \cup B) \cap C' = \{1, 3, 5, 6, 7, 9, 11, 12\} \cap \{0, 6, 7, 8, 9, 10, 11, 12\}$$
$$= \{6, 7, 9, 11, 12\}$$ TRY YOUR TURN 5

YOUR TURN 5   For the sets in Example 7, find $A \cup (B \cap C')$.

NOTE
1. As Example 7 shows, when forming sets, do not list the same element more than once. In our final answer, we listed the elements in numerical order to make it easier to see what elements are in the set, but the set is the same, regardless of the order of the elements.
2. As shown in the definitions, an element is in the *intersection* of sets A and B if it is in A *and* B. On the other hand, an element is in the *union* of sets A and B if it is in A *or* B (or both).
3. In mathematics, "A *or* B" implies A or B, or both. Since "or" includes the possibility of both, we will usually omit the words "or both".

EXAMPLE 8   Stocks

The following table gives the 52-week low and high prices, the closing price, and the change from the previous day for six stocks in the Standard & Poor's 100 on February 19, 2010. *Source: New York Stock Exchange.*

New York Stock Exchange				
Stock	Low	High	Close	Change
AT&T	21.44	28.73	25.10	−0.55
Coca-Cola	37.44	59.45	55.72	−0.34
FedEx	34.02	92.59	81.76	+2.07
McDonald's	50.44	65.75	64.74	+0.40
PepsiCo	45.39	64.48	62.66	+0.21
Walt Disney	15.14	32.75	31.23	+0.68

Let the universal set U consist of the six stocks listed in the table. Let A contain all stocks with a high price greater than \$50, B all stocks with a closing price between \$60 and \$70, C all stocks with a positive price change, and D all stocks with a low price less than \$40. Find the following.

a. A'

SOLUTION Set A' contains all the listed stocks that are not in set A, or those with a high price less than or equal to \$50, so

$$A' = \{\text{AT\&T, Disney}\}.$$

b. $A \cap C$

SOLUTION The intersection of A and C will contain those stocks that are in both sets A and C, or those with a high price greater than \$50 *and* a positive price change.

$$A \cap C = \{\text{FedEx, McDonald's, PepsiCo}\}$$

c. $D \cup B$

SOLUTION The union of D and B contains all stocks with a low price less than \$40 *or* a closing price between \$60 and \$70.

$$D \cup B = \{\text{AT\&T, Coca-Cola, FedEx, McDonald's, PepsiCo, Disney}\} = U$$

EXAMPLE 9 **Employment**

A department store classifies credit applicants by gender, marital status, and employment status. Let the universal set be the set of all applicants, M be the set of male applicants, S be the set of single applicants, and E be the set of employed applicants. Describe each set in words.

a. $M \cap E$

SOLUTION The set $M \cap E$ includes all applicants who are both male *and* employed; that is, employed male applicants.

b. $M' \cup S$

SOLUTION This set includes all applicants who are female (not male) *or* single. *All* female applicants and *all* single applicants are in this set.

c. $M' \cap S'$

SOLUTION These applicants are female *and* married (not single); thus, $M' \cap S'$ is the set of all married female applicants.

d. $M \cup E'$

SOLUTION $M \cup E'$ is the set of applicants that are male *or* unemployed. The set includes *all* male applicants and *all* unemployed applicants.

7.1 EXERCISES

In Exercises 1–10, write true or false for each statement.

1. $3 \in \{2, 5, 7, 9, 10\}$ **2.** $6 \in \{-2, 6, 9, 5\}$

3. $9 \notin \{2, 1, 5, 8\}$ **4.** $3 \notin \{7, 6, 5, 4\}$

5. $\{2, 5, 8, 9\} = \{2, 5, 9, 8\}$

6. $\{3, 7, 12, 14\} = \{3, 7, 12, 14, 0\}$

7. $\{\text{all whole numbers greater than 7 and less than 10}\} = \{8, 9\}$

8. $\{x \mid x \text{ is an odd integer}; 6 \le x \le 18\} = \{7, 9, 11, 15, 17\}$

9. $0 \in \emptyset$ **10.** $\emptyset \in \{\emptyset\}$

Let $A = \{2, 4, 6, 10, 12\}$, $B = \{2, 4, 8, 10\}$, $C = \{4, 8, 12\}$, $D = \{2, 10\}$, $E = \{6\}$, and $U = \{2, 4, 6, 8, 10, 12, 14\}$. Insert $\subseteq$ or $\not\subseteq$ to make the statement true.

11. A ___ U **12.** E ___ A **13.** A ___ E

14. B ___ C **15.** $\emptyset$ ___ A **16.** $\{0, 2\}$ ___ D

17. D ___ B **18.** A ___ C

19. Repeat Exercises 11–18 except insert $\subset$ or $\not\subset$ to make the statement true.

20. What is set-builder notation? Give an example.

Insert a number in each blank to make the statement true, using the sets for Exercises 11–18.

21. There are exactly ___ subsets of A.

22. There are exactly ___ subsets of B.

23. There are exactly ___ subsets of C.

24. There are exactly ___ subsets of D.

Insert $\cap$ or $\cup$ to make each statement true.

25. $\{5, 7, 9, 19\}$ ___ $\{7, 9, 11, 15\} = \{7, 9\}$

26. $\{8, 11, 15\}$ ___ $\{8, 11, 19, 20\} = \{8, 11\}$

27. $\{2, 1, 7\}$ ___ $\{1, 5, 9\} = \{1, 2, 5, 7, 9\}$

28. $\{6, 12, 14, 16\}$ ___ $\{6, 14, 19\} = \{6, 12, 14, 16, 19\}$

29. $\{3, 5, 9, 10\}$ ___ $\emptyset = \emptyset$

30. $\{3, 5, 9, 10\}$ ___ $\emptyset = \{3, 5, 9, 10\}$

31. $\{1, 2, 4\}$ ___ $\{1, 2, 4\} = \{1, 2, 4\}$

32. $\{0, 10\}$ ___ $\{10, 0\} = \{0, 10\}$

33. Describe the intersection and union of sets. How do they differ?

34. Is it possible for two nonempty sets to have the same intersection and union? If so, give an example.

Let $U = \{1, 2, 3, 4, 5, 6, 7, 8, 9\}$, $X = \{2, 4, 6, 8\}$, $Y = \{2, 3, 4, 5, 6\}$, and $Z = \{1, 2, 3, 8, 9\}$. List the members of each set, using set braces.

35. $X \cap Y$ **36.** $X \cup Y$

37. X' **38.** Y'

39. $X' \cap Y'$ **40.** $X' \cap Z$

41. $Y \cap (X \cup Z)$ **42.** $X' \cap (Y' \cup Z)$

43. $(X \cap Y') \cup (Z' \cap Y')$ **44.** $(X \cap Y) \cup (X' \cap Z)$

45. In Example 6, what set do you get when you calculate $(A \cap B) \cup (A \cap B')$?

46. Explain in words why $(A \cap B) \cup (A \cap B') = A$.

Let $U = \{$all students in this school$\}$, $M = \{$all students taking this course$\}$, $N = \{$all students taking accounting$\}$, and $P = \{$all students taking zoology$\}$. Describe each set in words.

47. M' **48.** $M \cup N$

49. $N \cap P$ **50.** $N' \cap P'$

51. Refer to the sets listed for Exercises 11–18. Which pairs of sets are disjoint?

52. Refer to the sets listed for Exercises 35–44. Which pairs are disjoint?

Refer to Example 8 in the text. Describe each set in Exercises 53–56 in words; then list the elements of each set.

53. B' **54.** $A \cap B$

55. $(A \cap B)'$ **56.** $(C \cup D)'$

57. Let $A = \{1, 2, 3, \{3\}, \{1, 4, 7\}\}$. Answer each of the following as *true* or *false*.

   a. $1 \in A$ **b.** $\{3\} \in A$ **c.** $\{2\} \in A$ **d.** $4 \in A$

   e. $\{\{3\}\} \subset A$ **f.** $\{1, 4, 7\} \in A$ **g.** $\{1, 4, 7\} \subseteq A$

58. Let $B = \{a, b, c, \{d\}, \{e, f\}\}$. Answer each of the following as *true* or *false*.

   a. $a \in B$ **b.** $\{b, c, d\} \subset B$ **c.** $\{d\} \in B$

   d. $\{d\} \subseteq B$ **e.** $\{e, f\} \in B$ **f.** $\{a, \{e, f\}\} \subset B$

   g. $\{e, f\} \subset B$

APPLICATIONS

Business and Economics

Mutual Funds The tables in the next column show five of the largest holdings of four major mutual funds on January 31, 2010. *Sources: fidelity.com, franklintempleton.com, janus.com, vanguard.com.*

Vanguard 500	Fidelity New Millennium Fund
Exxon Mobil	Pfizer
Apple	Cisco Systems
General Electric	Wal-Mart Stores
IBM	Apple
JPMorgan Chase & Co.	JPMorgan Chase & Co.

Janus Perkins Large Cap Value	Templeton Large Cap Value Fund
Exxon Mobil	IBM
General Electric	General Electric
Wal-Mart Stores	Hewlett-Packard
AT&T	Home Depot
JPMorgan Chase & Co.	Aflac

Let U be the smallest possible set that includes all the corporations listed, and V, F, J, and T be the set of top holdings for each mutual fund, respectively. Find each set:

59. $V \cap J$ **60.** $V \cap (F \cup T)$

61. $(J \cup F)'$ **62.** $J' \cap T'$

63. **Sales Calls** Suppose that Kendra Gallegos has appointments with 9 potential customers. Kendra will be ecstatic if all 9 of these potential customers decide to make a purchase from her. Of course, in sales there are no guarantees. How many different sets of customers may place an order with Kendra? (*Hint:* Each set of customers is a subset of the original set of 9 customers.)

Life Sciences

Health The following table shows some symptoms of an overactive thyroid and an underactive thyroid. *Source: The Merck Manual of Diagnosis and Therapy.*

Underactive Thyroid	Overactive Thyroid
Sleepiness, s	Insomnia, i
Dry hands, d	Moist hands, m
Intolerance of cold, c	Intolerance of heat, h
Goiter, g	Goiter, g

Let U be the smallest possible set that includes all the symptoms listed, N be the set of symptoms for an underactive thyroid, and O be the set of symptoms for an overactive thyroid. Find each set.

64. O' **65.** N'

66. $N \cap O$ **67.** $N \cup O$

68. $N \cap O'$

Social Sciences

69. **APPLY IT** **Electoral College** U.S. presidential elections are decided by the Electoral College, in which each of the 50 states, plus the District of Columbia, gives all of its votes to a candidate.* Ignoring the number of votes each state has in the Electoral College, but including all possible combinations of states that could be won by either candidate, how many outcomes are possible in the Electoral College if there are two candidates? (*Hint:* The states that can be won by a candidate form a subset of all the states.)

General Interest

70. Musicians A concert featured a cellist, a flutist, a harpist, and a vocalist. Throughout the concert, different subsets of the four musicians performed together, with at least two musicians playing each piece. How many subsets of at least two are possible?

Television Cable Services The following table lists some of the most popular cable television networks. Use this information for Exercises 71–76. *Source: The New York Times 2010 Almanac.*

Network	Subscribers (in millions)	Launch	Content
The Discovery Channel	98.0	1985	Nonfiction, nature, science
TNT	98.0	1988	Movies, sports, original programming
USA Network	97.5	1980	Sports, family entertainment
The Learning Channel (TLC)	97.3	1980	Original programming, family entertainment
TBS Superstation	97.3	1976	Movies, sports, original programming

List the elements of the following sets. For exercises 74–76, describe each set in words.

71. F, the set of networks that were launched before 1985.

72. G, the set of networks that feature sports.

73. H, the set of networks that have more than 97.6 million viewers.

*The exceptions are Maine and Nebraska, which allocate their electoral college votes according to the winner in each congressional district.

74. $F \cap H$ **75.** $G \cup H$ **76.** G'

77. Games In David Gale's game of Subset Takeaway, the object is for each player, at his or her turn, to pick a nonempty proper subset of a given set subject to the condition that no subset chosen earlier by either player can be a subset of the newly chosen set. The winner is the last person who can make a legal move. Consider the set $A = \{1, 2, 3\}$. Suppose Joe and Dorothy are playing the game and Dorothy goes first. If she chooses the proper subset $\{1\}$, then Joe cannot choose any subset that includes the element 1. Joe can, however, choose $\{2\}$ or $\{3\}$ or $\{2, 3\}$. Develop a strategy for Joe so that he can always win the game if Dorothy goes first. *Source: Scientific American.*

States In the following list of states, let $A = \{$states whose name contains the letter $e\}$, let $B = \{$states with a population of more than 4,000,000$\}$, and $C = \{$states with an area greater than 40,000 square miles$\}$. *Source: The New York Times 2010 Almanac.*

State	Population (1000s)	Area (sq. mi.)
Alabama	4662	52,419
Alaska	686	663,267
Colorado	4939	104,094
Florida	18,328	65,755
Hawaii	1288	10,931
Indiana	6377	36,418
Kentucky	4269	40,409
Maine	1316	35,385
Nebraska	1783	77,354
New Jersey	8683	8721

78. a. Describe in words the set $A \cup (B \cap C)'$.
    b. List all elements in the set $A \cup (B \cap C)'$.

79. a. Describe in words the set $(A \cup B)' \cap C$.
    b. List all elements in the set $(A \cup B)' \cap C$.

YOUR TURN ANSWERS

1. {Ohio, Oklahoma, Oregon}
2. True
3. $2^4 = 16$ subsets
4. {2, 4, 8}
5. {1, 3, 5, 6, 7, 9, 11,12}

7.2 Applications of Venn Diagrams

APPLY IT The responses to a survey of 100 households show that 76 have a DVD player, 21 have a Blue Ray player, and 12 have both. How many have neither a DVD player nor Blue Ray player?
In Example 3 we show how a Venn diagram can be used to sort out this information to answer the question.

Venn diagrams were used in the previous section to illustrate set union and intersection. The rectangular region of a Venn diagram represents the universal set U. Including only a single set A inside the universal set, as in Figure 4, divides U into two regions. Region 1

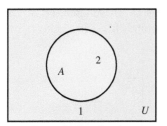

One set leads to 2 regions
(numbering is arbitrary).

FIGURE 4

represents those elements of U outside set A (that is, the elements in A'), and region 2 represents those elements belonging to set A. (The numbering of these regions is arbitrary.)

The Venn diagram in Figure 5(a) shows two sets inside U. These two sets divide the universal set into four regions. As labeled in Figure 5(a), region 1 represents the set whose elements are outside both set A and set B. Region 2 shows the set whose elements belong to A and not to B. Region 3 represents the set whose elements belong to both A and B. Which set is represented by region 4? (Again, the labeling is arbitrary.)

Two other situations can arise when representing two sets by Venn diagrams. If it is known that $A \cap B = \emptyset$, then the Venn diagram is drawn as in Figure 5(b). If it is known that $A \subseteq B$, then the Venn diagram is drawn as in Figure 5(c). For the material presented throughout this chapter we will only refer to Venn diagrams like the one in Figure 5(a), and note that some of the regions of the Venn diagram may be equal to the empty (or null) set.

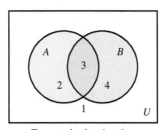

Two sets lead to 4 regions
(numbering is arbitrary).

(a)

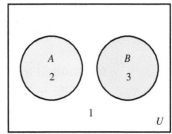

Two sets lead to 3 regions
(numbering is arbitrary).

(b)

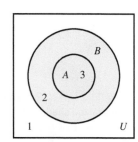

Two sets lead to 3 regions
(numbering is arbitrary).

(c)

FIGURE 5

EXAMPLE 1   **Venn Diagrams**

Draw Venn diagrams similar to Figure 5(a) and shade the regions representing each set.

(a) $A' \cap B$

SOLUTION   Set A' contains all the elements outside set A. As labeled in Figure 5(a), A' is represented by regions 1 and 4. Set B is represented by regions 3 and 4. The intersection of sets A' and B, the set $A' \cap B$, is given by the region common to both sets. The result is the set represented by region 4, which is blue in Figure 6. When looking for the intersection, remember to choose the area that is in one region *and* the other region.

In addition to the fact that region 4 in Figure 6 is $A' \cap B$, notice that region 1 is $A' \cap B'$, region 2 is $A \cap B'$, and region 3 is $A \cap B$.

FIGURE 6

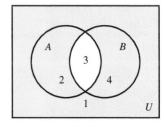

FIGURE 7

(b) $A' \cup B'$

YOUR TURN 1   Draw a Venn diagram and shade the region representing $A \cup B'$.

SOLUTION   Again, set A' is represented by regions 1 and 4, and set B' by regions 1 and 2. To find $A' \cup B'$, identify the region that represents the set of all elements in A', B', or both. The result, which is blue in Figure 7, includes regions 1, 2, and 4. When looking for the union, remember to choose the area that is in one region *or* the other region (or both).   TRY YOUR TURN 1

Venn diagrams also can be drawn with three sets inside U. These three sets divide the universal set into eight regions, which can be numbered (arbitrarily) as in Figure 8.

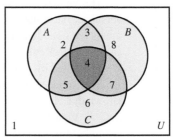

Three sets lead to 8 regions.
FIGURE 8

EXAMPLE 2   Venn Diagram

In a Venn diagram, shade the region that represents $A' \cup (B \cap C')$.

SOLUTION   First find $B \cap C'$. Set B is represented by regions 3, 4, 7, and 8, and set C' by regions 1, 2, 3, and 8. The overlap of these regions (regions 3 and 8) represents the set $B \cap C'$. Set A' is represented by regions 1, 6, 7, and 8. The union of the set represented by regions 3 and 8 and the set represented by regions 1, 6, 7, and 8 is the set represented by regions 1, 3, 6, 7, and 8, which are blue in Figure 9.   **TRY YOUR TURN 2**

YOUR TURN 2   Draw a Venn diagram and shade the region representing $A' \cap (B \cup C)$.

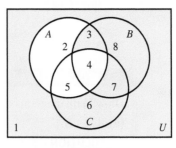

FIGURE 9

Applications   Venn diagrams can be used to analyze many applications, as illustrated in the following examples.

EXAMPLE 3   Entertainment Technology

A researcher collecting data on 100 households finds that

> 76 have a DVD player;
>
> 21 have a Blue Ray player; and
>
> 12 have both.

The researcher wants to answer the following questions.

(a) How many do not have a DVD player?

(b) How many have neither a DVD player nor a Blue Ray player?

(c) How many have a Blue Ray player but not a DVD player?

APPLY IT   **SOLUTION**   A Venn diagram like the one in Figure 10 will help sort out this information. In Figure 10(a), we put the number 12 in the region common to both a DVD player and a Blue Ray player, because 12 households have both. Of the 21 with a Blue Ray player, $21 - 12 = 9$ have no DVD player, so in Figure 10(b) we put 9 in the region for a Blue Ray player but no DVD player. Similarly, $76 - 12 = 64$ households have a DVD player but not a Blue Ray player, so we put 64 in that region. Finally, the diagram shows that $100 - 64 - 12 - 9 = 15$ households have neither a DVD player nor a Blue Ray player. Now we can answer the questions:

(a) $15 + 9 = 24$ do not have a DVD player.

(b) 15 have neither.

(c) 9 have a Blue Ray player but not a DVD player.

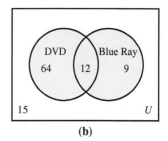

(a)   (b)

FIGURE 10

| EXAMPLE 4 | **Magazines** |

A survey of 77 freshman business students at a large university produced the following results.

25 of the students read *Bloomberg Businessweek*;

19 read *The Wall Street Journal*;

27 do not read *Fortune*;

11 read *Bloomberg Businessweek* but not *The Wall Street Journal*;

11 read *The Wall Street Journal* and *Fortune*;

13 read *Bloomberg Businessweek* and *Fortune*;

9 read all three.

Use this information to answer the following questions.

(a) How many students read none of the publications?

(b) How many read only *Fortune*?

(c) How many read *Bloomberg Businessweek* and *The Wall Street Journal*, but not *Fortune*?

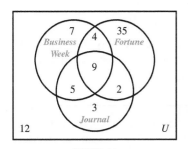

FIGURE 11

SOLUTION Since 9 students read all three publications, begin by placing 9 in the area that belongs to all three regions, as shown in Figure 11. Of the 13 students who read *Bloomberg Businessweek* and *Fortune*, 9 also read *The Wall Street Journal*. Therefore, only $13 - 9 = 4$ read just *Bloomberg Businessweek* and *Fortune*. Place the number 4 in the area of Figure 11 common only to *Bloomberg Businessweek* and *Fortune* readers.

In the same way, place $11 - 9 = 2$ in the region common only to *Fortune* and *The Wall Street Journal*. Of the 11 students who read *Bloomberg Businessweek* but not *The Wall Street Journal*, 4 read *Fortune*, so place $11 - 4 = 7$ in the region for those who read only *Bloomberg Businessweek*.

The data show that 25 students read *Bloomberg Businessweek*. However, $7 + 4 + 9 = 20$ readers have already been placed in the region representing *Bloomberg Businessweek*. The balance of this region will contain only $25 - 20 = 5$ students. These students read *Bloomberg Businessweek* and *The Wall Street Journal* but not *Fortune*. In the same way, $19 - (5 + 9 + 2) = 3$ students read only *The Wall Street Journal*.

Using the fact that 27 of the 77 students do not read *Fortune*, we know that 50 do read *Fortune*. We already have $4 + 9 + 2 = 15$ students in the region representing *Fortune*, leaving $50 - 15 = 35$ who read only *Fortune*.

A total of $7 + 4 + 35 + 5 + 9 + 2 + 3 = 65$ students are placed in the three circles in Figure 11. Since 77 students were surveyed, $77 - 65 = 12$ students read none of the three publications, and 12 is placed outside all three regions.

YOUR TURN 3 One hundred students were asked which fast food restaurants they had visited in the past month. The results are as follows:

47 ate at McDonald's;

46 ate at Taco Bell;

44 ate at Wendy's;

17 ate at McDonald's and Taco Bell;

19 ate at Taco Bell and Wendy's;

22 ate at Wendy's and McDonald's;

13 ate at all three.

Determine how many ate only at Taco Bell.

Now Figure 11 can be used to answer the questions asked above.

(a) There are 12 students who read none of the three publications.

(b) There are 35 students who read only *Fortune.*

(c) The overlap of the regions representing readers of *Bloomberg Businessweek* and *The Wall Street Journal* shows that 5 students read *Bloomberg Businessweek* and *The Wall Street Journal* but not *Fortune.* **TRY YOUR TURN 3**

| CAUTION | A common error in solving problems of this type is to make a circle represent one set and another circle represent its complement. In Example 4, with one circle representing those who read *Bloomberg Businessweek*, we did not draw another for those who do not read *Bloomberg Businessweek*. An additional circle is not only unnecessary (because those not in one set are automatically in the other) but very confusing, because the region outside or inside both circles must be empty. Similarly, if a problem involves men and women, do not draw one circle for men and another for women. Draw one circle; if you label it "women," for example, then men are automatically those outside the circle. |

EXAMPLE 5   Utility Maintenance

Jeff Friedman is a section chief for an electric utility company. The employees in his section cut down trees, climb poles, and splice wire. Friedman reported the following information to the management of the utility.

"Of the 100 employees in my section,

45 can cut trees;

50 can climb poles;

57 can splice wire;

22 can climb poles but can't cut trees;

20 can climb poles and splice wire;

25 can cut trees and splice wire;

14 can cut trees and splice wire but can't climb poles;

9 can't do any of the three (management trainees)."

FIGURE 12

The data supplied by Friedman lead to the numbers shown in Figure 12. Add the numbers from all of the regions to get the total number of employees:

$$9 + 3 + 14 + 23 + 11 + 9 + 17 + 13 = 99.$$

Friedman claimed to have 100 employees, but his data indicated only 99. Management decided that Friedman didn't qualify as a section chief, and he was reassigned as a night-shift meter reader in Guam. (*Moral:* He should have taken this course.)

In all the examples above, we started with a piece of information specifying the relationship with all the categories. This is usually the best way to begin solving problems of this type.

As we saw in the previous section, we use the symbol $n(A)$ to indicate the *number* of elements in a finite set A. The following statement about the number of elements in the union of two sets will be used later in our study of probability.

Union Rule for Sets

$$n(A \cup B) = n(A) + n(B) - n(A \cap B)$$

To prove this statement, let $x + y$ represent $n(A)$, y represent $n(A \cap B)$, and $y + z$ represent $n(B)$, as shown in Figure 13. Then

$$n(A \cup B) = x + y + z,$$
$$n(A) + n(B) - n(A \cap B) = (x + y) + (y + z) - y = x + y + z,$$

so $$n(A \cup B) = n(A) + n(B) - n(A \cap B).$$

FIGURE 13

EXAMPLE 6 School Activities

A group of 10 students meet to plan a school function. All are majoring in accounting or economics or both. Five of the students are economics majors and 7 are majors in accounting. How many major in both subjects?

SOLUTION Let A represent the set of accounting majors and B represent the set of economics majors. Use the union rule, with $n(A) = 5$, $n(B) = 7$, and $n(A \cup B) = 10$. Find $n(A \cap B)$.

$$n(A \cup B) = n(A) + n(B) - n(A \cap B)$$
$$10 = 5 + 7 - n(A \cap B),$$

so

$$n(A \cap B) = 5 + 7 - 10 = 2. \qquad \text{TRY YOUR TURN 4}$$

YOUR TURN 4 A group of students are sitting in the lounge. All are texting or listening to music or both. Eleven are listening to music and 15 are texting. Eight are doing both. How many students are in the lounge?

When A and B are disjoint, then $n(A \cap B) = 0$, so the union rule simplifies to $n(A \cup B) = n(A) + n(B)$.

CAUTION The rule $n(A \cup B) = n(A) + n(B)$ is only valid when A and B are disjoint. When A and B are *not* disjoint, use the rule $n(A \cup B) = n(A) + n(B) - n(A \cap B)$.

EXAMPLE 7 Endangered Species

The following table gives the number of threatened and endangered animal species in the world as of January, 2010. *Source: U.S. Fish and Wildlife Service.*

Endangered and Threatened Species			
	Endangered (E)	Threatened (T)	Totals
Amphibians and reptiles (A)	101	52	153
Arachnids and insects (I)	63	10	73
Birds (B)	256	23	279
Clams, crustaceans, corals and snails (C)	108	24	132
Fishes (F)	85	66	151
Mammals (M)	325	35	360
Totals	938	210	1148

Using the letters given in the table to denote each set, find the number of species in each of the following sets.

(a) $E \cap B$

SOLUTION The set $E \cap B$ consists of all species that are endangered *and* are birds. From the table, we see that there are 256 such species.

(b) $E \cup B$

SOLUTION The set $E \cup B$ consists of all species that are endangered *or* are birds. We include all 938 endangered species, plus the 23 bird species who are threatened but not endangered, for a total of 961. Alternatively, we could use the formula $n(E \cup B) = n(E) + n(B) - n(E \cap B) = 938 + 279 - 256 = 961$.

(c) $(F \cup M) \cap T'$

SOLUTION Begin with the set $F \cup M$, which is all species that are fish or mammals. This consists of the four categories with 85, 66, 325, and 35 species. Of this set, take those that are *not* threatened, for a total of $85 + 325 = 410$ species. This is the number of species of fish and mammals that are not threatened.

EXAMPLE 8 **Online Activities**

Suppose that a group of 150 students have done at least one of these activities online: purchasing an item, banking, and watching a video. In addition,

90 students have made an online purchase;

50 students have banked online;

70 students have watched an online video;

15 students have made an online purchase and watched an online video;

12 have banked online and watched an online video; and

10 students have done all three.

How many students have made an online purchase and banked online?

SOLUTION Let P represent the set of students who have made a purchase online, B the set who have banked online, and V the set who have watched a video online. Since 10 students did all three activities, begin by placing 10 in the area that belongs to all three regions, as shown in Figure 14. Of the 15 students who belong in sets P and V, 10 also belong to set B. Thus, only $15 - 10 = 5$ students were in the area of Figure 14 common only to sets P and V. Likewise, there are $12 - 10 = 2$ students who belong to only sets B and V. Since there are already $5 + 10 + 2 = 17$ students in set V, there are $70 - 17 = 53$ students in only set V.

We cannot use the information about set P, since there are two regions in P for which we have no information. Similarly, we cannot use the information about set B. In such cases, we label a region with the variable x. Here we place x in the region common only to P and B, as shown in Figure 14.

Of the 90 students in set P, the number who are only in set P must be $90 - x - 10 - 5 = 75 - x$, and this expression is placed in the appropriate region in Figure 14. Similarly, the number who are in only set B is $50 - x - 10 - 2 = 38 - x$. Notice that because all 150 students participated in at least one activity, there are no elements in the region outside the three circles.

Now that the diagram is filled out, we can determine the value of x by recalling that the total number of students was 150. Thus,

$$(75 - x) + 5 + x + 10 + (38 - x) + 2 + 53 = 150.$$

Simplifying, we have $183 - x = 150$, implying that $x = 33$. The number of students who made an online purchase and banked online is

$$33 + 10 = 43.$$

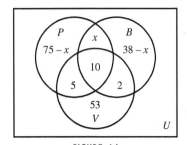

FIGURE 14

7.2 EXERCISES

Sketch a Venn diagram like the one in the figure, and use shading to show each set.

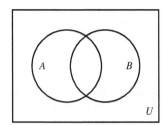

1. $B \cap A'$

2. $A \cup B'$

3. $A' \cup B$

4. $A' \cap B'$

5. $B' \cup (A' \cap B')$

6. $(A \cap B) \cup B'$

7. U'

8. $\emptyset'$

9. Three sets divide the universal set into at most _____ regions.

10. What does the notation $n(A)$ represent?

Sketch a Venn diagram like the one shown, and use shading to show each set.

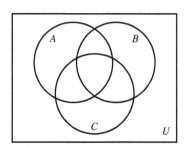

11. $(A \cap B) \cap C$

12. $(A \cap C') \cup B$

13. $A \cap (B \cup C')$

14. $A' \cap (B \cap C)$

15. $(A' \cap B') \cap C'$

16. $(A \cap B') \cap C$

17. $(A \cap B') \cup C'$

18. $A' \cap (B' \cup C)$

19. $(A \cup B') \cap C$

20. $A' \cup (B' \cap C')$

Use the union rule to answer the following questions.

21. If $n(A) = 5$, $n(B) = 12$, and $n(A \cap B) = 4$, what is $n(A \cup B)$?

22. If $n(A) = 15$, $n(B) = 30$, and $n(A \cup B) = 33$, what is $n(A \cap B)$?

23. Suppose $n(B) = 9$, $n(A \cap B) = 5$, and $n(A \cup B) = 22$. What is $n(A)$?

24. Suppose $n(A \cap B) = 5$, $n(A \cup B) = 38$, and $n(A) = 13$. What is $n(B)$?

Draw a Venn diagram and use the given information to fill in the number of elements for each region.

25. $n(U) = 41, n(A) = 16, n(A \cap B) = 12, n(B') = 20$

26. $n(A) = 28, n(B) = 12, n(A \cup B) = 32, n(A') = 19$

27. $n(A \cup B) = 24, n(A \cap B) = 6, n(A) = 11,$
$n(A' \cup B') = 25$

28. $n(A') = 31, n(B) = 25, n(A' \cup B') = 46, n(A \cap B) = 12$

29. $n(A) = 28, n(B) = 34, n(C) = 25, n(A \cap B) = 14,$
$n(B \cap C) = 15, n(A \cap C) = 11, n(A \cap B \cap C) = 9,$
$n(U) = 59$

30. $n(A) = 54, n(A \cap B) = 22, n(A \cup B) = 85,$
$n(A \cap B \cap C) = 4, n(A \cap C) = 15, n(B \cap C) = 16,$
$n(C) = 44, n(B') = 63$

31. $n(A \cap B) = 6, n(A \cap B \cap C) = 4, n(A \cap C) = 7,$
$n(B \cap C) = 4, n(A \cap C') = 11, n(B \cap C') = 8,$
$n(C) = 15, n(A' \cap B' \cap C') = 5$

32. $n(A) = 13, n(A \cap B \cap C) = 4, n(A \cap C) = 6,$
$n(A \cap B') = 6, n(B \cap C) = 6, n(B \cap C') = 11,$
$n(B \cup C) = 22, n(A' \cap B' \cap C') = 5$

In Exercises 33–36, show that the statement is true by drawing Venn diagrams and shading the regions representing the sets on each side of the equals sign.*

33. $(A \cup B)' = A' \cap B'$

34. $(A \cap B)' = A' \cup B'$

35. $A \cap (B \cup C) = (A \cap B) \cup (A \cap C)$

36. $A \cup (B \cap C) = (A \cup B) \cap (A \cup C)$

37. Use the union rule of sets to prove that $n(A \cup B \cup C) = n(A) + n(B) + n(C) - n(A \cap B) - n(A \cap C) - n(B \cap C) + n(A \cap B \cap C)$. (*Hint:* Write $A \cup B \cup C$ as $A \cup (B \cup C)$ and use the formula from Exercise 35.)

*The statements in Exercises 33 and 34 are known as De Morgan's Laws. They are named for the English mathematician Augustus De Morgan (1806–1871). They are analogous to De Morgan's Laws for logic seen in the previous chapter.

Business and Economics

Use Venn diagrams to answer the following questions.

38. Cooking Preferences Jeff Friedman, of Example 5 in the text, was again reassigned, this time to the home economics department of the electric utility. He interviewed 140 people in a suburban shopping center to discover some of their cooking habits. He obtained the following results:

58 use microwave ovens;
63 use electric ranges;
58 use gas ranges;
19 use microwave ovens and electric ranges;
17 use microwave ovens and gas ranges;
4 use both gas and electric ranges;
1 uses all three;
2 use none of the three.

Should he be reassigned one more time? Why or why not?

39. Harvesting Fruit Toward the middle of the harvesting season, peaches for canning come in three types, early, late, and extra late, depending on the expected date of ripening. During a certain week, the following data were recorded at a fruit delivery station:

34 trucks went out carrying early peaches;
61 carried late peaches;
50 carried extra late;
25 carried early and late;
30 carried late and extra late;
8 carried early and extra late;
6 carried all three;
9 carried only figs (no peaches at all).

a. How many trucks carried only late variety peaches?

b. How many carried only extra late?

c. How many carried only one type of peach?

d. How many trucks (in all) went out during the week?

40. Cola Consumption Market research showed that the adult residents of a certain small town in Georgia fit the following categories of cola consumption. (We assume here that no one drinks both regular cola and diet cola.)

Age	Drink Regular Cola (R)	Drink Diet Cola (D)	Drink No Cola (N)	Totals
21–25 (Y)	40	15	15	70
26–35 (M)	30	30	20	80
Over 35 (O)	10	50	10	70
Totals	80	95	45	220

Using the letters given in the table, find the number of people in each set.

a. $Y \cap R$

b. $M \cap D$

c. $M \cup (D \cap Y)$

d. $Y' \cap (D \cup N)$

e. $O' \cup N$

f. $M' \cap (R' \cap N')$

g. Describe the set $M \cup (D \cap Y)$ in words.

41. Investment Habits The following table shows the results of a survey taken by a bank in a medium-sized town in Tennessee. The survey asked questions about the investment habits of bank customers. (We assume here that no one invests in more than one of type of investment.)

Age	Stocks (S)	Bonds (B)	Savings Accounts (A)	Totals
18–29 (Y)	6	2	15	23
30–49 (M)	14	5	14	33
50 or over (O)	32	20	12	64
Totals	52	27	41	120

Using the letters given in the table, find the number of people in each set.

a. $Y \cap B$ **b.** $M \cup A$ **c.** $Y \cap (S \cup B)$

d. $O' \cup (S \cup A)$ **e.** $(M' \cup O') \cap B$

f. Describe the set $Y \cap (S \cup B)$ in words.

42. Investment Survey Most mathematics professors love to invest their hard-earned money. A recent survey of 150 math professors revealed that

111 invested in stocks;
98 invested in bonds;
100 invested in certificates of deposit;
80 invested in stocks and bonds;
83 invested in bonds and certificates of deposit;
85 invested in stocks and certificates of deposit;
9 did not invest in any of the three.

How many mathematics professors invested in stocks and bonds and certificates of deposit?

Life Sciences

43. Genetics After a genetics experiment on 50 pea plants, the number of plants having certain characteristics was tallied, with the following results.

22 were tall;
25 had green peas;
39 had smooth peas;
9 were tall and had green peas;
20 had green peas and smooth peas;
6 had all three characteristics;
4 had none of the characteristics.

a. Find the number of plants that were tall and had smooth peas.

b. How many plants were tall and had peas that were neither smooth nor green?

c. How many plants were not tall but had peas that were smooth and green?

44. Blood Antigens Human blood can contain the A antigen, the B antigen, both the A and B antigens, or neither antigen. A third antigen, called the Rh antigen, is important in human reproduction, and again may or may not be present in an

individual. Blood is called type A-positive if the individual has the A and Rh but not the B antigen. A person having only the A and B antigens is said to have type AB-negative blood. A person having only the Rh antigen has type O-positive blood. Other blood types are defined in a similar manner. Identify the blood types of the individuals in regions (a)–(h) below.

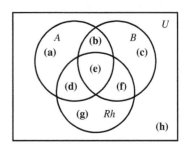

45. Blood Antigens (Use the diagram from Exercise 44.) In a certain hospital, the following data were recorded.

25 patients had the A antigen;
8 had the A and not the B antigen;
27 had the B antigen;
22 had the B and Rh antigens;
30 had the Rh antigen;
12 had none of the antigens;
16 had the A and Rh antigens;
15 had all three antigens.

How many patients

a. were represented? **b.** had exactly one antigen?

c. had exactly two antigens? **d.** had O-positive blood?

e. had AB-positive blood? **f.** had B-negative blood?

g. had O-negative blood? **h.** had A-positive blood?

46. Mortality The table lists the number of deaths in the United States during 2006 according to race and gender. Use this information and the letters given to find the number of people in each set. *Source: National Vital Statistics Reports.*

	White (W)	Black (B)	American Indian (I)	Asian or Pacific Islander (A)
Female (F)	1,055,221	141,369	6407	21,325
Male (M)	1,022,328	148,602	7630	23,382

a. F **b.** $F \cap (I \cup A)$

c. $M \cup B$ **d.** $W' \cup I' \cup A'$

e. In words, describe the set in part b.

47. Hockey The table lists the number of head and neck injuries for 319 ice hockey players wearing either a full shield or half shield in the Canadian Inter-University Athletics Union during one season. Using the letters given in the table, find the number of injuries in each set. *Source: JAMA.*

	Half Shield (H)	Full Shield (F)
Head and Face Injuries (A)	95	34
Concussions (B)	41	38
Neck Injuries (C)	9	7
Other Injuries (D)	202	150

a. $A \cap F$
b. $C \cap (H \cup F)$
c. $D \cup F$
d. $B' \cap C'$

Social Sciences

48. Military The number of female military personnel in 2009 is given in the following table. Use this information and the letters given to find the number of female military personnel in each set. *Source: Department of Defense.*

	Army (A)	Air Force (B)	Navy (C)	Marines (D)	Totals
Officers (O)	14,322	12,097	7884	1202	35,505
Enlisted (E)	59,401	51,965	42,225	11,749	165,340
Cadets & Midshipmen (M)	688	922	920	0	2530
Totals	74,411	64,984	51,029	12,951	203,375

a. $A \cup B$
b. $E \cup (C \cup D)$
c. $O' \cap M'$

U.S. Population The projected U.S. population in 2020 (in millions) by age and race or ethnicity is given in the following table. Use this information in Exercises 49–54. *Source: U.S. Bureau of the Census.*

	Non-Hispanic White (A)	Hispanic (B)	Black (C)	Asian (D)	American Indian (E)
Under 45 (F)	110.6	37.6	30.2	13.1	2.2
45–64 (G)	55.3	10.3	9.9	4.3	0.6
65 and over (H)	41.4	4.7	5.0	2.2	0.3
Totals	207.3	52.6	45.1	19.6	3.1

Using the letters given in the table, find the number of people in each set.

49. $A \cap F$
50. $G \cup B$
51. $G \cup (C \cap H)$
52. $F \cap (B \cup H)$
53. $H \cup D$
54. $G' \cap (A' \cap C')$

Marital Status The following table gives the population breakdown (in thousands) of the U.S. population in 2008 based on marital status and race or ethnic origin. *Source: New York Times 2010 Almanac.*

	White (W)	Black (B)	Hispanic (H)	Asian or Pacific Islander (A)
Never married (N)	54,205	13,547	12,021	3518
Married (M)	106,517	9577	16,111	6741
Widowed (I)	11,968	1740	1068	507
Divorced/ separated (D)	23,046	4590	3477	665

Find the number of people in each set. Describe each set in words.

55. $N \cap (B \cup H)$
56. $(M \cup I) \cap A$
57. $(D \cup W) \cap A'$
58. $M' \cap (B \cup A)$

General Interest

59. Chinese New Year A survey of people attending a Lunar New Year celebration in Chinatown yielded the following results:

    120 were women;
    150 spoke Cantonese;
    170 lit firecrackers;
    108 of the men spoke Cantonese;
    100 of the men did not light firecrackers;
    18 of the non-Cantonese-speaking women lit firecrackers;
    78 non-Cantonese-speaking men did not light firecrackers;
    30 of the women who spoke Cantonese lit firecrackers.

a. How many attended?

b. How many of those who attended did not speak Cantonese?

c. How many women did not light firecrackers?

d. How many of those who lit firecrackers were Cantonese-speaking men?

60. Native American Ceremonies At a pow-wow in Arizona, 75 Native American families from all over the Southwest came to participate in the ceremonies. A coordinator of the pow-wow took a survey and found that

    15 families brought food, costumes, and crafts;
    25 families brought food and crafts;
    42 families brought food;
    35 families brought crafts;
    14 families brought crafts but not costumes;
    10 families brought none of the three items;
    18 families brought costumes but not crafts.

a. How many families brought costumes and food?

b. How many families brought costumes?

c. How many families brought food, but not costumes?

d. How many families did not bring crafts?

e. How many families brought food or costumes?

61. Poultry Analysis A chicken farmer surveyed his flock with the following results. The farmer had

   9 fat red roosters;
   13 thin brown hens;
   15 red roosters;
   11 thin red chickens (hens and roosters);
   17 red hens;
   56 fat chickens (hens and roosters);
   41 roosters;
   48 hens.

Assume all chickens are thin or fat, red or brown, and hens (female) or roosters (male). How many chickens were

a. in the flock?   **b.** red?

c. fat roosters?   **d.** fat hens?

e. thin and brown?   **f.** red and fat?

YOUR TURN ANSWERS

1.   **2.** 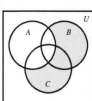   **3.** 23   **4.** 18

7.3 Introduction to Probability

APPLY IT   **What is the probability that a randomly selected person in the United States is Hispanic or Black?**
After introducing probability, we will answer this question in Exercise 58.

If you go to a supermarket and buy 5 pounds of peaches at 99 cents per pound, you can easily find the *exact* price of your purchase: $4.95. On the other hand, the produce manager of the market is faced with the problem of ordering peaches. The manager may have a good estimate of the number of pounds of peaches that will be sold during the day, but it is impossible to predict the *exact* amount. The number of pounds that customers will purchase during a day is *random*: the quantity cannot be predicted exactly. A great many problems that come up in applications of mathematics involve random phenomena—those for which exact prediction is impossible. The best that we can do is determine the *probability* of the possible outcomes.

Sample Spaces   In probability, an **experiment** is an activity or occurrence with an observable result. Each repetition of an experiment is called a **trial**. The possible results of each trial are called **outcomes**. The set of all possible outcomes for an experiment is the **sample space** for that experiment. A sample space for the experiment of tossing a coin is made up of the outcomes heads (*h*) and tails (*t*). If *S* represents this sample space, then

$$S = \{h, t\}.$$

EXAMPLE 1   **Sample Spaces**

Give the sample space for each experiment.

(a) A spinner like the one in Figure 15 is spun.

SOLUTION   The three outcomes are 1, 2, or 3, so the sample space is

$$\{1, 2, 3\}.$$

FIGURE 15

(b) For the purposes of a public opinion poll, respondents are classified as young, middle-aged, or senior, and as male or female.

SOLUTION A sample space for this poll could be written as a set of ordered pairs:

$$\{(\text{young, male}), (\text{young, female}), (\text{middle-aged, male}),$$
$$(\text{middle-aged, female}), (\text{senior, male}), (\text{senior, female})\}.$$

(c) An experiment consists of studying the numbers of boys and girls in families with exactly 3 children. Let *b* represent *boy* and *g* represent *girl*.

SOLUTION A three-child family can have 3 boys, written *bbb*, 3 girls, *ggg*, or various combinations, such as *bgg*. A sample space with four outcomes (not equally likely) is

$$S_1 = \{3 \text{ boys, 2 boys and 1 girl, 1 boy and 2 girls, 3 girls}\}.$$

Notice that a family with 3 boys or 3 girls can occur in just one way, but a family of 2 boys and 1 girl or 1 boy and 2 girls can occur in more than one way. If the *order* of the births is considered, so that *bgg* is different from *gbg* or *ggb*, for example, another sample space is

$$S_2 = \{bbb, bbg, bgb, gbb, bgg, gbg, ggb, ggg\}.$$

The second sample space, S_2, has equally likely outcomes if we assume that boys and girls are equally likely. This assumption, while not quite true, is approximately true, so we will use it throughout this book. The outcomes in S_1 are not equally likely, since there is more than one way to get a family with 2 boys and 1 girl (*bbg, bgb,* or *gbb*) or a family with 2 girls and 1 boy (*ggb, gbg,* or *bgg*), but only one way to get 3 boys (*bbb*) or 3 girls (*ggg*). **TRY YOUR TURN 1**

> **YOUR TURN 1** Two coins are tossed, and a head or a tail is recorded for each coin. Give a sample space where each outcome is equally likely.

CAUTION | An experiment may have more than one sample space, as shown in Example 1(c). The most convenient sample spaces have equally likely outcomes, but it is not always possible to choose such a sample space.

Events

An **event** is a subset of a sample space. If the sample space for tossing a coin is $S = \{h, t\}$, then one event is $E = \{h\}$, which represents the outcome "heads."

An ordinary die is a cube whose six different faces show the following numbers of dots: 1, 2, 3, 4, 5, and 6. If the die is fair (not "loaded" to favor certain faces over others), then any one of the faces is equally likely to come up when the die is rolled. The sample space for the experiment of rolling a single fair die is $S = \{1, 2, 3, 4, 5, 6\}$. Some possible events are listed below.

The die shows an even number: $E_1 = \{2, 4, 6\}$.

The die shows a 1: $E_2 = \{1\}$.

The die shows a number less than 5: $E_3 = \{1, 2, 3, 4\}$.

The die shows a multiple of 3: $E_4 = \{3, 6\}$.

Using the notation introduced earlier in this chapter, notice that $n(S) = 6, n(E_1) = 3, n(E_2) = 1, n(E_3) = 4,$ and $n(E_4) = 2$.

EXAMPLE 2 Events

For the sample space S_2 in Example 1(c), write the following events.

(a) Event *H*: the family has exactly two girls

SOLUTION Families with three children can have exactly two girls with either *bgg*, *gbg*, or *ggb*, so event *H* is

$$H = \{bgg, gbg, ggb\}.$$

(b) Event K: the three children are the same sex

SOLUTION Two outcomes satisfy this condition: all boys or all girls.

$$K = \{bbb, ggg\}$$

YOUR TURN 2 Two coins are tossed, and a head or a tail is recorded for each coin. Write the event E: the coins show exactly one head.

(c) Event J: the family has three girls

SOLUTION Only ggg satisfies this condition, so

$$J = \{ggg\}.$$

TRY YOUR TURN 2

In Example 2(c), event J had only one possible outcome, ggg. Such an event, with only one possible outcome, is a **simple event**. If event E equals the sample space S, then E is called a **certain event**. If event $E = \emptyset$, then E is called an **impossible event**.

EXAMPLE 3 Events

Suppose a coin is flipped until both a head and a tail appear, or until the coin has been flipped four times, whichever comes first. Write each of the following events in set notation.

(a) The coin is flipped exactly three times.

SOLUTION This means that the first two flips of the coin did not include both a head and a tail, so they must both be heads or both be tails. Because the third flip is the last one, it must show the side of the coin not yet seen. Thus the event is

$$\{hht, tth\}.$$

(b) The coin is flipped at least three times.

SOLUTION In addition to the outcomes listed in part (a), there is also the possibility that the coin is flipped four times, which only happens when the first three flips are all heads or all tails. Thus the event is

$$\{hht, tth, hhhh, hhht, tttt, ttth\}.$$

(c) The coin is flipped at least two times.

SOLUTION This event consists of the entire sample space:

$$S = \{ht, th, hht, tth, hhhh, hhht, tttt, ttth\}.$$

This is an example of a certain event.

(d) The coin is flipped fewer than two times.

SOLUTION The coin cannot be flipped fewer than two times under the rules described, so the event is the empty set $\emptyset$. This is an example of an impossible event.

Since events are sets, we can use set operations to find unions, intersections, and complements of events. A summary of the set operations for events is given below.

> **Set Operations for Events**
>
> Let E and F be events for a sample space S.
>
> $E \cap F$ occurs when both E **and** F occur;
>
> $E \cup F$ occurs when E **or** F **or both** occur;
>
> E' occurs when E does **not** occur.

EXAMPLE 4 Minimum-Wage Workers

A study of workers earning the minimum wage grouped such workers into various categories, which can be interpreted as events when a worker is selected at random. *Source: Economic Policy Institute.* Consider the following events:

E: worker is under 20;

F: worker is white;

G: worker is female.

Describe the following events in words.

(a) E'

SOLUTION E' is the event that the worker is 20 or over.

(b) $F \cap G'$

SOLUTION $F \cap G'$ is the event that the worker is white and not a female, that is, the worker is a white male.

(c) $E \cup G$

SOLUTION $E \cup G$ is the event that the worker is under 20 or is female. Note that this event includes all workers under 20, both male and female, and all female workers of any age. **TRY YOUR TURN 3**

YOUR TURN 3 Describe the following event in words: $E' \cap F'$.

Two events that cannot both occur at the same time, such as rolling an even number and an odd number with a single roll of a die, are called *mutually exclusive events*.

Mutually Exclusive Events

Events E and F are **mutually exclusive events** if $E \cap F = \emptyset$.

Any event E and its complement E' are mutually exclusive. By definition, mutually exclusive events are disjoint sets.

EXAMPLE 5 Mutually Exclusive Events

Let $S = \{1, 2, 3, 4, 5, 6\}$, the sample space for tossing a single die. Let $E = \{4, 5, 6\}$, and let $G = \{1, 2\}$. Then E and G are mutually exclusive events since they have no outcomes in common: $E \cap G = \emptyset$. See Figure 16.

$E \cap G = \emptyset$

FIGURE 16

Probability

For sample spaces with *equally likely* outcomes, the probability of an event is defined as follows.

Basic Probability Principle

Let S be a sample space of equally likely outcomes, and let event E be a subset of S. Then the **probability** that event E occurs is

$$P(E) = \frac{n(E)}{n(S)}.$$

By this definition, the probability of an event is a number that indicates the relative likelihood of the event.

CAUTION The basic probability principle only applies when the outcomes are equally likely.

EXAMPLE 6 Basic Probabilities

Suppose a single fair die is rolled. Use the sample space $S = \{1, 2, 3, 4, 5, 6\}$ and give the probability of each event.

(a) E: the die shows an even number

SOLUTION Here, $E = \{2, 4, 6\}$, a set with three elements. Since S contains six elements,

$$P(E) = \frac{3}{6} = \frac{1}{2}.$$

(b) *F*: the die shows a number less than 10

SOLUTION Event *F* is a certain event, with

$$F = \{1, 2, 3, 4, 5, 6\},$$

so that

$$P(F) = \frac{6}{6} = 1.$$

YOUR TURN 4 In Example 6, find the probability of event *H*: the die shows a number less than 5.

(c) *G*: the die shows an 8

SOLUTION This event is impossible, so

$$P(G) = 0.$$

TRY YOUR TURN 4

A standard deck of 52 cards has four suits: hearts (♥), clubs (♣), diamonds (♦), and spades (♠), with 13 cards in each suit. The hearts and diamonds are red, and the spades and clubs are black. Each suit has an ace (A), a king (K), a queen (Q), a jack (J), and cards numbered from 2 to 10. The jack, queen, and king are called *face cards* and for many purposes can be thought of as having values 11, 12, and 13, respectively. The ace can be thought of as the low card (value 1) or the high card (value 14). See Figure 17. We will refer to this standard deck of cards often in our discussion of probability.

FIGURE 17

EXAMPLE 7 **Playing Cards**

If a single playing card is drawn at random from a standard 52-card deck, find the probability of each event.

(a) Drawing an ace

SOLUTION There are 4 aces in the deck. The event "drawing an ace" is

{heart ace, diamond ace, club ace, spade ace}.

Therefore,

$$P(\text{ace}) = \frac{4}{52} = \frac{1}{13}.$$

(b) Drawing a face card

SOLUTION Since there are 12 face cards (three in each of the four suits),

$$P(\text{face card}) = \frac{12}{52} = \frac{3}{13}.$$

(c) Drawing a spade

SOLUTION The deck contains 13 spades, so

$$P(\text{spade}) = \frac{13}{52} = \frac{1}{4}.$$

(d) Drawing a spade or a heart

SOLUTION Besides the 13 spades, the deck contains 13 hearts, so

YOUR TURN 5 Find the probability of drawing a jack or a king.

$$P(\text{spade or heart}) = \frac{26}{52} = \frac{1}{2}.$$ TRY YOUR TURN 5

In the preceding examples, the probability of each event was a number between 0 and 1. The same thing is true in general. Any event E is a subset of the sample space S, so $0 \leq n(E) \leq n(S)$. Since $P(E) = n(E)/n(S)$, it follows that $0 \leq P(E) \leq 1$. Note that a certain event has probability 1 and an impossible event has probability 0, as seen in Example 6.

For any event E, $0 \leq P(E) \leq 1$.

Empirical Probability
In many real-life problems, it is not possible to establish exact probabilities for events. Instead, useful approximations are often found by drawing on past experience. The next example shows one approach to such **empirical probabilities**.

EXAMPLE 8 **Injuries**

The following table lists the estimated number of injuries in the United States associated with recreation equipment. *Source: National Safety Council.*

Recreation Equipment Injuries	
Equipment	Number of Injuries
Bicycles	515,871
Skateboards	143,682
Trampolines	107,345
Playground climbing equipment	77,845
Swings or swing sets	59,144

Find the probability that a randomly selected person whose injury is associated with recreation equipment was hurt on a trampoline.

SOLUTION We first find the total number of injuries. Verify that the amounts in the table sum to 903,887. The probability is then found by dividing the number of people injured on trampolines by the total number of people injured. Thus,

$$P(\text{Trampolines}) = \frac{107,345}{903,887} \approx 0.1188.$$

7.3 EXERCISES

1. What is meant by a "fair" coin or die?

2. What is the sample space for an experiment?

Write sample spaces for the experiments in Exercises 3–10.

3. A month of the year is chosen for a wedding.

4. A day in April is selected for a bicycle race.

5. A student is asked how many points she earned on a recent 80-point test.

6. A person is asked the number of hours (to the nearest hour) he watched television yesterday.

7. The management of an oil company must decide whether to go ahead with a new oil shale plant or to cancel it.

8. A record is kept each day for three days about whether a particular stock goes up or down.

9. A coin is tossed, and a die is rolled.

10. A box contains five balls, numbered 1, 2, 3, 4, and 5. A ball is drawn at random, the number on it recorded, and the ball replaced. The box is shaken, a second ball is drawn, and its number is recorded.

11. Define an event.

12. What is a simple event?

For the experiments in Exercises 13–18, write out the sample space S, choosing an S with equally likely outcomes, if possible. Then give the value of $n(S)$ and tell whether the outcomes in S are equally likely. Finally, write the indicated events in set notation.

13. A committee of 2 people is selected at random from 5 executives: Alam, Bartolini, Chinn, Dickson, and Ellsberg.

   a. Chinn is on the committee.

   b. Dickson and Ellsberg are not both on the committee.

   c. Both Alam and Chinn are on the committee.

14. Five states are being considered as the location for three new high-energy physics laboratories: California (CA), Colorado (CO), New Jersey (NJ), New York (NY), and Utah (UT). Three states will be chosen at random. Write elements of the sample space in the form (CA, CO, NJ).

   a. All three states border an ocean.

   b. Exactly two of the three states border an ocean.

   c. Exactly one of the three states is west of the Mississippi River.

15. Slips of paper marked with the numbers 1, 2, 3, 4, and 5 are placed in a box. After being mixed, two slips are drawn simultaneously.

   a. Both slips are marked with even numbers.

   b. One slip is marked with an odd number and the other is marked with an even number.

   c. Both slips are marked with the same number.

16. An unprepared student takes a three-question, true/false quiz in which he guesses the answers to all three questions, so each answer is equally likely to be correct or wrong.

   a. The student gets three answers wrong.

   b. The student gets exactly two answers correct.

   c. The student gets only the first answer correct.

17. A coin is flipped until two heads appear, up to a maximum of four flips. (If three tails are flipped, the coin is still tossed a fourth time to complete the experiment).

   a. The coin is tossed four times.

   b. Exactly two heads are tossed.

   c. No heads are tossed.

18. One jar contains four balls, labeled 1, 2, 3, and 4. A second jar contains five balls, labeled 1, 2, 3, 4, and 5. An experiment consists of taking one ball from the first jar, and then taking a ball from the second jar.

   a. The number on the first ball is even.

   b. The number on the second ball is even.

   c. The sum of the numbers on the two balls is 5.

   d. The sum of the numbers on the two balls is 1.

A single fair die is rolled. Find the probabilities of each event.

19. Getting a 2

20. Getting an odd number

21. Getting a number less than 5

22. Getting a number greater than 2

23. Getting a 3 or a 4

24. Getting any number except 3

A card is drawn from a well-shuffled deck of 52 cards. Find the probability of drawing the following.

25. A 9

26. A black card

27. A black 9

28. A heart

29. The 9 of hearts

30. A face card

31. A 2 or a queen

32. A black 7 or a red 8

33. A red card or a 10

34. A spade or a king

A jar contains 3 white, 4 orange, 5 yellow, and 8 black marbles. If a marble is drawn at random, find the probability that it is the following.

35. White

36. Orange

37. Yellow

38. Black

39. Not black

40. Orange or yellow

Which of Exercises 41–48 are examples of empirical probability?

41. The probability of heads on 5 consecutive tosses of a coin

42. The probability that a freshman entering college will graduate with a degree

43. The probability that a person is allergic to penicillin

44. The probability of drawing an ace from a standard deck of 52 cards

45. The probability that a person will get lung cancer from smoking cigarettes

46. A weather forecast that predicts a 70% chance of rain tomorrow

47. A gambler's claim that on a roll of a fair die, $P(\text{even}) = 1/2$

48. A surgeon's prediction that a patient has a 90% chance of a full recovery

49. The student sitting next to you in class concludes that the probability of the ceiling falling down on both of you before class ends is 1/2, because there are two possible outcomes—the ceiling will fall or not fall. What is wrong with this reasoning?

50. The following puzzler was given on the *Car Talk* radio program. *Source: Car Talk, Feb 24, 2001.*

   "Three different numbers are chosen at random, and one is written on each of three slips of paper. The slips are then placed face down on the table. The objective is to choose the slip upon which is written the largest number. Here are the rules: You can turn over any slip of paper and look at the amount written on it. If for any reason you think this is the largest, you're done; you keep it. Otherwise you discard it and turn over a second slip. Again, if you think this is the one with the biggest number, you keep that one and the game is over. If you don't, you discard that one too. . . . The chance of getting the highest number is one in three. Or is it? Is there a strategy by which you can improve the odds?"

The answer to the puzzler is that you can indeed improve the probability of getting the highest number by the following strategy. Pick one of the slips of paper, and after looking at the number, throw it away. Then pick a second slip; if it has a larger number than the first slip, stop. If not, pick the third slip. Find the probability of winning with this strategy.*

APPLICATIONS

Business and Economics

51. Survey of Workers The management of a firm wishes to check on the opinions of its assembly line workers. Before the workers are interviewed, they are divided into various categories. Define events E, F, and G as follows.

> E: worker is female
> F: worker has worked less than 5 years
> G: worker contributes to a voluntary retirement plan

Describe each event in words.

a. E' **b.** $E \cap F$ **c.** $E \cup G'$

d. F' **e.** $F \cup G$ **f.** $F' \cap G'$

52. Research Funding In 2008, funding for research and development in the United States totaled $397.6 billion dollars. Support came from various sources, as shown in the following table. *Source: National Science Foundation.*

Source	Amount (in billions of dollars)
Federal government	103.7
State and local government	3.5
Industry	267.8
Academic institutions	10.6
Other	12.0

Find the probability that funds for a particular project came from each source.

a. Federal government

b. Industry

c. Academic institutions

53. Investment Survey Exercise 42 of the previous section presented a survey of 150 mathematics professors. Use the information given in that exercise to find each probability.

a. A randomly chosen professor invested in stocks and bonds and certificates of deposit.

b. A randomly chosen professor invested in only bonds.

*This is a special case of the famous Googol problem. For more details, see "Recognizing the Maximum of a Sequence" by John P. Gilbert and Frederick Mosteller, *Journal of the American Statistical Association*, Vol. 61, No. 313, March 1966, pp. 35–73.

54. Labor Force The 2008 and the 2018 (projected) civilian labor forces by age are given in the following table. *Source: U.S. Department of Labor.*

Age (in years)	2008 (in millions)	2018 (in millions)
16 to 24	22.0	21.1
25 to 54	104.4	105.9
55 and over	27.9	39.8
Total	154.3	166.8

a. In 2008, find the probability that a member of the civilian labor force is age 55 or older.

b. In 2018, find the probability that a member of the civilian labor force is age 55 or over.

c. What do these projections imply about the future civilian labor force?

Life Sciences

55. Medical Survey For a medical experiment, people are classified as to whether they smoke, have a family history of heart disease, or are overweight. Define events E, F, and G as follows.

> E: person smokes
> F: person has a family history of heart disease
> G: person is overweight

Describe each event in words.

a. G' **b.** $F \cap G$ **c.** $E \cup G'$

56. Medical Survey Refer to Exercise 55. Describe each event in words.

a. $E \cup F$ **b.** $E' \cap F$ **c.** $F' \cup G'$

57. Causes of Death There were 2,424,059 U.S. deaths in 2007. They are listed according to cause in the following table. If a randomly selected person died in 2007, use this information to find the following probabilities. *Source: Centers for Disease Control and Prevention.*

Cause	Number of Deaths
Heart Disease	615,651
Cancer	560,187
Cerebrovascular disease	133,990
Chronic lower respiratory disease	129,311
Accidents	117,075
Alzheimer's disease	74,944
Diabetes mellitus	70,905
Influenza and pneumonia	52,847
All other causes	669,149

a. The probability that the cause of death was heart disease

b. The probability that the cause of death was cancer or heart disease

c. The probability that the cause of death was not an accident and was not diabetes mellitus

Social Sciences

58. APPLY IT **U.S. Population** The projected U.S. population (in thousands) by race in 2020 and 2050 is given in the table. *Source: Bureau of the Census.*

Race	2020	2050
White	207,393	207,901
Hispanic	52,652	96,508
Black	41,538	53,555
Asian and Pacific Islander	18,557	32,432
Other	2602	3535

Find the probability that a randomly selected person in the given year is of the race specified.

a. Hispanic in 2020   **b.** Hispanic in 2050

c. Black in 2020   **d.** Black in 2050

59. **Congressional Service** The following table gives the number of years of service of senators in the 111th Congress of the United States of America. Find the probability that a randomly selected senator of the 111th Congress served 20–29 years when Congress convened. *Source: Roll Call.*

Years of Service	Number of Senators
0–9	48
10–19	27
20–29	17
30–39	6
40 or more	2

60. **Civil War** Estimates of the Union Army's strength and losses for the battle of Gettysburg are given in the following table, where *strength* is the number of soldiers immediately preceding the battle and *loss* indicates a soldier who was killed, wounded, captured, or missing. *Source: Regimental Strengths and Losses of Gettysburg.*

Unit	Strength	Loss
I Corps (Reynolds)	12,222	6059
II Corps (Hancock)	11,347	4369
III Corps (Sickles)	10,675	4211
V Corps (Sykes)	10,907	2187
VI Corps (Sedgwick)	13,596	242
XI Corps (Howard)	9188	3801
XII Corps (Slocum)	9788	1082
Cavalry (Pleasonton)	11,851	610
Artillery (Tyler)	2376	242
Total	91,950	22,803

a. Find the probability that a randomly selected union soldier was from the XI Corps.

b. Find the probability that a soldier was lost in the battle.

c. Find the probability that a I Corps soldier was lost in the battle.

d. Which group had the highest probability of not being lost in the battle?

e. Which group had the highest probability of loss?

f. Explain why these probabilities vary.

61. **Civil War** Estimates of the Confederate Army's strength and losses for the battle of Gettysburg are given in the following table, where *strength* is the number of soldiers immediately preceding the battle and *loss* indicates a soldier who was killed, wounded, captured, or missing. *Source: Regimental Strengths and Losses at Gettysburg.*

Unit	Strength	Loss
I Corps (Longstreet)	20,706	7661
II Corps (Ewell)	20,666	6603
III Corps (Hill)	22,083	8007
Cavalry (Stuart)	6621	286
Total	70,076	22,557

a. Find the probability that a randomly selected confederate soldier was from the III Corps.

b. Find the probability that a confederate soldier was lost in the battle.

c. Find the probability that a I Corps soldier was lost in the battle.

d. Which group had the highest probability of not being lost in the battle?

e. Which group had the highest probability of loss?

General Interest

62. **Native American Ceremonies** Exercise 60 of the previous section presented a survey of families participating in a pow-wow in Arizona. Use the information given in that exercise to find each probability.

a. A randomly chosen family brought costumes and food.

b. A randomly chosen family brought crafts, but neither food nor costumes.

c. A randomly chosen family brought food or costumes.

63. **Chinese New Year** Exercise 59 of the previous section presented a survey of people attending a Lunar New Year celebration in Chinatown. Use the information given in that exercise to find each of the following probabilities.

a. A randomly chosen attendee speaks Cantonese.

b. A randomly chosen attendee does not speak Cantonese.

c. A randomly chosen attendee was a woman that did not light a firecracker.

YOUR TURN ANSWERS

1. $S = \{HH, HT, TH, TT\}$ **2.** $E = \{HT, TH\}$

3. $E' \cap F'$ is the event that the worker is 20 or over and is not white.

4. $P(H) = \dfrac{4}{6} = \dfrac{2}{3}.$ **5.** $P(\text{jack or a king}) = 8/52 = 2/13.$

7.4 Basic Concepts of Probability

APPLY IT   What is the probability that a dollar of advertising in the United States is spent on magazines or newspapers?

We will determine this probability in Example 8. But first we need to develop additional rules for calculating probability, beginning with the probability of a union of two events.

The Union Rule
To determine the probability of the union of two events E and F in a sample space S, use the union rule for sets,

$$n(E \cup F) = n(E) + n(F) - n(E \cap F),$$

which was proved in Section 7.2. Assuming that the events in the sample space S are equally likely, divide both sides by $n(S)$, so that

$$\frac{n(E \cup F)}{n(S)} = \frac{n(E)}{n(S)} + \frac{n(F)}{n(S)} - \frac{n(E \cap F)}{n(S)}$$

$$P(E \cup F) = P(E) + P(F) - P(E \cap F).$$

Although our derivation is valid only for sample spaces with equally likely events, the result is valid for any events E and F from any sample space, and is called the **union rule for probability**.

Union Rule for Probability
For any events E and F from a sample space S,

$$P(E \cup F) = P(E) + P(F) - P(E \cap F).$$

EXAMPLE 1   Probabilities with Playing Cards

If a single card is drawn from an ordinary deck of cards, find the probability that it will be a red or a face card.

SOLUTION   Let R represent the event "red card" and F the event "face card." There are 26 red cards in the deck, so $P(R) = 26/52$. There are 12 face cards in the deck, so $P(F) = 12/52$. Since there are 6 red face cards in the deck, $P(R \cap F) = 6/52$. By the union rule, the probability of the card being red or a face card is

YOUR TURN 1   In Example 1, find the probability of an ace or a club.

$$P(R \cup F) = P(R) + P(F) - P(R \cap F)$$

$$= \frac{26}{52} + \frac{12}{52} - \frac{6}{52} = \frac{32}{52} = \frac{8}{13}.$$ TRY YOUR TURN 1

EXAMPLE 2   Probabilities with Dice

Suppose two fair dice are rolled. Find each probability.

(a) The first die shows a 2, or the sum of the results is 6 or 7.

   SOLUTION   The sample space for the throw of two dice is shown in Figure 18 on the next page, where 1-1 represents the event "the first die shows a 1 and the second die shows a 1," 1-2 represents "the first die shows a 1 and the second die shows a 2," and so on. Let A represent the event "the first die shows a 2," and B represent the event "the sum of the results is 6 or 7." These events are indicated in Figure 18. From the diagram, event A has 6 elements, B has 11 elements, the intersection of A and B has 2 elements, and the sample space has 36 elements. Thus,

$$P(A) = \frac{6}{36}, \quad P(B) = \frac{11}{36}, \quad \text{and} \quad P(A \cap B) = \frac{2}{36}.$$

FIGURE 18

By the union rule,

$$P(A \cup B) = P(A) + P(B) - P(A \cap B)$$

$$P(A \cup B) = \frac{6}{36} + \frac{11}{36} - \frac{2}{36} = \frac{15}{36} = \frac{5}{12}.$$

(b) The sum of the results is 11, or the second die shows a 5.

SOLUTION $P(\text{sum is } 11) = 2/36$, $P(\text{second die shows a } 5) = 6/36$, and $P(\text{sum is } 11 \text{ and second die shows a } 5) = 1/36$, so

YOUR TURN 2 In Example 2, find the probability that the sum is 8, or both die show the same number.

$$P(\text{sum is } 11 \text{ or second die shows a } 5) = \frac{2}{36} + \frac{6}{36} - \frac{1}{36} = \frac{7}{36}.$$

TRY YOUR TURN 2

CAUTION | You may wonder why we did not use $S = \{2, 3, 4, 5, \ldots, 12\}$ as the sample space in Example 2. Remember, we prefer to use a sample space with equally likely outcomes. The outcomes in set S above are not equally likely—a sum of 2 can occur in just one way, a sum of 3 in two ways, a sum of 4 in three ways, and so on, as shown in Figure 18.

If events E and F are mutually exclusive, then $E \cap F = \emptyset$ by definition; hence, $P(E \cap F) = 0$. In this case the union rule simplifies to $P(E \cup F) = P(E) + P(F)$.

CAUTION | The rule $P(E \cup F) = P(E) + P(F)$ is only valid when E and F are mutually exclusive. When E and F are *not* mutually exclusive, use the rule $P(E \cup F) = P(E) + P(F) - P(E \cap F)$.

The Complement Rule
By the definition of E', for any event E from a sample space S,

$$E \cup E' = S \quad \text{and} \quad E \cap E' = \emptyset.$$

Since $E \cap E' = \emptyset$, events E and E' are mutually exclusive, so that

$$P(E \cup E') = P(E) + P(E').$$

However, $E \cup E' = S$, the sample space, and $P(S) = 1$. Thus

$$P(E \cup E') = P(E) + P(E') = 1.$$

Rearranging these terms gives the following useful rule for complements.

Complement Rule

$$P(E) = 1 - P(E') \quad \text{and} \quad P(E') = 1 - P(E).$$

EXAMPLE 3 Complement Rule

If a fair die is rolled, what is the probability that any number but 5 will come up?

SOLUTION If E is the event that 5 comes up, then E' is the event that any number but 5 comes up. Since $P(E) = 1/6$, we have $P(E') = 1 - 1/6 = 5/6$.

EXAMPLE 4 Complement Rule

If two fair dice are rolled, find the probability that the sum of the numbers rolled is greater than 3. Refer to Figure 18.

SOLUTION To calculate this probability directly, we must find the probabilities that the sum is 4, 5, 6, 7, 8, 9, 10, 11, or 12 and then add them. It is much simpler to first find the probability of the complement, the event that the sum is less than or equal to 3.

$$P(\text{sum} \le 3) = P(\text{sum is } 2) + P(\text{sum is } 3)$$

$$= \frac{1}{36} + \frac{2}{36}$$

$$= \frac{3}{36} = \frac{1}{12}$$

YOUR TURN 3 Find the probability that when two fair dice are rolled, the sum is less than 11.

Now use the fact that $P(E) = 1 - P(E')$ to get

$$P(\text{sum} > 3) = 1 - P(\text{sum} \le 3)$$

$$= 1 - \frac{1}{12} = \frac{11}{12}.$$ TRY YOUR TURN 3

Odds Sometimes probability statements are given in terms of **odds**, a comparison of $P(E)$ with $P(E')$. For example, suppose $P(E) = 4/5$. Then $P(E') = 1 - 4/5 = 1/5$. These probabilities predict that E will occur 4 out of 5 times and E' will occur 1 out of 5 times. Then we say the *odds in favor* of E are 4 to 1.

> Odds
>
> The **odds in favor** of an event E are defined as the ratio of $P(E)$ to $P(E')$, or
>
> $$\frac{P(E)}{P(E')}, \text{ where } P(E') \ne 0.$$

EXAMPLE 5 Odds in Favor of Rain

Suppose the weather forecaster says that the probability of rain tomorrow is $1/3$. Find the odds in favor of rain tomorrow.

SOLUTION Let E be the event "rain tomorrow." Then E' is the event "no rain tomorrow." Since $P(E) = 1/3, P(E') = 2/3$. By the definition of odds, the odds in favor of rain are

$$\frac{1/3}{2/3} = \frac{1}{2}, \quad \text{written} \quad 1 \text{ to } 2, \text{ or } 1:2.$$

YOUR TURN 4 If the probability of snow tomorrow is $3/10$, find the odds in favor of snow tomorrow.

On the other hand, the odds that it will *not* rain, or the *odds against* rain, are

$$\frac{2/3}{1/3} = \frac{2}{1}, \quad \text{written} \quad 2 \text{ to } 1, \text{ or } 2:1. \quad \text{TRY YOUR TURN 4}$$

If the odds in favor of an event are, say, 3 to 5, then the probability of the event is $3/8$, while the probability of the complement of the event is $5/8$. (Odds of 3 to 5 indicate

3 outcomes in favor of the event out of a total of 8 possible outcomes.) This example suggests the following generalization.

> If the odds favoring event E are m to n, then
> $$P(E) = \frac{m}{m+n} \quad \text{and} \quad P(E') = \frac{n}{m+n}.$$

EXAMPLE 6 Package Delivery

The odds that a particular package will be delivered on time are 25 to 2.

(a) Find the probability that the package will be delivered on time.

SOLUTION Odds of 25 to 2 show 25 favorable chances out of $25 + 2 = 27$ chances altogether:

$$P(\text{package will be delivered on time}) = \frac{25}{25+2} = \frac{25}{27}.$$

(b) Find the odds against the package being delivered on time.

SOLUTION Using the complement rule, there is a 2/27 chance that the package will not be delivered on time. So the odds against the package being delivered on time are

$$\frac{P(\text{package will not be delivered on time})}{P(\text{package will be delivered on time})} = \frac{2/27}{25/27} = \frac{2}{25},$$

or $2 : 25$.

YOUR TURN 5 If the odds that a package will be delivered on time are 17 to 3, find the probability that the package will not be delivered on time.

TRY YOUR TURN 5

EXAMPLE 7 Odds in Horse Racing

If the odds in favor of a particular horse's winning a race are 5 to 7, what is the probability that the horse will win the race?

SOLUTION The odds indicate chances of 5 out of 12 ($5 + 7 = 12$) that the horse will win, so

$$P(\text{winning}) = \frac{5}{12}.$$

YOUR TURN 6 If the odds against a particular horse winning a race are 7 to 3, what is the probability the horse will win the race?

Race tracks generally give odds *against* a horse winning. In this case, the track would give the odds as 7 to 5. Of course, race tracks, casinos, and other gambling establishments need to give odds that are more favorable to the house than those representing the actual probabilities, because they need to make a profit.

TRY YOUR TURN 6

Probability Distribution

A table listing each possible outcome of an experiment and its corresponding probability is called a **probability distribution**. The assignment of probabilities may be done in any reasonable way (on an empirical basis, as in the next example, or by theoretical reasoning, as in Section 7.3), provided that it satisfies the following conditions.

Properties of Probability

Let S be a sample space consisting of n distinct outcomes, $s_1, s_2, \ldots, s_n$. An acceptable probability assignment consists of assigning to each outcome s_i a number p_i (the probability of s_i) according to these rules.

1. The probability of each outcome is a number between 0 and 1.

$$0 \le p_1 \le 1, \quad 0 \le p_2 \le 1, \ldots, \quad 0 \le p_n \le 1$$

2. The sum of the probabilities of all possible outcomes is 1.

$$p_1 + p_2 + p_3 + \cdots + p_n = 1$$

EXAMPLE 8 Advertising Volume

The following table lists U.S. advertising volume in millions of dollars by medium in 2008. *Source: Advertising Age.*

Advertising Volume	
Medium	Expenditures
Television	65,137
Magazines	28,580
Newspapers	25,059
Internet	9727
Radio	9501
Outdoor	3964

(a) Construct a probability distribution for the probability that a dollar of advertising is spent on each medium.

SOLUTION We first find the total spent and then divide the amount spent on each medium by the total. Verify that the amounts in the table sum to 141,968. The probability that a dollar is spent on newspapers, for example, is $P(\text{newspapers}) = 25,059/141,968 \approx 0.1765$. Similarly, we could divide each amount by 141,968, with the results (rounded to four decimal places) shown in the following table.

Advertising Volume	
Medium	Probabilities
Television	0.4588
Magazines	0.2013
Newspapers	0.1765
Internet	0.0685
Radio	0.0669
Outdoor	0.0279

Verify that this distribution satisfies the conditions for probability. Each probability is between 0 and 1, so the first condition holds. The probabilities in this table sum to 0.9999. In theory, to satisfy the second condition, they should total 1.0000, but this does not always occur when the individual numbers are rounded.

(b) Find the probability that a dollar of advertising in the United States is spent on newspapers or magazines.

APPLY IT

SOLUTION The categories in the table are mutually exclusive simple events. Thus, to find the probability that an advertising dollar is spent on newspapers or magazines, we use the union rule to calculate

$$P(\text{newspapers or magazines}) = 0.1765 + 0.2013 = 0.3778.$$

We could get this same result by summing the amount spent on newspapers and magazines, and dividing the total by 141,968.

Thus, more than a third of all advertising dollars are spent on these two media, a figure that should be of interest to both advertisers and the owners of the various media.

Probability distributions are discussed further in the next chapter.

EXAMPLE 9 Clothing

Susan is a college student who receives heavy sweaters from her aunt at the first sign of cold weather. Susan has determined that the probability that a sweater is the wrong size is 0.47, the probability that it is a loud color is 0.59, and the probability that it is both the wrong size and a loud color is 0.31.

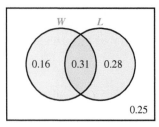

FIGURE 19

(a) Find the probability that the sweater is the correct size and not a loud color.

SOLUTION Let W represent the event "wrong size," and L represent "loud color." Place the given information on a Venn diagram, starting with 0.31 in the intersection of the regions W and L (see Figure 19). As stated earlier, event W has probability 0.47. Since 0.31 has already been placed inside the intersection of W and L,

$$0.47 - 0.31 = 0.16$$

goes inside region W, but outside the intersection of W and L, that is, in the region $W \cap L'$. In the same way,

$$0.59 - 0.31 = 0.28$$

goes inside the region for L, and outside the overlap, that is, in the region $L \cap W'$.

Using regions W and L, the event we want is $W' \cap L'$. From the Venn diagram in Figure 19, the labeled regions have a total probability of

$$0.16 + 0.31 + 0.28 = 0.75.$$

Since the entire region of the Venn diagram must have probability 1, the region outside W and L, or $W' \cap L'$, has probability

$$1 - 0.75 = 0.25.$$

The probability is 0.25 that the sweater is the correct size and not a loud color.

(b) Find the probability that the sweater is the correct size or is not loud.

SOLUTION The corresponding region, $W' \cup L'$, has probability

$$0.25 + 0.16 + 0.28 = 0.69.$$

7.4 EXERCISES

 1. Define mutually exclusive events in your own words.

2. Explain the union rule for mutually exclusive events.

Decide whether the events in Exercises 3–8 are mutually exclusive.

3. Owning a dog and owning an MP3 player

4. Being a business major and being from Texas

5. Being retired and being 70 years old

6. Being a teenager and being 70 years old

7. Being one of the ten tallest people in the United States and being under 4 feet tall

8. Being male and being a nurse

Two dice are rolled. Find the probabilities of rolling the given sums.

9. a. 2   **b.** 4   **c.** 5   **d.** 6

10. a. 8   **b.** 9   **c.** 10   **d.** 13

11. a. 9 or more   **b.** Less than 7

    c. Between 5 and 8 (exclusive)

12. a. Not more than 5   **b.** Not less than 8

    c. Between 3 and 7 (exclusive)

Two dice are rolled. Find the probabilities of the following events.

13. The first die is 3 or the sum is 8.

14. The second die is 5 or the sum is 10.

One card is drawn from an ordinary deck of 52 cards. Find the probabilities of drawing the following cards.

15. a. A 9 or 10

    b. A red card or a 3

    c. A 9 or a black 10

    d. A heart or a black card

    e. A face card or a diamond

16. a. Less than a 4 (count aces as ones)

    b. A diamond or a 7

    c. A black card or an ace

    d. A heart or a jack

    e. A red card or a face card

Kristi Perez invites 13 relatives to a party: her mother, 2 aunts, 3 uncles, 2 brothers, 1 male cousin, and 4 female cousins. If the chances of any one guest arriving first are equally likely, find the probabilities that the first guest to arrive is as follows.

17. a. A brother or an uncle   **b.** A brother or a cousin

   c. A brother or her mother

18. a. An uncle or a cousin   **b.** A male or a cousin

   c. A female or a cousin

The numbers 1, 2, 3, 4, and 5 are written on slips of paper, and 2 slips are drawn at random one at a time without replacement. Find the probabilities in Exercises 19 and 20.

19. a. The sum of the numbers is 9.

   b. The sum of the numbers is 5 or less.

   c. The first number is 2 or the sum is 6.

20. a. Both numbers are even.

   b. One of the numbers is even or greater than 3.

   c. The sum is 5 or the second number is 2.

Use Venn diagrams to work Exercises 21 and 22.

21. Suppose $P(E) = 0.26$, $P(F) = 0.41$, and $P(E \cap F) = 0.16$. Find the following.

   a. $P(E \cup F)$ **b.** $P(E' \cap F)$

   c. $P(E \cap F')$ **d.** $P(E' \cup F')$

22. Let $P(Z) = 0.42$, $P(Y) = 0.35$, and $P(Z \cup Y) = 0.59$. Find each probability.

   a. $P(Z' \cap Y')$ **b.** $P(Z' \cup Y')$

   c. $P(Z' \cup Y)$ **d.** $P(Z \cap Y')$

23. Three unusual dice, A, B, and C, are constructed such that die A has the numbers 3, 3, 4, 4, 8, 8; die B has the numbers 1, 1, 5, 5, 9, 9; and die C has the numbers 2, 2, 6, 6, 7, 7.

   a. If dice A and B are rolled, find the probability that B beats A, that is, the number that appears on die B is greater than the number that appears on die A.

   b. If dice B and C are rolled, find the probability that C beats B.

   c. If dice A and C are rolled, find the probability that A beats C.

   d. Which die is better? Explain.

24. In the "Ask Marilyn" column of *Parade* magazine, a reader wrote about the following game: You and I each roll a die. If your die is higher than mine, you win. Otherwise, I win. The reader thought that the probability that each player wins is $1/2$. Is this correct? If not, what is the probability that each player wins? *Source: Parade magazine.*

25. Define what is meant by odds.

26. On page 134 of Roger Staubach's autobiography, *First Down, Lifetime to Go*, Staubach makes the following statement regarding his experience in Vietnam: *Source: First Down, Lifetime to Go.*

> "Odds against a direct hit are very low but when your life is in danger, you don't worry too much about the odds."

Is this wording consistent with our definition of odds, for and against? How could it have been said so as to be technically correct?

A single fair die is rolled. Find the odds in favor of getting the results in Exercises 27–30.

27. 3   **28.** 4, 5, or 6

29. 2, 3, 4, or 5   **30.** Some number less than 6

31. A marble is drawn from a box containing 3 yellow, 4 white, and 11 blue marbles. Find the odds in favor of drawing the following.

   a. A yellow marble   **b.** A blue marble

   c. A white marble   **d.** Not drawing a white marble

32. Two dice are rolled. Find the odds of rolling the following. (Refer to Figure 18.)

   a. A sum of 3   **b.** A sum of 7 or 11

   c. A sum less than 5   **d.** Not a sum of 6

33. What is a probability distribution?

34. What conditions must hold for a probability distribution to be acceptable?

An experiment is conducted for which the sample space is $S = \{s_1, s_2, s_3, s_4, s_5\}$. Which of the probability assignments in Exercises 35–40 are possible for this experiment? If an assignment is not possible, tell why.

35.

Outcomes	s_1	s_2	s_3	s_4	s_5
Probabilities	0.09	0.32	0.21	0.25	0.13

36.

Outcomes	s_1	s_2	s_3	s_4	s_5
Probabilities	0.92	0.03	0	0.02	0.03

37.

Outcomes	s_1	s_2	s_3	s_4	s_5
Probabilities	1/3	1/4	1/6	1/8	1/10

38.

Outcomes	s_1	s_2	s_3	s_4	s_5
Probabilities	1/5	1/3	1/4	1/5	1/10

39.

Outcomes	s_1	s_2	s_3	s_4	s_5
Probabilities	0.64	−0.08	0.30	0.12	0.02

40.

Outcomes	s_1	s_2	s_3	s_4	s_5
Probabilities	0.05	0.35	0.5	0.2	−0.3

One way to solve a probability problem is to repeat the experiment many times, keeping track of the results. Then the probability can be approximated using the basic definition of the probability of an event E: $P(E) = n(E)/n(S)$, where E occurs $n(E)$ times out of $n(S)$ trials of an experiment. This is called the Monte Carlo method of finding probabilities. If physically repeating the experiment is too tedious, it may be simulated using a random-number generator, available on most computers and scientific or graphing calculators. To simulate a coin toss or the roll of a die on the TI-84 Plus, change the setting to fixed decimal mode with 0 digits displayed, and enter `rand` or rand*6+.5, respectively. **For a coin toss, interpret 0 as a head and 1 as a tail. In either case, the** ENTER **key can be pressed repeatedly to perform multiple simulations.**

41. Suppose two dice are rolled. Use the Monte Carlo method with at least 50 repetitions to approximate the following probabilities. Compare with the results of Exercise 11.

  a. P(the sum is 9 or more)

  b. P(the sum is less than 7)

42. Suppose two dice are rolled. Use the Monte Carlo method with at least 50 repetitions to approximate the following probabilities. Compare with the results of Exercise 12.

  a. P(the sum is not more than 5)

  b. P(the sum is not less than 8)

43. Suppose three dice are rolled. Use the Monte Carlo method with at least 100 repetitions to approximate the following probabilities.

  a. P(the sum is 5 or less)

  b. P(neither a 1 nor a 6 is rolled)

44. Suppose a coin is tossed 5 times. Use the Monte Carlo method with at least 50 repetitions to approximate the following probabilities.

  a. P(exactly 4 heads)

  b. P(2 heads and 3 tails)

45. The following description of the classic "Linda problem" appeared in the *New Yorker:* "In this experiment, subjects are told, 'Linda is thirty-one years old, single, outspoken, and very bright. She majored in philosophy. As a student, she was deeply concerned with issues of discrimination and social justice and also participated in antinuclear demonstrations.' They are then asked to rank the probability of several possible descriptions of Linda today. Two of them are 'bank teller' and 'bank teller and active in the feminist movement.'" Many people rank the second event as more likely. Explain why this violates basic concepts of probability. *Source: New Yorker.*

46. You are given $P(A \cup B) = 0.7$ and $P(A \cup B') = 0.9$. Determine $P(A)$. Choose one of the following. *Source: Society of Actuaries.*

  a. 0.2   **b.** 0.3   **c.** 0.4   **d.** 0.6   **e.** 0.8

APPLICATIONS

Business and Economics

47. Defective Merchandise Suppose that 8% of a certain batch of calculators have a defective case, and that 11% have defective batteries. Also, 3% have both a defective case and defective batteries. A calculator is selected from the batch at random. Find the probability that the calculator has a good case and good batteries.

48. Profit The probability that a company will make a profit this year is 0.74.

  a. Find the probability that the company will not make a profit this year.

  b. Find the odds against the company making a profit.

49. Credit Charges The table shows the probabilities of a person accumulating specific amounts of credit card charges over a 12-month period. Find the probabilities that a person's total charges during the period are the following.

  a. $500 or more   **b.** Less than $1000

  c. $500 to $2999   **d.** $3000 or more

Charges	Probability
Under $100	0.21
$100–$499	0.17
$500–$999	0.16
$1000–$1999	0.15
$2000–$2999	0.12
$3000–$4999	0.08
$5000–$9999	0.07
$10,000 or more	0.04

50. Employment The table shows the projected probabilities of a worker employed by different occupational groups in 2018. *Source: U.S. Department of Labor.*

Occupation	Probability
Management and business	0.1047
Professional	0.2182
Service	0.2024
Sales	0.1015
Office and administrative support	0.1560
Farming, fishing, forestry	0.0061
Construction	0.0531
Production	0.0585
Other	0.0995

If a worker in 2018 is selected at random, find the following.

  a. The probability that the worker is in sales or service.

  b. The probability that the worker is not in construction.

  c. The odds in favor of the worker being in production.

51. Labor Force The following table gives the 2018 projected civilian labor force probability distribution by age and gender. *Source: U.S. Department of Labor.*

Age	Male	Female	Total
16–24	0.066	0.061	0.127
25–54	0.343	0.291	0.634
55 and over	0.122	0.117	0.239
Total	0.531	0.469	1.000

Find the probability that a randomly selected worker is the following.

  a. Female and 16 to 24 years old

  b. 16 to 54 years old

  c. Male or 25 to 54 years old

  d. Female or 16 to 24 years old

Life Sciences

52. Body Types A study on body types gave the following results: 45% were short; 25% were short and overweight; and 24% were tall and not overweight. Find the probabilities that a person is the following.

a. Overweight

b. Short, but not overweight

c. Tall and overweight

53. Color Blindness Color blindness is an inherited characteristic that is more common in males than in females. If M represents male and C represents red-green color blindness, we use the relative frequencies of the incidences of males and red-green color blindness as probabilities to get

$P(C) = 0.039, P(M \cap C) = 0.035, P(M \cup C) = 0.491.$

Source: Parsons' Diseases of the Eye.

Find the following probabilities.

a. $P(C')$ **b.** $P(M)$ **c.** $P(M')$

d. $P(M' \cap C')$ **e.** $P(C \cap M')$ **f.** $P(C \cup M')$

54. Genetics Gregor Mendel, an Austrian monk, was the first to use probability in the study of genetics. In an effort to understand the mechanism of character transmittal from one generation to the next in plants, he counted the number of occurrences of various characteristics. Mendel found that the flower color in certain pea plants obeyed this scheme:

Pure red crossed with pure white produces red.

From its parents, the red offspring received genes for both red (R) and white (W), but in this case red is *dominant* and white *recessive*, so the offspring exhibits the color red. However, the offspring still carries both genes, and when two such offspring are crossed, several things can happen in the third generation. The table below, which is called a *Punnet square*, shows the equally likely outcomes.

		Second Parent R	Second Parent W
First Parent	R	RR	RW
	W	WR	WW

Use the fact that red is dominant over white to find the following. Assume that there are an equal number of red and white genes in the population.

a. P(a flower is red)

b. P(a flower is white)

55. Genetics Mendel found no dominance in snapdragons, with one red gene and one white gene producing pink-flowered offspring. These second-generation pinks, however, still carry one red and one white gene, and when they are crossed, the next generation still yields the Punnet square from Exercise 54. Find each probability.

a. P(red)

b. P(pink)

c. P(white)

(Mendel verified these probability ratios experimentally and did the same for many characteristics other than flower color. His work, published in 1866, was not recognized until 1890.)

56. Genetics In most animals and plants, it is very unusual for the number of main parts of the organism (such as arms, legs, toes, or flower petals) to vary from generation to generation. Some species, however, have *meristic variability,* in which the number of certain body parts varies from generation to generation. One researcher studied the front feet of certain guinea pigs and produced the following probabilities. *Source: Genetics.*

$P(\text{only four toes, all perfect}) = 0.77$
$P(\text{one imperfect toe and four good ones}) = 0.13$
$P(\text{exactly five good toes}) = 0.10$

Find the probability of each event.

a. No more than four good toes

b. Five toes, whether perfect or not

57. Doctor Visit The probability that a visit to a primary care physician's (PCP) office results in neither lab work nor referral to a specialist is 35%. Of those coming to a PCP's office, 30% are referred to specialists and 40% require lab work. Determine the probability that a visit to a PCP's office results in both lab work and referral to a specialist. Choose one of the following. (*Hint:* Use the union rule for probability.) *Source: Society of Actuaries.*

a. 0.05   **b.** 0.12   **c.** 0.18

d. 0.25   **e.** 0.35

58. Shoulder Injuries Among a large group of patients recovering from shoulder injuries, it is found that 22% visit both a physical therapist and a chiropractor, whereas 12% visit neither of these. The probability that a patient visits a chiropractor exceeds by 0.14 the probability that a patient visits a physical therapist. Determine the probability that a randomly chosen member of this group visits a physical therapist. Choose one of the following. (*Hint:* Use the union rule for probability, and let $x = P$(patient visits a physical therapist).) *Source: Society of Actuaries.*

a. 0.26   **b.** 0.38   **c.** 0.40

d. 0.48   **e.** 0.62

59. Health Plan An insurer offers a health plan to the employees of a large company. As part of this plan, the individual employees may choose exactly two of the supplementary coverages A, B, and C, or they may choose no supplementary coverage. The proportions of the company's employees that choose coverages A, B, and C are 1/4, 1/3, and 5/12, respectively. Determine the probability that a randomly chosen employee will choose no supplementary coverage. Choose one of the following. (*Hint:* Draw a Venn diagram with three sets, and let $x = P(A \cap B)$. Use the fact that 4 of the 8 regions in the Venn diagram have a probability of 0.) *Source: Society of Actuaries.*

a. 0   **b.** 47/144   **c.** 1/2

d. 97/144   **e.** 7/9

Social Sciences

60. Presidential Candidates In 2002, *The New York Times* columnist William Safire gave the following odds against various prominent Democrats receiving their party's presidential nomination in 2004.

Al Gore: 2 to 1
Tom Daschle: 4 to 1
John Kerry: 4 to 1
Chris Dodd: 4 to 1
Joe Lieberman: 5 to 1
Joe Biden: 5 to 1
Pat Leahy: 6 to 1
Russell Feingold: 8 to 1
John Edwards: 9 to 1
Dick Gephardt: 15 to 1

John Allen Paulos observed that there is something wrong with those odds. Translate these odds into probabilities of winning the nomination, and then explain why these are not possible. *Sources: The New York Times and ABC News.*

61. Earnings The following data were gathered for 130 adult U.S. workers: 55 were women; 3 women earned more than $40,000; and 62 men earned $40,000 or less. Find the probability that an individual is

a. a woman earning $40,000 or less;

b. a man earning more than $40,000;

c. a man or is earning more than $40,000;

d. a woman or is earning $40,000 or less.

62. Expenditures for Music A survey of 100 people about their music expenditures gave the following information: 38 bought rock music; 20 were teenagers who bought rock music; and 26 were teenagers. Find the probabilities that a person is

a. a teenager who buys nonrock music;

b. someone who buys rock music or is a teenager;

c. not a teenager;

d. not a teenager, but a buyer of rock music.

63. Refugees In a refugee camp in southern Mexico, it was found that 90% of the refugees came to escape political oppression, 80% came to escape abject poverty, and 70% came to escape both. What is the probability that a refugee in the camp was not poor nor seeking political asylum?

64. Community Activities At the first meeting of a committee to plan a local Lunar New Year celebration, the persons attending are 3 Chinese men, 4 Chinese women, 3 Vietnamese women, 2 Vietnamese men, 4 Korean women, and 2 Korean men. A chairperson is selected at random. Find the probabilities that the chairperson is the following.

a. Chinese

b. Korean or a woman

c. A man or Vietnamese

d. Chinese or Vietnamese

e. Korean and a woman

65. Elections If the odds that a given candidate will win an election are 3 to 2, what is the probability that the candidate will lose?

66. Military There were 203,375 female military personnel in 2009 in various ranks and military branches, as listed in the table. *Source: Department of Defense.*

	Army (A)	Air Force (B)	Navy (C)	Marines (D)
Officers (O)	14,322	12,097	7884	1202
Enlisted (E)	59,401	51,965	42,225	11,749
Cadets & Midshipmen (M)	688	922	920	0

a. Convert the numbers in the table to probabilities.

b. Find the probability that a randomly selected woman is in the Army.

c. Find the probability that a randomly selected woman is an officer in the Navy or Marine Corps.

d. $P(A \cup B)$

e. $P(E \cup (C \cup D))$

67. Perceptions of Threat Research has been carried out to measure the amount of intolerance that citizens of Russia have for left-wing Communists and right-wing Fascists, as indicated in the table below. Note that the numbers are given as percents and each row sums to 100 (except for rounding). *Source: Political Research Quarterly.*

Russia	None at All	Don't Know	Not Very Much	Somewhat	Extremely
Left-Wing Communists	47.8	6.7	31.0	10.5	4.1
Right-Wing Fascists	3.0	3.2	7.1	27.1	59.5

a. Find the probability that a randomly chosen citizen of Russia would be somewhat or extremely intolerant of right-wing Fascists.

b. Find the probability that a randomly chosen citizen of Russia would be completely tolerant of left-wing Communists.

c. Compare your answers to parts a and b and provide possible reasons for these numbers.

68. Perceptions of Threat Research has been carried out to measure the amount of intolerance that U.S. citizens have for left-wing Communists and right-wing Fascists, as indicated in the table. Note that the numbers are given as percents and each row sums to 100 (except for rounding). *Source: Political Research Quarterly.*

United States	None at All	Don't Know	Not Very Much	Somewhat	Extremely
Left-Wing Communists	13.0	2.7	33.0	34.2	17.1
Right-Wing Fascists	10.1	3.3	20.7	43.1	22.9

    a. Find the probability that a randomly chosen U.S. citizen would have at least some intolerance of right-wing Fascists.

    b. Find the probability that a randomly chosen U.S. citizen would have at least some intolerance of left-wing Communists.

    c. Compare your answers to parts a and b and provide possible reasons for these numbers.

    d. Compare these answers to the answers to Exercise 67.

General Interest

69. Olympics In recent winter Olympics, each part of the women's figure skating program has 12 judges, but the scores of only 9 of the judges are randomly selected for the final results. As we will see in the next chapter, there are 220 possible ways for the 9 judges whose scores are counted to be selected. *The New York Times* examined those 220 possibilities for the short program in the 2006 Olympics, based on the published scores of the judges, and listed what the results would have been for each, as shown below. *Source: The New York Times.*

    a. The winner of the short program was Sasha Cohen. For a random combination of 9 judges, what is the probability of that outcome?

    b. The second place finisher in the short program was Irina Slutskaya. For a random combination of 9 judges, what is the probability of that outcome?

    c. The third place finisher in the short program was Shizuka Arakawa. For a random combination of 9 judges, what is the probability of that outcome? Do not include outcomes that include a tie.

70. Book of Odds The following table gives the probabilities that a particular event will occur. Convert each probability to the odds in favor of the event. *Source: The Book of Odds.*

Event	Probability for the Event
An NFL pass will be intercepted.	0.03
A U.S. president owned a dog during his term in office.	0.65
A woman owns a pair of high heels.	0.61
An adult smokes.	0.21
A flight is cancelled.	0.02

71. Book of Odds The following table gives the odds that a particular event will occur. Convert each odd to the probability that the event will occur. *Source: The Book of Odds.*

Event	Odds for the Event
A powerball entry will win the jackpot.	1 to 195,199,999
An adult will be struck by lightning during a year.	1 to 835,499
An adult will file for personal bankruptcy during a year.	1 to 157.6
A person collects stamps.	1 to 59.32

YOUR TURN ANSWERS

1. $16/52 = 4/13$ **2.** $10/36 = 5/18$ **3.** $33/36 = 11/12$
4. 3 to 7 or 3:7   **5.** $3/20$ **6.** $3/10$

Outcome	1. Slutskaya 2. Cohen 3. Arakawa	1. Slutskaya 2. Arakawa 3. Cohen	1. Slutskaya 2, 3. Arakawa and Cohen tied	1. Cohen 2. Slutskaya 3. Arakawa	1. Cohen 2. Arakawa 3. Slutskaya
Number of Possible Judging Combinations	92	33	3	67	25

7.5 Conditional Probability; Independent Events

APPLY IT **What is the probability that a broker who uses research picks stocks that go up?**

The manager for a brokerage firm has noticed that some of the firm's stockbrokers have selected stocks based on the firm's research, while other brokers tend to follow their own instincts. To see whether the research department performs better than the brokers' instincts, the manager surveyed 100 brokers, with results as shown in the following table.

	Results of Stockbroker Survey		
	Picked Stocks That Went Up (A)	Didn't Pick Stocks That Went Up (A')	Totals
Used Research (B)	30	15	45
Didn't Use Research (B')	30	25	55
Totals	60	40	100

Letting A represent the event "picked stocks that went up," and letting B represent the event "used research," we can find the following probabilities.

$$P(A) = \frac{60}{100} = 0.6 \qquad P(A') = \frac{40}{100} = 0.4$$

$$P(B) = \frac{45}{100} = 0.45 \qquad P(B') = \frac{55}{100} = 0.55$$

APPLY IT   To answer the question asked at the beginning of this section, suppose we want to find the probability that a broker using research will pick stocks that go up. From the table, of the 45 brokers who use research, 30 picked stocks that went up, with

$$P(\text{broker who uses research picks stocks that go up}) = \frac{30}{45} \approx 0.6667.$$

This is a different number than the probability that a broker picks stocks that go up, 0.6, since we have additional information (the broker uses research) that has *reduced the sample space*. In other words, we found the probability that a broker picks stocks that go up, A, given the additional information that the broker uses research, B. This is called the *conditional probability* of event A, given that event B has occurred. It is written $P(A\,|\,B)$ and read as "the probability of A given B." In this example,

$$P(A|B) = \frac{30}{45}.$$

To generalize this result, assume that E and F are two events for a particular experiment and that all events in the sample space S are equally likely. We want to find $P(E\,|\,F)$, the probability that E occurs given F has occurred. Since we assume that F has occurred, reduce the sample space to F: look only at the elements inside F. See Figure 20. Of those $n(F)$ elements, there are $n(E \cap F)$ elements where E also occurs. This makes

$$P(E|F) = \frac{n(E \cap F)}{n(F)}.$$

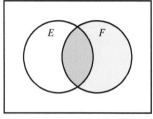

Event F has a total of $n(F)$ elements.

FIGURE 20

This equation can also be written as the quotient of two probabilities. Divide numerator and denominator by $n(S)$ to get

$$P(E|F) = \frac{n(E \cap F)/n(S)}{n(F)/n(S)} = \frac{P(E \cap F)}{P(F)}.$$

This last result motivates the definition of conditional probability.

> **Conditional Probability**
>
> The **conditional probability** of event E given event F, written $P(E|F)$, is
>
> $$P(E|F) = \frac{P(E \cap F)}{P(F)}, \quad \text{where } P(F) \neq 0.$$

Although the definition of conditional probability was motivated by an example with equally likely outcomes, it is valid in all cases. However, for *equally likely outcomes*, conditional probability can be found by directly applying the definition, or by first reducing the sample space to event F, and then finding the number of outcomes in F that are also in event E. Thus,

$$P(E|F) = \frac{n(E \cap F)}{n(F)}.$$

In the preceding example, the conditional probability could have also been found using the definition of conditional probability:

$$P(A|B) = \frac{P(A \cap B)}{P(B)} = \frac{30/100}{45/100} = \frac{30}{45} = \frac{2}{3}.$$

EXAMPLE 1 **Stocks**

Use the information given in the chart at the beginning of this section to find the following probabilities.

(a) $P(B|A)$

SOLUTION This represents the probability that the broker used research, given that the broker picked stocks that went up. Reduce the sample space to A. Then find $n(A \cap B)$ and $n(A)$.

$$P(B|A) = \frac{P(B \cap A)}{P(A)} = \frac{n(A \cap B)}{n(A)} = \frac{30}{60} = \frac{1}{2}$$

If a broker picked stocks that went up, then the probability is $1/2$ that the broker used research.

(b) $P(A'|B)$

SOLUTION In words, this is the probability that a broker picks stocks that do not go up, even though he used research.

$$P(A'|B) = \frac{n(A' \cap B)}{n(B)} = \frac{15}{45} = \frac{1}{3}$$

YOUR TURN 1 In Example 1, find $P(A|B')$.

(c) $P(B'|A')$

SOLUTION Here, we want the probability that a broker who picked stocks that did not go up did not use research.

$$P(B'|A') = \frac{n(B' \cap A')}{n(A')} = \frac{25}{40} = \frac{5}{8} \quad \text{TRY YOUR TURN 1}$$

Venn diagrams are useful for illustrating problems in conditional probability. A Venn diagram for Example 1, in which the probabilities are used to indicate the number in the set defined by each region, is shown in Figure 21. In the diagram, $P(B|A)$ is found by reducing the sample space to just set A. Then $P(B|A)$ is the ratio of the number in that part of set B that is also in A to the number in set A, or $0.3/0.6 = 0.5$.

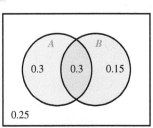

$P(A) = 0.3 + 0.3 = 0.6$

FIGURE 21

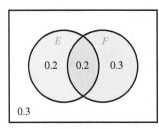

FIGURE 22

YOUR TURN 2 Given $P(E) = 0.56$, $P(F) = 0.64$, and $P(E \cup F) = 0.80$, find $P(E \mid F)$.

EXAMPLE 2   Conditional Probabilities

Given $P(E) = 0.4$, $P(F) = 0.5$, and $P(E \cup F) = 0.7$, find $P(E \mid F)$.

SOLUTION   Find $P(E \cap F)$ first. By the union rule,

$$P(E \cup F) = P(E) + P(F) - P(E \cap F)$$
$$0.7 = 0.4 + 0.5 - P(E \cap F)$$
$$P(E \cap F) = 0.2.$$

$P(E \mid F)$ is the ratio of the probability of that part of E that is in F to the probability of F, or

$$P(E \mid F) = \frac{P(E \cap F)}{P(F)} = \frac{0.2}{0.5} = \frac{2}{5}. \qquad \text{TRY YOUR TURN 2}$$

The Venn diagram in Figure 22 illustrates Example 2.

EXAMPLE 3   Tossing Coins

Two fair coins were tossed, and it is known that at least one was a head. Find the probability that both were heads.

SOLUTION   At first glance, the answer may appear to be $1/2$, but this is not the case. The sample space has four equally likely outcomes, $S = \{hh, ht, th, tt\}$. Because of the condition that at least one coin was a head, the sample space is reduced to $\{hh, ht, th\}$. Since only one outcome in this reduced sample space is 2 heads,

$$P(2 \text{ heads} \mid \text{at least 1 head}) = \frac{1}{3}.$$

Alternatively, we could use the conditional probability definition. Define two events:

$$E_1 = \text{at least 1 head} = \{hh, ht, th\}$$

and

YOUR TURN 3   In Example 3, find the probability of exactly one head, given that there is at least one tail.

$$E_2 = 2 \text{ heads} = \{hh\}.$$

Since there are four equally likely outcomes, $P(E_1) = 3/4$ and $P(E_1 \cap E_2) = 1/4$. Therefore,

$$P(E_2 \mid E_1) = \frac{P(E_2 \cap E_1)}{P(E_1)} = \frac{1/4}{3/4} = \frac{1}{3}. \qquad \text{TRY YOUR TURN 3}$$

EXAMPLE 4   Playing Cards

Two cards are drawn from a standard deck, one after another without replacement. Find the probability that the second card is red, given that the first card is red.

SOLUTION   According to the conditional probability formula,

$$P(\text{second card is red} \mid \text{first card is red})$$
$$= \frac{P(\text{second card is red and the first card is red})}{P(\text{first card is red})}.$$

We will soon see how to compute probabilities such as the one in the numerator. But there is a much simpler way to calculate this conditional probability. We only need to observe that with one red card gone, there are 51 cards left, 25 of which are red, so

$$P(\text{second card is red} \mid \text{first card is red}) = \frac{25}{51}.$$

It is important not to confuse $P(A|B)$ with $P(B|A)$. For example, in a criminal trial, a prosecutor may point out to the jury that the probability of the defendant's DNA profile matching that of a sample taken at the scene of the crime, given that the defendant is innocent, $P(D|I)$, is very small. What the jury must decide, however, is the probability that the defendant is innocent, given that the defendant's DNA profile matches the sample, $P(I|D)$. Confusing the two is an error sometimes called "the prosecutor's fallacy," and the 1990 conviction of a rape suspect in England was overturned by a panel of judges, who ordered a retrial, because the fallacy made the original trial unfair. *Source: New Scientist.*

In the next section, we will see how to compute $P(A|B)$ when we know $P(B|A)$.

Product Rule

If $P(E) \neq 0$ and $P(F) \neq 0$, then the definition of conditional probability shows that

$$P(E|F) = \frac{P(E \cap F)}{P(F)} \quad \text{and} \quad P(F|E) = \frac{P(F \cap E)}{P(E)}.$$

Using the fact that $P(E \cap F) = P(F \cap E)$, and solving each of these equations for $P(E \cap F)$, we obtain the following rule.

Product Rule of Probability
If E and F are events, then $P(E \cap F)$ may be found by either of these formulas.

$$P(E \cap F) = P(F) \cdot P(E|F) \quad \text{or} \quad P(E \cap F) = P(E) \cdot P(F|E)$$

The product rule gives a method for finding the probability that events E and F both occur, as illustrated by the next few examples.

EXAMPLE 5 Business Majors

In a class with 2/5 women and 3/5 men, 25% of the women are business majors. Find the probability that a student chosen from the class at random is a female business major.

YOUR TURN 4 At a local college, 4/5 of the students live on campus. Of those who live on campus, 25% have cars on campus. Find the probability that a student lives on campus and has a car.

SOLUTION Let B and W represent the events "business major" and "woman," respectively. We want to find $P(B \cap W)$. By the product rule,

$$P(B \cap W) = P(W) \cdot P(B|W).$$

Using the given information, $P(W) = 2/5 = 0.4$ and $P(B|W) = 0.25$. Thus,

$$P(B \cap W) = 0.4(0.25) = 0.10. \quad \text{TRY YOUR TURN 4}$$

The next examples show how a tree diagram is used with the product rule to find the probability of a sequence of events.

EXAMPLE 6 Advertising

A company needs to hire a new director of advertising. It has decided to try to hire either person A or B, who are assistant advertising directors for its major competitor. To decide between A and B, the company does research on the campaigns managed by either A or B (no campaign is managed by both) and finds that A is in charge of twice as many advertising campaigns as B. Also, A's campaigns have satisfactory results 3 out of 4 times, while B's campaigns have satisfactory results only 2 out of 5 times. Suppose one of the competitor's advertising campaigns (managed by A or B) is selected randomly.

We can represent this situation using a tree diagram as follows. Let A denote the event "Person A manages the job" and B the event "person B manages the job." Notice that A and

B are complementary events. Since A does twice as many jobs as B, we have $P(A) = 2/3$ and $P(B) = 1/3$, as noted on the first-stage branches of the tree in Figure 23.

Let *S* be the event "satisfactory results" and *U* the event "unsatisfactory results." When A manages the job, the probability of satisfactory results is 3/4 and of unsatisfactory results 1/4 as noted on the second-stage branches. Similarly, the probabilities when B manages the job are noted on the remaining second-stage branches. The composite branches labeled 1 to 4 represent the four mutually exclusive possibilities for the managing and outcome of the selected campaign.

(a) Find the probability that A is in charge of the selected campaign and that it produces satisfactory results.

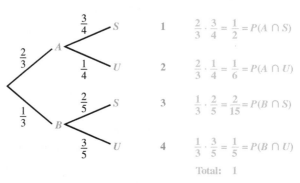

FIGURE 23

SOLUTION We are asked to find $P(A \cap S)$. We know that when A does the job, the probability of success is 3/4, that is, $P(S|A) = 3/4$. Hence, by the product rule,

$$P(A \cap S) = P(A) \cdot P(S|A) = \frac{2}{3} \cdot \frac{3}{4} = \frac{1}{2}.$$

The event $A \cap S$ is represented by branch 1 of the tree, and, as we have just seen, its probability is the product of the probabilities of the pieces that make up that branch.

(b) Find the probability that B runs the campaign and that it produces satisfactory results.

SOLUTION We must find $P(B \cap S)$. The event is represented by branch 3 of the tree, and, as before, its probability is the product of the probabilities of the pieces of that branch:

$$P(B \cap S) = P(B) \cdot P(S|B) = \frac{1}{3} \cdot \frac{2}{5} = \frac{2}{15}.$$

(c) What is the probability that the selected campaign is satisfactory?

SOLUTION The event *S* is the union of the mutually exclusive events $A \cap S$ and $B \cap S$, which are represented by branches 1 and 3 of the diagram. By the union rule,

$$P(S) = P(A \cap S) + P(B \cap S) = \frac{1}{2} + \frac{2}{15} = \frac{19}{30}.$$

Thus, the probability of an event that appears on several branches is the sum of the probabilities of each of these branches.

(d) What is the probability that the selected campaign is unsatisfactory?

SOLUTION $P(U)$ can be read from branches 2 and 4 of the tree.

$$P(U) = \frac{1}{6} + \frac{1}{5} = \frac{11}{30}$$

Alternatively, since *U* is the complement of *S*,

YOUR TURN 5 In Example 6, what is the probability that A is in charge of the selected campaign and that it produces unsatisfactory results?

$$P(U) = 1 - P(S) = 1 - \frac{19}{30} = \frac{11}{30}.$$

TRY YOUR TURN 5

EXAMPLE 7 **Environmental Inspections**

The Environmental Protection Agency is considering inspecting 6 plants for environmental compliance: 3 in Chicago, 2 in Los Angeles, and 1 in New York. Due to a lack of inspectors, they decide to inspect two plants selected at random, one this month and one next month, with each plant equally likely to be selected, but no plant selected twice. What is the probability that 1 Chicago plant and 1 Los Angeles plant are selected?

SOLUTION A tree diagram showing the various possible outcomes is given in Figure 24. In this diagram, the events of inspecting a plant in Chicago, Los Angeles, and New York are represented by C, LA, and NY, respectively. For the first inspection, $P(C \text{ first}) = 3/6 = 1/2$ because 3 of the 6 plants are in Chicago, and all plants are equally likely to be selected. Likewise, $P(LA \text{ first}) = 1/3$ and $P(NY \text{ first}) = 1/6$.

For the second inspection, we first note that one plant has been inspected and, therefore, removed from the list, leaving 5 plants. For example, $P(LA \text{ second} | C \text{ first}) = 2/5$ since 2 of the 5 remaining plants are in Los Angeles. The remaining second inspection probabilities are calculated in the same manner.

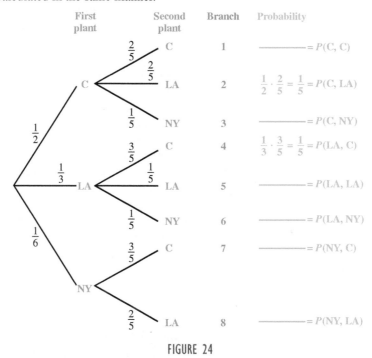

FIGURE 24

We want to find the probability of selecting exactly 1 Chicago plant and 1 Los Angeles plant. This event can occur in two ways: inspecting Chicago this month and Los Angeles next month (branch 2 of the tree diagram), or inspecting Los Angeles this month and Chicago next month (branch 4). For branch 2,

$$P(C \text{ first}) \cdot P(LA \text{ second} \mid C \text{ first}) = \frac{1}{2} \cdot \frac{2}{5} = \frac{1}{5}.$$

For branch 4, where Los Angeles is inspected first,

$$P(LA \text{ first}) \cdot P(C \text{ second} \mid LA \text{ first}) = \frac{1}{3} \cdot \frac{3}{5} = \frac{1}{5}.$$

Since the two events are mutually exclusive, the final probability is the sum of these two probabilities.

$$P(1 \text{ C}, 1 \text{ LA}) = P(C \text{ first}) \cdot P(LA \text{ second} | C \text{ first})$$
$$+ P(LA \text{ first}) \cdot P(C \text{ second} | LA \text{ first})$$
$$= \frac{2}{5}$$

YOUR TURN 6 In Example 7, what is the probability that 1 New York plant and 1 Chicago plant are selected?

TRY YOUR TURN 6

─FOR REVIEW─
You may wish to refer to the picture of a deck of cards shown in Figure 17 (Section 7.3) and the description accompanying it.

The product rule is often used with *stochastic processes*, which are mathematical models that evolve over time in a probabilistic manner. For example, selecting factories at random for inspection is such a process, in which the probabilities change with each successive selection.

EXAMPLE 8 **Playing Cards**

Two cards are drawn from a standard deck, one after another without replacement.

(a) Find the probability that the first card is a heart and the second card is red.

SOLUTION Start with the tree diagram in Figure 25. On the first draw, since there are 13 hearts among the 52 cards, the probability of drawing a heart is $13/52 = 1/4$. On the second draw, since a (red) heart has been drawn already, there are 25 red cards in the remaining 51 cards. Thus, the probability of drawing a red card on the second draw, given that the first is a heart, is $25/51$. By the product rule of probability,

$$P(\text{heart first and red second})$$
$$= P(\text{heart first}) \cdot P(\text{red second}|\text{heart first})$$
$$= \frac{1}{4} \cdot \frac{25}{51} = \frac{25}{204} \approx 0.123.$$

(b) Find the probability that the second card is red.

SOLUTION To solve this, we need to fill out the bottom branch of the tree diagram in Figure 25. Unfortunately, if the first card is not a heart, it is not clear how to find the probability that the second card is red, because it depends upon whether the first card is red or black. One way to solve this problem would be to divide the bottom branch into two separate branches: diamond and black card (club or spade).

There is a simpler way, however, since we don't care whether or not the first card is a heart, as we did in part (a). Instead, we'll consider whether the first card is red or black and then do the same for the second card. The result, with the corresponding probabilities, is in Figure 26. The probability that the second card is red is found by multiplying the probabilities along the two branches and adding.

$$P(\text{red second}) = \frac{1}{2} \cdot \frac{25}{51} + \frac{1}{2} \cdot \frac{26}{51}$$
$$= \frac{1}{2}$$

The probability is $1/2$, exactly the same as the probability that any card is red. If we know nothing about the first card, there is no reason for the probability of the second card to be anything other than $1/2$.

FIGURE 25

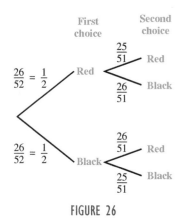

FIGURE 26

Independent Events
Suppose, in Example 8(a), that we draw the two cards *with replacement* rather than without replacement (that is, we put the first card back before drawing the second card). If the first card is a heart, then the probability of drawing a red card on the second draw is $26/52$, rather than $25/51$, because there are still 52 cards in the deck, 26 of them red. In this case, $P(\text{red second}|\text{heart first})$ is the same as $P(\text{red second})$. The value of the second card is not affected by the value of the first card. We say that the event that the second card is red is *independent* of the event that the first card is a heart since the knowledge of the first card does not influence what happens to the second card. On the other hand, when we draw without replacement, the events that the first card is a heart and that the second card is red are *dependent* events. The fact that the first card is a heart means there is one less red card in the deck, influencing the probability that the second card is red.

As another example, consider tossing a fair coin twice. If the first toss shows heads, the probability that the next toss is heads is still $1/2$. Coin tosses are independent events, since the outcome of one toss does not influence the outcome of the next toss. Similarly, rolls of a fair die are independent events.

On the other hand, the events "the milk is old" and "the milk is sour" are dependent events; if the milk is old, there is an increased chance that it is sour. Also, in the example at the beginning of this section, the events A (broker picked stocks that went up) and B (broker used research) are dependent events, because information about the use of research affected the probability of picking stocks that go up. That is, $P(A|B)$ is different from $P(A)$.

If events E and F are independent, then the knowledge that E has occurred gives no (probability) information about the occurrence or nonoccurrence of event F. That is, $P(F)$ is exactly the same as $P(F|E)$, or

$$P(F|E) = P(F).$$

This, in fact, is the formal definition of independent events.

Independent Events

Events E and F are **independent events** if

$$P(F|E) = P(F) \quad \text{or} \quad P(E|F) = P(E).$$

If the events are not independent, they are **dependent events**.

When E and F are independent events, then $P(F|E) = P(F)$ and the product rule becomes

$$P(E \cap F) = P(E) \cdot P(F|E) = P(E) \cdot P(F).$$

Conversely, if this equation holds, then it follows that $P(F) = P(F|E)$. Consequently, we have this useful fact:

Product Rule for Independent Events

Events E and F are independent events if and only if

$$P(E \cap F) = P(E) \cdot P(F).$$

EXAMPLE 9 Calculator

A calculator requires a keystroke assembly and a logic circuit. Assume that 99% of the keystroke assemblies are satisfactory and 97% of the logic circuits are satisfactory. Find the probability that a finished calculator will be satisfactory.

SOLUTION If the failure of a keystroke assembly and the failure of a logic circuit are independent events, then

$$P(\text{satisfactory calculator})$$
$$= P(\text{satisfactory keystroke assembly}) \cdot P(\text{satisfactory logic circuit})$$
$$= (0.99)(0.97) \approx 0.96.$$

YOUR TURN 7 The probability that you roll a five on a single die is 1/6. Find the probability you roll two five's in a row.

(The probability of a defective calculator is $1 - 0.96 = 0.04$.)　　TRY YOUR TURN 7

CAUTION　It is common for students to confuse the ideas of *mutually exclusive* events and *independent* events. Events E and F are mutually exclusive if $E \cap F = \emptyset$. For example, if a family has exactly one child, the only possible outcomes are $B = \{\text{boy}\}$ and $G = \{\text{girl}\}$. These two events are mutually exclusive. The events are *not* independent, however, since $P(G|B) = 0$ (if a family with only one child has a boy, the probability it has a girl is then 0). Since $P(G|B) \neq P(G)$, the events are not independent.

Of all the families with exactly two children, the events $G_1 = \{\text{first child is a girl}\}$ and $G_2 = \{\text{second child is a girl}\}$ are independent, since $P(G_2|G_1)$ equals $P(G_2)$. However, G_1 and G_2 are not mutually exclusive, since $G_1 \cap G_2 = \{\text{both children are girls}\} \neq \emptyset$.

To show that two events E and F are independent, show that $P(F|E) = P(F)$ or that $P(E|F) = P(E)$ or that $P(E \cap F) = P(E) \cdot P(F)$. Another way is to observe that knowledge of one outcome does not influence the probability of the other outcome, as we did for coin tosses.

NOTE In some cases, it may not be apparent from the physical description of the problem whether two events are independent or not. For example, it is not obvious whether the event that a baseball player gets a hit tomorrow is independent of the event that he got a hit today. In such cases, it is necessary to calculate whether $P(F|E) = P(F)$, or, equivalently, whether $P(E \cap F) = P(E) \cdot P(F)$.

EXAMPLE 10 **Snow in Manhattan**

On a typical January day in Manhattan the probability of snow is 0.10, the probability of a traffic jam is 0.80, and the probability of snow or a traffic jam (or both) is 0.82. Are the event "it snows" and the event "a traffic jam occurs" independent?

SOLUTION Let S represent the event "it snows" and T represent the event "a traffic jam occurs." We must determine whether

$$P(T|S) = P(T) \quad \text{or} \quad P(S|T) = P(S).$$

We know $P(S) = 0.10$, $P(T) = 0.8$, and $P(S \cup T) = 0.82$. We can use the union rule (or a Venn diagram) to find $P(S \cap T) = 0.08$, $P(T|S) = 0.8$, and $P(S|T) = 0.1$. Since

$$P(T|S) = P(T) = 0.8 \quad \text{and} \quad P(S|T) = P(S) = 0.1,$$

the events "it snows" and "a traffic jam occurs" are independent. **TRY YOUR TURN 8**

YOUR TURN 8 The probability that you do your math homework is 0.8, the probability that you do your history assignment is 0.7, and the probability of you doing your math homework or your history assignment is 0.9. Are the events "do your math homework" and "do your history assignment" independent?

Although we showed $P(T|S) = P(T)$ and $P(S|T) = P(S)$ in Example 10, only one of these results is needed to establish independence. It is also important to note that independence of events does not necessarily follow intuition; it is established from the mathematical definition of independence.

7.5 EXERCISES

If a single fair die is rolled, find the probabilities of the following results.

1. A 2, given that the number rolled was odd
2. A 4, given that the number rolled was even
3. An even number, given that the number rolled was 6
4. An odd number, given that the number rolled was 6.

If two fair dice are rolled, find the probabilities of the following results.

5. A sum of 8, given that the sum is greater than 7
6. A sum of 6, given that the roll was a "double" (two identical numbers)
7. A double, given that the sum was 9
8. A double, given that the sum was 8.

If two cards are drawn without replacement from an ordinary deck, find the probabilities of the following results.

9. The second is a heart, given that the first is a heart.
10. The second is black, given that the first is a spade.
11. The second is a face card, given that the first is a jack.
12. The second is an ace, given that the first is not an ace.
13. A jack and a 10 are drawn.
14. An ace and a 4 are drawn.
15. Two black cards are drawn.
16. Two hearts are drawn.
17. In your own words, explain how to find the conditional probability $P(E|F)$.
18. In your own words, define independent events.

Decide whether each of the following pairs of events are dependent or independent.

19. A red and a green die are rolled. A is the event that the red die comes up even, and B is the event that the green die comes up even.
20. C is the event that it rains more than 10 days in Chicago next June, and D is the event that it rains more than 15 days.
21. E is the event that a resident of Texas lives in Dallas, and F is the event that a resident of Texas lives in either Dallas or Houston.
22. A coin is flipped. G is the event that today is Tuesday, and H is the event that the coin comes up heads.

In the previous section, we described an experiment in which the numbers 1, 2, 3, 4, and 5 are written on slips of paper, and 2 slips are drawn at random one at a time without replacement. Find each probability in Exercises 23 and 24.

23. The probability that the first number is 3, given the following.

a. The sum is 7.

b. The sum is 8.

24. The probability that the sum is 8, given the following.

a. The first number is 5.

b. The first number is 4.

25. Suppose two dice are rolled. Let A be the event that the sum of the two dice is 7. Find an event B related to numbers on the dice such that A and B are

a. independent;

b. dependent.

26. Your friend asks you to explain how the product rule for independent events differs from the product rule for dependent events. How would you respond?

27. Another friend asks you to explain how to tell whether two events are dependent or independent. How would you reply? (Use your own words.)

28. A student reasons that the probability in Example 3 of both coins being heads is just the probability that the other coin is a head, that is, $1/2$. Explain why this reasoning is wrong.

29. Let A and B be independent events with $P(A) = \frac{1}{4}$ and $P(B) = \frac{1}{5}$. Find $P(A \cap B)$ and $P(A \cup B)$.

30. If A and B are events such that $P(A) = 0.5$ and $P(A \cup B) = 0.7$, find $P(B)$ when

a. A and B are mutually exclusive;

b. A and B are independent.

31. The following problem, submitted by Daniel Hahn of Blairstown, Iowa, appeared in the "Ask Marilyn" column of *Parade* magazine. *Source: Parade magazine.*

"You discover two booths at a carnival. Each is tended by an honest man with a pair of covered coin shakers. In each shaker is a single coin, and you are allowed to bet upon the chance that both coins in that booth's shakers are heads after the man in the booth shakes them, does an inspection, and can tell you that at least one of the shakers contains a head. The difference is that the man in the first booth always looks inside both of his shakers, whereas the man in the second booth looks inside only one of the shakers. Where will you stand the best chance?"

32. The following question was posed in *Chance News* by Craig Fox and Yoval Rotenstrich. You are playing a game in which a fair coin is flipped and a fair die is rolled. You win a prize if both the coin comes up heads and a 6 is rolled on the die. Now suppose the coin is tossed and the die is rolled, but you are not allowed to see either result. You are told, however, that either the head or the 6 occurred. You are then offered the chance to cancel the game and play a new game in which a die is rolled (there is no coin), and you win a prize if a 6 is rolled. *Source: Chance News.*

a. Is it to your advantage to switch to the new game, or to stick with the original game? Answer this question by calculating your probability of winning in each case.

b. Many people erroneously think that it's better to stick with the original game. Discuss why this answer might seem intuitive, but why it is wrong.

33. Suppose a male defendant in a court trial has a mustache, beard, tattoo, and an earring. Suppose, also, that an eyewitness has identified the perpetrator as someone with these characteristics. If the respective probabilities for the male population in this region are 0.35, 0.30, 0.10, and 0.05, is it fair to multiply these probabilities together to conclude that the probability that a person having these characteristics is 0.000525, or 21 in 40,000, and thus decide that the defendant must be guilty?

34. In a two-child family, if we assume that the probabilities of a male child and a female child are each 0.5, are the events *all children are the same sex* and *at most one male* independent? Are they independent for a three-child family?

35. Laura Johnson, a game show contestant, could win one of two prizes: a shiny new Porsche or a shiny new penny. Laura is given two boxes of marbles. The first box has 50 pink marbles in it and the second box has 50 blue marbles in it. The game show host will pick someone from the audience to be blindfolded and then draw a marble from one of the two boxes. If a pink marble is drawn, she wins the Porsche. Otherwise, Laura wins the penny. Can Laura increase her chances of winning by redistributing some of the marbles from one box to the other? Explain. *Source: Car Talk.*

APPLICATIONS

Business and Economics

Banking   The Midtown Bank has found that most customers at the tellers' windows either cash a check or make a deposit. The following table indicates the transactions for one teller for one day.

	Cash Check	No Check	Totals
Make Deposit	60	20	80
No Deposit	30	10	40
Totals	90	30	120

Letting C represent "cashing a check" and D represent "making a deposit," express each probability in words and find its value.

36. $P(C|D)$ **37.** $P(D'|C)$ **38.** $P(C'|D')$

39. $P(C'|D)$ **40.** $P[(C \cap D)']$

41. Airline Delays   In February 2010, the major U.S. airline with the fewest delays was United Airlines, for which 77.3% of their flights arrived on time. Assume that the event that a given flight arrives on time is independent of the event that another flight arrives on time. *Source: U.S. Department of Transportation.*

a. Katie O'Connor plans to take four separate flights for her publisher next month on United Airlines. Assuming that the airline has the same on-time performance as in February 2010, what is the probability that all four flights arrive on time?

b. Discuss how realistic it is to assume that the on-time arrivals of the different flights are independent.

42. Backup Computers   Corporations where a computer is essential to day-to-day operations, such as banks, often have a second backup computer in case the main computer fails. Suppose there is a 0.003 chance that the main computer will fail in a given time period and a 0.005 chance that the backup computer will fail while the main computer is being repaired. Assume these failures represent independent events, and find the fraction of the time that the corporation can assume it will have computer service. How realistic is our assumption of independence?

43. ATM Transactions Among users of automated teller machines (ATMs), 92% use ATMs to withdraw cash, and 32% use them to check their account balance. Suppose that 96% use ATMs to either withdraw cash or check their account balance (or both). Given a woman who uses an ATM to check her account balance, what is the probability that she also uses an ATM to get cash? *Source: Chicago Tribune.*

Quality Control A bicycle factory runs two assembly lines, A and B. If 95% of line A's products pass inspection, while only 85% of line B's products pass inspection, and 60% of the factory's bikes come off assembly line A (the rest off B), find the probabilities that one of the factory's bikes did not pass inspection and came off the following.

44. Assembly line A   **45.** Assembly line B

46. Find the probability that one of the factory's bikes did not pass inspection.

Life Sciences

47. Genetics Both of a certain pea plant's parents had a gene for red and a gene for white flowers. (See Exercise 54 in Section 7.4.) If the offspring has red flowers, find the probability that it combined a gene for red and a gene for white (rather than 2 for red).

48. Medical Experiment A medical experiment showed that the probability that a new medicine is effective is 0.75, the probability that a patient will have a certain side effect is 0.4, and the probability that both events occur is 0.3. Decide whether these events are dependent or independent.

Genetics Assuming that boy and girl babies are equally likely, fill in the remaining probabilities on the tree diagram below and use that information to find the probability that a family with three children has all girls, given the following.

49. The first is a girl.

50. The third is a girl.

51. The second is a girl.

52. At least 2 are girls.

53. At least 1 is a girl.

Color Blindness The following table shows frequencies for red-green color blindness, where M represents "person is male" and C represents "person is color-blind." Use this table to find the following probabilities. (See Exercise 53, Section 7.4.)

	M	M'	Totals
C	0.035	0.004	0.039
C'	0.452	0.509	0.961
Totals	0.487	0.513	1.000

54. $P(M)$ **55.** $P(C)$

56. $P(M \cap C)$ **57.** $P(M \cup C)$

58. $P(M|C)$ **59.** $P(C|M)$

60. $P(M'|C)$

61. Are the events C and M, described above, dependent? What does this mean?

62. Color Blindness A scientist wishes to determine whether there is a relationship between color blindness (C) and deafness (D).

a. Suppose the scientist found the probabilities listed in the table. What should the findings be? (See Exercises 54–61.)

b. Explain what your answer tells us about color blindness and deafness.

	D	D'	Totals
C	0.0008	0.0392	0.0400
C'	0.0192	0.9408	0.9600
Totals	0.0200	0.9800	1.0000

63. Overweight According to a recent report, 68.3% of men and 64.1% of women in the United States were overweight. Given that 49.3% of Americans are men and 50.7% are women, find the probability that a randomly selected American fits the following description. *Source: JAMA.*

a. An overweight man

b. Overweight

c. Are the events "male" and "overweight" independent?

Hockey The table below lists the number of head and neck injuries for 319 ice hockey players' exposures wearing either a full shield or half shield in the Canadian Inter-University Athletics Union. *Source: JAMA.*

For a randomly selected injury, find each probability.

64. $P(A)$ **65.** $P(C|F)$

66. $P(A|H)$ **67.** $P(B'|H')$

	Half Shield (H)	Full Shield (F)	Totals
Head and Face Injuries (A)	95	34	129
Concussions (B)	41	38	79
Neck Injuries (C)	9	7	16
Other Injuries (D)	202	150	352
Totals	347	229	576

68. Are the events A and H independent events?*

69. Blood Pressure   A doctor is studying the relationship between blood pressure and heartbeat abnormalities in her patients. She tests a random sample of her patients and notes their blood pressures (high, low, or normal) and their heartbeats (regular or irregular). She finds that:

  (**i**) 14% have high blood pressure.

  (**ii**) 22% have low blood pressure.

  (**iii**) 15% have an irregular heartbeat.

  (**iv**) Of those with an irregular heartbeat, one-third have high blood pressure.

  (**v**) Of those with normal blood pressure, one-eighth have an irregular heartbeat.

What portion of the patients selected have a regular heartbeat and low blood pressure? Choose one of the following. (*Hint:* Make a table similar to the one for Exercises 54–61.) *Source: Society of Actuaries.*

  a. 2%   **b.** 5%   **c.** 8%   **d.** 9%   **e.** 20%

70. Breast Cancer   To explain why the chance of a woman getting breast cancer in the next year goes up each year, while the chance of a woman getting breast cancer in her lifetime goes down, Ruma Falk made the following analogy. Suppose you are looking for a letter that you may have lost. You have 8 drawers in your desk. There is a probability of 0.1 that the letter is in any one of the 8 drawers and a probability of 0.2 that the letter is not in any of the drawers. *Source: Chance News.*

  a. What is the probability that the letter is in drawer 1?

  b. Given that the letter is not in drawer 1, what is the probability that the letter is in drawer 2?

  c. Given that the letter is not in drawer 1 or 2, what is the probability that the letter is in drawer 3?

  d. Given that the letter is not in drawers 1–7, what is the probability that the letter is in drawer 8?

  e. Based on your answers to parts a–d, what is happening to the probability that the letter is in the next drawer?

  f. What is the probability that the letter is in some drawer?

  g. Given that the letter is not in drawer 1, what is the probability that the letter is in some drawer?

  h. Given that the letter is not in drawer 1 or 2, what is the probability that the letter is in some drawer?

  i. Given that the letter is not in drawers 1–7, what is the probability that the letter is in some drawer?

  j. Based on your answers to parts f–i, what is happening to the probability that the letter is in some drawer?

71. Twins   A 1920 study of 17,798 pairs of twins found that 5844 consisted of two males, 5612 consisted of two females, and 6342 consisted of a male and a female. Of course, all of the

mixed-gender pairs were not identical twins. The same-gender pairs may or may not have been identical twins. The goal here is to use the data to estimate p, the probability that a pair of twins is identical.

  a. Use the data to find the proportion of twins who were male.

  b. Denoting your answer from part a by $P(B)$, show that the probability that a pair of twins is male is

$$pP(B) + (1 - p)(P(B))^2.$$

  (*Hint:* Draw a tree diagram. The first set of branches should be identical and not identical. Then note that if one member of a pair of identical twins is male, the other must also be male.)

  c. Using your answers from parts a and b, plus the fact that 5844 of the 17,798 twin pairs were male, find an estimate for the value of p.

  d. Find an expression, similar to the one in part b, for the probability that a pair of twins is female.

  e. Using your answers from parts a and d, plus the fact that 5612 of the 17,798 twin pairs were female, find an estimate for the value of p.

  f. Find an expression, similar to those in parts b and d, for the probability that a pair of twins consists of one male and one female.

  g. Using your answers from parts a and f, plus the fact that 6342 of the 17,798 twin pairs consisted of one male and one female, find an estimate for the value of p.

Social Sciences

72. Working Women   A survey has shown that 52% of the women in a certain community work outside the home. Of these women, 64% are married, while 86% of the women who do not work outside the home are married. Find the probabilities that a woman in that community can be categorized as follows.

  a. Married

  b. A single woman working outside the home

73. Cigarette Smokers   The following table gives a recent estimate (in millions) of the smoking status among persons 25 years of age and over and their highest level of education. *Source: National Health Interview Survey.*

Education	Current Smoker	Former Smoker	Non-Smoker	Total
Less than a high school diploma	7.90	6.66	14.12	28.68
High school diploma or GED	14.38	13.09	25.70	53.17
Some college	12.41	13.55	28.65	54.61
Bachelor's degree or higher	4.97	12.87	38.34	56.18
Total	39.66	46.17	106.81	192.64

  a. Find the probability that a person is a current smoker.

  b. Find the probability that a person has less than a high school diploma.

*We are assuming here and in other exercises that the events consist entirely of the numbers given in the table. If the numbers are interpreted as a sample of all people fitting the description of the events, then testing for independence is more complicated, requiring a technique from statistics known as a *contingency table*.

c. Find the probability that a person is a current smoker and has less than a high school diploma.

d. Find the probability that a person is a current smoker, given that the person has less than a high school diploma.

e. Are the events "current smoker" and "less than a high school diploma" independent events?

Physical Sciences

74. Rain Forecasts In a letter to the journal *Nature*, Robert A. J. Matthews gives the following table of outcomes of forecast and weather over 1000 1-hour walks, based on the United Kingdom's Meteorological office's 83% accuracy in 24-hour forecasts. *Source: Nature.*

	Rain	No Rain	Totals
Forecast of Rain	66	156	222
Forecast of No Rain	14	764	778
Totals	80	920	1000

a. Verify that the probability that the forecast called for rain, given that there was rain, is indeed 83%. Also verify that the probability that the forecast called for no rain, given that there was no rain, is also 83%.

b. Calculate the probability that there was rain, given that the forecast called for rain.

c. Calculate the probability that there was no rain, given that the forecast called for no rain.

d. Observe that your answer to part c is higher than 83% and that your answer to part b is much lower. Discuss which figure best describes the accuracy of the weather forecast in recommending whether or not you should carry an umbrella.

75. Earthquakes There are seven geologic faults (and possibly more) capable of generating a magnitude 6.7 earthquake in the region around San Francisco. Their probabilities of rupturing by the year 2032 are 27%, 21%, 11%, 10%, 4%, 3%, and 3%. *Source: Science News.*

a. Calculate the probability that at least one of these faults erupts by the year 2032, assuming that these are independent events.

b. Scientists forecast a 62% chance of an earthquake with magnitude at least 6.7 in the region around San Francisco by the year 2032. Compare this with your answer from part a. Consider the realism of the assumption of independence. Also consider the role of roundoff. For example, the probability of 10% for one of the faults is presumably rounded to the nearest percent, with the actual probability between 9.5% and 10.5%.

76. Reliability The probability that a key component of a space rocket will fail is 0.03.

a. How many such components must be used as backups to ensure that the probability of at least one of the components working is 0.999999 or more?

b. Is it reasonable to assume independence here?

General Interest

77. Titanic The table at the bottom of the page lists the number of passengers who were on the Titanic and the number of passengers who survived, according to class of ticket. Use this information to determine the following (round answers to four decimal places). *Source: Mathematics Teacher.*

a. What is the probability that a randomly selected passenger was second class?

b. What is the overall probability of surviving?

c. What is the probability of a first-class passenger surviving?

d. What is the probability of a child who was also in the third class surviving?

e. Given that the survivor is from first class, what is the probability that she was a woman?

f. Given that a male has survived, what is the probability that he was in third class?

g. Are the events third-class survival and male survival independent events? What does this imply?

78. Real Estate A real estate agent trying to sell you an attractive beachfront house claims that it will not collapse unless it is subjected simultaneously to extremely high winds and extremely high waves. According to weather service records, there is a 0.001 probability of extremely high winds, and the same for extremely high waves. The real estate agent claims, therefore, that the probability of both occurring is $(0.001)(0.001) = 0.000001$. What is wrong with the agent's reasoning?

79. Age and Loans Suppose 20% of the population are 65 or over, 26% of those 65 or over have loans, and 53% of those under 65 have loans. Find the probabilities that a person fits into the following categories.

a. 65 or over and has a loan

b. Has a loan

80. Women Joggers In a certain area, 15% of the population are joggers and 40% of the joggers are women. If 55% of those who do not jog are women, find the probabilities that

	Children		Women		Men		Totals	
	On	Survived	On	Survived	On	Survived	On	Survived
First Class	6	6	144	140	175	57	325	203
Second Class	24	24	165	76	168	14	357	114
Third Class	79	27	93	80	462	75	634	182
Totals	109	57	402	296	805	146	1316	499

an individual from that community fits the following descriptions.

a. A woman jogger

b. A man who is not a jogger

c. A woman

d. Are the events that a person is a woman and a person is a jogger independent? Explain.

81. Diet Soft Drinks Two-thirds of the population are on a diet at least occasionally. Of this group, 4/5 drink diet soft drinks, while 1/2 of the rest of the (nondieting) population drink diet soft drinks. Find the probabilities that a person fits into the following categories.

a. Drinks diet soft drinks

b. Diets, but does not drink diet soft drinks

82. Driver's License Test The Motor Vehicle Department has found that the probability of a person passing the test for a driver's license on the first try is 0.75. The probability that an individual who fails on the first test will pass on the second try is 0.80, and the probability that an individual who fails the first and second tests will pass the third time is 0.70. Find the probabilities that an individual will do the following.

a. Fail both the first and second tests

b. Fail three times in a row

c. Require at least two tries

83. Ballooning A pair of mathematicians in a hot air balloon were told that there are four independent burners, any one of which is sufficient to keep the balloon aloft. If the probability of any one burner failing during a flight is 0.001, what is the probability that the balloon will crash due to all four burners failing?

84. Speeding Tickets A smooth-talking young man has a 1/3 probability of talking a policeman out of giving him a speeding ticket. The probability that he is stopped for speeding during a given weekend is 1/2. Find the probabilities of the events in parts a and b.

a. He will receive no speeding tickets on a given weekend.

b. He will receive no speeding tickets on 3 consecutive weekends.

c. We have assumed that what happens on the second or third weekend is the same as what happened on the first weekend. Is this realistic? Will driving habits remain the same after getting a ticket?

85. Luxury Cars In one area, 4% of the population drive luxury cars. However, 17% of the CPAs drive luxury cars. Are the events "person drives a luxury car" and "person is a CPA" independent?

86. Studying A teacher has found that the probability that a student studies for a test is 0.60, the probability that a student gets a good grade on a test is 0.70, and the probability that both occur is 0.52.

a. Are these events independent?

b. Given that a student studies, find the probability that the student gets a good grade.

c. Given that a student gets a good grade, find the probability that the student studied.

87. Basketball A basketball player is fouled and now faces a one-and-one free throw situation. She shoots the first free throw. If she misses it, she scores 0 points. If she makes the first free throw, she gets to shoot a second free throw. If she misses the second free throw, she scores only one point for the first shot. If she makes the second free throw, she scores two points (one for each made shot). *Source: Mathematics Teacher.*

a. If her free-throwing percentage for this season is 60%, calculate the probability that she scores 0 points, 1 point, or 2 points.

b. Determine the free-throwing percentage necessary for the probability of scoring 0 points to be the same as the probability of scoring 2 points.* (*Hint:* Let p be the free-throwing percentage, and then solve $p^2 = 1 - p$ for p. Use only the positive value of p.)

88. Basketball The same player from Exercise 87 is now shooting two free throws (that is, she gets to shoot a second free throw whether she makes or misses the first shot.) Assume her free-throwing percentage is still 60%. Find the probability she scores 0 points, 1 point, or 2 points. *Source: Mathematics Teacher.*

89. Football A football coach whose team is 14 points behind needs two touchdowns to win. Each touchdown is worth 6 points. After a touchdown, the coach can choose either a 1-point kick, which is almost certain to succeed, or a 2-point conversion, which is roughly half as likely to succeed. After the first touchdown, the coach must decide whether to go for 1 or 2 points. If the 2-point conversion is successful, the almost certain 1-point kick after the second touchdown will win the game. If the 2-point conversion fails, the team can try another 2-point conversion after the second touchdown to tie. Some coaches, however, prefer to go for the almost certain 1-point kick after the first touchdown, hoping that the momentum will help them get a 2-point conversion after the second touchdown and win the game. They fear that an unsuccessful 2-point conversion after the first touchdown will discourage the team, which can then at best tie. *Source: The Mathematics Teacher.*

a. Draw a tree diagram for the 1-point kick after the first touchdown and the 2-point conversion after the second touchdown. Letting the probability of success for the 1-point kick and the 2-point conversion be k and r, respectively, show that

$$P(\text{win}) = kr,$$
$$P(\text{tie}) = r(1 - k), \text{ and}$$
$$P(\text{lose}) = 1 - r.$$

b. Consider the case of trying for a 2-point conversion after the first touchdown. If it succeeds, try a 1-point kick after the second touchdown. If the 2-point conversion fails, try

---

* The solution is the reciprocal of the number $\frac{1 + \sqrt{5}}{2}$, known as the golden ratio or the divine proportion. This number has great significance in architecture, science, and mathematics.

another one after the second touchdown. Draw a tree diagram and use it to show that

$$P(\text{win}) = kr,$$
$$P(\text{tie}) = r(2 - k - r), \quad \text{and}$$
$$P(\text{lose}) = (1 - r)^2.$$

c. What can you say about the probability of winning under each strategy?

d. Given that $r < 1$, which strategy has a smaller probability of losing? What does this tell you about the value of the two strategies?

7.6 Bayes' Theorem

APPLY IT What is the probability that a particular defective item was produced by a new machine operator?
This question will be answered in Example 2 using Bayes' theorem, discussed in this section.

Suppose the probability that an applicant is hired, *given the applicant is qualified*, is known. The manager might also be interested in the probability that the applicant is qualified, *given the applicant was hired*. More generally, if $P(E|F)$ is known for two events E and F, then $P(F|E)$ can be found using a tree diagram. Since $P(E|F)$ is known, the first outcome is either F or F'. Then for each of these outcomes, either E or E' occurs, as shown in Figure 27.

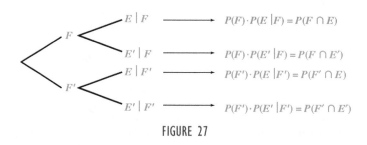

FIGURE 27

The four cases have the probabilities shown on the right. Notice $P(E \cap F)$ is the first case and $P(E)$ is the sum of the first and third cases in the tree diagram. By the definition of conditional probability,

$$P(F|E) = \frac{P(F \cap E)}{P(E)} = \frac{P(F) \cdot P(E|F)}{P(F) \cdot P(E|F) + P(F') \cdot P(E|F')}.$$

This result is a special case of Bayes' theorem, which is generalized later in this section.

Bayes' Theorem (Special Case)

$$P(F|E) = \frac{P(F) \cdot P(E|F)}{P(F) \cdot P(E|F) + P(F') \cdot P(E|F')}$$

EXAMPLE 1 **Worker Errors**

For a fixed length of time, the probability of a worker error on a certain production line is 0.1, the probability that an accident will occur when there is a worker error is 0.3, and the probability that an accident will occur when there is no worker error is 0.2. Find the probability of a worker error if there is an accident.

SOLUTION Let E represent the event of an accident, and let F represent the event of worker error. From the information given,

$$P(F) = 0.1, \qquad P(E|F) = 0.3, \qquad \text{and} \qquad P(E|F') = 0.2.$$

These probabilities are shown on the tree diagram in Figure 28.

Find $P(F|E)$ by dividing the probability that both E and F occur, given by branch 1, by the probability that E occurs, given by the sum of branches 1 and 3.

$$P(F|E) = \frac{P(F) \cdot P(E|F)}{P(F) \cdot P(E|F) + P(F') \cdot P(E|F')}$$

$$= \frac{(0.1)(0.3)}{(0.1)(0.3) + (0.9)(0.2)} = \frac{0.03}{0.21} = \frac{1}{7} \approx 0.1429$$

TRY YOUR TURN 1

YOUR TURN 1 The probability that a student will pass a math exam is 0.8 if he or she attends the review session and 0.65 if he or she does not attend the review session. Sixty percent of the students attend the review session. What is the probability that, given a student passed, the student attended the review session?

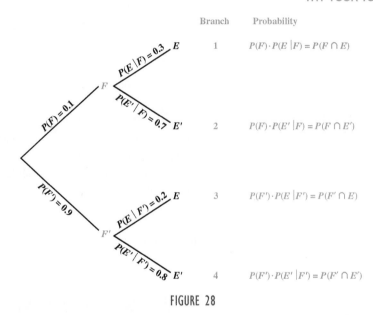

FIGURE 28

The special case of Bayes' theorem can be generalized to more than two events with the tree diagram in Figure 29. This diagram shows the paths that can produce an event E. We assume that the events $F_1, F_2, \ldots, F_n$ are mutually exclusive events (that is, disjoint events) whose union is the sample space, and that E is an event that has occurred. See Figure 30.

FIGURE 29

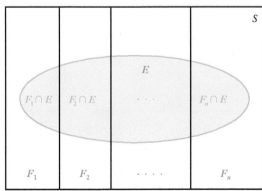

FIGURE 30

The probability $P(F_i|E)$, where $1 \le i \le n$, can be found by dividing the probability for the branch containing $P(E|F_i)$ by the sum of the probabilities of all the branches producing event E.

Bayes' Theorem

$$P(F_i|E) = \frac{P(F_i) \cdot P(E|F_i)}{P(F_1) \cdot P(E|F_1) + P(F_2) \cdot P(E|F_2) + \cdots + P(F_n) \cdot P(E|F_n)}$$

This result is known as **Bayes' theorem**, after the Reverend Thomas Bayes (1702–1761), whose paper on probability was published about three years after his death.

The statement of Bayes' theorem can be daunting. Actually, it is easier to remember the formula by thinking of the tree diagram that produced it. Go through the following steps.

Using Bayes' Theorem

1. Start a tree diagram with branches representing $F_1, F_2, \ldots, F_n$. Label each branch with its corresponding probability.

2. From the end of each of these branches, draw a branch for event E. Label this branch with the probability of getting to it, $P(E|F_i)$.

3. You now have n different paths that result in event E. Next to each path, put its probability—the product of the probabilities that the first branch occurs, $P(F_i)$, and that the second branch occurs, $P(E|F_i)$; that is, the product $P(F_i) \cdot P(E|F_i)$, which equals $P(F_i \cap E)$.

4. $P(F_i|E)$ is found by dividing the probability of the branch for F_i by the sum of the probabilities of all the branches producing event E.

EXAMPLE 2 Machine Operators

Based on past experience, a company knows that an experienced machine operator (one or more years of experience) will produce a defective item 1% of the time. Operators with some experience (up to one year) have a 2.5% defect rate, and new operators have a 6% defect rate. At any one time, the company has 60% experienced operators, 30% with some experience, and 10% new operators. Find the probability that a particular defective item was produced by a new operator.

APPLY IT

SOLUTION   Let E represent the event "item is defective," F_1 represent "item was made by an experienced operator," F_2 represent "item was made by an operator with some experience," and F_3 represent "item was made by a new operator." Then

$$P(F_1) = 0.60 \qquad P(E|F_1) = 0.01$$
$$P(F_2) = 0.30 \qquad P(E|F_2) = 0.025$$
$$P(F_3) = 0.10 \qquad P(E|F_3) = 0.06.$$

We need to find $P(F_3|E)$, the probability that an item was produced by a new operator, given that it is defective. First, draw a tree diagram using the given information, as in Figure 31. The steps leading to event E are shown in red.

Find $P(F_3|E)$ with the bottom branch of the tree in Figure 31: Divide the probability for this branch by the sum of the probabilities of all the branches leading to E, or

$$P(F_3|E) = \frac{0.10(0.06)}{0.60(0.01) + 0.30(0.025) + 0.10(0.06)} = \frac{0.006}{0.0195} = \frac{4}{13} \approx 0.3077.$$

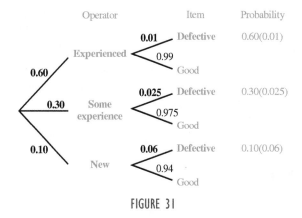

FIGURE 31

YOUR TURN 2 The English department at a small college has found that 12% of freshmen test into English I, 68% test into English II, and 20% test into English III. Eighty percent of students in English I will seek help from the writing center, 40% of those in English II, and 11% of those in English III. Given that a student received help from the writing center, find the probability that the student is in English I.

In a similar way, the probability that the defective item was produced by an operator with some experience is

$$P(F_2|E) = \frac{0.30(0.025)}{0.60(0.01) + 0.30(0.025) + 0.10(0.06)} = \frac{0.0075}{0.0195} = \frac{5}{13} \approx 0.3846.$$

Finally, the probability that the defective item was produced by an experienced operator is $P(F_1|E) = 4/13 \approx 0.3077$. Check that $P(F_1|E) + P(F_2|E) + P(F_3|E) = 1$ (that is, the defective item was made by *someone*). TRY YOUR TURN 2

EXAMPLE 3 Manufacturing

A manufacturer buys items from six different suppliers. The fraction of the total number of items obtained from each supplier, along with the probability that an item purchased from that supplier is defective, are shown in the following table.

Manufacturing Supplies		
Supplier	Fraction of Total Supplied	Probability of Defect
1	0.05	0.04
2	0.12	0.02
3	0.16	0.07
4	0.23	0.01
5	0.35	0.03
6	0.09	0.05

Find the probability that a defective item came from supplier 5.

SOLUTION Let F_1 be the event that an item came from supplier 1, with F_2, F_3, F_4, F_5, and F_6 defined in a similar manner. Let E be the event that an item is defective. We want to find $P(F_5|E)$. Use the probabilities in the table above to prepare a tree diagram, or work with the rows of the table to get

$$P(F_5|E) = \frac{(0.35)(0.03)}{(0.05)(0.04) + (0.12)(0.02) + (0.16)(0.07) + (0.23)(0.01) + (0.35)(0.03) + (0.09)(0.05)}$$

$$= \frac{0.0105}{0.0329} \approx 0.319.$$

There is about a 32% chance that a defective item came from supplier 5. Even though supplier 5 has only 3% defectives, his probability of being "guilty" is relatively high, about 32%, because of the large fraction supplied by 5.

CAUTION | Notice that the 0.04 in the upper right of the previous table represents the probability of a defective item *given* that the item came from supplier 1. In contrast, the probability of 0.035 in the table for Exercises 54–61 of the previous section represents the probability that a person is color-blind *and* male. The tables in this section represent probability in a different way than those of the previous section. Tables that you encounter outside of this course might represent probability in either way. You can usually tell what is intended by the context, but be careful!

7.6 EXERCISES

For two events M and N, $P(M) = 0.4$, $P(N|M) = 0.3$, and $P(N|M') = 0.4$. Find the following.

1. $P(M|N)$ **2.** $P(M'|N)$

For mutually exclusive events R_1, R_2, and R_3, we have $P(R_1) = 0.15$, $P(R_2) = 0.55$, and $P(R_3) = 0.30$. Also, $P(Q|R_1) = 0.40$, $P(Q|R_2) = 0.20$, and $P(Q|R_3) = 0.70$. Find the following.

3. $P(R_1|Q)$ **4.** $P(R_2|Q)$

5. $P(R_3|Q)$ **6.** $P(R_1'|Q)$

Suppose you have three jars with the following contents: 2 black balls and 1 white ball in the first, 1 black ball and 2 white balls in the second, and 1 black ball and 1 white ball in the third. One jar is to be selected, and then 1 ball is to be drawn from the selected jar. If the probabilities of selecting the first, second, or third jar are 1/2, 1/3, and 1/6, respectively, find the probabilities that if a white ball is drawn, it came from the following jars.

7. The second jar **8.** The third jar

APPLICATIONS

Business and Economics

9. Employment Test A manufacturing firm finds that 70% of its new hires turn out to be good workers and 30% become poor workers. All current workers are given a reasoning test. Of the good workers, 85% pass it; 35% of the poor workers pass it. Assume that these figures will hold true in the future. If the company makes the test part of its hiring procedure and only hires people who meet the previous requirements and pass the test, what percent of the new hires will turn out to be good workers?

Job Qualifications Of all the people applying for a certain job, 75% are qualified and 25% are not. The personnel manager claims that she approves qualified people 85% of the time; she approves an unqualified person 20% of the time. Find each probability.

10. A person is qualified if he or she was approved by the manager.

11. A person is unqualified if he or she was approved by the manager.

Quality Control A building contractor buys 70% of his cement from supplier A and 30% from supplier B. A total of 90% of the bags from A arrive undamaged, while 95% of the bags from B arrive undamaged. Give the probabilities that a damaged bag is from the following sources.

12. Supplier A **13.** Supplier B

Appliance Reliability Companies A, B, and C produce 15%, 40%, and 45%, respectively, of the major appliances sold in a certain area. In that area, 1% of the company A appliances, $1\frac{1}{2}\%$ of the company B appliances, and 2% of the company C appliances need service within the first year. Suppose a defective appliance is chosen at random; find the probabilities that it was manufactured by the following companies.

14. Company A **15.** Company B

Television Advertising On a given weekend in the fall, a tire company can buy television advertising time for a college football game, a baseball game, or a professional football game. If the company sponsors the college football game, there is a 70% chance of a high rating, a 50% chance if they sponsor a baseball game, and a 60% chance if they sponsor a professional football game. The probabilities of the company sponsoring these various games are 0.5, 0.2, and 0.3, respectively. Suppose the company does get a high rating; find the probabilities that it sponsored the following.

16. A college football game

17. A professional football game

18. Auto Insurance An auto insurance company insures drivers of all ages. An actuary compiled the following statistics on the company's insured drivers:

Age of Driver	Probability of Accident	Portion of Company's Insured Drivers
16–20	0.06	0.08
21–30	0.03	0.15
31–65	0.02	0.49
66–99	0.04	0.28

A randomly selected driver that the company insures has an accident. Calculate the probability that the driver was age 16–20. Choose one of the following. *Source: Society of Actuaries.*

a. 0.13 **b.** 0.16 **c.** 0.19 **d.** 0.23 **e.** 0.40

19. Life Insurance An insurance company issues life insurance policies in three separate categories: standard, preferred, and ultra-preferred. Of the company's policyholders, 50% are standard, 40% are preferred, and 10% are ultra-preferred. Each standard policyholder has probability 0.010 of dying in the next year, each preferred policyholder has probability 0.005 of dying in the next year, and each ultra-preferred policyholder has probability 0.001 of dying in the next year. A policyholder dies in the next year. What is the probability that the deceased policyholder was ultra-preferred? Choose one of the following. *Source: Society of Actuaries.*

a. 0.0001   **b.** 0.0010   **c.** 0.0071   **d.** 0.0141   **e.** 0.2817

20. Automobile Collisions An actuary studied the likelihood that different types of drivers would be involved in at least one collision during any one-year period. The results of the study are presented below.

Type of Driver	Percentage of All Drivers	Probability of at Least One Collision
Teen	8%	0.15
Young Adult	16%	0.08
Midlife	45%	0.04
Senior	31%	0.05
Total	100%	

Given that a driver has been involved in at least one collision in the past year, what is the probability that the driver is a young adult driver? Choose one of the following. *Source: Society of Actuaries.*

a. 0.06   **b.** 0.16   **c.** 0.19   **d.** 0.22   **e.** 0.25

21. Shipping Errors The following information pertains to three shipping terminals operated by Krag Corp. *Source: CPA Examination.*

Terminal	Percentage of Cargo Handled	Percentage of Error
Land	50	2
Air	40	4
Sea	10	14

Krag's internal auditor randomly selects one set of shipping documents, ascertaining that the set selected contains an error. Which of the following gives the probability that the error occurred in the Land Terminal?

a. 0.02   **b.** 0.10

c. 0.25   **d.** 0.50

22. Mortgage Defaults A bank finds that the relationship between mortgage defaults and the size of the down payment is given by the following table.

Down Payment	Number of Mortgages with This Down Payment	Probability of Default
5%	1260	0.06
10%	700	0.04
20%	560	0.02
25%	280	0.01

a. If a default occurs, what is the probability that it is on a mortgage with a 5% down payment?

b. What is the probability that a mortgage that is paid to maturity has a 10% down payment?

Life Sciences

23. Colorectal Cancer Researchers found that only one out of 24 physicians could give the correct answer to the following problem: "The probability of colorectal cancer can be given as 0.3%. If a person has colorectal cancer, the probability that the hemoccult test is positive is 50%. If a person does not have colorectal cancer, the probability that he still tests positive is 3%. What is the probability that a person who tests positive actually has colorectal cancer?" What is the correct answer? *Source: Science.*

24. Hepatitis Blood Test The probability that a person with certain symptoms has hepatitis is 0.8. The blood test used to confirm this diagnosis gives positive results for 90% of people with the disease and 5% of those without the disease. What is the probability that an individual who has the symptoms and who reacts positively to the test actually has hepatitis?

25. Sensitivity and Specificity The *sensitivity* of a medical test is defined as the probability that a test will be positive given that a person has a disease, written $P(T^+|D^+)$. The *specificity* of a test is defined as the probability that a test will be negative given that the person does not have the disease, written $P(T^-|D^-)$. For example, the sensitivity and specificity for breast cancer during a mammography exam are approximately 79.6% and 90.2%, respectively. *Source: National Cancer Institute.*

a. It is estimated that 0.5% of U.S. women under the age 40 have breast cancer. Find the probability that a woman under 40 who tests positive during a mammography exam actually has breast cancer.

b. Given that a woman under 40 tests negative during a mammography exam, find the probability that she does not have breast cancer.

c. According to the National Cancer Institute, failure to diagnose breast cancer is the most common cause of medical malpractice litigation. Given a woman under 40 tests negative for breast cancer, find the probability that she does have breast cancer.

d. It is estimated that 1.5% of U.S. women over the age of 50 have breast cancer. Find the probability that a woman over 50 who tests positive actually has breast cancer.

26. Test for HIV Clinical studies have demonstrated that rapid HIV tests have a sensitivity (probability that a test will be positive given that a person has the disease) of approximately 99.9% and a specificity (probability that a test will be negative given that the person does not have the disease) of approximately 99.8%. *Source: Centers for Disease Control and Prevention*

a. In some HIV clinics, the prevalence of HIV was high, about 5%. Find the probability a person actually has HIV, given that the test came back positive from one of these clinics.

b. In other clinics, like a family planning clinic, the prevalence of HIV was low, about 0.1%. Find the probability that a person actually has HIV, given that the test came back positive from one of these clinics.

c. The answers in parts a and b are significantly different. Explain why.

27. Smokers A health study tracked a group of persons for five years. At the beginning of the study, 20% were classified as heavy smokers, 30% as light smokers, and 50% as non-smokers. Results of the study showed that light smokers were twice as likely as nonsmokers to die during the five-year study but only half as likely as heavy smokers. A randomly selected participant from the study died over the five-year period. Calculate the probability that the participant was a heavy smoker. Choose one of the following. (*Hint:* Let $x = P$(a nonsmoker dies).) *Source: Society of Actuaries.*

a. 0.20　**b.** 0.25　**c.** 0.35　**d.** 0.42　**e.** 0.57

28. Emergency Room Upon arrival at a hospital's emergency room, patients are categorized according to their condition as critical, serious, or stable. In the past year:

　(i) 10% of the emergency room patients were critical;

　(ii) 30% of the emergency room patients were serious;

　(iii) the rest of the emergency room patients were stable;

　(iv) 40% of the critical patients died;

　(v) 10% of the serious patients died; and

　(vi) 1% of the stable patients died.

Given that a patient survived, what is the probability that the patient was categorized as serious upon arrival? Choose one of the following. *Source: Society of Actuaries.*

a. 0.06　**b.** 0.29　**c.** 0.30　**d.** 0.39　**e.** 0.64

29. Blood Test A blood test indicates the presence of a particular disease 95% of the time when the disease is actually present. The same test indicates the presence of the disease 0.5% of the time when the disease is not present. One percent of the population actually has the disease. Calculate the probability that a person has the disease, given that the test indicates the presence of the disease. Choose one of the following. *Source: Society of Actuaries.*

a. 0.324　**b.** 0.657　**c.** 0.945　**d.** 0.950　**e.** 0.995

30. Circulation The probability that a randomly chosen male has a circulation problem is 0.25. Males who have a circulation problem are twice as likely to be smokers as those who do not have a circulation problem. What is the conditional probability that a male has a circulation problem, given that he is a smoker? Choose one of the following. *Source: Society of Actuaries.*

a. 1/4　**b.** 1/3　**c.** 2/5　**d.** 1/2　**e.** 2/3

Social Sciences

31. Alcohol Abstinence The Harvard School of Public Health completed a study on alcohol consumption on college campuses in 2001. They concluded that 20.7% of women attending all-women colleges abstained from alcohol, compared to 18.6% of women attending coeducational colleges. Approximately 4.7% of women college students attend all-women schools. *Source: Harvard School of Public Health.*

a. What is the probability that a randomly selected female student abstains from alcohol?

b. If a randomly selected female student abstains from alcohol, what is the probability she attends a coeducational college?

32. Murder During the murder trial of O. J. Simpson, Alan Dershowitz, an advisor to the defense team, stated on television that only about 0.1% of men who batter their wives actually murder them. Statistician I. J. Good observed that even if, given that a husband is a batterer, the probability he is guilty of murdering his wife is 0.001, what we really want to know is the probability that the husband is guilty, given that the wife was murdered. Good estimates the probability of a battered wife being murdered, given that her husband is not guilty, as 0.001. The probability that she is murdered if her husband is guilty is 1, of course. Using these numbers and Dershowitz's 0.001 probability of the husband being guilty, find the probability that the husband is guilty, given that the wife was murdered. *Source: Nature.*

Never-Married Adults by Age Group The following tables give the proportion of men and of women 18 and older in each age group in 2009, as well as the proportion in each group who have never been married. *Source: U.S Census Bureau.*

Age	Men Proportion of Population	Proportion Never Married
18–24	0.132	0.901
25–34	0.186	0.488
35–44	0.186	0.204
45–64	0.348	0.118
65 or over	0.148	0.044

Age	Women Proportion of Population	Proportion Never Married
18–24	0.121	0.825
25–34	0.172	0.366
35–44	0.178	0.147
45–64	0.345	0.092
65 or over	0.184	0.040

33. Find the probability that a randomly selected man who has never married is between 35 and 44 years old (inclusive).

34. Find the probability that a randomly selected woman who has been married is between 18 and 24 (inclusive).

35. Find the probability that a randomly selected woman who has never been married is between 45 and 64 (inclusive).

36. Seat Belt Effectiveness A 2009 federal study showed that 63.8% of occupants involved in a fatal car crash wore seat belts. Of those in a fatal crash who wore seat belts, 2% were ejected from the vehicle. For those not wearing seat belts, 36% were ejected from the vehicle. *Source: National Highway Traffic Safety Administration.*

    a. Find the probability that a randomly selected person in a fatal car crash who was ejected from the vehicle was wearing a seat belt.

    b. Find the probability that a randomly selected person in a fatal car crash who was not ejected from the vehicle was not wearing a seat belt.

Smokers by Age Group The following table gives the proportion of U.S. adults in each age group in 2008, as well as the proportion in each group who smoke. *Source: Centers for Disease Control and Prevention.*

Age	Proportion of Population	Proportion that Smoke
18 – 44 years	0.49	0.23
45 – 64 years	0.34	0.22
64 – 74 years	0.09	0.12
75 years and over	0.08	0.06

37. Find the probability that a randomly selected adult who smokes is between 18 and 44 years of age (inclusive).

38. Find the probability that a randomly selected adult who does not smoke is between 45 and 64 years of age (inclusive).

General Interest

39. Terrorists John Allen Paulos has pointed out a problem with massive, untargeted wiretaps. To illustrate the problem, he supposes that one out of every million Americans has terrorist ties. Furthermore, he supposes that the terrorist profile is 99% accurate, so that if a person has terrorist ties, the profile will pick them up 99% of the time, and if the person does not have terrorist ties, the profile will accidentally pick them up only 1% of the time. Given that the profile has picked up a person, what is the probability that the person actually has terrorist ties? Discuss how your answer affects your opinion on domestic wiretapping. *Source: Who's Counting.*

40. Three Prisoners The famous "problem of three prisoners" is as follows.

Three men, A, B, and C, were in jail. A knew that one of them was to be set free and the other two were to be executed. But he didn't know who was the one to be spared. To the jailer who did know, A said, "Since two out of the three will be executed, it is certain that either B or C will be, at least. You will give me no information about my own chances if you give me the name of one man, B or C, who is going to be executed." Accepting this argument after some thinking, the jailer said "B will be executed." Thereupon A felt happier because now either he or C would go free, so his chance had increased from 1/3 to 1/2. *Source: Cognition.*

    a. Assume that initially each of the prisoners is equally likely to be set free. Assume also that if both B and C are to be executed, the jailer is equally likely to name either B or C. Show that A is wrong, and that his probability of being freed, given that the jailer says B will be executed, is still 1/3.

    b. Now assume that initially the probabilities of A, B, and C being freed are 1/4, 1/4, and 1/2, respectively. As in part a, assume also that if both B and C are to be executed, the jailer is equally likely to name either B or C. Now show that A's probability of being freed, given that the jailer says B will be executed, actually drops to 1/5. Discuss the reasonableness of this answer, and why this result might violate someone's intuition.

YOUR TURN ANSWERS

1. 0.6486   **2.** 0.2462

7 CHAPTER REVIEW

SUMMARY

We began this chapter by introducing sets, which are collections of objects. We introduced the following set operations:

- complement (A' is the set of elements not in A),
- intersection ($A \cap B$ is the set of elements belonging to both set A and set B), and
- union ($A \cup B$ is the set of elements belonging to either set A or set B or both).

We used tree diagrams and Venn diagrams to define and study concepts in set operations as well as in probability. We introduced the following terms:

- experiment (an activity or occurrence with an observable result),
- trial (a repetition of an experiment),
- outcome (a result of a trial),
- sample space (the set of all possible outcomes for an experiment), and
- event (a subset of a sample space).

We investigated how to compute various probabilities and we explored some of the properties of probability. In particular, we studied the following concepts:

- empirical probability (based on how frequently an event actually occurred),
- conditional probability (in which some other event is assumed to have occurred),

- odds (an alternative way of expressing probability),
- independent events (in which the occurrence of one event does not affect the probability of another), and
- Bayes' theorem (used to calculate certain types of conditional probability).

Throughout the chapter, many applications of probability were introduced and analyzed. In the next two chapters, we will employ these techniques to further our study into the fields of probability and statistics.

Sets Summary

Number of Subsets   A set of k distinct elements has 2^k subsets.

Disjoint Sets   If sets A and B are disjoint, then
$$A \cap B = \emptyset \quad \text{and} \quad n(A \cap B) = 0.$$

Union Rule for Sets   For any sets A and B,
$$n(A \cup B) = n(A) + n(B) - n(A \cap B).$$

Probability Summary

Basic Probability Principle   Let S be a sample space of equally likely outcomes, and let event E be a subset of S. Then the probability that event E occurs is
$$P(E) = \frac{n(E)}{n(S)}.$$

Mutually Exclusive Events   If E and F are mutually exclusive events,
$$E \cap F = \emptyset \quad \text{and} \quad P(E \cap F) = 0.$$

Union Rule   For any events E and F from a sample space S,
$$P(E \cup F) = P(E) + P(F) - P(E \cap F).$$

Complement Rule $P(E) = 1 - P(E') \quad \text{and} \quad P(E') = 1 - P(E)$

Odds   The odds in favor of event E are $\dfrac{P(E)}{P(E')}$, where $P(E') \neq 0$.

If the odds favoring event E are m to n, then
$$P(E) = \frac{m}{m+n} \quad \text{and} \quad P(E') = \frac{n}{m+n}.$$

Properties of Probability
1. For any event E in sample space S, $0 \leq P(E) \leq 1$.
2. The sum of the probabilities of all possible distinct outcomes is 1.

Conditional Probability   The conditional probability of event E, given that event F has occurred, is
$$P(E|F) = \frac{P(E \cap F)}{P(F)}, \quad \text{where } P(F) \neq 0.$$

For equally likely outcomes, conditional probability is found by reducing the sample space to event F; then
$$P(E|F) = \frac{n(E \cap F)}{n(F)}.$$

Product Rule of Probability   If E and F are events, then $P(E \cap F)$ may be found by either of these formulas.
$$P(E \cap F) = P(F) \cdot P(E|F) \quad \text{or} \quad P(E \cap F) = P(E) \cdot P(F|E)$$

Independent Events   If E and F are independent events,
$$P(E|F) = P(E), \quad P(F|E) = P(F), \quad \text{and} \quad P(E \cap F) = P(E) \cdot P(F).$$

Bayes' Theorem $P(F_i|E) = \dfrac{P(F_i) \cdot P(E|F_i)}{P(F_1) \cdot P(E|F_1) + P(F_2) \cdot P(E|F_2) + \cdots + P(F_n) \cdot P(E|F_n)}$

KEY TERMS

7.1
set
element (member)
empty set (or null set)
set-builder notation
universal set
subset
tree diagram
Venn diagram
complement

intersection
disjoint sets
union

7.2
union rule for sets

7.3
experiment
trial
outcome

sample space
event
simple event
certain event
impossible event
mutually exclusive events
probability
empirical probability

7.4
union rule for probability

odds
probability distribution

7.5
conditional probability
product rule
independent events
dependent events

7.6
Bayes' theorem

REVIEW EXERCISES

CONCEPT CHECK

Determine whether each of the following statements is true or false, and explain why.

1. A set is a subset of itself.

2. A set has more subsets than it has elements.

3. The union of two sets always has more elements than either set.

4. The intersection of two sets always has fewer elements than either set.

5. The number of elements in the union of two sets can be found by adding the number of elements in each set.

6. The probability of an event is always at least 0 and no larger than 1.

7. The probability of the union of two events can be found by adding the probability of each event.

8. The probability of drawing the Queen of Hearts from a deck of cards is an example of empirical probability.

9. If two events are mutually exclusive, then they are independent.

10. The probability of two independent events can be found by multiplying the probabilities of each event.

11. The probability of an event E given an event F is the same as the probability of F given E.

12. Bayes' theorem can be useful for calculating conditional probability.

PRACTICE AND EXPLORATIONS

Write true or false for each statement.

13. $9 \in \{8, 4, -3, -9, 6\}$

14. $4 \notin \{3, 9, 7\}$

15. $2 \notin \{0, 1, 2, 3, 4\}$

16. $0 \in \{0, 1, 2, 3, 4\}$

17. $\{3, 4, 5\} \subseteq \{2, 3, 4, 5, 6\}$

18. $\{1, 2, 5, 8\} \subseteq \{1, 2, 5, 10, 11\}$

19. $\{3, 6, 9, 10\} \subseteq \{3, 9, 11, 13\}$

20. $\emptyset \subseteq \{1\}$

21. $\{2, 8\} \not\subseteq \{2, 4, 6, 8\}$

22. $0 \subseteq \emptyset$

In Exercises 23–32, let $U = \{a, b, c, d, e, f, g, h\}$, $K = \{c, d, e, f, h\}$, and $R = \{a, c, d, g\}$. Find the following.

23. The number of subsets of K

24. The number of subsets of R

25. K'

26. R'

27. $K \cap R$

28. $K \cup R$

29. $(K \cap R)'$

30. $(K \cup R)'$

31. $\emptyset'$

32. U'

In Exercises 33–38, let

$U = \{$all employees of the K. O. Brown Company$\}$;
$A = \{$employees in the accounting department$\}$;
$B = \{$employees in the sales department$\}$;
$C = \{$female employees$\}$;
$D = \{$employees with an MBA degree$\}$.

Describe each set in words.

33. $A \cap C$

34. $B \cap D$

35. $A \cup D$

36. $A' \cap D$

37. $B' \cap C'$

38. $(B \cup C)'$

Draw a Venn diagram and shade each set.

39. $A \cup B'$

40. $A' \cap B$

41. $(A \cap B) \cup C$

42. $(A \cup B)' \cap C$

Write the sample space S for each experiment, choosing an S with equally likely outcomes, if possible.

43. Rolling a die

44. Drawing a card from a deck containing only the 13 spades

45. Measuring the weight of a person to the nearest half pound (the scale will not measure more than 300 lb)

46. Tossing a coin 4 times

A jar contains 5 balls labeled 3, 5, 7, 9, and 11, respectively, while a second jar contains 4 red and 2 green balls. An experiment consists of pulling 1 ball from each jar, in turn. In Exercises 47–50, write each set using set notation.

47. The sample space

48. Event E: the number on the first ball is greater than 5

49. Event F: the second ball is green

50. Are the outcomes in the sample space in Exercise 47 equally likely?

In Exercises 51–58, find the probability of each event when a single card is drawn from an ordinary deck.

51. A heart

52. A red queen

53. A face card or a heart

54. Black or a face card

55. Red, given that it is a queen

56. A jack, given that it is a face card

57. A face card, given that it is a king

58. A king, given that it is not a face card

59. Describe what is meant by disjoint sets.

60. Describe what is meant by mutually exclusive events.

61. How are disjoint sets and mutually exclusive events related?

62. Define independent events.

63. Are independent events always mutually exclusive? Are they ever mutually exclusive?

64. An uproar has raged since September 1990 over the answer to a puzzle published in *Parade* magazine, a supplement of the Sunday newspaper. In the "Ask Marilyn" column, Marilyn vos Savant answered the following question: "Suppose you're on a game show, and you're given the choice of three doors. Behind one door is a car; behind the others, goats. You pick a door, say number 1, and the host, who knows what's behind the other doors, opens another door, say number 3, which has a goat. He then says to you, 'Do you want to pick door number 2?' Is it to your advantage to take the switch?"

Ms. vos Savant estimates that she has since received some 10,000 letters; most of them, including many from mathematicians and statisticians, disagreed with her answer. Her answer has been debated by both professionals and amateurs and tested in classes at all levels from grade school to graduate school. But by performing the experiment repeatedly, it can be shown that vos Savant's answer was correct. Find the probabilities of getting the car if you switch or do not switch, and then answer the question yourself. (*Hint:* Consider the sample space.) *Source: Parade Magazine.*

Find the odds in favor of a card drawn from an ordinary deck being the following.

65. A club

66. A black jack

67. A red face card or a queen

68. An ace or a club

Find the probabilities of getting the following sums when two fair dice are rolled.

69. 8

70. 0

71. At least 10

72. No more than 5

73. An odd number greater than 8

74. 12, given that the sum is greater than 10

75. 7, given that at least one die shows a 4

76. At least 9, given that at least one die shows a 5

77. Suppose $P(E) = 0.51$, $P(F) = 0.37$, and $P(E \cap F) = 0.22$. Find the following.

a. $P(E \cup F)$ **b.** $P(E \cap F')$ **c.** $P(E' \cup F)$

d. $P(E' \cap F')$

78. An urn contains 10 balls: 4 red and 6 blue. A second urn contains 16 red balls and an unknown number of blue balls. A single ball is drawn from each urn. The probability that both balls are the same color is 0.44. Calculate the number of blue balls in the second urn. Choose one of the following. *Source: Society of Actuaries.*

a. 4   **b.** 20   **c.** 24   **d.** 44   **e.** 64

79. Box A contains 5 red balls and 1 black ball; box B contains 2 red balls and 3 black balls. A box is chosen, and a ball is selected from it. The probability of choosing box A is 3/8. If the selected ball is black, what is the probability that it came from box A?

80. Find the probability that the ball in Exercise 79 came from box B, given that it is red.

APPLICATIONS

Business and Economics

Appliance Repairs   Of the appliance repair shops listed in the phone book, 80% are competent and 20% are not. A competent shop can repair an appliance correctly 95% of the time; an incompetent shop can repair an appliance correctly 55% of the time. Suppose an appliance was repaired correctly. Find the probabilities that it was repaired by the following.

81. A competent shop

82. An incompetent shop

Suppose an appliance was repaired incorrectly. Find the probabilities that it was repaired by the following.

83. A competent shop

84. An incompetent shop

85. Find the probability that an appliance brought to a shop chosen at random is repaired correctly.

86. Are the events that a repair shop is competent and that the repair is done correctly independent? Explain.

87. Sales   A company sells printers and copiers. Let E be the event "a customer buys a printer," and let F be the event "a customer buys a copier." Write the following using $\cap$, $\cup$, or $'$ as necessary.

a. A customer buys neither machine.

b. A customer buys at least one of the machines.

88. Defective Items   A sample shipment of five hair dryers is chosen at random. The probability of exactly 0, 1, 2, 3, 4, or 5 hair dryers being defective is given in the following table.

Number Defective	0	1	2	3	4	5
Probability	0.34	0.26	0.18	0.12	0.07	0.03

Find the probabilities that the following numbers of hair dryers are defective.

a. No more than 3   **b.** At least 3

89. Defective Items A manufacturer buys items from four different suppliers. The fraction of the total number of items that is obtained from each supplier, along with the probability that an item purchased from that supplier is defective, is shown in the table below.

Supplier	Fraction of Total Supplied	Probability of Defective
1	0.17	0.01
2	0.39	0.02
3	0.35	0.05
4	0.09	0.03

a. Find the probability that a randomly selected item is defective.

b. Find the probability that a defective item came from supplier 4.

c. Find the probability that a defective item came from supplier 2.

d. Are the events that an item came from supplier 4 and that the item is defective independent? Explain.

90. Car Buyers The table shows the results of a survey of buyers of a certain model of car.

Car Type	Satisfied	Not Satisfied	Totals
New	300	100	
Used	450		600
Totals		250	

a. Complete the table.

b. How many buyers were surveyed?

c. How many bought a new car and were satisfied?

d. How many were not satisfied?

e. How many bought used cars?

f. How many of those who were not satisfied had purchased a used car?

g. Rewrite the event stated in part f using the expression "given that."

h. Find the probability of the outcome in parts f and g.

i. Find the probability that a used-car buyer is not satisfied.

j. You should have different answers in parts h and i. Explain why.

k. Are the events that a car is new and that the customer is satisfied independent? Explain.

91. Auto Insurance An insurance company examines its pool of auto insurance customers and gathers the following information:

 (i) All customers insure at least one car.

 (ii) 70% of the customers insure more than one car.

 (iii) 20% of the customers insure a sports car.

 (iv) Of those customers who insure more than one car, 15% insure a sports car.

Calculate the probability that a randomly selected customer insures exactly one car and that car is not a sports car. Choose one of the following. (*Hint:* Draw a tree diagram, and let x be the probability that a customer who insures exactly one car insures a sports car.) *Source: Society of Actuaries.*

 a. 0.13   **b.** 0.21   **c.** 0.24   **d.** 0.25   **e.** 0.30

92. Auto Insurance An auto insurance company has 10,000 policyholders. Each policyholder is classified as:

 (i) young or old;

 (ii) male or female; and

 (iii) married or single.

Of these policyholders, 3000 are young, 4600 are male, and 7000 are married. The policyholders can also be classified as 1320 young males, 3010 married males, and 1400 young married persons. Finally, 600 of the policyholders are young married males. How many of the company's policyholders are young, female, and single? Choose one of the following. *Source: Society of Actuaries.*

 a. 280   **b.** 423   **c.** 486   **d.** 880   **e.** 896

93. Auto Insurance An actuary studying the insurance preferences of automobile owners makes the following conclusions:

 (i) An automobile owner is twice as likely to purchase collision coverage as disability coverage.

 (ii) The event that an automobile owner purchases collision coverage is independent of the event that he or she purchases disability coverage.

 (iii) The probability that an automobile owner purchases both collision and disability coverages is 0.15.

What is the probability that an automobile owner purchases neither collision nor disability coverage? Choose one of the following. *Source: Society of Actuaries.*

 a. 0.18   **b.** 0.33   **c.** 0.48   **d.** 0.67   **e.** 0.82

94. Insurance An insurance company estimates that 40% of policyholders who have only an auto policy will renew next year and 60% of policyholders who have only a homeowners policy will renew next year. The company estimates that 80% of policyholders who have both an auto and a homeowners policy will renew at least one of these policies next year. Company records show that 65% of policyholders have an auto policy, 50% of policyholders have a homeowners policy, and 15% of policyholders have both an auto and a homeowners policy. Using the company's estimates, calculate the percentage of policyholders that will renew at least one policy next year. Choose one of the following. *Source: Society of Actuaries.*

 a. 20   **b.** 29   **c.** 41   **d.** 53   **e.** 70

Life Sciences

95. Sickle Cell Anemia The square on the next page shows the four possible (equally likely) combinations when both parents are carriers of the sickle cell anemia trait. Each carrier parent has normal cells (N) and trait cells (T).

a. Complete the table.

b. If the disease occurs only when two trait cells combine, find the probability that a child born to these parents will have sickle cell anemia.

c. The child will carry the trait but not have the disease if a normal cell combines with a trait cell. Find this probability.

d. Find the probability that the child is neither a carrier nor has the disease.

	Second Parent	
	N_2	T_2
First Parent	N_1	N_1T_2
	T_1	

96. Blood Antigens   In Exercise 44 of Section 7.2, we described the eight types of human blood. The percentage of the population having each type is as follows:

O$^+$: 38%;   O$^-$: 8%;   A$^+$: 32%;   A$^-$: 7%;
B$^+$: 9%;   B$^-$: 2%;   AB$^+$: 3%;   AB$^-$: 1%.

When a person receives a blood transfusion, it is important that the blood be compatible, which means that it introduces no new antigens into the recipient's blood. The following diagram helps illustrate what blood types are compatible. *Source: The Mathematics Teacher.*

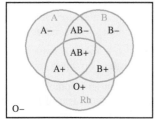

The universal blood type is O$^-$, since it has none of the additional antigens. The circles labeled A, B, and Rh contain blood types with the A antigen, B antigen, and Rh antigen, respectively. A person with O$^-$ blood can only be transfused with O$^-$ blood, because any other type would introduce a new antigen. Thus the probability that blood from a random donor is compatible is just 8%. A person with AB$^+$ blood already has all antigens, so the probability that blood from a random donor is compatible is 100%. Find the probability that blood from a random donor is compatible with a person with each blood type.

a. O$^+$ **b.** A$^+$ **c.** B$^+$

d. A$^-$ **e.** B$^-$ **f.** AB$^-$

97. Risk Factors   An actuary is studying the prevalence of three health risk factors, denoted by A, B, and C, within a population of women. For each of the three factors, the probability is 0.1 that a woman in the population has only this risk factor (and no others). For any two of the three factors, the probability is 0.12 that she has exactly these two risk factors (but not the other). The probability that a woman has all three risk factors, given that she has A and B, is 1/3. What is the probability that a woman has none of the three risk factors, given that she does not have risk factor A? Choose one of the following. *Source: Society of Actuaries.*

a. 0.280   **b.** 0.311   **c.** 0.467   **d.** 0.484   **e.** 0.700

Social Sciences

98. Elections   In the 2008 presidential election, over 130 million people voted, of which 46.3% were male and 53.7% were female. Of the male voters, 49% voted for Barack Obama and 48% voted for John McCain. Of the female voters, 56% voted for Obama and 43% voted for McCain. *Source: U.S. Census and The New York Times.*

a. Find the percentage of voters who voted for Obama.

b. Find the probability that a randomly selected voter for Obama was male.

c. Find the probability that a randomly selected voter for Obama was female.

99. Television Viewing Habits   A telephone survey of television viewers revealed the following information:

    20 watch situation comedies;
    19 watch game shows;
    27 watch movies;
    19 watch movies but not game shows;
    15 watch situation comedies but not game shows;
    10 watch both situation comedies and movies;
     3 watch all three;
     7 watch none of these.

a. How many viewers were interviewed?

b. How many viewers watch comedies and movies but not game shows?

c. How many viewers watch only movies?

d. How many viewers do not watch movies?

100. Randomized Response Method for Getting Honest Answers to Sensitive Questions   There are many personal questions that most people would rather not answer. In fact, when a person is asked such a question, a common response is to provide a false answer. In 1965, Stanley Warner developed a method to assure that the identity of an individual who answers a question remains anonymous, thus assuring an honest answer to the question. For this method, instead of one sensitive question being asked to a person, there are two questions, one sensitive and one non-sensitive, and which question the person answers depends on a randomized procedure. The interviewer, who doesn't know which question a person is answering, simply records the answer given as either "Yes" or "No." In this way, there is no way of knowing to which question the person answered "Yes" or "No." Then, using conditional probability, we can estimate the percentage of people who answer "Yes" to the sensitive question. For example, suppose that the two questions are

    A: Does your birth year end in an odd digit? (Nonsensitive)
    B: Have you ever intentionally cheated on an examination? (Sensitive)

We already know that $P(\text{"Yes"} \mid \text{Question } A) = 1/2$, since half the years are even and half are odd. The answer we seek is $P(\text{"Yes"} \mid \text{Question } B)$. In this experiment, a student is asked to flip a coin and answer question A if the coin comes up heads and otherwise answer question B. Note that the interviewer does not know the outcome of the coin flip or which question is being answered. The percentage of students answering "Yes" is used to approximate $P(\text{"Yes"})$, which is then used to estimate the percentage of students who have cheated on an examination. *Source: Journal of the American Statistical Association.*

a. Use the fact that the event "Yes" is the union of the event "Yes and Question A" with the event "Yes and Question B" to prove that

$$P(\text{"Yes"} \mid \text{Question } B)$$
$$= \frac{P(\text{"Yes"}) - P(\text{"Yes"} \mid \text{Question } A) \cdot P(\text{Question } A)}{P(\text{Question } B)}.$$

b. If this technique is tried on 100 subjects and 60 answered "Yes," what is the approximated probability that a person randomly selected from the group has intentionally cheated on an examination?

101. Police Lineup To illustrate the difficulties with eyewitness identifications from police lineups, John Allen Paulos considers a "lineup" of three pennies, in which we know that two are fair (innocent) and the third (the culprit) has a 75% probability of landing heads. The probability of picking the culprit by chance is, of course, 1/3. Suppose we observe three heads in a row on one of the pennies. If we then guess that this penny is the culprit, what is the probability that we're right? *Source: Who's Counting.*

102. SIDS On July 15, 2005, a panel in England ruled that Roy Meadow, a renowned expert on child abuse and co-founder of London's Royal College of Paediatrics and Child Health, should be erased from the register of physicians in Britain for his faulty statistics at the trial of Sally Clark, who was convicted of murdering her first two babies. Meadow testified at the trial that the probability of a baby dying of sudden death syndrome (SIDS) is 1/8543. He then calculated that the probability of two babies in a family dying of SIDS is $(1/8543)^2 \approx 1/73{,}000{,}000$. With such a small probability of both babies dying of SIDS, he concluded that the babies were instead murdered. What assumption did Meadow make in doing this calculation? Discuss reasons why this assumption may be invalid. (*Note:* Clark spent three years in prison before her conviction was reversed.) *Source: Science.*

Physical Sciences

103. Earthquake It has been reported that government scientists have predicted that the odds for a major earthquake occurring in the San Francisco Bay area during the next 30 years are 9 to 1. What is the probability that a major earthquake will occur during the next 30 years in San Francisco? *Source: The San Francisco Chronicle.*

General Interest

104. Making a First Down A first down is desirable in football—it guarantees four more plays by the team making it, assuming no score or turnover occurs in the plays. After getting a first down, a team can get another by advancing the ball at least 10 yards. During the four plays given by a first down, a team's position will be indicated by a phrase such as "third and 4," which means that the team has already had two of its four plays, and that 4 more yards are needed to get 10 yards necessary for another first down. An article in a management journal offers the following results for 189 games for a particular National Football League season. "Trials" represents the number of times a team tried to make a first down, given that it was currently playing either a third or a fourth down. Here, n represents the number of yards still needed for a first down. *Source: Management Science.*

n	Trials	Successes	Probability of Making First Down with n Yards to Go
1	543	388	
2	327	186	
3	356	146	
4	302	97	
5	336	91	

a. Complete the table.

b. Why is the sum of the answers in the table not equal to 1?

105. States Of the 50 United States, the following is true:

24 are west of the Mississippi River (western states);*

22 had populations less than 3.6 million in the 2010 census (small states);

26 begin with the letters A through M (early states);

9 are large late (beginning with the letters N through Z) eastern states;

14 are small western states;

11 are small early states;

7 are small early western states.

a. How many western states had populations more than 3.6 million in the 2010 census and begin with the letters N through Z?

b. How many states east of the Mississippi had populations more than 3.6 million in the 2010 census?

106. Music Country-western songs often emphasize three basic themes: love, prison, and trucks. A survey of the local country-western radio station produced the following data:

12 songs were about a truckdriver who was in love while in prison;

13 were about a prisoner in love;

28 were about a person in love;

18 were about a truckdriver in love;

33 were about people not in prison;

18 were about prisoners;

15 were about truckdrivers who were in prison;

16 were about truckdrivers who were not in prison.

a. How many songs were surveyed?

Find the number of songs about

b. truckdrivers;

c. prisoners who are not truckdrivers or in love;

d. prisoners who are in love but are not truckdrivers;

e. prisoners who are not truckdrivers;

f. people not in love.

107. Gambling The following puzzle was featured on the Puzzler part of the radio program *Car Talk* on February 23, 2002. A con man puts three cards in a bag; one card is green on both sides, one is red on both sides, and the third is green on one side and red on the other. He lets you pick one card out of the bag and put it on a table, so you can see that a red side is face up, but neither of you can see the other side. He offers to bet you even money that the other side is also red. In other words, if you bet $1, you lose if the other side is red but get back $2 if the other side is green. Is this a good bet? What is the probability that the other side is red? *Source: Car Talk.*

108. Missiles In his novel *Debt of Honor*, Tom Clancy writes the following:

"There were ten target points—missile silos, the intelligence data said, and it pleased the Colonel [Zacharias] to be eliminating the hateful things, even though the price of that was the lives of other

*We count here states such as Minnesota, which has more than half of its area to the west of the Mississippi.

men. There were only three of them [bombers], and his bomber, like the others, carried only eight weapons [smart bombs]. The total number of weapons carried for the mission was only twenty-four, with two designated for each silo, and Zacharias's last four for the last target. Two bombs each. Every bomb had a 95% probability of hitting within four meters of the aim point, pretty good numbers really, except that this sort of mission had precisely no margin for error. Even the paper probability was less than half a percent chance of a double miss, but that number times ten targets meant a 5% chance that [at least] one missile would survive, and that could not be tolerated." *Source: Debt of Honor.*

Determine whether the calculations in this quote are correct by the following steps.

a. Given that each bomb had a 95% probability of hitting the missile silo on which it was dropped, and that two bombs were dropped on each silo, what is the probability of a double miss?

b. What is the probability that a specific silo was destroyed (that is, that at least one bomb of the two bombs struck the silo)?

c. What is the probability that all ten silos were destroyed?

d. What is the probability that at least one silo survived? Does this agree with the quote?

e. What assumptions need to be made for the calculations in parts a through d to be valid? Discuss whether these assumptions seem reasonable.

109. **Viewing Habits** A survey of a group's viewing habits over the last year revealed the following information:

  (i) 28% watched gymnastics;

  (ii) 29% watched baseball;

  (iii) 19% watched soccer;

  (iv) 14% watched gymnastics and baseball;

  (v) 12% watched baseball and soccer;

  (vi) 10% watched gymnastics and soccer;

  (vii) 8% watched all three sports.

Calculate the percentage of the group that watched none of the three sports during the last year. Choose one of the following. *Source: Society of Actuaries.*

  a. 24   **b.** 36   **c.** 41   **d.** 52   **e.** 60

EXTENDED APPLICATION

MEDICAL DIAGNOSIS

When a patient is examined, information (typically incomplete) is obtained about his or her state of health. Probability theory provides a mathematical model appropriate for this situation, as well as a procedure for quantitatively interpreting such partial information to arrive at a reasonable diagnosis. *Source: Some Mathematical Models in Biology.*

To develop a model, we list the states of health that can be distinguished in such a way that the patient can be in one and only one state at the time of the examination. For each state of health H, we associate a number, $P(H)$, between 0 and 1 such that the sum of all these numbers is 1. This number $P(H)$ represents the probability, before examination, that a patient is in the state of health H, and $P(H)$ may be chosen subjectively from medical experience, using any information available prior to the examination. The probability may be most conveniently established from clinical records; that is, a mean probability is established for patients in general, although the number would vary from patient to patient. Of course, the more information that is brought to bear in establishing $P(H)$, the better the diagnosis.

For example, limiting the discussion to the condition of a patient's heart, suppose there are exactly three states of health, with probabilities as follows.

State of Health, H		$P(H)$
H_1	Patient has a normal heart	0.8
H_2	Patient has minor heart irregularities	0.15
H_3	Patient has a severe heart condition	0.05

Having selected $P(H)$, the information from the examination is processed. First, the results of the examination must be classified. The examination itself consists of observing the state of a number of characteristics of the patient. Let us assume that the examination for a heart condition consists of a stethoscope examination and a cardiogram. The outcome of such an examination, C, might be one of the following:

C_1 = stethoscope shows normal heart
    and cardiogram shows normal heart;

C_2 = stethoscope shows normal heart
    and cardiogram shows minor irregularities;

and so on.

It remains to assess for each state of health H the conditional probability $P(C|H)$ of each examination outcome C using only the knowledge that a patient is in a given state of health. (This may be based on the medical knowledge and clinical experience of the doctor.) The conditional probabilities $P(C|H)$ will not vary from patient to patient (although they should be reviewed periodically), so that they may be built into a diagnostic system.

Suppose the result of the examination is C_1. Let us assume the following probabilities:

$$P(C_1|H_1) = 0.9,$$
$$P(C_1|H_2) = 0.4,$$
$$P(C_1|H_3) = 0.1.$$

Now, for a given patient, the appropriate probability associated with each state of health H, after examination, is $P(H|C)$, where C is the outcome of the examination. This can be calculated by using Bayes' theorem. For example, to find $P(H_1|C_1)$—that is, the probability that

the patient has a normal heart given that the examination showed a normal stethoscope examination and a normal cardiogram—we use Bayes' theorem as follows:

$$P(H_1|C_1)$$
$$= \frac{P(C_1|H_1)P(H_1)}{P(C_1|H_1)P(H_1) + P(C_1|H_2)P(H_2) + P(C_1|H_3)P(H_3)}$$
$$= \frac{(0.9)(0.8)}{(0.9)(0.8) + (0.4)(0.15) + (0.1)(0.05)} \approx 0.92.$$

Hence, the probability is about 0.92 that the patient has a normal heart on the basis of the examination results. This means that in 8 out of 100 patients, some abnormality will be present and not be detected by the stethoscope or the cardiogram.

EXERCISES

1. Find $P(H_2|C_1)$.
2. Assuming the following probabilities, find $P(H_1|C_2)$.

$$P(C_2|H_1) = 0.2 \qquad P(C_2|H_2) = 0.8 \qquad P(C_2|H_3) = 0.3$$

3. Assuming the probabilities of Exercise 2, find $P(H_3|C_2)$.

DIRECTIONS FOR GROUP PROJECT

Find an article on medical decision making from a medical journal and develop a doctor–patient scenario for that particular decision. Then create a role-playing activity where the doctor and nurse present the various options and the mathematics associated with making such a decision to a patient. Make sure to present the mathematics in a manner that the average patient might understand. (Hint: Many leading medical journals include articles on medical decision making. One particular journal that certainly includes such research is Medical Decision Making.)

8 Counting Principles; Further Probability Topics

If you have 31 ice cream flavors available, how many different three-scoop cones can you make? The answer, which is surprisingly large, involves counting permutations or combinations, the subject of the first two sections in this chapter. The counting formulas we will develop have important applications in probability theory.

f we flip two coins and record heads or tails for each coin, we can list the four possible outcomes in the sample space as $S = \{hh, ht, th, tt\}$. But what if we flip 10 coins? As we shall see, there are over 1000 possible outcomes, which makes a list of the sample space impractical. Fortunately, there are methods for counting the outcomes in a set without actually listing them. We introduce these methods in the first two sections, and then we use this approach in the third section to find probabilities. In the fourth section, we introduce binomial experiments, which consist of repeated independent trials with only two possible outcomes, and develop a formula for binomial probabilities. The final section continues the discussion of probability distributions that we began in Chapter 7.

8.1 The Multiplication Principle; Permutations

APPLY IT In how many ways can seven panelists be seated in a row of seven chairs? *Before we answer this question in Example 8, we will begin with a simpler example.*

Suppose a breakfast consists of one pastry, for which you can choose a bagel, a muffin, or a donut, and one beverage, for which you can choose coffee or juice. How many different breakfasts can you have? For each of the 3 pastries there are 2 different beverages, or a total of $3 \cdot 2 = 6$ different breakfasts, as shown in Figure 1. This example illustrates a general principle of counting, called the **multiplication principle.**

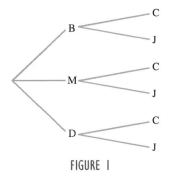

FIGURE 1

> ## Multiplication Principle
> Suppose n choices must be made, with
>
> $$m_1 \text{ ways to make choice 1,}$$
> $$m_2 \text{ ways to make choice 2,}$$
>
> and so on, with
>
> $$m_n \text{ ways to make choice } n.$$
>
> Then there are
>
> $$m_1 \cdot m_2 \cdot \cdots \cdot m_n$$
>
> different ways to make the entire sequence of choices.

EXAMPLE 1 Combination Lock

A certain combination lock can be set to open to any 3-letter sequence.

(a) How many sequences are possible?

SOLUTION Since there are 26 letters in the alphabet, there are 26 choices for each of the 3 letters. By the multiplication principle, there are $26 \cdot 26 \cdot 26 = 17{,}576$ different sequences.

(b) How many sequences are possible if no letter is repeated?

SOLUTION There are 26 choices for the first letter. It cannot be used again, so there are 25 choices for the second letter and then 24 choices for the third letter. Consequently, the number of such sequences is $26 \cdot 25 \cdot 24 = 15{,}600$. **TRY YOUR TURN 1**

YOUR TURN 1 A combination lock can be set to open to any 4-digit sequence. How many sequences are possible? How many sequences are possible if no digit is repeated?

EXAMPLE 2   Morse Code

Morse code uses a sequence of dots and dashes to represent letters and words. How many sequences are possible with at most 3 symbols?

SOLUTION   "At most 3" means "1 or 2 or 3" here. Each symbol may be either a dot or a dash. Thus the following number of sequences are possible in each case.

Morse Code	
Number of Symbols	**Number of Sequences**
1	**2**
2	**2 · 2 = 4**
3	**2 · 2 · 2 = 8**

Altogether, $2 + 4 + 8 = 14$ different sequences are possible.

EXAMPLE 3   I Ching

yin   yang

FIGURE 2

An ancient Chinese philosophical work known as the *I Ching (Book of Changes)* is often used as an oracle from which people can seek and obtain advice. The philosophy describes the duality of the universe in terms of two primary forces: *yin* (passive, dark, receptive) and *yang* (active, light, creative). Figure 2 shows the traditional symbol for yin and yang. The yin energy can also be represented by a broken line (– –) and the yang by a solid line (—). These lines are written on top of one another in groups of three, known as *trigrams*. For example, the trigram ☱ is called *Tui*, the Joyous, and has the image of a lake.

(a) How many trigrams are there altogether?

SOLUTION   Think of choosing between the 2 types of lines for each of the 3 positions in the trigram. There will be 2 choices for each position, so there are $2 \cdot 2 \cdot 2 = 8$ different trigrams.

(b) The trigrams are grouped together, one on top of the other, in pairs known as *hexagrams*. Each hexagram represents one aspect of the *I Ching* philosophy. How many hexagrams are there?

SOLUTION   For each position in the hexagram there are 8 possible trigrams, giving $8 \cdot 8 = 64$ hexagrams.

EXAMPLE 4   Books

A teacher has 5 different books that he wishes to arrange side by side. How many different arrangements are possible?

YOUR TURN 2   A teacher is lining up 8 students for a spelling bee. How many different line-ups are possible?

SOLUTION   Five choices will be made, one for each space that will hold a book. Any of the 5 books could be chosen for the first space. There are 4 choices for the second space, since 1 book has already been placed in the first space; there are 3 choices for the third space, and so on. By the multiplication principle, the number of different possible arrangements is $5 \cdot 4 \cdot 3 \cdot 2 \cdot 1 = 120$.   TRY YOUR TURN 2

FOR REVIEW

The natural numbers, also referred to as the positive integers, are the numbers 1, 2, 3, 4, etc.

The use of the multiplication principle often leads to products such as $5 \cdot 4 \cdot 3 \cdot 2 \cdot 1$, the product of all the natural numbers from 5 down to 1. If n is a natural number, the symbol $n!$ (read "*n factorial*") denotes the product of all the natural numbers from n down to 1. If $n = 1$, this formula is understood to give $1! = 1$.

Factorial Notation

For any natural number n,

$$n! = n(n - 1)(n - 2) \cdots (3)(2)(1).$$

Also, by definition,

$$0! = 1.$$

With this symbol, the product $5 \cdot 4 \cdot 3 \cdot 2 \cdot 1$ can be written as 5!. Also, $3! = 3 \cdot 2 \cdot 1 = 6$. The definition of $n!$ could be used to show that $n[(n - 1)]! = n!$ for all natural numbers $n \ge 2$. It is helpful if this result also holds for $n = 1$. This can happen only if 0! equals 1, as defined above.

As n gets large, $n!$ grows very quickly. For example, $5! = 120$, while $10! = 3{,}628{,}800$. Most calculators can be used to determine $n!$ for small values of n. A calculator with a 10-digit display and scientific notation capability will usually give the exact value of $n!$ for $n \le 13$, and approximate values of $n!$ for $14 \le n \le 69$. The value of 70! is approximately 1.198×10^{100}, which is too large for most calculators. To get a sense of how large 70! is, suppose a computer counted the numbers from 1 to 70! at a rate of 1 billion numbers per second. If the computer started when the universe began, by now it would have calculated only a tiny fraction of the total.

TECHNOLOGY NOTE

On many graphing calculators, the factorial of a number is accessible through a menu. On the TI-84 Plus, for example, this menu is found by pressing the MATH key, selecting PRB (for probability), and then selecting the !.

EXAMPLE 5 Books

YOUR TURN 3 A teacher wishes to place 5 out of 8 different books on her shelf. How many arrangements of 5 books are possible?

Suppose the teacher in Example 4 wishes to place only 3 of the 5 books on his desk. How many arrangements of 3 books are possible?

SOLUTION The teacher again has 5 ways to fill the first space, 4 ways to fill the second space, and 3 ways to fill the third. Since he wants to use only 3 books, only 3 spaces can be filled (3 events) instead of 5, for $5 \cdot 4 \cdot 3 = 60$ arrangements.   **TRY YOUR TURN 3**

Permutations

The answer 60 in Example 5 is called the number of *permutations* of 5 things taken 3 at a time. A **permutation** of r (where $r \ge 1$) elements from a set of n elements is any specific ordering or arrangement, *without repetition*, of the r elements. Each rearrangement of the r elements is a different permutation. The number of permutations of n things taken r at a time (with $r \le n$) is written $P(n, r)$.* Based on the work in Example 5,

$$P(5, 3) = 5 \cdot 4 \cdot 3 = 60.$$

Factorial notation can be used to express this product as follows.

$$5 \cdot 4 \cdot 3 = 5 \cdot 4 \cdot 3 \cdot \frac{2 \cdot 1}{2 \cdot 1} = \frac{5 \cdot 4 \cdot 3 \cdot 2 \cdot 1}{2 \cdot 1} = \frac{5!}{2!} = \frac{5!}{(5 - 3)!}$$

This example illustrates the general rule of permutations, which can be stated as follows.

Permutations

If $P(n, r)$ (where $r \le n$) is the number of permutations of n elements taken r at a time, then

$$P(n, r) = \frac{n!}{(n - r)!}.$$

*An alternate notation for $P(n, r)$ is $_nP_r$.

CAUTION   The letter P here represents *permutations*, not *probability*. In probability notation, the quantity in parentheses describes an *event*. In permutations notation, the quantity in parentheses always comprises *two numbers*.

The proof of the permutations rule follows the discussion in Example 5. There are n ways to choose the first of the r elements, $n - 1$ ways to choose the second, and $n - r + 1$ ways to choose the rth element, so that

$$P(n, r) = n(n - 1)(n - 2)\cdots(n - r + 1).$$

Now multiply on the right by $(n - r)!/(n - r)!$.

$$P(n, r) = n(n - 1)(n - 2)\cdots(n - r + 1) \cdot \frac{(n - r)!}{(n - r)!}$$

$$= \frac{n(n - 1)(n - 2)\cdots(n - r + 1)(n - r)!}{(n - r)!}$$

$$= \frac{n!}{(n - r)!}$$

Because we defined 0! equal to 1, the formula for permutations gives the special case

$$P(n, n) = \frac{n!}{(n - n)!} = \frac{n!}{0!} = \frac{n!}{1} = n!.$$

This result also follows from the multiplication principle, because $P(n, n)$ gives the number of permutations of n objects, and there are n choices for the first object, $n - 1$ for the second, and so on, down to just 1 choice for the last object. Example 4 illustrated this idea.

> **$P(n, n)$**
>
> The number of permutations of a set with n elements is $n!$; that is $P(n, n) = n!$.

EXAMPLE 6   Permutations of Letters

Find the following.

(a) The number of permutations of the letters A, B, and C.

SOLUTION   By the formula $P(n, n) = n!$, with $n = 3$,

$$P(3, 3) = 3! = 3 \cdot 2 \cdot 1 = 6.$$

The 6 *permutations* (or *arrangements*) are ABC, ACB, BAC, BCA, CAB, CBA.

(b) The number of permutations if just 2 of the letters A, B, and C are to be used

SOLUTION   Find $P(3, 2)$.

$$P(3, 2) = \frac{3!}{(3 - 2)!} = \frac{3!}{1!} = 3! = 6$$

This result is exactly the same answer as in part (a). This is because, in the case of $P(3, 3)$, after the first 2 choices are made, the third is already determined, as shown in the table below.

YOUR TURN 4   Find the number of permutations of the letters L, M, N, O, P, and Q, if just three of the letters are to be used.

Permutations of Three Letters						
First Two Letters	AB	AC	BA	BC	CA	CB
Third Letter	C	B	C	A	B	A

TRY YOUR TURN 4

To find $P(n, r)$, we can use either the permutations formula or direct application of the multiplication principle, as the following example shows.

EXAMPLE 7 **Politics**

In a recent election, eight candidates sought the Democratic nomination for president. In how many ways could voters rank their first, second, and third choices?

Method 1
Calculating By Hand

SOLUTION This is the same as finding the number of permutations of 8 elements taken 3 at a time. Since there are 3 choices to be made, the multiplication principle gives $P(8, 3) = 8 \cdot 7 \cdot 6 = 336$. Alternatively, use the permutations formula to get

$$P(8, 3) = \frac{8!}{(8 - 3)!} = \frac{8!}{5!} = \frac{8 \cdot 7 \cdot 6 \cdot 5 \cdot 4 \cdot 3 \cdot 2 \cdot 1}{5 \cdot 4 \cdot 3 \cdot 2 \cdot 1} = 8 \cdot 7 \cdot 6 = 336.$$

Method 2
Graphing Calculator

Graphing calculators have the capacity to compute permutations. For example, on a TI-84 Plus, $P(8, 3)$ can be calculated by inputting 8 followed by `nPr` (found in the `MATH-PRB` menu), and a 3 yielding 336, as shown in Figure 3.

FIGURE 3

Method 3
Spreadsheet

Spreadsheets can also compute permutations. For example, in Microsoft Excel, $P(8, 3)$ can be calculated by inputting 8 and 3 in cells, say, A1 and B1, and then typing "`=FACT(A1)/FACT(A1-B1)`" in cell C1 or, for that matter, any other cell.

CAUTION When calculating the number of permutations with the formula, do not try to cancel unlike factorials. For example,

$$\frac{8!}{4!} \neq 2! = 2 \cdot 1 = 2.$$

$$\frac{8!}{4!} = \frac{8 \cdot 7 \cdot 6 \cdot 5 \cdot 4 \cdot 3 \cdot 2 \cdot 1}{4 \cdot 3 \cdot 2 \cdot 1} = 8 \cdot 7 \cdot 6 \cdot 5 = 1680.$$

Always write out the factors first, then cancel where appropriate.

EXAMPLE 8 **Television Panel**

A televised talk show will include 4 women and 3 men as panelists.

(a) In how many ways can the panelists be seated in a row of 7 chairs?

APPLY IT

SOLUTION Find $P(7, 7)$, the total number of ways to seat 7 panelists in 7 chairs.

$$P(7, 7) = 7! = 7 \cdot 6 \cdot 5 \cdot 4 \cdot 3 \cdot 2 \cdot 1 = 5040$$

There are 5040 ways to seat the 7 panelists.

(b) In how many ways can the panelists be seated if the men and women are to be alternated?

SOLUTION Use the multiplication principle. In order to alternate men and women, a woman must be seated in the first chair (since there are 4 women and only 3 men), any of the men next, and so on. Thus there are 4 ways to fill the first seat, 3 ways to fill the second seat, 3 ways to fill the third seat (with any of the 3 remaining women), and so on. This gives

$$\underbrace{4}_{W_1} \cdot \underbrace{3}_{M_1} \cdot \underbrace{3}_{W_2} \cdot \underbrace{2}_{M_2} \cdot \underbrace{2}_{W_3} \cdot \underbrace{1}_{M_3} \cdot \underbrace{1}_{W_4} = 144$$

ways to seat the panelists.

(c) In how many ways can the panelists be seated if the men must sit together, and the women must also sit together?

SOLUTION Use the multiplication principle. We first must decide how to arrange the two groups (men and women). There are 2! ways of doing this. Next, there are 4! ways of arranging the women and 3! ways of arranging the men, for a total of

$$2!\, 4!\, 3! = 2 \cdot 24 \cdot 6 = 288$$

ways.

(d) In how many ways can one woman and one man from the panel be selected?

SOLUTION There are 4 ways to pick the woman and 3 ways to pick the man, for a total of

$$4 \cdot 3 = 12$$

ways.

YOUR TURN 5 Two freshmen, 2 sophomores, 2 juniors, and 3 seniors are on a panel. In how many ways can the panelists be seated if each class must sit together?

TRY YOUR TURN 5

If the n objects in a permutation are not all distinguishable—that is, if there are n_1 of type 1, n_2 of type 2, and so on for r different types, then the number of **distinguishable permutations** is

$$\frac{n!}{n_1!\, n_2! \cdots n_r!}.$$

For example, suppose we want to find the number of permutations of the numbers 1, 1, 4, 4, 4. We cannot distinguish between the two 1's or among the three 4's, so using 5! would give too many distinguishable arrangements. Since the two 1's are indistinguishable and account for 2! of the permutations, we divide 5! by 2!. Similarly, we also divide by 3! to account for the three indistinguishable 4's. This gives

$$\frac{5!}{2!\, 3!} = 10$$

permutations.

EXAMPLE 9 Mississippi

In how many ways can the letters in the word *Mississippi* be arranged?

SOLUTION This word contains 1 m, 4 i's, 4 s's, and 2 p's. To use the formula, let $n = 11$, $n_1 = 1$, $n_2 = 4$, $n_3 = 4$, and $n_4 = 2$ to get

$$\frac{11!}{1!\, 4!\, 4!\, 2!} = 34{,}650$$

YOUR TURN 6 In how many ways can the letters in the word *Tennessee* be arranged?

arrangements.

TRY YOUR TURN 6

NOTE If Example 9 had asked for the number of ways that the letters in a word with 11 *different* letters could be arranged, the answer would be 11! = 39,916,800.

EXAMPLE 10 Yogurt

A student buys 3 cherry yogurts, 2 raspberry yogurts, and 2 blueberry yogurts. She puts them in her dormitory refrigerator to eat one a day for the next week. Assuming yogurts of

YOUR TURN 7 A student has 4 pairs of identical blue socks, 5 pairs of identical brown socks, 3 pairs of identical black socks, and 2 pairs of identical white socks. In how many ways can he select socks to wear for the next two weeks?

the same flavor are indistinguishable, in how many ways can she select yogurts to eat for the next week?

SOLUTION   This problem is again one of distinguishable permutations. The 7 yogurts can be selected in 7! ways, but since the 3 cherry, 2 raspberry, and 2 blueberry yogurts are indistinguishable, the total number of distinguishable orders in which the yogurts can be selected is

$$\frac{7!}{3!\,2!\,2!} = 210.$$

TRY YOUR TURN 7

8.1   EXERCISES

In Exercises 1–12, evaluate the factorial or permutation.

1. 6!

2. 7!

3. 15!

4. 16!

5. $P(13, 2)$

6. $P(12, 3)$

7. $P(38, 17)$

8. $P(33, 19)$

9. $P(n, 0)$

10. $P(n, n)$

11. $P(n, 1)$

12. $P(n, n - 1)$

13. How many different types of homes are available if a builder offers a choice of 6 basic plans, 3 roof styles, and 2 exterior finishes?

14. A menu offers a choice of 3 salads, 8 main dishes, and 7 desserts. How many different meals consisting of one salad, one main dish, and one dessert are possible?

15. A couple has narrowed down the choice of a name for their new baby to 4 first names and 5 middle names. How many different first- and middle-name arrangements are possible?

16. In a club with 16 members, how many ways can a slate of 3 officers consisting of president, vice-president, and secretary/treasurer be chosen?

17. Define *permutation* in your own words.

18. Explain the difference between *distinguishable* and *indistinguishable* permutations.

19. In Example 6, there are six 3-letter permutations of the letters A, B, and C. How many 3-letter subsets (unordered groups of letters) are there?

20. In Example 6, how many unordered 2-letter subsets of the letters A, B, and C are there?

21. Find the number of distinguishable permutations of the letters in each word.

a. initial   **b.** little   **c.** decreed

22. A printer has 5 A's, 4 B's, 2 C's, and 2 D's. How many different "words" are possible that use all these letters? (A "word" does not have to have any meaning here.)

23. Wing has different books to arrange on a shelf: 4 blue, 3 green, and 2 red.

a. In how many ways can the books be arranged on a shelf?

b. If books of the same color are to be grouped together, how many arrangements are possible?

c. In how many distinguishable ways can the books be arranged if books of the same color are identical but need not be grouped together?

d. In how many ways can you select 3 books, one of each color, if the order in which the books are selected does not matter?

e. In how many ways can you select 3 books, one of each color, if the order in which the books are selected matters?

24. A child has a set of differently shaped plastic objects. There are 3 pyramids, 4 cubes, and 7 spheres.

a. In how many ways can she arrange the objects in a row if each is a different color?

b. How many arrangements are possible if objects of the same shape must be grouped together and each object is a different color?

c. In how many distinguishable ways can the objects be arranged in a row if objects of the same shape are also the same color but need not be grouped together?

d. In how many ways can you select 3 objects, one of each shape, if the order in which the objects are selected does not matter and each object is a different color?

e. In how many ways can you select 3 objects, one of each shape, if the order in which the objects are selected matters and each object is a different color?

25. If you already knew the value of 9!, how could you find the value of 10! quickly?

26. Given that 450! is approximately equal to $1.7333687 \times 10^{1000}$ (to 8 digits of accuracy), find 451! to 7 digits of accuracy.

27. When calculating $n!$, the number of ending zeros in the answer can be determined prior to calculating the actual number by finding the number of times 5 can be factored from $n!$. For example, 7! only has one 5 occurring in its calculation, and so there is only one ending zero in 5040. The number 10! has two 5's (one from the 5 and one from the 10) and so there must be two ending zeros in the answer 3,628,800. Use this idea to determine the number of zeros that occur in the following factorials, and then explain why this works.

a. 13!   **b.** 27!   **c.** 75!

28. Because of the view screen, calculators only show a fixed number of digits, often 10 digits. Thus, an approximation of a number will be shown by only including the 10 largest place values of the number. Using the ideas from the previous exercise, determine if the following numbers are correct or if they are incorrect by checking if they have the correct number of ending zeros. (*Note:* Just because a number has the correct number of zeros does not imply that it is correct.)

a. $12! = 479,001,610$

b. $23! = 25,852,016,740,000,000,000,000$

c. $15! = 1,307,643,680,000$

d. $14! = 87,178,291,200$

29. Some students find it puzzling that $0! = 1$, and think that $0!$ should equal 0. If this were true, what would be the value of $P(4, 4)$ using the permutations formula?

APPLICATIONS

Business and Economics

30. Automobile Manufacturing   An automobile manufacturer produces 8 models, each available in 7 different exterior colors, with 4 different upholstery fabrics and 5 interior colors. How many varieties of automobile are available?

31. Marketing   In a recent marketing campaign, Olive Garden Italian Restaurant® offered a "Never-Ending Pasta Bowl." The customer could order an array of pasta dishes, selecting from 7 types of pasta and 6 types of sauce, including 2 with meat.

a. If the customer selects one pasta type and one sauce type, how many different "pasta bowls" can a customer order?

b. How many different "pasta bowls" can a customer order without meat?

32. Investments   Natalie Graham's financial advisor has given her a list of 9 potential investments and has asked her to select and rank her favorite five. In how many different ways can she do this?

33. Scheduling   A local television station has eleven slots for commercials during a special broadcast. Six restaurants and 5 stores have bought slots for the broadcast.

a. In how many ways can the commercials be arranged?

b. In how many ways can the commercials be arranged so that the restaurants are grouped together and the stores are grouped together?

c. In how many ways can the commercials be arranged so that the restaurant and store commercials are alternating?

Life Sciences

34. Drug Sequencing   Twelve drugs have been found to be effective in the treatment of a disease. It is believed that the sequence in which the drugs are administered is important in the effectiveness of the treatment. In how many different sequences can 5 of the 12 drugs be administered?

35. Insect Classification   A biologist is attempting to classify 52,000 species of insects by assigning 3 initials to each species. Is it possible to classify all the species in this way? If not, how many initials should be used?

36. Science Conference   At an annual college science conference, student presentations are scheduled one after another in the afternoon session. This year, 5 students are presenting in

biology, 5 students are presenting in chemistry, and 2 students are presenting in physics.

a. In how many ways can the presentations be scheduled?

b. In how many ways can the presentations be scheduled so that each subject is grouped together?

c. In how many ways can the presentations be scheduled if the conference must begin and end with a physics presentation?

Social Sciences

37. Social Science Experiment   In an experiment on social interaction, 6 people will sit in 6 seats in a row. In how many ways can this be done?

38. Election Ballots   In an election with 3 candidates for one office and 6 candidates for another office, how many different ballots may be printed?

General Interest

39. Baseball Teams   A baseball team has 19 players. How many 9-player batting orders are possible?

40. Union Elections   A chapter of union Local 715 has 35 members. In how many different ways can the chapter select a president, a vice-president, a treasurer, and a secretary?

41. Programming Music   A concert to raise money for an economics prize is to consist of 5 works: 2 overtures, 2 sonatas, and a piano concerto.

a. In how many ways can the program be arranged?

b. In how many ways can the program be arranged if an overture must come first?

42. Programming Music   A zydeco band from Louisiana will play 5 traditional and 3 original Cajun compositions at a concert. In how many ways can they arrange the program if

a. they begin with a traditional piece?

b. an original piece will be played last?

43. Radio Station Call Letters   How many different 4-letter radio station call letters can be made if

a. the first letter must be K or W and no letter may be repeated?

b. repeats are allowed, but the first letter is K or W?

c. the first letter is K or W, there are no repeats, and the last letter is R?

44. Telephone Numbers   How many 7-digit telephone numbers are possible if the first digit cannot be zero and

a. only odd digits may be used?

b. the telephone number must be a multiple of 10 (that is, it must end in zero)?

c. the telephone number must be a multiple of 100?

d. the first 3 digits are 481?

e. no repetitions are allowed?

Telephone Area Codes   **Several years ago, the United States began running out of telephone numbers. Telephone companies introduced new area codes as numbers were used up, and eventually almost all area codes were used up.**

45. a. Until recently, all area codes had a 0 or 1 as the middle digit, and the first digit could not be 0 or 1. How many area codes are there with this arrangement? How many telephone numbers does the current 7-digit sequence permit per area code? (The 3-digit sequence that follows the area code cannot start with 0 or 1. Assume there are no other restrictions.)

b. The actual number of area codes under the previous system was 152. Explain the discrepancy between this number and your answer to part a.

46. The shortage of area codes was avoided by removing the restriction on the second digit. (This resulted in problems for some older equipment, which used the second digit to determine that a long-distance call was being made.) How many area codes are available under the new system?

47. License Plates For many years, the state of California used 3 letters followed by 3 digits on its automobile license plates.

a. How many different license plates are possible with this arrangement?

b. When the state ran out of new numbers, the order was reversed to 3 digits followed by 3 letters. How many new license plate numbers were then possible?

c. Several years ago, the numbers described in b were also used up. The state then issued plates with 1 letter followed by 3 digits and then 3 letters. How many new license plate numbers will this provide?

48. Social Security Numbers A social security number has 9 digits. How many social security numbers are there? The U.S. population in 2010 was about 309 million. Is it possible for every U.S. resident to have a unique social security number? (Assume no restrictions.)

49. Postal Zip Codes The U.S. Postal Service currently uses 5-digit zip codes in most areas. How many zip codes are possible if there are no restrictions on the digits used? How many would be possible if the first number could not be 0?

50. Postal Zip Codes The U.S. Postal Service is encouraging the use of 9-digit zip codes in some areas, adding 4 digits after the usual 5-digit code. How many such zip codes are possible with no restrictions?

51. Games The game of Sets uses a special deck of cards. Each card has either one, two, or three identical shapes, all of the same color and style. There are three possible shapes: squiggle, diamond, and oval. There are three possible colors: green, purple, and red. There are three possible styles: solid, shaded, or outline. The deck consists of all possible combinations of shape, color, style, and number of shapes. How many cards are in the deck? *Source: Sets.*

52. Games In the game of Scattergories, the players take 12 turns. In each turn, a 20-sided die is rolled; each side has a letter. The players must then fill in 12 categories (e.g., vegetable, city, etc.) with a word beginning with the letter rolled. Considering that a game consists of 12 rolls of the 20-sided die, and that rolling the same side more than once is allowed, how many possible games are there? *Source: Milton Bradley.*

53. Games The game of Twenty Questions consists of asking 20 questions to determine a person, place, or thing that the other person is thinking of. The first question, which is always "Is it an animal, vegetable, or mineral?" has three possible answers. All the other questions must be answered "Yes" or "No." How many possible objects can be distinguished in this game, assuming that all 20 questions are asked? Are 20 questions enough?

54. Traveling Salesman In the famous Traveling Salesman Problem, a salesman starts in any one of a set of cities, visits every city in the set once, and returns to the starting city. He would like to complete this circuit with the shortest possible distance.

a. Suppose the salesman has 10 cities to visit. Given that it does not matter what city he starts in, how many different circuits can he take?

b. The salesman decides to check all the different paths in part a to see which is shortest, but realizes that a circuit has the same distance whichever direction it is traveled. How many different circuits must he check?

c. Suppose the salesman has 70 cities to visit. Would it be feasible to have a computer check all the different circuits? Explain your reasoning.

55. Circular Permutations Circular permutations arise in applications involving arrangements around a closed loop, as in the previous exercise. Here are two examples.

a. A ferris wheel has 20 seats. How many ways can 20 students arrange themselves on the ferris wheel if each student takes a different seat? We consider two arrangements to be identical if they differ only by rotations of the wheel.

b. A necklace is to be strung with 15 beads, each of a different color. In how many ways can the beads be arranged? We consider two arrangements to be identical if they differ only by rotations of the necklace or by flipping the necklace over. (*Hint:* If every arrangement is counted twice, the correct number of arrangements can be found by dividing by 2.)

YOUR TURN ANSWERS

1. 10,000; 5040   **2.** 40,320   **3.** 6720   **4.** 120
5. 1152   **6.** 3780   **7.** 2,522,520

8.2 Combinations

APPLY IT In how many ways can a manager select 4 employees for promotion from 12 eligible employees?

As we shall see in Example 5, permutations alone cannot be used to answer this question, but combinations will provide the answer.

In the previous section, we saw that there are 60 ways that a teacher can arrange 3 of 5 different books on his desk. That is, there are 60 permutations of 5 books taken 3 at a time.

Suppose now that the teacher does not wish to arrange the books on his desk but rather wishes to choose, without regard to order, any 3 of the 5 books for a book sale to raise money for his school. In how many ways can this be done?

At first glance, we might say 60 again, but this is incorrect. The number 60 counts all possible *arrangements* of 3 books chosen from 5. The following 6 arrangements, however, would all lead to the same set of 3 books being given to the book sale.

mystery-biography-textbook	biography-textbook-mystery
mystery-textbook-biography	textbook-biography-mystery
biography-mystery-textbook	textbook-mystery-biography

The list shows 6 different *arrangements* of 3 books, but only one *subset* of 3 books. A subset of items listed *without regard to order* is called a **combination**. The number of combinations of 5 things taken 3 at a time is written $C(5, 3)$.* Since they are subsets, combinations are *not ordered*.

To evaluate $C(5, 3)$, start with the $5 \cdot 4 \cdot 3$ *permutations* of 5 things taken 3 at a time. Since combinations are not ordered, find the number of combinations by dividing the number of permutations by the number of ways each group of 3 can be ordered; that is, divide by 3!.

$$C(5, 3) = \frac{5 \cdot 4 \cdot 3}{3!} = \frac{5 \cdot 4 \cdot 3}{3 \cdot 2 \cdot 1} = 10$$

There are 10 ways that the teacher can choose 3 books for the book sale.

Generalizing this discussion gives the following formula for the number of combinations of n elements taken r at a time:

$$C(n, r) = \frac{P(n, r)}{r!}.$$

Another version of this formula is found as follows.

$$C(n, r) = \frac{P(n, r)}{r!}$$

$$= \frac{n!}{(n - r)!} \cdot \frac{1}{r!} \qquad P(n, r) = \frac{n!}{(n - r)!}.$$

$$= \frac{n!}{(n - r)! \, r!}$$

The steps above lead to the following result.

Combinations

If $C(n, r)$, denotes the number of combinations of n elements taken r at a time, where $r \le n$, then

$$C(n, r) = \frac{n!}{(n - r)! \, r!}.$$

EXAMPLE 1 **Committees**

How many committees of 3 people can be formed from a group of 8 people?

Method 1
Calculating By Hand

SOLUTION A committee is an unordered group, so use the combinations formula for $C(8, 3)$.

$$C(8, 3) = \frac{8!}{5!3!} = \frac{8 \cdot 7 \cdot 6 \cdot 5 \cdot 4 \cdot 3 \cdot 2 \cdot 1}{5 \cdot 4 \cdot 3 \cdot 2 \cdot 1 \cdot 3 \cdot 2 \cdot 1} = \frac{8 \cdot 7 \cdot 6}{3 \cdot 2 \cdot 1} = 56$$

*Other common notations for $C(n, r)$ are $_nC_r$, C_r^n, and $\binom{n}{r}$.

Method 2
Graphing Calculator

Graphing calculators have the capacity to compute combinations. For example, on a TI-84 Plus, $C(8, 3)$ can be calculated by inputting 8 followed by nCr (found in the MATH-PRB menu) and a 3 yielding 56, as shown in Figure 4.

```
8 nCr 3
                    56
■
```

FIGURE 4

Method 3
Spreadsheet

Spreadsheets can also compute combinations. For example, in Microsoft Excel, $C(8, 3)$ can be calculated by inputting 8 and 3 in cells, say, A1 and B1, and then typing "=FACT(A1)/(FACT(A1-B1)*FACT(B1))" in cell C1 or, for that matter, any other cell. The command "= MULTINOMIAL(5, 3)" also gives this answer.

YOUR TURN 1 How many committees of 4 people can be formed from a group of 10 people?

TRY YOUR TURN 1

Example 1 shows an alternative way to compute $C(n, r)$. Take r or $n - r$, whichever is smaller. Write the factorial of this number in the denominator. In the numerator, write out a sufficient number of factors of $n!$ so there is one factor in the numerator for each factor in the denominator. For example, to calculate $C(8, 3)$ or $C(8, 5)$ write

$$\frac{8 \cdot 7 \cdot 6}{3 \cdot 2 \cdot 1} = 56.$$

The factors that are omitted (written in color in Example 1) cancel out of the numerator and denominator, so need not be included.

Notice from the previous discussion that $C(8, 3) = C(8, 5)$. (See Exercise 25 for a generalization of this idea.) One interpretation of this fact is that the number of ways to form a committee of 3 people chosen from a group of 8 is the same as the number of ways to choose the 5 people who are not on the committee.

Notice that this is *not* true with permutations: $P(8, 3) \neq P(8, 5)$.

EXAMPLE 2 **Lawyers**

Three lawyers are to be selected from a group of 30 to work on a special project.

(a) In how many different ways can the lawyers be selected?

SOLUTION Here we wish to know the number of 3-element combinations that can be formed from a set of 30 elements. (We want combinations, not permutations, since order within the group of 3 doesn't matter.)

$$C(30, 3) = \frac{30!}{27!3!} = \frac{30 \cdot 29 \cdot 28 \cdot 27!}{27! \cdot 3 \cdot 2 \cdot 1} \qquad 30! = 30 \cdot 29 \cdot 28 \cdot 27!$$

$$= \frac{30 \cdot 29 \cdot 28}{3 \cdot 2 \cdot 1}$$

$$= 4060$$

There are 4060 ways to select the project group.

(b) In how many ways can the group of 3 be selected if a certain lawyer must work on the project?

SOLUTION Since 1 lawyer already has been selected for the project, the problem is reduced to selecting 2 more from the remaining 29 lawyers.

$$C(29, 2) = \frac{29!}{27! \, 2!} = \frac{29 \cdot 28 \cdot 27!}{27! \cdot 2 \cdot 1} = \frac{29 \cdot 28}{2 \cdot 1} = 29 \cdot 14 = 406$$

In this case, the project group can be selected in 406 ways.

(c) In how many ways can a nonempty group of at most 3 lawyers be selected from these 30 lawyers?

SOLUTION Here, by "at most 3" we mean "1 or 2 or 3." (The number 0 is excluded because the group is nonempty.) Find the number of ways for each case.

Case	Number of Ways
1	$C(30, 1) = \dfrac{30!}{29!\, 1!} = \dfrac{30 \cdot 29!}{29!\, (1)} = 30$
2	$C(30, 2) = \dfrac{30!}{28!\, 2!} = \dfrac{30 \cdot 29 \cdot 28!}{28! \cdot 2 \cdot 1} = 435$
3	$C(30, 3) = \dfrac{30!}{27!\, 3!} = \dfrac{30 \cdot 29 \cdot 28 \cdot 27!}{27! \cdot 3 \cdot 2 \cdot 1} = 4060$

YOUR TURN 2 From a class of 15 students, a group of 3 or 4 students will be selected to work on a special project. In how many ways can a group of 3 or 4 students be selected?

The total number of ways to select at most 3 lawyers will be the sum

$$30 + 435 + 4060 = 4525.$$ **TRY YOUR TURN 2**

EXAMPLE 3   Sales

A salesman has 10 accounts in a certain city.

(a) In how many ways can he select 3 accounts to call on?

SOLUTION Within a selection of 3 accounts, the arrangement of the calls is not important, so there are

$$C(10, 3) = \frac{10!}{7!\, 3!} = \frac{10 \cdot 9 \cdot 8}{3 \cdot 2 \cdot 1} = 120$$

ways he can make a selection of 3 accounts.

(b) In how many ways can he select at least 8 of the 10 accounts to use in preparing a report?

SOLUTION "At least 8" means "8 or more," which is "8 or 9 or 10." First find the number of ways to choose in each case.

-FOR REVIEW-

Notice in Example 3 that to calculate the number of ways to select 8 or 9 or 10 accounts, we added the three numbers found. The union rule for sets from Chapter 7 says that when A and B are disjoint sets, the number of elements in A or B is the number of elements in A plus the number in B.

Case	Number of Ways
8	$C(10, 8) = \dfrac{10!}{2!\, 8!} = \dfrac{10 \cdot 9}{2 \cdot 1} = 45$
9	$C(10, 9) = \dfrac{10!}{1!\, 9!} = \dfrac{10}{1} = 10$
10	$C(10, 10) = \dfrac{10!}{0!\, 10!} = 1$

He can select at least 8 of the 10 accounts in $45 + 10 + 1 = 56$ ways.

CAUTION When we are making a first decision *and* a second decision, we *multiply* to find the total number of ways. When we are making a decision in which the first choice *or* the second choice are valid choices, we *add* to find the total number of ways.

The formulas for permutations and combinations given in this section and in the previous section will be very useful in solving probability problems in the next section. Any difficulty in using these formulas usually comes from being unable to differentiate between them. Both permutations and combinations give the number of ways to choose r objects from a set of n objects. The differences between permutations and combinations are outlined in the following table.

Permutations	Combinations
Different orderings or arrangements of the r objects are different permutations.	Each choice or subset of r objects gives one combination. Order within the group of r objects does not matter.
$$P(n, r) = \frac{n!}{(n-r)!}$$	$$C(n, r) = \frac{n!}{(n-r)!\,r!}$$
Clue words: arrangement, schedule, order	Clue words: group, committee, set, sample
Order matters!	Order does not matter!

In the next examples, concentrate on recognizing which formula should be applied.

EXAMPLE 4 Permutations and Combinations

For each problem, tell whether permutations or combinations should be used to solve the problem.

(a) How many 4-digit code numbers are possible if no digits are repeated?

SOLUTION Since changing the order of the 4 digits results in a different code, use permutations.

(b) A sample of 3 light bulbs is randomly selected from a batch of 15. How many different samples are possible?

SOLUTION The order in which the 3 light bulbs are selected is not important. The sample is unchanged if the items are rearranged, so combinations should be used.

(c) In a baseball conference with 8 teams, how many games must be played so that each team plays every other team exactly once?

SOLUTION Selection of 2 teams for a game is an *unordered* subset of 2 from the set of 8 teams. Use combinations again.

(d) In how many ways can 4 patients be assigned to 6 different hospital rooms so that each patient has a private room?

YOUR TURN 3 Solve the problems in Example 4.

SOLUTION The room assignments are an *ordered* selection of 4 rooms from the 6 rooms. Exchanging the rooms of any 2 patients within a selection of 4 rooms gives a different assignment, so permutations should be used. **TRY YOUR TURN 3**

EXAMPLE 5 Promotions

A manager must select 4 employees for promotion; 12 employees are eligible.

(a) In how many ways can the 4 be chosen?

APPLY IT

SOLUTION Since there is no reason to differentiate among the 4 who are selected, use combinations.

$$C(12, 4) = \frac{12!}{8!\,4!} = 495$$

YOUR TURN 4 In how many ways can a committee of 3 be chosen from a group of 20 students? In how many ways can three officers (president, treasurer, and secretary) be selected from a group of 20 students?

(b) In how many ways can 4 employees be chosen (from 12) to be placed in 4 different jobs?

SOLUTION In this case, once a group of 4 is selected, they can be assigned in many different ways (or arrangements) to the 4 jobs. Therefore, this problem requires permutations.

$$P(12, 4) = \frac{12!}{8!} = 11,880$$

TRY YOUR TURN 4

FOR REVIEW

Example 6 involves a standard deck of 52 playing cards, as shown in Figure 17 in Chapter 7. Recall the discussion that accompanies the photograph.

EXAMPLE 6 **Playing Cards**

Five cards are dealt from a standard 52-card deck.

(a) How many such hands have only face cards?

SOLUTION The face cards are the king, queen, and jack of each suit. Since there are 4 suits, there are 12 face cards. The arrangement of the 5 cards is not important, so use combinations to get

$$C(12, 5) = \frac{12!}{7!\,5!} = 792.$$

(b) How many such hands have a full house of aces and eights (3 aces and 2 eights)?

SOLUTION The arrangement of the 3 aces or the 2 eights does not matter, so we use combinations. There are $C(4, 3)$ ways to get 3 aces from the four aces in the deck, and $C(4, 2)$ ways to get 2 eights. By the multiplication principle we get

$$C(4, 3) \cdot C(4, 2) = 4 \cdot 6 = 24.$$

(c) How many such hands have exactly 2 hearts?

SOLUTION There are 13 hearts in the deck, so the 2 hearts will be selected from those 13 cards. The other 3 cards must come from the remaining 39 cards that are not hearts. Use combinations and the multiplication principle to get

$$C(13, 2) \cdot C(39, 3) = 78 \cdot 9139 = 712{,}842.$$

Notice that the two numbers in red in the combinations add up to 52, the total number of cards, and the two numbers in blue add up to 5, the number of cards in a hand.

(d) How many such hands have cards of a single suit?

SOLUTION Since the arrangement of the 5 cards is not important, use combinations. The total number of ways that 5 cards of a particular suit of 13 cards can occur is $C(13, 5)$. There are four different suits, so the multiplication principle gives

$$4 \cdot C(13, 5) = 4 \cdot 1287 = 5148$$

ways to deal 5 cards of the same suit. **TRY YOUR TURN 5**

YOUR TURN 5 How many five card hands have exactly 2 aces?

As Example 6 shows, often both combinations and the multiplication principle must be used in the same problem.

EXAMPLE 7 **Soup**

To illustrate the differences between permutations and combinations in another way, suppose 2 cans of soup are to be selected from 4 cans on a shelf: noodle (N), bean (B), mushroom (M), and tomato (T). As shown in Figure 5(a), there are 12 ways to select 2 cans from the 4 cans if the order matters (if noodle first and bean second is considered different from bean, then

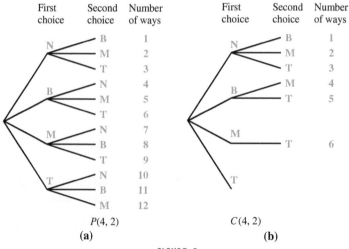

FIGURE 5

noodle, for example). On the other hand, if order is unimportant, then there are 6 ways to choose 2 cans of soup from the 4, as illustrated in Figure 5(b).

CAUTION It should be stressed that not all counting problems lend themselves to either permutations or combinations. Whenever a tree diagram or the multiplication principle can be used directly, it's often best to use it.

8.2 EXERCISES

1. Define combinations in your own words.

2. Explain the difference between a permutation and a combination.

Evaluate each combination.

3. $C(8, 3)$ 4. $C(12, 5)$

5. $C(44, 20)$ 6. $C(40, 18)$

7. $C(n, 0)$ 8. $C(n, n)$

9. $C(n, 1)$ 10. $C(n, n - 1)$

11. In how many ways can a hand of 6 clubs be chosen from an ordinary deck?

12. In how many ways can a hand of 6 red cards be chosen from an ordinary deck?

13. Five cards are marked with the numbers 1, 2, 3, 4, and 5, then shuffled, and 2 cards are drawn.

  a. How many different 2-card combinations are possible?

  b. How many 2-card hands contain a number less than 3?

14. An economics club has 31 members.

  a. If a committee of 4 is to be selected, in how many ways can the selection be made?

  b. In how many ways can a committee of at least 1 and at most 3 be selected?

15. Use a tree diagram for the following.

  a. Find the number of ways 2 letters can be chosen from the set {L, M, N} if order is important and repetition is allowed.

  b. Reconsider part a if no repeats are allowed.

  c. Find the number of combinations of 3 elements taken 2 at a time. Does this answer differ from part a or b?

16. Repeat Exercise 15 using the set {L, M, N, P}.

In Exercises 17–24, decide whether each exercise involves permutations or combinations, and then solve the problem.

17. In a club with 9 male and 11 female members, how many 5-member committees can be chosen that have

  a. all men?   **b.** all women?

  c. 3 men and 2 women?

18. In Exercise 17, how many committees can be selected that have

  a. at least 4 women?   **b.** no more than 2 men?

19. In a game of musical chairs, 12 children will sit in 11 chairs arranged in a row (one will be left out). In how many ways can

this happen, if we count rearrangements of the children in the chairs as different outcomes?

20. A group of 3 students is to be selected from a group of 14 students to take part in a class in cell biology.

  a. In how many ways can this be done?

  b. In how many ways can the group who will not take part be chosen?

21. Marbles are being drawn without replacement from a bag containing 16 marbles.

  a. How many samples of 2 marbles can be drawn?

  b. How many samples of 4 marbles can be drawn?

  c. If the bag contains 3 yellow, 4 white, and 9 blue marbles, how many samples of 2 marbles can be drawn in which both marbles are blue?

22. There are 7 rotten apples in a crate of 26 apples.

  a. How many samples of 3 apples can be drawn from the crate?

  b. How many samples of 3 could be drawn in which all 3 are rotten?

  c. How many samples of 3 could be drawn in which there are two good apples and one rotten one?

23. A bag contains 5 black, 1 red, and 3 yellow jelly beans; you take 3 at random. How many samples are possible in which the jelly beans are

  a. all black?   **b.** all red?

  c. all yellow?   **d.** 2 black and 1 red?

  e. 2 black and 1 yellow?   **f.** 2 yellow and 1 black?

  g. 2 red and 1 yellow?

24. In how many ways can 5 out of 9 plants be arranged in a row on a windowsill?

25. Show that $C(n, r) = C(n, n - r)$.

26. Padlocks with digit dials are often referred to as "combination locks." According to the mathematical definition of combination, is this an accurate description? Explain.

27. The following problem was posed on National Public Radio's *Weekend Edition*: In how many points can 6 circles intersect? *Source: National Public Radio.*

  a. Find the answer for 6 circles.

  b. Find the general answer for *n* circles.

28. How many different dominoes can be formed from the numbers 0...6? (*Hint:* A domino may have the same number of dots on both halves of it or it may have a different number of dots on each half.)

APPLICATIONS

Business and Economics

29. Work Assignments From a group of 8 newly hired office assistants, 3 are selected. Each of these 3 assistants will be assigned to a different manager. In how many ways can they be selected and assigned?

30. Assembly Line Sampling Five items are to be randomly selected from the first 50 items on an assembly line to determine the defect rate. How many different samples of 5 items can be chosen?

31. Sales Schedules A salesperson has the names of 6 prospects.

a. In how many ways can she arrange her schedule if she calls on all 6?

b. In how many ways can she arrange her schedule if she can call on only 4 of the 6?

32. Worker Grievances A group of 9 workers decides to send a delegation of 3 to their supervisor to discuss their grievances.

a. How many delegations are possible?

b. If it is decided that a particular worker must be in the delegation, how many different delegations are possible?

c. If there are 4 women and 5 men in the group, how many delegations would include at least 1 woman?

33. Hamburger Variety Hamburger Hut sells regular hamburgers as well as a larger burger. Either type can include cheese, relish, lettuce, tomato, mustard, or catsup.

a. How many different hamburgers can be ordered with exactly three extras?

b. How many different regular hamburgers can be ordered with exactly three extras?

c. How many different regular hamburgers can be ordered with at least five extras?

34. Ice Cream Flavors Baskin-Robbins advertises that it has 31 flavors of ice cream.

a. How many different double-scoop cones can be made? Assume that the order of the scoops matters.

b. How many different triple-scoop cones can be made?

c. How many different double-scoop cones can be made if order doesn't matter?

Life Sciences

35. Research Participants From a group of 16 smokers and 22 nonsmokers, a researcher wants to randomly select 8 smokers and 8 nonsmokers for a study. In how many ways can the study group be selected?

36. Plant Hardiness In an experiment on plant hardiness, a researcher gathers 6 wheat plants, 3 barley plants, and 2 rye plants. She wishes to select 4 plants at random.

a. In how many ways can this be done?

b. In how many ways can this be done if exactly 2 wheat plants must be included?

Social Sciences

37. Legislative Committee A legislative committee consists of 5 Democrats and 4 Republicans. A delegation of 3 is to be selected to visit a small Pacific island republic.

a. How many different delegations are possible?

b. How many delegations would have all Democrats?

c. How many delegations would have 2 Democrats and 1 Republican?

d. How many delegations would include at least 1 Republican?

38. Political Committee From 10 names on a ballot, 4 will be elected to a political party committee. In how many ways can the committee of 4 be formed if each person will have a different responsibility, and different assignments of responsibility are considered different committees?

39. Judges When Paul Martinek, publisher of *Lawyers Weekly USA*, was a guest on the television news program *The O'Reilly Factor*, he discussed a decision by a three-judge panel, chosen at random from judges in the Ninth Circuit in California. The judges had ruled that the mandatory recitation of the Pledge of Allegience is unconstitutional because of the phrase "under God." According to Martinek, "Because there are 45 judges in the Ninth Circuit, there are 3000 different combinations of three-judge panels." Is this true? If not, what is the correct number? *Source: Mathematics Teacher.*

General Interest

40. Bridge How many different 13-card bridge hands can be selected from an ordinary deck?

41. Poker Five cards are chosen from an ordinary deck to form a hand in poker. In how many ways is it possible to get the following results?

a. 4 queens   **b.** No face card

c. Exactly 2 face cards   **d.** At least 2 face cards

e. 1 heart, 2 diamonds, and 2 clubs

42. Poker In poker, a flush consists of 5 cards with the same suit, such as 5 diamonds.

a. Find the number of ways of getting a flush consisting of cards with values from 5 to 10 by listing all the possibilities.

b. Find the number of ways of getting a flush consisting of cards with values from 5 to 10 by using combinations.

43. Baseball If a baseball coach has 5 good hitters and 4 poor hitters on the bench and chooses 3 players at random, in how many ways can he choose at least 2 good hitters?

44. Softball The coach of the Morton Valley Softball Team has 6 good hitters and 8 poor hitters. He chooses 3 hitters at random.

a. In how many ways can he choose 2 good hitters and 1 poor hitter?

b. In how many ways can he choose 3 good hitters?

c. In how many ways can he choose at least 2 good hitters?

45. Flower Selection Five orchids from a collection of 20 are to be selected for a flower show.

a. In how many ways can this be done?

b. In how many ways can the 5 be selected if 2 special plants from the 20 must be included?

46. Lottery A state lottery game requires that you pick 6 different numbers from 1 to 99. If you pick all 6 winning numbers, you win the jackpot.

  a. How many ways are there to choose 6 numbers if order is not important?

  b. How many ways are there to choose 6 numbers if order matters?

47. Lottery In Exercise 46, if you pick 5 of the 6 numbers correctly, you win $250,000. In how many ways can you pick exactly 5 of the 6 winning numbers without regard to order?

48. Committees Suppose that out of 19 members of a club, two committees are to be formed. A nominating committee is to consist of 7 members, and a public relations committee is to consist of 5 members. No one can be on both committees.

  a. Calculate the number of ways that the two committees can be formed, assuming that the nominating committee is formed first.

  b. Calculate the number of ways that the two committees can be formed, assuming that the public relations committee is formed first. Verify that this answer is the same as that of part a.

  c. Suppose the 7 members of the nominating committee wear red T-shirts, the 5 members of the public relations committee wear yellow T-shirts, and the remaining members of the club wear white T-shirts. A photographer lines up the members of the club to take a picture, but the picture is so blurry that people wearing the same color T-shirt are indistinguishable. In how many distinguishable ways can the club members line up? Explain why this answer is the same as the answers to parts a and b.

49. Committee A small department of 5 people decides to form a hiring committee. The only restriction on the size of the committee is that it must have at least 2 members.

  a. Calculate the number of different committees possible by adding up the number of committees of different sizes.

  b. Calculate the number of different committees possible by taking the total number of subsets of the 5 members and subtracting the number of committees that are invalid because they have too few members.

50. License Plates Officials from a particular state are considering a new type of license plate consisting of three letters followed by three numbers. If the letters cannot be repeated and must be in alphabetical order, calculate the number of possible distinct license plates.

51. Passwords A certain website requires users to log on using a security password.

  a. If passwords must consist of six letters, followed by a single digit, determine the total number of possible distinct passwords.

  b. If passwords must consist of six non-repetitive letters, followed by a single digit, determine the total number of possible distinct passwords.

52. Pizza Varieties A television commercial for Little Caesars pizza announced that with the purchase of two pizzas, one could receive free any combination of up to five toppings on each pizza. The commercial shows a young child waiting in line at Little Caesars who calculates that there are 1,048,576 possibilities for the toppings on the two pizzas. *Source: The Mathematics Teacher.*

  a. Verify the child's calculation. Use the fact that Little Caesars has 11 toppings to choose from. Assume that the order of the two pizzas matters; that is, if the first pizza has combination 1 and the second pizza has combination 2, that is different from combination 2 on the first pizza and combination 1 on the second.

  b. In a letter to *The Mathematics Teacher*, Joseph F. Heiser argued that the two combinations described in part a should be counted as the same, so the child has actually overcounted. Give the number of possibilities if the order of the two pizzas doesn't matter.

53. Pizza In an ad for Pizza Hut, Jessica Simpson explains to the Muppets that there are more than 6 million possibilities for their 4forAll Pizza. Griffin Weber and Glenn Weber wrote an article explaining that the number of possibilities is far more than 6 million, as described below. *Source: The College Mathematics Journal.*

  a. Each pizza can have up to 3 toppings, out of 17 possible choices, or can be one of four specialty pizzas. Calculate the number of different pizzas possible.

  b. Out of the total possible pizzas calculated in the first part of this exercise, a 4forAll Pizza consists of four pizzas in a box. Keeping in mind that the four pizzas could all be different, or there could be two or three different pizzas in the box, or all four pizzas could be the same, calculate the total number of 4forAll Pizzas possible.

  c. The article considers another way of counting the number in part b. Suppose that only 8 pizzas were available, and they were listed in a row with lines separating each type, as in the following diagram:

$$A|B|C|D|E|F|G|H.$$

A person orders 4 pizzas by placing 4 X's in the desired places on the diagram, after which the letters can be ignored. For example, an order for 2 of A, 1 of C, and 1 of G would look like the following diagram.

$$XX||X||||X|$$

The number of ways this can be done is then the number of ways of arranging 11 objects, 4 of which are X and the other 7 of which are vertical lines, or

$$C(11, 4) = 330.$$

Use similar reasoning to verify the answer to part b.

54. Cereal The Post Corporation once introduced the cereal, *Create a Crunch*™, in which the consumers could combine ingredients to create their own unique cereal. Each box contained 8 packets of food goods. There were four types of cereal: Frosted Alpha Bits®, Cocoa Pebbles®, Fruity Pebbles®, and

Honey Comb®. Also included in the box were four "Add-Ins": granola, blue rice cereal, marshmallows, and sprinkles.

a. What is the total number of breakfasts that could be made if a breakfast is defined as any one or more cereals or add-ins?

b. If Sara Ouellette chose to mix one type of cereal with one add-in, how many different breakfasts could she make?

c. If Kristen Schmitt chose to mix two types of cereal with three add-ins, how many different breakfasts could she make?

d. If Matthew Pastier chose to mix at least one type of cereal with at least one type of add-in, how many breakfasts could he make?

e. If Inga Moffitt's favorite cereal is Fruity Pebbles®, how many different cereals could she make if each of her mixtures must include this cereal?

55. Appetizers Applebee's restaurant recently advertised "Ultimate Trios," where the customer was able to pick any three trio-sized appetizers from a list of nine options. The ad claimed that there were over 200 combinations.

a. If each customer's selection must be a different item, how many meal combinations are possible?

b. If each customer can select the same item two or even three times in each trio, how many different trios are possible?

c. Using the answers to parts a and b, discuss that restaurant's claim.

d. Two of the trio items, the Buffalo chicken wings and the boneless Buffalo wings, each have five different sauce options. This implies that there are actually 17 different trio choices that are available to a customer. In this scenario, how many different trio meal combinations are possible? (Assume that each of the three selected items is different.)

e. How many different trios are possible if 2 of the items are different flavored boneless Buffalo wings? (Assume that the third item is not a boneless Buffalo wing.)

56. Football Writer Gregg Easterbrook, discussing ESPN's unsuccessful attempt to predict the winners for the six National Football League (NFL) divisions and the six wild-card slots, claimed that there were 180 different ways to make this forecast. Reader

Milton Eisner wrote in to tell him that the actual number is much larger. To make the calculation, note that at the time the NFL consisted of two conferences, each of which consisted of three divisions. Five of the divisions had five teams, while the other had six. There was one winner from each of the six divisions, plus three wild-card slots from each of the two conferences. How many ways could the six division winners and six wild-card slots have been chosen? *Source: Slate Magazine.*

57. Music In the opera *Amahl and the Night Visitors,* the shepherds sing a chorus involving 18 different names, a challenge for singers trying to remember the names in the correct order. (Two of the three authors of this textbook have sung this chorus in public.)

a. In how many ways can the names be arranged?

b. Not all the arrangements of names in part a could be sung, because 10 of the names have 3 syllables, 4 have 2 syllables, and 4 have 4 syllables. Of the 6 lines in the chorus, 4 lines consist of a 3-syllable name repeated, followed by a 2-syllable and then a 4-syllable name (e.g., Emily, Emily, Michael, Bartholomew), and 2 lines consist of a 3-syllable name repeated, followed by two more 3-syllable names (e.g., Josephine, Josephine, Angela, Jeremy). No names are repeated except where we've indicated. (If you think this is confusing, you should try memorizing the chorus.) How many arrangements of the names could fit this pattern?

58. Olympics In recent Winter Olympics, there were 12 judges for each part of the women's figure skating program, but the scores of only 9 of the judges were randomly selected for the final results. *Source: The New York Times.*

a. In how many ways can the 9 judges whose scores are counted be selected?

b. Women's figure skating consists of a short program and a long program, with different judges for each part. How many different sets of judges' scores are possible for the entire event?

YOUR TURN ANSWERS

1. 210 **2.** 1820 **3. a.** 5040 **b.** 455 **c.** 28 **d.** 360
4. 1140; 6840 **5.** 103,776

8.3 Probability Applications of Counting Principles

APPLY IT If 3 engines are tested from a shipping container packed with 12 diesel engines, 2 of which are defective, what is the probability that at least 1 of the defective engines will be found (in which case the container will not be shipped)?

This problem, which is solved in Example 3, could theoretically be solved with a tree diagram, but it would require a tree with a large number of branches. Many of the probability problems involving *dependent* events that were solved earlier by using tree diagrams can also be solved by using permutations or combinations. Permutations and combinations are especially helpful when the numbers involved are large.

To compare the method of using permutations or combinations with the method of tree diagrams used in Section 7.5, the first example repeats Example 7 from that section.

EXAMPLE 1 Environmental Inspections

The Environmental Protection Agency is considering inspecting 6 plants for environmental compliance: 3 in Chicago, 2 in Los Angeles, and 1 in New York. Due to a lack of inspectors, they decide to inspect 2 plants selected at random, 1 this month and 1 next month, with each plant equally likely to be selected, but no plant is selected twice. What is the probability that 1 Chicago plant and 1 Los Angeles plant are selected?

SOLUTION

Method 1
Multiplication Principle

To find the probability, we use the probability fraction, $P(E) = n(E)/n(S)$, where E is the event that 1 Chicago plant and 1 Los Angeles plant is selected and S is the sample space. We will use the multiplication principle since the plants are selected one at a time, and the first is inspected this month while the second is inspected next month.

To calculate the numerator, we find the number of elements in E. There are two ways to select a Chicago plant and a Los Angeles plant: Chicago first and Los Angeles second, or Los Angeles first and Chicago second. The Chicago plant can be selected from the 3 Chicago plants in $C(3, 1)$ ways, and the Los Angeles plant can be selected from the 2 Los Angeles plants in $C(2, 1)$ ways. Using the multiplication principle, we can select a Chicago plant then a Los Angeles plant in $C(3, 1) \cdot C(2, 1)$ ways, and a Los Angeles plant then a Chicago plant in $C(2, 1) \cdot C(3, 1)$ ways. By the union rule, we can select one Chicago plant and one Los Angeles plant in

$$C(3, 1) \cdot C(2, 1) + C(2, 1) \cdot C(3, 1) \text{ ways,}$$

giving the numerator of the probability fraction.

For the denominator, we calculate the number of elements in the sample space. There are 6 ways to select the first plant and 5 ways to select the second, for a total of $6 \cdot 5$ ways. The required probability is

$$P(1 \text{ C and } 1 \text{ LA}) = \frac{C(3, 1) \cdot C(2, 1) + C(2, 1) \cdot C(3, 1)}{6 \cdot 5}$$

$$= \frac{3 \cdot 2 + 2 \cdot 3}{6 \cdot 5} = \frac{12}{30} = \frac{2}{5}.$$

This agrees with the answer found in Example 7 of Section 7.5.

FOR REVIEW

The use of combinations to solve probability problems depends on the basic probability principle introduced in Section 7.3 and repeated here:
Let S be a sample space with equally likely outcomes, and let event E be a subset of S. Then the probability that event E occurs, written $P(E)$, is

$$P(E) = \frac{n(E)}{n(S)},$$

where $n(E)$ and $n(S)$ represent the number of elements in sets E and S.

Method 2
Combinations

This example can be solved more simply by observing that the probability that 1 Chicago plant and 1 Los Angeles plant are selected should not depend upon the order in which the plants are selected, so we may use combinations. The numerator is simply the number of ways of selecting 1 Chicago plant out of 3 Chicago plants and 1 Los Angeles plant out of 2 Los Angeles plants. The denominator is just the number of ways of selecting 2 plants out of 6. Then

$$P(1 \text{ C and } 1 \text{ LA}) = \frac{C(3, 1) \cdot C(2, 1)}{C(6, 2)} = \frac{6}{15} = \frac{2}{5}.$$

This helps explain why combinations tend to be used more often than permutations in probability. Even if order matters in the original problem, it is sometimes possible to ignore order and use combinations. Be careful to do this only when the final result does not depend on the order of events. Order often does matter. (If you don't believe this, try getting dressed tomorrow morning and then taking your shower.)

Method 3
Tree Diagram

In Section 7.5, we found this probability using the tree diagram shown in Figure 6 on the next page. Two of the branches correspond to drawing 1 Chicago plant and 1 Los Angeles plant. The probability for each branch is calculated by multiplying the probabilities along

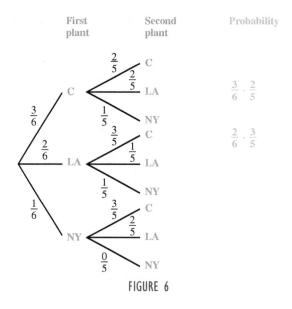

First plant   Second plant   Probability

FIGURE 6

YOUR TURN 1 In Example 1, what is the probability that 1 New York plant and 1 Chicago plant are selected?

the branch, as we did in the previous chapter. The resulting probabilities for the two branches are then added, giving the result

$$P(1 \text{ C and } 1 \text{ LA}) = \frac{3}{6} \cdot \frac{2}{5} + \frac{2}{6} \cdot \frac{3}{5} = \frac{2}{5}.$$

TRY YOUR TURN 1

CAUTION   The problems in the first two sections of this chapter asked how many ways a certain operation can be done. The problems in this section ask what is the probability that a certain event occurs; the solution involves answering questions about how many ways the event and the operation can be done.

- If a problem asks how many ways something can be done, the answer must be a nonnegative integer.
- If a problem asks for a probability, the answer must be a number between 0 and 1.

EXAMPLE 2   Nursing

From a group of 22 nurses, 4 are to be selected to present a list of grievances to management.

(a) In how many ways can this be done?

SOLUTION   Four nurses from a group of 22 can be selected in $C(22, 4)$ ways. (Use combinations, since the group of 4 is an unordered set.)

$$C(22, 4) = \frac{22!}{18! \, 4!} = \frac{(22)(21)(20)(19)}{(4)(3)(2)(1)} = 7315$$

There are 7315 ways to choose 4 people from 22.

(b) One of the nurses is Lori Hales. Find the probability that Hales will be among the 4 selected.

SOLUTION   The probability that Hales will be selected is given by $n(E)/n(S)$, where E is the event that the chosen group includes Hales, and S is the sample space for the experiment of choosing a group of 4. There is only $C(1, 1) = 1$ way to choose Hales. The number of ways that the other 3 nurses can be chosen from the remaining 21 nurses is

$$C(21, 3) = \frac{21!}{18! \, 3!} = 1330.$$

The probability that Hales will be one of the 4 chosen is

$$P(\text{Hales is chosen}) = \frac{n(E)}{n(S)} = \frac{C(1,1) \cdot C(21,3)}{C(22,4)} = \frac{1330}{7315} \approx 0.1818.$$

Notice that the two numbers in red in the numerator, 1 and 21, add up to the number in red in the denominator, 22. This indicates that the 22 nurses have been split into two groups, one of size 1 (Hales) and the other of size 21 (the other nurses). Similarly, the green numbers indicate that the 4 nurses chosen consist of two groups of size 1 (Hales) and size 3 (the other nurses chosen).

YOUR TURN 2 If 8 of the 22 nurses are men in Example 2, what is the probability that exactly 2 men are among the 4 nurses selected?

(c) Find the probability that Hales will not be selected.

SOLUTION The probability that Hales will not be chosen is $1 - 0.1818 = 0.8182$.

TRY YOUR TURN 2

EXAMPLE 3 Diesel Engines

When shipping diesel engines abroad, it is common to pack 12 engines in one container. Suppose that a company has received complaints from its customers that many of the engines arrive in nonworking condition. To help solve this problem, the company decides to make a spot check of containers after loading. The company will test 3 engines from a container at random; if any of the 3 are nonworking, the container will not be shipped until each engine in it is checked. Suppose a given container has 2 nonworking engines. Find the probability that the container will not be shipped.

APPLY IT

SOLUTION The container will not be shipped if the sample of 3 engines contains 1 or 2 defective engines. If $P(1 \text{ defective})$ represents the probability of exactly 1 defective engine in the sample, then

$$P(\text{not shipping}) = P(1 \text{ defective}) + P(2 \text{ defective}).$$

There are $C(12,3)$ ways to choose the 3 engines for testing:

$$C(12,3) = \frac{12!}{9! \, 3!} = 220.$$

There are $C(2,1)$ ways of choosing 1 defective engine from the 2 in the container, and for each of these ways, there are $C(10,2)$ ways of choosing 2 good engines from among the 10 in the container. By the multiplication principle, there are

$$C(2,1) \cdot C(10,2) = \frac{2!}{1! \, 1!} \cdot \frac{10!}{8! \, 2!} = 2 \cdot 45 = 90$$

ways of choosing a sample of 3 engines containing 1 defective engine with

$$P(1 \text{ defective}) = \frac{90}{220} = \frac{9}{22}.$$

There are $C(2,2)$ ways of choosing 2 defective engines from the 2 defective engines in the container, and $C(10,1)$ ways of choosing 1 good engine from among the 10 good engines, for

$$C(2,2) \cdot C(10,1) = 1 \cdot 10 = 10$$

ways of choosing a sample of 3 engines containing 2 defective engines. Finally,

$$P(2 \text{ defective}) = \frac{10}{220} = \frac{1}{22}$$

and

$$P(\text{not shipping}) = P(1 \text{ defective}) + P(2 \text{ defective})$$
$$= \frac{9}{22} + \frac{1}{22} = \frac{10}{22} \approx 0.4545.$$

YOUR TURN 3 Suppose the container in Example 3 has 4 nonworking engines. Find the probability that the container will not be shipped.

Notice that the probability is $1 - 0.4545 = 0.5455$ that the container will be shipped, even though it has 2 defective engines. The management must decide whether this probability is acceptable; if not, it may be necessary to test more than 3 engines from a container.

TRY YOUR TURN 3

─ FOR REVIEW ─

Recall from Section 7.4 that if E and E' are complements, then $P(E') = 1 - P(E)$. In Example 3, the event "0 defective in the sample" is the complement of the event "1 or 2 defective in the sample," since there are only 0 or 1 or 2 defective engines possible in the sample of 3 engines.

Observe that in Example 3, the complement of finding 1 or 2 defective engines is finding 0 defective engines. Then instead of finding the sum $P(1\text{ defective}) + P(2\text{ defective})$, the result in Example 3 could be found as $1 - P(0\text{ defective})$.

$$P(\text{not shipping}) = 1 - P(0\text{ defective in sample})$$
$$= 1 - \frac{C(2,0) \cdot C(10,3)}{C(12,3)}$$
$$= 1 - \frac{1(120)}{220}$$
$$= 1 - \frac{120}{220} = \frac{100}{220} \approx 0.4545$$

EXAMPLE 4 **Poker**

In a common form of the card game *poker*, a hand of 5 cards is dealt to each player from a deck of 52 cards. There are a total of

$$C(52,5) = \frac{52!}{47!\,5!} = 2{,}598{,}960$$

such hands possible. Find the probability of getting each of the following hands.

(a) A hand containing only hearts, called a *heart flush*

SOLUTION There are 13 hearts in a deck, with

$$C(13,5) = \frac{13!}{8!\,5!} = \frac{(13)(12)(11)(10)(9)}{(5)(4)(3)(2)(1)} = 1287$$

different hands containing only hearts. The probability of a heart flush is

$$P(\text{heart flush}) = \frac{C(13,5) \cdot C(39,0)}{C(52,5)} = \frac{1287}{2{,}598{,}960} \approx 0.0004952.$$

You don't really need the $C(39,0)$, since this just equals 1, but it might help to remind you that you are choosing none of the 39 cards that remain after the hearts are removed.

(b) A flush of any suit (5 cards of the same suit)

SOLUTION There are 4 suits in a deck, so

$$P(\text{flush}) = 4 \cdot P(\text{heart flush}) = 4 \cdot 0.0004952 \approx 0.001981.$$

(c) A full house of aces and eights (3 aces and 2 eights)

SOLUTION There are $C(4,3)$ ways to choose 3 aces from among the 4 in the deck, and $C(4,2)$ ways to choose 2 eights.

$$P(3\text{ aces, }2\text{ eights}) = \frac{C(4,3) \cdot C(4,2) \cdot C(44,0)}{C(52,5)} = \frac{4 \cdot 6 \cdot 1}{2{,}598{,}960} \approx 0.000009234$$

(d) Any full house (3 cards of one value, 2 of another)

SOLUTION

Method I
Standard Procedure

The 13 values in a deck give 13 choices for the first value. As in part (c), there are $C(4,3)$ ways to choose the 3 cards from among the 4 cards that have that value. This leaves 12 choices for the second value (order *is* important here, since a full house of 3 aces and 2 eights is not the same as a full house of 3 eights and 2 aces). From the 4 cards that have the second value, there are $C(4, 2)$ ways to choose 2. The probability of any full house is then

$$P(\text{full house}) = \frac{13 \cdot C(4, 3) \cdot 12 \cdot C(4, 2)}{2,598,960} \approx 0.001441.$$

Method 2
Alternative Procedure

As an alternative way of counting the numerator, first count the number of different values in the hand.* Since there are 13 values from which to choose, and we need 2 different values (one for the set of 3 cards and one for the set of 2), there are $C(13, 2)$ ways to choose the values. Next, of the two values chosen, select the value for which there are 3 cards, which can be done $C(2, 1)$ ways. This automatically determines that the other value is the one for which there are 2 cards. Next, choose the suits for each value. For the value with 3 cards, there are $C(4, 3)$ values of the suits, and for the value with 2 cards, there are $C(4, 2)$ values. Putting this all together,

$$P(\text{full house}) = \frac{C(13, 2) \cdot C(2, 1) \cdot C(4, 3) \cdot C(4, 2)}{2,598,960} \approx 0.001441.$$

YOUR TURN 4 In Example 4, what is the probability of a hand containing two pairs, one of aces and the other of kings? (This hand contains 2 aces, 2 kings, and a fifth card that is neither an ace nor a king.)

TRY YOUR TURN 4

EXAMPLE 5 **Letters**

Each of the letters w, y, o, m, i, n, and g is placed on a separate slip of paper. A slip is pulled out, and its letter is recorded in the order in which the slip was drawn. This is done four times.

(a) If the slip is not replaced after the letter is recorded, find the probability that the word "wing" is formed.

SOLUTION The sample space contains all possible arrangements of the seven letters, taken four at a time. Since order matters, use *permutations* to find the number of arrangements in the sample space.

$$P(7, 4) = \frac{7!}{3!} = 7 \cdot 6 \cdot 5 \cdot 4 = 840$$

Since there is only one way that the word "wing" can be formed, the required probability is $1/840 \approx 0.001190$.

YOUR TURN 5 Find the probability that the word "now" is formed if 3 slips are chosen without replacement in Example 5. Find the probability that the word "now" is formed if 3 slips are chosen with replacement.

(b) If the slip is replaced after the letter is recorded, find the probability that the word "wing" is formed.

SOLUTION Since the letters can be repeated, there are 7 possible outcomes for each draw of the slip. To calculate the number of arrangements in the sample space, use the *multiplication principle*. The number of arrangements in the sample space is $7^4 = 2401$, and the required probability is $1/2401 \approx 0.0004165$.

TRY YOUR TURN 5

EXAMPLE 6 **Birthdays**

Suppose a group of n people is in a room. Find the probability that at least 2 of the people have the same birthday.

SOLUTION "Same birthday" refers to the month and the day, not necessarily the same year. Also, ignore leap years, and assume that each day in the year is equally likely as a birthday. To see how to proceed, we first look at the case in which $n = 5$ and find the probability that *no 2 people* from among 5 people have the same birthday. There are 365 different birthdays possible for the first of the 5 people, 364 for the second (so that the people have different birthdays), 363 for the third, and so on. The number of ways the

*We learned this approach from Professor Peter Grassi of Hofstra University.

5 people can have different birthdays is thus the number of permutations of 365 days taken 5 at a time or

$$P(365, 5) = 365 \cdot 364 \cdot 363 \cdot 362 \cdot 361.$$

The number of ways that 5 people can have the same birthday or different birthdays is

$$365 \cdot 365 \cdot 365 \cdot 365 \cdot 365 = (365)^5.$$

Finally, the *probability* that none of the 5 people have the same birthday is

$$\frac{P(365, 5)}{365^5} = \frac{365 \cdot 364 \cdot 363 \cdot 362 \cdot 361}{365 \cdot 365 \cdot 365 \cdot 365 \cdot 365} \approx 0.9729.$$

The probability that at least 2 of the 5 people *do* have the same birthday is $1 - 0.9729 = 0.0271$.

Now this result can be extended to more than 5 people. Generalizing, the probability that no 2 people among n people have the same birthday is

$$\frac{P(365, n)}{365^n}.$$

The probability that at least 2 of the n people *do* have the same birthday is

$$1 - \frac{P(365, n)}{365^n}.$$

The following table shows this probability for various values of n.

Number of People, n	Probability That Two Have the Same Birthday
5	0.0271
10	0.1169
15	0.2529
20	0.4114
22	0.4757
23	0.5073
25	0.5687
30	0.7063
35	0.8144
40	0.8912
50	0.9704
366	1

The probability that 2 people among 23 have the same birthday is 0.5073, a little more than half. Many people are surprised at this result; it seems that a larger number of people should be required.

FIGURE 7

TECHNOLOGY NOTE

Using a graphing calculator, we can graph the probability formula in the previous example as a function of n, but care must be taken that the graphing calculator evaluates the function at integer points. Figure 7 was produced on a TI-84 Plus by letting $Y_1 = 1 - (365 \text{ nPr } X)/365^{\wedge}X$ on $0 \le x \le 47$. (This domain ensures integer values for x.) Notice that the graph does not extend past $x = 39$. This is because $P(365, n)$ and 365^n are too large for the calculator when $n \ge 40$.

An alternative way of doing the calculations that does not run into such large numbers is based on the concept of conditional probability. The probability that the first person's birthday does not match any so far is $365/365$. The probability that the second person's birthday does not match the first's is $364/365$. The probability that the third person's birthday does not match the first's or the second's is 363/365. By the product rule of probability, the probability that none of the first 3 people have matching birthdays is

$$\frac{365}{365} \cdot \frac{364}{365} \cdot \frac{363}{365}.$$

Similarly, the probability that no two people in a group of 40 have the same birthday is

$$\frac{365}{365} \cdot \frac{364}{365} \cdot \frac{363}{365} \cdots \cdots \frac{326}{365}.$$

This probability can be calculated (and then subtracted from 1 to get the probability we seek) without overflowing the calculator by multiplying each fraction times the next, rather then trying to compute the entire numerator and the entire denominator. The calculations are somewhat tedious to do by hand but can be programmed on a graphing calculator or computer.

As we saw in Examples 1 and 4(d), probability can sometimes be calculated in more than one way. We now look at one more example of this.

EXAMPLE 7   Fruit

Ray and Nate are arranging a row of fruit at random on a table. They have 5 apples, 6 oranges, and 7 lemons. What is the probability that all fruit of the same kind are together?

SOLUTION

Method 1
Distinguishable Permutations

Ray can't tell individual pieces of fruit of the same kind apart. All apples look the same to him, as do all oranges and all lemons. So in the denominator of the probability, he calculates the number of distinguishable ways to arrange the 18 pieces of fruit, given that all apples are indistinguishable, as are all oranges and all lemons.

$$\frac{18!}{5!\,6!\,7!} = 14{,}702{,}688$$

As for the numerator, the only choice is how to arrange the 3 kinds of fruit, for which there are $3! = 6$ ways. Thus

$$P(\text{all fruit of the same kind are together}) = \frac{6}{14{,}702{,}688} \approx 4.081 \times 10^{-7}.$$

Method 2
Permutations

Nate has better eyesight than Ray and can tell the individual pieces of fruit apart. So in the denominator of the probability, he calculates the number of ways to arrange the 18 pieces of fruit, which is

$$18! \approx 6.4024 \times 10^{15}.$$

For the numerator, he first must choose how to arrange the 3 kinds of fruit, for which there are 3! ways. Then there are 5! ways to arrange the apples, 6! ways to arrange the oranges, and 7! ways to arrange the lemons, for a total number of possibilities of

$$3!\,5!\,6!\,7! = 2{,}612{,}736{,}000.$$

Therefore,

YOUR TURN 6   If Ray and Nate arrange 2 kiwis, 3 apricots, 4 pineapples, and 5 coconuts in a row at random, what is the probability that all fruit of the same kind are together?

$$P(\text{all fruit of the same kind are together}) = \frac{2{,}612{,}736{,}000}{6.4024 \times 10^{15}} \approx 4.081 \times 10^{-7}.$$

The results for Method 1 and Method 2 are the same. The probability does not depend on whether a person can distinguish individual pieces of the same kind of fruit.

TRY YOUR TURN 6

8.3 EXERCISES

A basket contains 7 red apples and 4 yellow apples. A sample of 3 apples is drawn. Find the probabilities that the sample contains the following.

1. All red apples

2. All yellow apples

3. 2 yellow and 1 red apple

4. More red than yellow apples

In a club with 9 male and 11 female members, a 5-member committee will be randomly chosen. Find the probability that the committee contains the following.

5. All men

6. All women

7. 3 men and 2 women

8. 2 men and 3 women

9. At least 4 women

10. No more than 2 men

Two cards are drawn at random from an ordinary deck of 52 cards.

11. How many 2-card hands are possible?

Find the probability that the 2-card hand described above contains the following.

12. 2 aces

13. At least 1 ace

14. All spades

15. 2 cards of the same suit

16. Only face cards

17. No face cards

18. No card higher than 8 (count ace as 1)

Twenty-six slips of paper are each marked with a different letter of the alphabet and placed in a basket. A slip is pulled out, its letter recorded (in the order in which the slip was drawn), and the slip is replaced. This is done 5 times. Find the probabilities that the following "words" are formed.

19. Chuck

20. A word that starts with "p"

21. A word with no repetition of letters

22. A word that contains no "*x*," "*y*," or "*z*"

23. Discuss the relative merits of using tree diagrams versus combinations to solve probability problems. When would each approach be most appropriate?

24. Several examples in this section used the rule $P(E') = 1 - P(E)$. Explain the advantage (especially in Example 6) of using this rule.

For Exercises 25–28, refer to Example 6 in this section.

25. A total of 43 men have served as president through 2010.* Set up the probability that, if 43 men were selected at random, at least 2 have the same birthday.[†]

26. Set up the probability that at least 2 of the 100 U.S. senators have the same birthday.

27. What is the probability that at least 2 of the 435 members of the House of Representatives have the same birthday?

28. Argue that the probability that in a group of *n* people *exactly one pair* have the same birthday is

$$C(n, 2) \cdot \frac{P(365, n - 1)}{365^n}.$$

29. After studying all night for a final exam, a bleary-eyed student randomly grabs 2 socks from a drawer containing 9 black, 6 brown, and 2 blue socks, all mixed together. What is the probability that she grabs a matched pair?

30. Three crows, 4 blue jays, and 5 starlings sit in a random order on a section of telephone wire. Find the probability that birds of a feather flock together, that is, that all birds of the same type are sitting together.

31. If the letters l, i, t, t, l, and e are chosen at random, what is the probability that they spell the word "little"?

32. If the letters M, i, s, s, i, s, s, i, p, p, and i are chosen at random, what is the probability that they spell the word "Mississippi"?

33. An elevator has 4 passengers and stops at 7 floors. It is equally likely that a person will get off at any one of the 7 floors. Find the probability that at least 2 passengers leave at the same floor. (*Hint:* Compare this with the birthday problem.)

34. On National Public Radio, the *Weekend Edition* program posed the following probability problem: Given a certain number of balls, of which some are blue, pick 5 at random. The probability that all 5 are blue is 1/2. Determine the original number of balls and decide how many were blue. *Source: Weekend Edition.*

35. A reader wrote to the "Ask Marilyn" column in *Parade* magazine, "You have six envelopes to pick from. Two-thirds (that is, four) are empty. One-third (that is, two) contain a $100 bill. You're told to choose 2 envelopes at random. Which is more likely: (1) that you'll get at least one $100 bill, or (2) that you'll get no $100 bill at all?" Find the two probabilities. *Source: Parade Magazine.*

APPLICATIONS

Business and Economics

Quality Control A shipment of 11 printers contains 2 that are defective. Find the probability that a sample of the following sizes, drawn from the 11, will not contain a defective printer.

36. 1   37. 2   38. 3   39. 4

---

*Although Obama is the 44th President, the 22nd and 24th Presidents were the same man: Grover Cleveland.

[†]In fact, James Polk and Warren Harding were both born on November 2.

Refer to Example 3. The managers feel that the probability of 0.5455 that a container will be shipped even though it contains 2 defective engines is too high. They decide to increase the sample size chosen. Find the probabilities that a container will be shipped even though it contains 2 defective engines, if the sample size is increased to the following.

40. 4   **41.** 5

42. Sales Presentations Heidi Shadix and Boyd Shepherd are among 9 representatives making presentations at the annual sales meeting. The presentations are randomly ordered. Find the probability that Heidi is the first presenter and Boyd is the last presenter.

43. Sales Schedule Dan LaChapelle has the name of 6 prospects, including a customer in Scottsdale. He randomly arranges his schedule to call on only 4 of the 6 prospects. Find the probability that the customer from Scottsdale is not called upon.

Social Sciences

44. Election Ballots Five names are put on a ballot in a randomly selected order. What is the probability that they are not in alphabetical order?

45. Native American Council At the first meeting of a committee to plan a Northern California pow-wow, there were 3 women and 3 men from the Miwok tribe, 2 men and 3 women from the Hoopa tribe, and 4 women and 5 men from the Pomo tribe. If the ceremony subcouncil consists of 5 people and is randomly selected, find the probabilities that the subcouncil contains the following:

a. 3 men and 2 women;

b. exactly 3 Miwoks and 2 Pomos;

c. 2 Miwoks, 2 Hoopas, and a Pomo;

d. 2 Miwoks, 2 Hoopas, and 2 Pomos;

e. more women than men;

f. exactly 3 Hoopas;

g. at least 2 Pomos.

46. Education A school in Bangkok requires that students take an entrance examination. After the examination, there is a drawing in which 5 students are randomly selected from each group of 40 for automatic acceptance into the school, regardless of their performance on the examination. The drawing consists of placing 35 red and 5 green pieces of paper into a box. Each student picks a piece of paper from the box and then does not return the piece of paper to the box. The 5 lucky students who pick the green pieces are automatically accepted into the school. *Source: Mathematics Teacher.*

a. What is the probability that the first person wins automatic acceptance?

b. What is the probability that the last person wins automatic acceptance?

c. If the students are chosen by the order of their seating, does this give the student who goes first a better chance of winning than the second, third, . . . person? (*Hint:* Imagine that the 40 pieces of paper have been mixed up and laid in a row so that the first student picks the first piece of paper, the second student picks the second piece of paper, and so on.)

47. Education At a conference promoting excellence in education for African Americans in Detroit, special-edition books were selected to be given away in contests. There were 9 books written by Langston Hughes, 5 books by James Baldwin, and 7 books by Toni Morrison. The judge of one contest selected 6 books at random for prizes. Find the probabilities that the selection consisted of the following.

a. 3 Hughes and 3 Morrison books

b. Exactly 4 Baldwin books

c. 2 Hughes, 3 Baldwin, and 1 Morrison book

d. At least 4 Hughes books

e. Exactly 4 books written by males (Morrison is female)

f. No more than 2 books written by Baldwin

General Interest

Poker **Find the probabilities of the following hands at poker. Assume aces are either high or low.**

48. Royal flush (5 highest cards of a single suit)

49. Straight flush (5 in a row in a single suit, but not a royal flush)

50. Four of a kind (4 cards of the same value)

51. Straight (5 cards in a row, not all of the same suit), with ace either high or low

52. Three of a kind (3 cards of one value, with the other cards of two different values)

53. Two pairs (2 cards of one value, 2 of another value, and 1 of a third value)

54. One pair (2 cards of one value, with the other cards of three different values)

Bridge **A bridge hand is made up of 13 cards from a deck of 52. Find the probabilities that a hand chosen at random contains the following.**

55. Only hearts

56. At least 3 aces

57. Exactly 2 aces and exactly 2 kings

58. 6 of one suit, 4 of another, and 3 of another

Texas Hold'Em **In a version of poker called Texas Hold'Em, each player has 2 cards, and by the end of the round an additional 5 cards are on the table, shared by all the players. (For more about poker hands, see Example 4 and Exercises 48–54.) Each player's hand consists of the best 5 cards out of the 7 cards available to that player. For example, if a player holds 2 kings, and on the table there is one king and 4 cards with 4 other values, then the player has three of a kind. It's possible that the player has an even better hand. Perhaps five of the seven cards are of the same suit, making a flush, or the other 4 cards are queen, jack, 10, and 9, so the player has a straight. For Exercises 59–64, calculate the probability of each hand in Texas Hold'Em, but for simplicity, ignore the possibility that the cards might form an even better hand.**

59. One pair (2 cards of one value, with the other cards of five different values)

60. Two pairs (2 cards of one value, 2 of another, with the other cards of three different values)

61. Three of a kind (3 cards of one value, with the other cards of four different values)

62. Four of a kind (4 cards of one value, with the other cards of three different values)

63. Flush (at least 5 cards of the same suit)

64. Full house (3 cards of one value and two of another. Careful: The two unused cards could be a pair of another value or two different cards of other values. Also, the 7 cards could consist of 3 cards of one value, 3 of second value, and one card of a third value. We won't consider the case of 3 cards of one value and 4 of another, because even though this forms a full house, it also forms four of a kind, which is better.)

65. Suppose you are playing Texas Hold'Em and you've just received your two cards. You observe that they are both hearts. You get excited, because if at least 3 of the 5 cards that are on the table are hearts, you'll have a flush, which means that you'll likely win the round. Given that your two cards are hearts, and you know nothing of any other cards, what is the probability that you'll have a flush by the time all 5 cards are on the table?

66. Lottery In the previous section, we found the number of ways to pick 6 different numbers from 1 to 99 in a state lottery. Assuming order is unimportant, what is the probability of picking all 6 numbers correctly to win the big prize?

67. Lottery In Exercise 66, what is the probability of picking exactly 5 of the 6 numbers correctly?

68. Lottery An article in *The New York Times* discussing the odds of winning the lottery stated, "And who cares if a game-theory professor once calculated the odds of winning as equal to a poker player's chance of drawing four royal flushes in a row, all in spades—then getting up from the card table and meeting four strangers, all with the same birthday?" Calculate this probability. Does this probability seem comparable to the odds of winning the lottery? (Ignore February 29 as a birthday, and assume that all four strangers have the same birthday as each other, not necessarily the same as the poker player.) *Source: The New York Times Magazine.*

69. Lottery A reader wrote to the "Ask Marilyn" column in *Parade* magazine, "A dozen glazed doughnuts are riding on the answer to this question: Are the odds of winning in a lotto drawing higher when picking 6 numbers out of 49 or when picking 5 numbers out of 52?" Calculate each probability to answer the question. *Source: Parade Magazine.*

70. Lottery On October 22, 2005, the Powerball Lottery had a record jackpot of $340 million, which was a record at the time. To enter the lottery, 5 numbers are picked between 1 and 55, plus a bonus number between 1 and 42. All 6 numbers must be correct to win the jackpot.

a. What is the probability of winning the jackpot with a single ticket?

b. In an article for the *Minneapolis Star Tribune*, mathematician Douglas Arnold was quoted as saying, "If you were to select a group of Powerball numbers every minute for 138 years, you would have about a 50 percent chance of picking the winning Powerball ticket." Calculate the actual probability, using an estimate of 365.25 for the number of days in the year. (Arnold later told *Chance News* that this was an "off-the-top-of-my-head calculation" made when a reporter called.) *Sources: Minneapolis Star Tribune and Chance News.*

71. Canadian Lottery In June 2004, Canada introduced a change in its lottery that violated the usual convention that the smaller the probability of an event, the bigger the prize. In this lottery, participants have to guess six numbers from 1 to 49. Six numbers between 1 and 49 are then drawn at random, plus a seventh "bonus number." *Source: Chance.*

a. A fifth prize of $10 goes to those who correctly guess exactly three of the six numbers, but do not guess the bonus number. Find the probability of winning fifth prize.

b. A sixth prize of $5 goes to those who correctly guess exactly two of the six numbers plus the bonus number. Find the probability of winning sixth prize, and compare this with the probability of winning fifth prize.

72. Barbie A controversy arose in 1992 over the Teen Talk Barbie doll, each of which was programmed with four sayings randomly picked from a set of 270 sayings. The controversy was over the saying, "Math class is tough," which some felt gave a negative message toward girls doing well in math. In an interview with *Science*, a spokeswoman for Mattel, the makers of Barbie, said that "There's a less than 1% chance you're going to get a doll that says math class is tough." Is this figure correct? If not, give the correct figure. *Source: Science.*

73. Football During the 1988 college football season, the Big Eight Conference ended the season in a "perfect progression," as shown in the following table. *Source: The American Statistician.*

Won	Lost	Team
7	0	Nebraska (NU)
6	1	Oklahoma (OU)
5	2	Oklahoma State (OSU)
4	3	Colorado (CU)
3	4	Iowa State (ISU)
2	5	Missouri (MU)
1	6	Kansas (KU)
0	7	Kansas State (KSU)

Someone wondered what the probability of such an outcome might be.

a. How many games do the 8 teams play?

b. Assuming no ties, how many different outcomes are there for all the games together?

c. In how many ways could the 8 teams end in a perfect progression?

d. Assuming that each team had an equally likely probability of winning each game, find the probability of a perfect progression with 8 teams.

e. Find a general expression for the probability of a perfect progression in an *n*-team league with the same assumptions.

74. Unluckiest Fan During the 2009 season, the Washington Nationals baseball team won 59 games and lost 103 games. Season ticket holder Stephen Krupin reported in an interview that he watched the team lose all 19 games that he attended that season. The interviewer speculated that this must be a record for bad luck. *Source: Chance News.*

a. Based on the full 2009 season record, calculate the probability that a person would attend 19 Washington Nationals games and the Nationals would lose all 19 games.

b. However, Mr. Krupin only attended home games. The Nationals had 33 wins and 48 losses at home in 2009. Calculate the probability that a person would attend 19 Washington Nationals home games and the Nationals would lose all 19 games.

75. Bingo Bingo has become popular in the United States, and it is an efficient way for many organizations to raise money. The bingo card has 5 rows and 5 columns of numbers from 1 to 75, with the center given as a free cell. Balls showing one of the 75 numbers are picked at random from a container. If the drawn number appears on a player's card, then the player covers the number. In general, the winner is the person who first has a card with an entire row, column, or diagonal covered. *Source: Mathematics Teacher.*

a. Find the probability that a person will win bingo after just four numbers are called.

b. An L occurs when the first column and the bottom row are both covered. Find the probability that an L will occur in the fewest number of calls.

c. An X-out occurs when both diagonals are covered. Find the probability that an X-out occurs in the fewest number of calls.

d. If bingo cards are constructed so that column one has 5 of the numbers from 1 to 15, column two has 5 of the numbers from 16 to 30, column three has 4 of the numbers from 31 to 45, column four has 5 of the numbers from 46 to 60, and column five has 5 of the numbers from 61 to 75, how many different bingo cards could be constructed? (*Hint:* Order matters!)

76. Suppose a box contains 3 red and 3 blue balls. A ball is selected at random and removed, without observing its color. The box now either contains 3 red and 2 blue balls or 2 red and 3 blue balls. *Source: 40 Puzzles and Problems in Probability and Mathematical Statistics.*

a. Nate removes a ball at random from the box, observes its color, and puts the ball back. He performs this experiment a total of 6 times, and each time the ball is blue. What is the probability that a red ball was initially removed from the box? (*Hint:* Use Bayes' Theorem.)

b. Ray removes a ball at random from the box, observes its color, and puts the ball back. He performs this experiment a total of 80 times. Out of these, the ball was blue 44 times and red 36 times. What is the probability that a red ball was initially removed from the box?

c. Many people intuitively think that Nate's experiment gives more convincing evidence than Ray's experiment that a red ball was removed. Explain why this is wrong.

YOUR TURN ANSWERS

1. 1/5　　**2.** 0.3483　　**3.** 0.7455　　**4.** 0.0006095
5. 1/210; 1/343　　**6.** 9.514×10^{-6}

8.4 Binomial Probability

APPLY IT　What is the probability that 3 out of 6 randomly selected college students attend more than one institution during their college career?
We will calculate this probability in Example 2.

The question above involves an experiment that is repeated 6 times. Many probability problems are concerned with experiments in which an event is repeated many times. Other examples include finding the probability of getting 7 heads in 8 tosses of a coin, of hitting a target 6 times out of 6, and of finding 1 defective item in a sample of 15 items. Probability problems of this kind are called **Bernoulli trials** problems, or **Bernoulli processes**, named after the Swiss mathematician Jakob Bernoulli (1654–1705), who is well known for his work in probability theory. In each case, some outcome is designated a success and any other outcome is considered a failure. This labeling is arbitrary and does not necessarily have anything to do with real success or failure. Thus, if the probability of a success in a single trial is p, the probability of failure will be $1 - p$. A Bernoulli trials problem, or **binomial experiment**, must satisfy the following conditions.

Binomial Experiment

1. The same experiment is repeated a fixed number of times.
2. There are only two possible outcomes, success and failure.
3. The repeated trials are independent, so that the probability of success remains the same for each trial.

EXAMPLE 1   Sleep

The chance that an American falls asleep with the TV on at least three nights a week is 1/4. Suppose a researcher selects 5 Americans at random and is interested in the probability that all 5 are "TV sleepers." *Source: Harper's Magazine.*

FOR REVIEW

Recall that if A and B are independent events,

$$P(A \text{ and } B) = P(A)P(B).$$

SOLUTION   Here the experiment, selecting a person, is repeated 5 times. If selecting a TV sleeper is labeled a success, then getting a "non-TV sleeper" is labeled a failure. The 5 trials are almost independent. There is a very slight dependence; if, for example, the first person selected is a TV sleeper, then there is one less TV sleeper to choose from when we select the next person (assuming we never select the same person twice). When selecting a small sample out of a large population, however, the probability changes negligibly, so researchers consider such trials to be independent. Thus, the probability that all 5 in our sample are sleepers is

$$\frac{1}{4} \cdot \frac{1}{4} \cdot \frac{1}{4} \cdot \frac{1}{4} \cdot \frac{1}{4} = \left(\frac{1}{4}\right)^5 \approx 0.0009766.$$

Now suppose the problem in Example 1 is changed to that of finding the probability that exactly 4 of the 5 people in the sample are TV sleepers. This outcome can occur in more than one way, as shown below, where s represents a success (a TV sleeper) and f represents a failure (a non-TV sleeper).

outcome 1: s s s s f
outcome 2: s s s f s
outcome 3: s s f s s
outcome 4: s f s s s
outcome 5: f s s s s

Keep in mind that since the probability of success is 1/4, the probability of failure is $1 - 1/4 = 3/4$. The probability, then, of each of these 5 outcomes is

$$\left(\frac{1}{4}\right)^4 \left(\frac{3}{4}\right).$$

Since the 5 outcomes represent mutually exclusive events, add the 5 identical probabilities, which is equivalent to multiplying the above probability by 5. The result is

$$P(4 \text{ of the 5 people are TV sleepers}) = 5\left(\frac{1}{4}\right)^4 \left(\frac{3}{4}\right) = \frac{15}{4^5} \approx 0.01465.$$

In the same way, we can compute the probability of selecting 3 TV sleepers in our sample of 5. The probability of any one way of achieving 3 successes and 2 failures will be

$$\left(\frac{1}{4}\right)^3 \left(\frac{3}{4}\right)^2.$$

Rather than list all the ways of achieving 3 successes out of 5 trials, we will count this number using combinations. The number of ways to select 3 elements out of a set of 5 is $C(5, 3) = 5!/(2! \, 3!) = 10$, giving

$$P(3 \text{ of the 5 people are TV sleepers}) = 10\left(\frac{1}{4}\right)^3 \left(\frac{3}{4}\right)^2 = \frac{90}{4^5} \approx 0.08789.$$

A similar argument works in the general case.

Binomial Probability

If p is the probability of success in a single trial of a binomial experiment, the probability of x successes and $n - x$ failures in n independent repeated trials of the experiment, known as **binomial probability**, is

$$P(x \text{ successes in } n \text{ trials}) = C(n, x) \cdot p^x \cdot (1 - p)^{n-x}.$$

EXAMPLE 2   College Students

A recent survey found that 59% of college students attend more than one institution during their college career. Suppose a sample of 6 students is chosen. Assuming that each student's college attendance pattern is independent of the others, find the probability of each of the following. *Source: The New York Times.*

(a) Exactly 3 of the 6 students attend more than one institution.

APPLY IT

SOLUTION   Think of the 6 students chosen as 6 independent trials. A success occurs if the student attends more than one institution. Then this is a binomial experiment with $n = 6$ and $p = P(\text{attend more than one institution}) = 0.59$. To find the probability that exactly 3 students attend more than one institution, let $x = 3$ and use the binomial probability formula.

$$\begin{aligned} P(\text{exactly 3 of 6 students}) &= C(6, 3)(0.59)^3(1 - 0.59)^{6-3} \\ &= 20(0.59)^3(0.41)^3 \\ &= 20(0.2054)(0.06892) \\ &\approx 0.2831 \end{aligned}$$

YOUR TURN 1 Find the probability that exactly 2 of the 6 students in Example 2 attend more than 1 institution.

(b) None of the 6 students attend more than one institution.

SOLUTION Let $x = 0$.

$$\begin{aligned} P(\text{exactly 0 of 6 students}) &= C(6, 0)(0.59)^0(1 - 0.59)^6 \\ &= 1(1)(0.41)^6 \approx 0.00475 \quad \text{TRY YOUR TURN 1} \end{aligned}$$

EXAMPLE 3   Coin Toss

Find the probability of getting exactly 7 heads in 8 tosses of a fair coin.

SOLUTION   The probability of success (getting a head in a single toss) is $1/2$. The probability of a failure (getting a tail) is $1 - 1/2 = 1/2$. Thus,

YOUR TURN 2 In Example 3, find the probability of getting exactly 4 heads in 8 tosses of a fair coin.

$$P(\text{7 heads in 8 tosses}) = C(8, 7)\left(\frac{1}{2}\right)^7\left(\frac{1}{2}\right)^1 = 8\left(\frac{1}{2}\right)^8 = 0.03125.$$

TRY YOUR TURN 2

EXAMPLE 4   Defective Items

Assuming that selection of items for a sample can be treated as independent trials, and that the probability that any 1 item is defective is 0.01, find the following.

(a) The probability of 1 defective item in a random sample of 15 items from a production line

SOLUTION   Here, a "success" is a defective item. Since selecting each item for the sample is assumed to be an independent trial, the binomial probability formula applies. The probability of success (a defective item) is 0.01, while the probability of failure (an acceptable item) is 0.99. This makes

$$\begin{aligned} P(\text{1 defective in 15 items}) &= C(15, 1)(0.01)^1(0.99)^{14} \\ &= 15(0.01)(0.99)^{14} \\ &\approx 0.1303. \end{aligned}$$

(b) The probability of at most 1 defective item in a random sample of 15 items from a production line

SOLUTION "At most 1" means 0 defective items or 1 defective item. Since 0 defective items is equivalent to 15 acceptable items,

$$P(\text{0 defective}) = (0.99)^{15} \approx 0.8601.$$

YOUR TURN 3 In Example 4, find the probability of 2 or 3 defective items in a random sample of 15 items from a production line.

Use the union rule, noting that 0 defective and 1 defective are mutually exclusive events, to get

$$P(\text{at most 1 defective}) = P(0 \text{ defective}) + P(1 \text{ defective})$$
$$\approx 0.8601 + 0.1303$$
$$= 0.9904. \qquad \text{TRY YOUR TURN 3}$$

EXAMPLE 5 Checkout Scanners

The Federal Trade Commission (FTC) monitors pricing accuracy to ensure that consumers are charged the correct price at the checkout. According to the FTC, 29% of stores that use checkout scanners do not accurately charge customers. *Source: Federal Trade Commission.*

(a) If you shop at 3 stores that use checkout scanners, what is the probability that you will be incorrectly charged in at least one store?

SOLUTION We can treat this as a binomial experiment, letting $n = 3$ and $p = 0.29$. We need to find the probability of "at least 1" incorrect charge, which means 1 or 2 or 3 incorrect charges. To make our calculation simpler, we will use the complement. We will find the probability of being charged incorrectly in none of the 3 stores, that is, $P(0 \text{ incorrect charges})$, and then find $1 - P(0 \text{ incorrect charges})$.

$$P(0 \text{ incorrect charges}) = C(3, 0)(0.29)^0(0.71)^3$$
$$= 1(1)(0.357911) \approx 0.3579$$
$$P(\text{at least one}) = 1 - P(0 \text{ incorrect charges})$$
$$\approx 1 - 0.3579 = 0.6421$$

(b) If you shop at 3 stores that use checkout scanners, what is the probability that you will be incorrectly charged in at most one store?

SOLUTION "At most one" means 0 or 1, so

$$P(0 \text{ or } 1) = P(0) + P(1)$$
$$= C(3, 0)(0.29)^0(0.71)^3 + C(3, 1)(0.29)^1(0.71)^2$$
$$= 1(1)(0.357911) + 3(0.29)(0.5041) \approx 0.7965.$$

YOUR TURN 4 In Example 5, if you shop at 4 stores that use checkout scanners, find the probability that you will be charged incorrectly in at least one store.

TRY YOUR TURN 4

The triangular array of numbers shown below is called **Pascal's triangle** in honor of the French mathematician Blaise Pascal (1623–1662), who was one of the first to use it extensively. The triangle was known long before Pascal's time and appears in Chinese and Islamic manuscripts from the eleventh century.

Pascal's Triangle

The array provides a quick way to find binomial probabilities. The nth row of the triangle, where $n = 0, 1, 2, 3, \ldots$, gives the coefficients $C(n, r)$ for $r = 0, 1, 2, 3, \ldots, n$. For example, for $n = 4$, $1 = C(4, 0)$, $4 = C(4, 1)$, $6 = C(4, 2)$, and so on. Each number in the triangle is the sum of the two numbers directly above it. For example, in the row for

$n = 4$, 1 is the sum of 1, the only number above it, 4 is the sum of 1 and 3, 6 is the sum of 3 and 3, and so on. Adding in this way gives the sixth row:

$$1 \quad 6 \quad 15 \quad 20 \quad 15 \quad 6 \quad 1.$$

Notice that Pascal's triangle tells us, for example, that $C(4, 1) + C(4, 2) = C(5, 2)$ (that is, $4 + 6 = 10$). Using the combinations formula, it can be shown that, in general, $C(n, r) + C(n, r + 1) = C(n + 1, r + 1)$. This is left as an exercise.

EXAMPLE 6 Pascal's Triangle

Use Pascal's triangle to find the probability in Example 5 that if you shop at 6 stores that use checkout scanners, at least 3 will charge you incorrectly

SOLUTION   The probability of success is 0.29. Since at least 3 means 3, 4, 5, or 6,

$$\begin{aligned} P(\text{at least } 3) &= P(3) + P(4) + P(5) + P(6) \\ &= C(6, 3)(0.29)^3(0.71)^3 + C(6, 4)(0.29)^4(0.71)^2 \\ &\quad + C(6, 5)(0.29)^5(0.71)^1 + C(6, 6)(0.29)^6(0.71)^0. \end{aligned}$$

Use the sixth row of Pascal's triangle for the combinations to get

$$\begin{aligned} P(\text{at least } 3) &= 20(0.29)^3(0.71)^3 + 15(0.29)^4(0.71)^2 \\ &\quad + 6(0.29)^5(0.71)^1 + 1(0.29)^6(0.71)^0 \\ &= 0.1746 + 0.0535 + 0.0087 + 0.0006 \\ &= 0.2374. \end{aligned}$$

> **YOUR TURN 5**   In Example 5, find the probability that if you shop at 6 stores with checkout scanners, at most 3 stores will charge you incorrectly.

TRY YOUR TURN 5

EXAMPLE 7 Independent Jury

If each member of a 9-person jury acts independently of each other and makes the correct determination of guilt or innocence with probability 0.65, find the probability that the majority of jurors will reach a correct verdict. *Source: Frontiers in Economics.*

Method 1
Calculating By Hand

SOLUTION   Since the jurors in this particular situation act independently, we can treat this as a binomial experiment. Thus, the probability that the majority of the jurors will reach the correct verdict is given by

$$\begin{aligned} P(\text{at least } 5) &= C(9, 5)(0.65)^5(0.35)^4 + C(9, 6)(0.65)^6(0.35)^3 \\ &\quad + C(9, 7)(0.65)^7(0.35)^2 + C(9, 8)(0.65)^8(0.35)^1 + C(9, 9)(0.65)^9 \\ &= 0.2194 + 0.2716 + 0.2162 + 0.1004 + 0.0207 \\ &= 0.8283. \end{aligned}$$

Method 2
Graphing Calculator

Some graphing calculators provide binomial probabilities. On a TI-84 Plus, for example, the command `binompdf(9, .65, 5)`, found in the DISTR menu, gives 0.21939, which is the probability that $x = 5$. Alternatively, the command `binomcdf(9, .65, 4)` gives 0.17172 as the probability that 4 or fewer jurors will make the correct decision. Subtract 0.17172 from 1 to get 0.82828 as the probability that the majority of the jurors will make the correct decision. This value rounds to 0.8283, which is in agreement with Method 1. Often, graphing calculators are more accurate than calculations by hand due to the accumulation of rounding errors when doing successive calculations by hand.

Method 3
Spreadsheet

Some spreadsheets also provide binomial probabilities. In Microsoft Excel, for example, the command "=BINOMDIST(5, 9, .65, 0)" gives 0.21939, which is the probability that $x = 5$. Alternatively, the command "=BINOMDIST (4, 9, .65, 1)" gives 0.17172 as the probability that 4 or fewer jurors will make the correct decision. Subtract 0.17172 from 1 to get 0.82828 as the probability that the majority of the jurors will make the correct decision. This value agrees with the value found in Methods 1 and 2.

8.4 EXERCISES

Suppose that a family has 5 children. Also, suppose that the probability of having a girl is 1/2. Find the probabilities that the family has the following children.

1. Exactly 2 girls and 3 boys

2. Exactly 3 girls and 2 boys

3. No girls

4. No boys

5. At least 4 girls

6. At least 3 boys

7. No more than 3 boys

8. No more than 4 girls

A die is rolled 12 times. Find the probabilities of rolling the following.

9. Exactly 12 ones

10. Exactly 6 ones

11. Exactly 1 one

12. Exactly 2 ones

13. No more than 3 ones

14. No more than 1 one

A certain unfair coin lands on heads 1/4 of the time. This coin is tossed 6 times. Find the probabilities of getting the following.

15. All heads

16. Exactly 3 heads

17. No more than 3 heads

18. At least 3 heads

19. How do you identify a probability problem that involves a binomial experiment?

20. How is Pascal's triangle used to find probabilities?

21. Using the definition of combination in Section 8.2, prove that

$$C(n, r) + C(n, r + 1) = C(n + 1, r + 1)$$

(This is the formula underlying Pascal's triangle.)

In Exercises 22 and 23, argue that the use of binomial probabilities is not applicable and, thus, the probabilities that are computed are not correct.

22. In England, a woman was found guilty of smothering her two infant children. Much of the Crown's case against the lady was based on the testimony from a pediatrician who indicated that the chances of two crib deaths occurring in both siblings was only about 1 in 73 million. This number was calculated by assuming that the probability of a single crib death is 1 in 8543 and the probability of two crib deaths is 1 in 8543^2 (i.e., binomial). (See Chapter 7 Review Exercise 102.) *Source: Science.*

23. A contemporary radio station in Boston has a contest in which a caller is asked his or her date of birth. If the caller's date of birth, including the day, month, and year of birth, matches a predetermined date, the caller wins $1 million. Assuming that there were 36,525 days in the twentieth century and the contest was run 51 times on consecutive days, the probability that the grand prize will be won is

$$1 - \left(1 - \frac{1}{36,525}\right)^{51} \approx 0.0014.$$

Source: Chance News.

APPLICATIONS

Business and Economics

Management   The survey discussed in Example 5 also found that customers are charged incorrectly for 1 out of every 30 items, on average. Suppose a customer purchases 15 items. Find the following probabilities.

24. A customer is charged incorrectly on 3 items.

25. A customer is not charged incorrectly for any item.

26. A customer is charged incorrectly on at least one item.

27. A customer is charged incorrectly on at least 2 items.

28. A customer is charged incorrectly on at most 2 items.

Credit Cards   A survey of consumer finance found that 25.4% of credit-card-holding families hardly ever pay off the balance. Suppose a random sample of 20 credit-card-holding families is taken. Find the probabilities of each of the following results. *Source: Statistical Abstract of the United States.*

29. Exactly 6 families hardly ever pay off the balance.

30. Exactly 9 families hardly ever pay off the balance.

31. At least 4 families hardly ever pay off the balance.

32. At most 5 families hardly ever pay off the balance.

Personnel Screening   A company gives prospective workers a 6-question, multiple-choice test. Each question has 5 possible answers, so that there is a 1/5 or 20% chance of answering a question correctly just by guessing. Find the probabilities of getting the following results by chance.

33. Exactly 2 correct answers

34. No correct answers

35. At least 4 correct answers

36. No more than 3 correct answers

Quality Control   A factory tests a random sample of 20 transistors for defects. The probability that a particular transistor will be defective has been established by past experience as 0.05.

37. What is the probability that there are no defective transistors in the sample?

38. What is the probability that the number of defective transistors in the sample is at most 2?

39. Quality Control   The probability that a certain machine turns out a defective item is 0.05. Find the probabilities that in a run of 75 items, the following results are obtained.

   a. Exactly 5 defective items

   b. No defective items

   c. At least 1 defective item

40. Survey Results   A company is taking a survey to find out whether people like its product. Its last survey indicated that 70% of the population like the product. Based on that, in a sample of 58 people, find the probabilities of the following.

   a. All 58 like the product.

   b. From 28 to 30 (inclusive) like the product.

41. Pecans   Pecan producers blow air through the pecans so that the lighter ones are blown out. The lighter-weight pecans are generally bad and the heavier ones tend to be better. These "blow outs" and "good nuts" are often sold to tourists along the highway. Suppose 60% of the "blow outs" are good, and 80% of the "good nuts" are good. *Source: Irvin R. Hentzel.*

   a. What is the probability that if you crack and check 20 "good nuts" you will find 8 bad ones?

   b. What is the probability that if you crack and check 20 "blow outs" you will find 8 bad ones?

   c. If we assume that 70% of the roadside stands sell "good nuts," and that out of 20 nuts we find 8 that are bad, what is the probability that the nuts are "blow outs"?

42. Hurricane Insurance   A company prices its hurricane insurance using the following assumptions:

   (i)   In any calendar year, there can be at most one hurricane.

   (ii) In any calendar year, the probability of a hurricane is 0.05.

   (iii) The number of hurricanes in any calendar year is independent of the number of hurricanes in any other calendar year.

   Using the company's assumptions, calculate the probability that there are fewer than 3 hurricanes in a 20-year period. Choose one of the following. *Source: Society of Actuaries.*

   a. 0.06   **b.** 0.19   **c.** 0.38   **d.** 0.62   **e.** 0.92

Life Sciences

Breast Cancer   **A recent study found that 85% of breast-cancer cases are detectable by mammogram. Suppose a random sample of 15 women with breast cancer are given mammograms. Find the probability of each of the following results, assuming that detection in the cases is independent.** *Source: Harper's Index.*

43. All of the cases are detectable.

44. None of the cases are detectable.

45. Not all cases are detectable.

46. More than half of the cases are detectable.

Births of Twins   **The probability that a birth will result in twins is 0.012. Assuming independence (perhaps not a valid assumption), what are the probabilities that out of 100 births in a hospital, there will be the following numbers of sets of twins?**

47. Exactly 2 sets of twins

48. At most 2 sets of twins

49. Effects of Radiation   The probability of a mutation of a given gene under a dose of 1 roentgen of radiation is approximately 2.5×10^{-7}. What is the probability that in 10,000 genes, at least 1 mutation occurs?

50. Flu Inoculations   A flu vaccine has a probability of 80% of preventing a person who is inoculated from getting the flu. A county health office inoculates 83 people. Find the probabilities of the following.

   a. Exactly 10 of the people inoculated get the flu.

   b. No more than 4 of the people inoculated get the flu.

   c. None of the people inoculated get the flu.

51. Color Blindness   The probability that a male will be colorblind is 0.042. Find the probabilities that in a group of 53 men, the following will be true.

   a. Exactly 5 are color-blind.

   b. No more than 5 are color-blind.

   c. At least 1 is color-blind.

52. Pharmacology   In placebo-controlled trials of Pravachol®, a drug that is prescribed to lower cholesterol, 7.3% of the patients who were taking the drug experienced nausea/ vomiting, whereas 7.1% of the patients who were taking the placebo experienced nausea/vomiting. *Source: Bristol-Myers Squibb Company.*

   a. If 100 patients who are taking Pravachol® are selected, what is the probability that 10 or more will experience nausea/ vomiting?

   b. If a second group of 100 patients receives a placebo, what is the probability that 10 or more will experience nausea/vomiting?

   c. Since 7.3% is larger than 7.1%, do you believe that the Pravachol® causes more people to experience nausea/ vomiting than a placebo? Explain.

53. Genetic Fingerprinting   The use of DNA has become an integral part of many court cases. When DNA is extracted from cells and body fluids, genetic information is represented by bands of information, which look similar to a bar code at a grocery store. It is generally accepted that in unrelated people, the probability of a particular band matching is 1 in 4. *Source: University of Exeter.*

   a. If 5 bands are compared in unrelated people, what is the probability that all 5 of the bands match? (Express your answer in terms of "1 chance in ?".)

   b. If 20 bands are compared in unrelated people, what is the probability that all 20 of the bands match? (Express your answer in terms of "1 chance in ?".)

   c. If 20 bands are compared in unrelated people, what is the probability that 16 or more bands match? (Express your answer in terms of "1 chance in ?".)

   d. If you were deciding paternity and there were 16 matches out of 20 bands compared, would you believe that the person being tested was the father? Explain.

54. Salmonella   According to *The Salt Lake Tribune*, the Coffee Garden in Salt Lake City ran into trouble because of their four-egg quiche:

"A Salt Lake County Health Department inspector paid a visit recently and pointed out that research by the Food and Drug Administration indicates that one in four eggs carries *Salmonella* bacterium, so restaurants should never use more than three eggs when preparing quiche.

The manager on duty wondered aloud if simply throwing out three eggs from each dozen and using the remaining nine in four-egg quiches would serve the same purpose.

The inspector wasn't sure, but she said she would research it." *Source: The Salt Lake Tribune.*

a. Assuming that one in four eggs carries *Salmonella*, and that the event that any one egg is infected is independent of whether any other egg is infected, find the probability that at least one of the eggs in a four-egg quiche carries *Salmonella*.

b. Repeat part a for a three-egg quiche.

c. Discuss whether the assumption of independence is justified.

d. Discuss whether the inspector's reasoning makes sense.

55. Herbal Remedies According to Dr. Peter A.G.M. De Smet of the Netherlands, "If an herb caused an adverse reaction in 1 in 1,000 users, a traditional healer would have to treat 4,800 patients with that herb (i.e., one new patient every single working day for more than 18 years) to have a 95 percent chance of observing the reaction in more than one user." Verify this calculation by finding the probability of observing more than one reaction in 4800 patients, given that 1 in 1000 has a reaction. *Source: The New England Journal of Medicine.*

56. Vaccines A hospital receives 1/5 of its flu vaccine shipments from Company X and the remainder of its shipments from other companies. Each shipment contains a very large number of vaccine vials. For Company X's shipments, 10% of the vials are ineffective. For every other company, 2% of the vials are ineffective. The hospital tests 30 randomly selected vials from a shipment and finds that one vial is ineffective. What is the probability that this shipment came from Company X? Choose one of the following. (*Hint:* Find the probability that one out of 30 vials is ineffective, given that the shipment came from Company X and that the shipment came from other companies. Then use Bayes' theorem.) *Source: Society of Actuaries.*

a. 0.10   **b.** 0.14   **c.** 0.37   **d.** 0.63   **e.** 0.86

57. Health Study A study is being conducted in which the health of two independent groups of ten policyholders is being monitored over a one-year period of time. Individual participants in the study drop out before the end of the study with probability 0.2 (independently of the other participants). What is the probability that at least 9 participants complete the study in one of the two groups, but not in both groups? Choose one of the following. *Source: Society of Actuaries.*

a. 0.096   **b.** 0.192   **c.** 0.235   **d.** 0.376   **e.** 0.469

Social Sciences

58. Women Working A recent study found that 60% of working mothers would prefer to work part-time if money were not a concern. Find the probability that if 10 working mothers are selected at random, that at least 3 of them would prefer to work part-time. *Source: Pew Research Center.*

Volunteering A recent survey found that 83% of first-year college students were involved in volunteer work at least occasionally. Suppose a random sample of 12 college students is taken. Find the probabilities of each of the following results. *Source: The New York Times.*

59. Exactly 7 students volunteered at least occasionally.

60. Exactly 9 students volunteered at least occasionally.

61. At least 9 students volunteered at least occasionally.

62. At most 9 students volunteered at least occasionally.

63. Minority Enrollment According to the U.S. Department of Education, 32.2% of all students enrolled in degree-granting institutions (those that grant associate's or higher degrees) belong to minorities. Find the probabilities of the following results in a random sample of 10 students enrolled in degree-granting institutions. *Source: National Center for Education Statistics.*

a. Exactly 2 belong to a minority.

b. Three or fewer belong to a minority.

c. Exactly 5 do not belong to a minority.

d. Six or more do not belong to a minority.

64. Cheating According to a poll conducted by *U.S. News and World Report*, 84% of college students believe they need to cheat to get ahead in the world today. *Source: U.S. News and World Report.*

a. Do the results of this poll indicate that 84% of all college students cheat? Explain.

b. If this result is accurate and 100 college students are asked if they believe that cheating is necessary to get ahead in the world, what is the probability that 90 or more of the students will answer affirmatively to the question?

65. Education A study by Cleveland Clinic tracked a cohort of very-low-birth-weight infants for twenty years. The results of the study indicated that 74% of the very-low-birth-weight babies graduated from high school during this time period. The study also reported that 83% of the comparison group of normal-birth-weight babies graduated from high school during the same period. *Source: The New England Journal of Medicine.*

a. If 40 very-low-birth-weight babies were tracked through high school, what is the probability that at least 30 will graduate from high school by age 20?

b. If 40 babies from the comparison group were tracked through high school, what is the probability that at least 30 will graduate from high school by age 20?

66. War Dead A newspaper article questioned whether soldiers and marines from some states bear greater risks in Afghanistan and Iraq than those from others. Out of 644,066 troops deployed as of the time of the article, 1174 had been killed, for a probability of being killed of $p = 1174/644,066$. Assume the deaths are independent.* *Source: Valley News.*

a. Vermont had 9 deaths out of 1613 troops deployed. Find the probability of at least this many deaths.

*For further statistical analysis, see http://www.dartmouth.edu/~chance/ForWiki/GregComments.pdf.

b. Massachusetts had 28 deaths out of 7146 troops deployed. Find the probability of at least this many deaths.

c. Florida had 54 deaths out of 62,572 troops deployed. Find the probability of at most this many deaths.

d. Discuss why the assumption of independence may be questionable.

67. Sports In many sports championships, such as the World Series in baseball and the Stanley Cup final series in hockey, the winner is the first team to win four games. For this exercise, assume that each game is independent of the others, with a constant probability p that one specified team (say, the National League team) wins.

a. Find the probability that the series lasts for four, five, six, and seven games when $p = 0.5$. (*Hint:* Suppose the National

League wins the series, so they must win the last game. Consider how the previous games might come out. Then consider the probability that the American League wins.)

b. Morrison and Schmittlein have found that the Stanley Cup finals can be described by letting $p = 0.73$ be the probability that the better team wins each game. Find the probability that the series lasts for four, five, six, and seven games. *Source: Chance.*

c. Some have argued that the assumption of independence does not apply. Discuss this issue. *Source: Mathematics Magazine.*

YOUR TURN ANSWERS

1. 0.1475   **2.** 0.2734   **3.** 0.009617
4. 0.7459   **5.** 0.9372

8.5 Probability Distributions; Expected Value

APPLY IT   **What is the expected payback for someone who buys one ticket in a raffle?**
In Example 3, we will calculate the expected payback or expected value of this raffle.

We shall see that the *expected value* of a probability distribution is a type of average. Probability distributions were introduced briefly in Chapter 7 on Sets and Probability. Now we take a more complete look at probability distributions. A probability distribution depends on the idea of a *random variable*, so we begin with that.

Random Variables
When researchers carry out an experiment it is necessary to quantify the possible outcomes of the experiment. This process will enable the researcher to recognize individual outcomes and analyze the data. The most common way to keep track of the individual outcomes of the experiment is to assign a numerical value to each of the different possible outcomes of the experiment. For example, if a coin is tossed 2 times, the possible outcomes are: *hh*, *ht*, *th*, and *tt*. For each of these possible outcomes, we could record the number of heads. Then the outcome, which we will label *x*, is one of the numbers 0, 1, or 2. Of course, we could have used other numbers, like 00, 01, 10, and 11, to indicate these same outcomes, but the values of 0, 1, and 2 are simpler and provide an immediate description of the exact outcome of the experiment. Notice that using this random variable also gives us a way to readily know how many tails occurred in the experiment. Thus, in some sense, the values of *x* are random, so *x* is called a **random variable.**

> **Random Variable**
> A **random variable** is a function that assigns a real number to each outcome of an experiment.

Probability Distribution
A table that lists the possible values of a random variable, together with the corresponding probabilities, is called a **probability distribution**. The sum of the probabilities in a probability distribution must always equal 1. (The sum in some distributions may vary slightly from 1 because of rounding.)

EXAMPLE 1   Computer Monitors

A shipment of 12 computer monitors contains 3 broken monitors. A shipping manager checks a sample of four monitors to see if any are broken. Give the probability distribution for the number of broken monitors that the shipping manager finds.

SOLUTION Let x represent the random variable "number of broken monitors found by the manager." Since there are 3 broken monitors, the possible values of x are 0, 1, 2, and 3. We can calculate the probability of each x using the methods of Section 8.3. There are 3 broken monitors, and 9 unbroken monitors, so the number of ways of choosing 0 broken monitors (which implies 4 unbroken monitors) is $C(3, 0) \cdot C(9, 4)$. The number of ways of choosing a sample of 4 monitors is $C(12, 4)$. Therefore, the probability of choosing 0 broken monitors is

$$P(0) = \frac{C(3, 0) \cdot C(9, 4)}{C(12, 4)} = \frac{1\left(\dfrac{9 \cdot 8 \cdot 7 \cdot 6}{4 \cdot 3 \cdot 2 \cdot 1}\right)}{\left(\dfrac{12 \cdot 11 \cdot 10 \cdot 9}{4 \cdot 3 \cdot 2 \cdot 1}\right)} = \frac{126}{495} = \frac{14}{55}.$$

Similarly, the probability of choosing 1 broken monitor is

$$P(1) = \frac{C(3, 1) \cdot C(9, 3)}{C(12, 4)} = \frac{3 \cdot 84}{495} = \frac{252}{495} = \frac{28}{55}.$$

The probability of choosing 2 broken monitors is

$$P(2) = \frac{C(3, 2) \cdot C(9, 2)}{C(12, 4)} = \frac{3 \cdot 36}{495} = \frac{108}{495} = \frac{12}{55}.$$

The probability of choosing 3 broken monitors is

$$P(3) = \frac{C(3, 3) \cdot C(9, 1)}{C(12, 4)} = \frac{1 \cdot 9}{495} = \frac{9}{495} = \frac{1}{55}.$$

YOUR TURN 1 Suppose the inspector in Example 1 chose only two monitors to inspect. Find the probability distribution for the number of broken monitors.

The results can be put in a table, called a probability distribution.

Probability Distribution of Broken Monitors in Sample			
x	0	1	2	3
$P(x)$	14/55	28/55	12/55	1/55

TRY YOUR TURN 1

Instead of writing the probability distribution as a table, we could write the same information as a set of ordered pairs:

$$\{(0, 14/55), (1, 28/55), (2, 12/55), (3, 1/55)\}.$$

There is just one probability for each value of the random variable. Thus, a probability distribution defines a function, called a **probability distribution function**, or simply a **probability function**. We shall use the terms "probability distribution" and "probability function" interchangeably.

The information in a probability distribution is often displayed graphically as a special kind of bar graph called a **histogram**. The bars of a histogram all have the same width, usually 1. (The widths might be different from 1 when the values of the random variable are not consecutive integers.) The heights of the bars are determined by the probabilities. A histogram for the data in Example 1 is given in Figure 8. A histogram shows important characteristics of a distribution that may not be readily apparent in tabular form, such as the relative sizes of the probabilities and any symmetry in the distribution.

The area of the bar above $x = 0$ in Figure 8 is the product of 1 and 14/55, or $1 \cdot 14/55 = 14/55$. Since each bar has a width of 1, its area is equal to the probability that corresponds to that value of x. The probability that a particular value will occur is thus given by the area of the appropriate bar of the graph. For example, the probability that one or more monitors is broken is the sum of the areas for $x = 1$, $x = 2$, and $x = 3$. This area, shown in pink in Figure 9, corresponds to 41/55 of the total area, since

$$P(x \geq 1) = P(x = 1) + P(x = 2) + P(x = 3)$$
$$= 28/55 + 12/55 + 1/55 = 41/55.$$

FIGURE 8

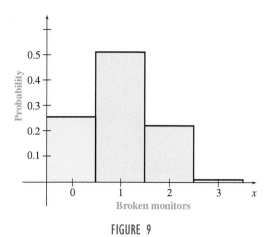

FIGURE 9

EXAMPLE 2   Probability Distributions

(a) Give the probability distribution for the number of heads showing when two coins are tossed.

SOLUTION   Let x represent the random variable "number of heads." Then x can take on the values 0, 1, or 2. Now find the probability of each outcome. To find the probability of 0, 1, or 2 heads, we can either use binomial probability, or notice that there are 4 outcomes in the sample space: $\{hh, ht, th, tt\}$. The results are shown in the table with Figure 10.

Probability Distribution of Heads		
x	0	1	2
$P(x)$	1/4	1/2	1/4

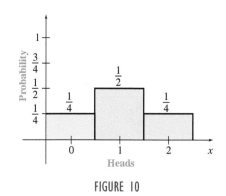

FIGURE 10

YOUR TURN 2   Find the probability distribution and draw a histogram for the number of tails showing when three coins are tossed.

(b) Draw a histogram for the distribution in the table. Find the probability that at least one coin comes up heads.

SOLUTION   The histogram is shown in Figure 10. The portion in pink represents

$$P(x \geq 1) = P(x = 1) + P(x = 2)$$
$$= \frac{3}{4}.$$

TRY YOUR TURN 2

Expected Value
In working with probability distributions, it is useful to have a concept of the typical or average value that the random variable takes on. In Example 2, for instance, it seems reasonable that, on the average, one head shows when two coins are tossed. This does not tell what will happen the next time we toss two coins; we may get two heads, or we may get none. If we tossed two coins many times, however, we would expect that, in the long run, we would average about one head for each toss of two coins.

A way to solve such problems in general is to imagine flipping two coins 4 times. Based on the probability distribution in Example 2, we would expect that 1 of the 4 times we would get 0 heads, 2 of the 4 times we would get 1 head, and 1 of the 4 times we would get 2 heads. The total number of heads we would get, then, is

$$0 \cdot 1 + 1 \cdot 2 + 2 \cdot 1 = 4.$$

The expected numbers of heads per toss is found by dividing the total number of heads by the total number of tosses, or

$$\frac{0 \cdot 1 + 1 \cdot 2 + 2 \cdot 1}{4} = 0 \cdot \frac{1}{4} + 1 \cdot \frac{1}{2} + 2 \cdot \frac{1}{4} = 1.$$

Notice that the expected number of heads turns out to be the sum of the three values of the random variable x multiplied by their corresponding probabilities. We can use this idea to define the *expected value* of a random variable as follows.

Expected Value

Suppose the random variable x can take on the n values $x_1, x_2, x_3, \ldots, x_n$. Also, suppose the probabilities that these values occur are, respectively, $p_1, p_2, p_3, \ldots, p_n$. Then the **expected value** of the random variable is

$$E(x) = x_1 p_1 + x_2 p_2 + x_3 p_3 + \cdots + x_n p_n.$$

EXAMPLE 3 Computer Monitors

In Example 1, find the expected number of broken monitors that the shipping manager finds.

SOLUTION   Using the values in the first table in this section and the definition of expected value, we find that

$$E(x) = 0 \cdot \frac{14}{55} + 1 \cdot \frac{28}{55} + 2 \cdot \frac{12}{55} + 3 \cdot \frac{1}{55} = 1.$$

On average, the shipping manager will find 1 broken monitor in the sample of 4. On reflection, this seems natural; 3 of the 12 monitors, or $1/4$ of the total, are broken. We should expect, then, that $1/4$ of the sample of 4 monitors are broken.

Physically, the expected value of a probability distribution represents a balance point. If we think of the histogram in Figure 8 as a series of weights with magnitudes represented by the heights of the bars, then the system would balance if supported at the point corresponding to the expected value.

EXAMPLE 4 Symphony Orchestra

Suppose a local symphony decides to raise money by raffling an HD television worth $400, a dinner for two worth $80, and 2 CDs worth $20 each. A total of 2000 tickets are sold at $1 each. Find the expected payback for a person who buys one ticket in the raffle.

APPLY IT

Method 1
Direct Calculation

SOLUTION

Here the random variable represents the possible amounts of payback, where payback = amount won − cost of ticket. The payback of the person winning the television is $400 (amount won) − $1 (cost of ticket) = $399. The payback for each losing ticket is $0 − $1 = −$1.

The paybacks of the various prizes, as well as their respective probabilities, are shown in the table on the next page. The probability of winning $19 is $2/2000$ because there are 2 prizes worth $20. We have not reduced the fractions in order to keep all the denominators equal. Because there are 4 winning tickets, there are 1996 losing tickets, so the probability of winning −$1 is $1996/2000$.

Probability Distribution of Prize Winnings				
x	$399	$79	$19	−$1
$P(x)$	1/2000	1/2000	2/2000	1996/2000

The expected payback for a person buying one ticket is

$$399\left(\frac{1}{2000}\right) + 79\left(\frac{1}{2000}\right) + 19\left(\frac{2}{2000}\right) + (-1)\left(\frac{1996}{2000}\right) = -\frac{1480}{2000}$$
$$= -0.74.$$

On average, a person buying one ticket in the raffle will lose $0.74, or 74¢.

It is not possible to lose 74¢ in this raffle: either you lose $1, or you win a prize worth $400, $80, or $20, minus the $1 you pay to play. But if you bought tickets in many such raffles over a long period of time, you would lose 74¢ per ticket on average. It is important to note that the expected value of a random variable may be a number that can never occur in any one trial of the experiment.

Method 2
Alternate Procedure

YOUR TURN 3 Suppose that there is a $5 raffle with prizes worth $1000, $500, and $250. Suppose 1000 tickets are sold and you purchase a ticket. Find your expected payback for this raffle.

An alternative way to compute expected value in this and other examples is to calculate the expected amount won and then subtract the cost of the ticket afterward. The amount won is either $400 (with probability 1/2000), $80 (with probability 1/2000), $20 (with probability 2/2000), or $0 (with probability 1996/2000). The expected payback for a person buying one ticket is then

$$400\left(\frac{1}{2000}\right) + 80\left(\frac{1}{2000}\right) + 20\left(\frac{2}{2000}\right) + 0\left(\frac{1996}{2000}\right) - 1 = -\frac{1480}{2000}$$
$$= -0.74.$$

TRY YOUR TURN 3

EXAMPLE 5 **Friendly Wager**

Each day Donna and Mary toss a coin to see who buys coffee ($1.20 a cup). One tosses and the other calls the outcome. If the person who calls the outcome is correct, the other buys the coffee; otherwise the caller pays. Find Donna's expected payback.

SOLUTION   Assume that an honest coin is used, that Mary tosses the coin, and that Donna calls the outcome. The possible results and corresponding probabilities are shown below.

Possible Results				
Result of Toss	Heads	Heads	Tails	Tails
Call	Heads	Tails	Heads	Tails
Caller Wins?	Yes	No	No	Yes
Probability	1/4	1/4	1/4	1/4

Donna wins a $1.20 cup of coffee whenever the results and calls match, and she loses a $1.20 cup when there is no match. Her expected payback is

$$(1.20)\left(\frac{1}{4}\right) + (-1.20)\left(\frac{1}{4}\right) + (-1.20)\left(\frac{1}{4}\right) + (1.20)\left(\frac{1}{4}\right) = 0.$$

This implies that, over the long run, Donna neither wins nor loses.

A game with an expected value of 0 (such as the one in Example 5) is called a **fair game**. Casinos do not offer fair games. If they did, they would win (on average) $0, and have a hard time paying the help! Casino games have expected winnings for the house that vary from 1.5 cents per dollar to 60 cents per dollar. Exercises 47–52 at the end of the section ask you to find the expected payback for certain games of chance.

The idea of expected value can be very useful in decision making, as shown by the next example.

EXAMPLE 6 Life Insurance

At age 50, you receive a letter from Mutual of Mauritania Insurance Company. According to the letter, you must tell the company immediately which of the following two options you will choose: take $20,000 at age 60 (if you are alive, $0 otherwise) or $30,000 at age 70 (again, if you are alive, $0 otherwise). Based *only* on the idea of expected value, which should you choose?

SOLUTION Life insurance companies have constructed elaborate tables showing the probability of a person living a given number of years into the future. From a recent such table, the probability of living from age 50 to 60 is 0.88, while the probability of living from age 50 to 70 is 0.64. The expected values of the two options are given below.

$$\text{First option: } (20{,}000)(0.88) + (0)(0.12) = 17{,}600$$
$$\text{Second option: } (30{,}000)(0.64) + (0)(0.36) = 19{,}200$$

Based strictly on expected values, choose the second option.

EXAMPLE 7 Bachelor's Degrees

According to the National Center for Education Statistics, 78.7% of those earning bachelor's degrees in education in the United States in 2006–2007 were female. Suppose 5 holders of bachelor's degrees in education from 2006 to 2007 are picked at random. *Source: National Center for Education Statistics.*

(a) Find the probability distribution for the number that are female.

SOLUTION We first note that each of the 5 people in the sample is either female (with probability 0.787) or male (with probability 0.213). As in the previous section, we may assume that the probability for each member of the sample is independent of that of any other. Such a situation is described by binomial probability with $n = 5$ and $p = 0.787$, for which we use the binomial probability formula

$$P(x \text{ successes in } n \text{ trials}) = C(n, x) \cdot p^x \cdot (1 - p)^{n-x},$$

where x is the number of females in the sample. For example, the probability of 0 females is

$$P(x = 0) = C(5, 0)(0.787)^0(0.213)^5 \approx 0.0004.$$

Similarly, we could calculate the probability that x is any value from 0 to 5, resulting in the probability distribution below (with all probabilities rounded to four places).

Probability Distribution of Female Education Graduate					
x	0	1	2	3	4	5
$P(x)$	0.0004	0.0081	0.0599	0.2211	0.4086	0.3019

YOUR TURN 4 In the same survey quoted in Example 7, 81.6% of those earning bachelor's degrees in engineering were male. Suppose 5 holders of bachelor's degrees in engineering were picked at random, find the expected number of male engineers.

(b) Find the expected number of females in the sample of 5 people.

SOLUTION Using the formula for expected value, we have

$$E(x) = 0(0.0004) + 1(0.0081) + 2(0.0599) + 3(0.2211)$$
$$+ 4(0.4086) + 5(0.3019) = 3.935.$$

On average, 3.935 of the people in the sample of 5 will be female.

TRY YOUR TURN 4

There is another way to get the answer in part (b) of the previous example. Because 78.7% of those earning bachelor's degrees in education in the United States in 2006–2007 are female, it is reasonable to expect 78.7% of our sample to be female. Thus, 78.7% of 5 is $5(0.787) = 3.935$. Notice that what we have done is to multiply n by p. It can be shown that this method always gives the expected value for binomial probability.

Expected Value for Binomial Probability

For binomial probability, $E(x) = np$. In other words, the expected number of successes is the number of trials times the probability of success in each trial.

EXAMPLE 8 Female Children

Suppose a family has 3 children.

(a) Find the probability distribution for the number of girls.

SOLUTION Assuming girls and boys are equally likely, the probability distribution is binomial with $n = 3$ and $p = 1/2$. Letting x be the number of girls in the formula for binomial probability, we find, for example,

$$P(x = 0) = C(3, 0)\left(\frac{1}{2}\right)^0\left(\frac{1}{2}\right)^3 = \frac{1}{8}.$$

The other values are found similarly, and the results are shown in the following table.

Probability Distribution of Number of Girls			
x	0	1	2	3
$P(x)$	1/8	3/8	3/8	1/8

We can verify this by noticing that in the sample space S of all 3-child families, there are eight equally likely outcomes: $S = \{ggg, ggb, gbg, gbb, bgg, bgb, bbg, bbb\}$. One of the outcomes has 0 girls, three have 1 girl, three have 2 girls, and one has 3 girls.

(b) Find the expected number of girls in a 3-child family using the distribution from part (a).

SOLUTION Using the formula for expected value, we have

$$\text{Expected number of girls} = 0\left(\frac{1}{8}\right) + 1\left(\frac{3}{8}\right) + 2\left(\frac{3}{8}\right) + 3\left(\frac{1}{8}\right)$$

$$= \frac{12}{8} = 1.5.$$

On average, a 3-child family will have 1.5 girls. This result agrees with our intuition that, on average, half the children born will be girls.

(c) Find the expected number of girls in a 3-child family using the formula for expected value for binomial probability.

SOLUTION Using the formula $E(x) = np$ with $n = 3$ and $p = 1/2$, we have

$$\text{Expected number of girls} = 3\left(\frac{1}{2}\right) = 1.5.$$

This agrees with our answer from part (b), as it must. **TRY YOUR TURN 5**

YOUR TURN 5 Find the expected number of girls in a family of a dozen children.

8.5 EXERCISES

For each experiment described below, let x determine a random variable, and use your knowledge of probability to prepare a probability distribution.

1. Four coins are tossed, and the number of heads is noted.

2. Two dice are rolled, and the total number of points is recorded.

3. Three cards are drawn from a deck. The number of aces is counted.

4. Two balls are drawn from a bag in which there are 4 white balls and 2 black balls. The number of black balls is counted.

Draw a histogram for the following, and shade the region that gives the indicated probability.

5. Exercise 1; $P(x \leq 2)$

6. Exercise 2; $P(x \geq 11)$

7. Exercise 3; $P(\text{at least one ace})$

8. Exercise 4; $P(\text{at least one black ball})$

Find the expected value for each random variable.

9.

x	2	3	4	5
P(x)	0.1	0.4	0.3	0.2

10.

y	4	6	8	10
P(y)	0.4	0.4	0.05	0.15

11.

z	9	12	15	18	21
P(z)	0.14	0.22	0.38	0.19	0.07

12.

x	30	32	36	38	44
P(x)	0.31	0.29	0.26	0.09	0.05

Find the expected value for the random variable x having the probability function shown in each graph.

13.

14.

15.

16.

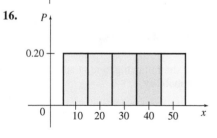

17. For the game in Example 5, find Mary's expected payback. Is it a fair game?

18. Suppose one day Mary brings a 2-headed coin and uses it to toss for the coffee. Since Mary tosses, Donna calls.

   a. Is this still a fair game?

   b. What is Donna's expected payback if she calls heads?

   c. What is Donna's expected payback if she calls tails?

Solve each exercise. Many of these exercises require the use of combinations.

19. Suppose 3 marbles are drawn from a bag containing 3 yellow and 4 white marbles.

   a. Draw a histogram for the number of yellow marbles in the sample.

   b. What is the expected number of yellow marbles in the sample?

20. Suppose 5 apples in a barrel of 25 apples are known to be rotten.

   a. Draw a histogram for the number of rotten apples in a sample of 2 apples.

   b. What is the expected number of rotten apples in a sample of 2 apples?

21. Suppose a die is rolled 4 times.

   a. Find the probability distribution for the number of times 1 is rolled.

   b. What is the expected number of times 1 is rolled?

22. A delegation of 3 is selected from a city council made up of 5 liberals and 6 conservatives.

   a. What is the expected number of liberals in the delegation?

   b. What is the expected number of conservatives in the delegation?

23. From a group of 3 women and 5 men, a delegation of 2 is selected. Find the expected number of women in the delegation.

24. In a club with 20 senior and 10 junior members, what is the expected number of junior members on a 4-member committee?

25. If 2 cards are drawn at one time from a deck of 52 cards, what is the expected number of diamonds?

26. Suppose someone offers to pay you $5 if you draw 2 diamonds in the game in Exercise 25. He says that you should pay 50 cents for the chance to play. Is this a fair game?

27. Your friend missed class the day probability distributions were discussed. How would you explain probability distribution to him?

28. Explain what expected value means in your own words.

29. Four slips of paper numbered 2, 3, 4, and 5 are in a hat. You draw a slip, note the result, and then draw a second slip and note the result (without replacing the first).

   a. Find the probability distribution for the sum of the two slips.

   b. Draw a histogram for the probability distribution in part a.

   c. Find the odds that the sum is even.

   d. Find the expected value of the sum.

APPLICATIONS

Business and Economics

30. Complaints A local used-car dealer gets complaints about his cars as shown in the table below. Find the expected number of complaints per day.

Number of Complaints per Day	0	1	2	3	4	5	6
Probability	0.02	0.06	0.16	0.25	0.32	0.13	0.06

31. Payout on Insurance Policies An insurance company has written 100 policies for $100,000, 500 policies for $50,000, and 1000 policies for $10,000 for people of age 20. If experience shows that the probability that a person will die at age 20 is 0.0012, how much can the company expect to pay out during the year the policies were written?

32. Device Failure An insurance policy on an electrical device pays a benefit of $4000 if the device fails during the first year. The amount of the benefit decreases by $1000 each successive year until it reaches 0. If the device has not failed by the beginning of any given year, the probability of failure during that year is 0.4. What is the expected benefit under this policy? Choose one of the following. *Source: Society of Actuaries.*

  a. $2234 **b.** $2400 **c.** $2500 **d.** $2667 **e.** $2694

33. Pecans Refer to Exercise 41 in Section 8.4. Suppose that 60% of the pecan "blow outs" are good, and 80% of the "good nuts" are good.

  a. If you purchase 50 pecans, what is the expected number of good nuts you will find if you purchase "blow outs"?

  b. If you purchase 50 pecans, what is the expected number of bad nuts you will find if you have purchased "good nuts"?

34. Rating Sales Accounts Levi Strauss and Company uses expected value to help its salespeople rate their accounts. For each account, a salesperson estimates potential additional volume and the probability of getting it. The product of these figures gives the expected value of the potential, which is added to the existing volume. The totals are then classified as A, B, or C, as follows: $40,000 or below, class C; from $40,000 up to and including $55,000, class B; above $55,000, class A. Complete the table below for one salesperson. *Source: James McDonald.*

35. Tour Bus A tour operator has a bus that can accommodate 20 tourists. The operator knows that tourists may not show up, so he sells 21 tickets. The probability that an individual tourist will not show up is 0.02, independent of all other tourists. Each ticket costs $50, and is non-refundable if a tourist fails to show up. If a tourist shows up and a seat is not available, the tour operator has to pay $100 (ticket cost + $50 penalty) to the tourist. What is the expected revenue of the tour operator? Choose one of the following. *Source: Society of Actuaries.*

  a. $935 **b.** $950 **c.** $967 **d.** $976 **e.** $985

Life Sciences

36. Animal Offspring In a certain animal species, the probability that a healthy adult female will have no offspring in a given year is 0.29, while the probabilities of 1, 2, 3, or 4 offspring are, respectively, 0.23, 0.18, 0.16, and 0.14. Find the expected number of offspring.

37. Ear Infections Otitis media, or middle ear infection, is initially treated with an antibiotic. Researchers have compared two antibiotics, amoxicillin and cefaclor, for their cost effectiveness. Amoxicillin is inexpensive, safe, and effective. Cefaclor is also safe. However, it is considerably more expensive and it is generally more effective. Use the tree diagram below (where the costs are estimated as the total cost of medication, office visit, ear check, and hours of lost work) to answer the following. *Source: Journal of Pediatric Infectious Disease.*

  a. Find the expected cost of using each antibiotic to treat a middle ear infection.

  b. To minimize the total expected cost, which antibiotic should be chosen?

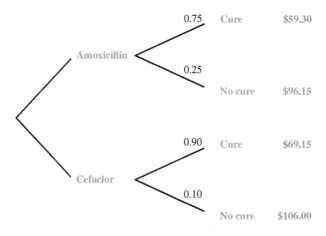

Account Number	Existing Volume	Potential Additional Volume	Probability of Getting It	Expected Value of Potential	Existing Volume + Expected Value of Potential	Class
1	$15,000	$10,000	0.25	$2500	$17,500	C
2	$40,000	$0	—	—	$40,000	C
3	$20,000	$10,000	0.20			
4	$50,000	$10,000	0.10			
5	$5000	$50,000	0.50			
6	$0	$100,000	0.60			
7	$30,000	$20,000	0.80			

38. Hospitalization Insurance An insurance policy pays an individual $100 per day for up to 3 days of hospitalization and $25 per day for each day of hospitalization thereafter. The number of days of hospitalization, X, is a discrete random variable with probability function

$$P(X = k) = \begin{cases} \dfrac{6-k}{15} & \text{for } k = 1, 2, 3, 4, 5 \\ 0 & \text{otherwise.} \end{cases}$$

Calculate the expected payment for hospitalization under this policy. Choose one of the following. *Source: Society of Actuaries.*

a. $85   **b.** $163   **c.** $168   **d.** $213   **e.** $255

Social Sciences

39. Education Recall from Exercise 65 in Section 8.4 that a study from Cleveland Clinic reported that 74% of very-low-birth-weight babies graduate from high school by age 20. If 250 very-low-birth-weight babies are followed through high school, how many would you expect to graduate from high school? *Source: The New England Journal of Medicine.*

40. Cheating Recall from Exercise 64 in Section 8.4 that a poll conducted by *U.S. News and World Report* reported that 84% of college students believe they need to cheat to get ahead in the world today. If 500 college students were surveyed, how many would you expect to say that they need to cheat to get ahead in the world today? *Source: U.S. News and World Report.*

41. Samuel Alito When Supreme Court Justice Samuel Alito was on the U.S. Court of Appeals for the 3rd Circuit, he dissented in the successful appeal of a first-degree murder case. The prosecution used its peremptory challenges to eliminate all African Americans from the jury, as it had in three other first-degree murder trials in the same county that year. According to a majority of the judges, "An amateur with a pocket calculator can calculate the number of blacks that would have served had the State used its strikes in a racially proportionate manner. In the four capital cases there was a total of 82 potential jurors on the venires who were not removed for cause, of whom eight, or 9.76%, were black. If the prosecution had used its peremptory challenges in a manner proportional to the percentage of blacks in the overall venire, then only 3 of the 34 jurors peremptorily struck (8.82%) would have been black and 5 of the 48 actual jurors (10.42%) would have been black. Instead, none of the 48 jurors were black. Admittedly, there was no statistical analysis of these figures presented by either side in the post-conviction proceeding. But is it really necessary to have a sophisticated analysis by a statistician to conclude that there is little chance of randomly selecting four consecutive all white juries?" *Source: findlaw.com.*

a. Using binomial probability, calculate the probability that no African Americans would be selected out of 48 jurors if the percentage African American is 9.76%.

☎ **b.** Binomial probability is not entirely accurate in this case, because the jurors were selected without replacement, so the

selections were not independent. Recalculate the probability in part a using combinations.

c. In his dissent, Judge Alito wrote, "Statistics can be very revealing—and also terribly misleading in the hands of 'an amateur with a pocket calculator.' . . . Although only about 10% of the population is left-handed, left-handers have won five of the last six presidential elections. Our 'amateur with a calculator' would conclude that 'there is little chance of randomly selecting' left-handers in five out of six presidential elections. But does it follow that the voters cast their ballots based on whether a candidate was right- or left-handed?" Given the figures quoted by Judge Alito, what is the probability that at least 5 out of the last 6 presidents elected would be left-handed?

d. The majority of the judges, in disagreeing with Judge Alito, said, "The dissent has overlooked the obvious fact that there is no provision in the Constitution that protects persons from discrimination based on whether they are right-handed or left handed." Furthermore, according to *Chance News*, only 2 of the last 6 men elected president were left-handed. What is the probability that at least 2 out of the last 6 presidents elected would be left-handed? *Source: Chance News.*

Physical Sciences

42. Seeding Storms One of the few methods that can be used in an attempt to cut the severity of a hurricane is to *seed* the storm. In this process, silver iodide crystals are dropped into the storm. Unfortunately, silver iodide crystals sometimes cause the storm to *increase* its speed. Wind speeds may also increase or decrease even with no seeding. Use the table below to answer the following. *Source: Science.*

a. Find the expected amount of damage under each option, "seed" and "do not seed."

b. To minimize total expected damage, what option should be chosen?

	Change in wind speed	Probability	Property damage (millions of dollars)
Seed	+32%	0.038	335.8
	+16%	0.143	191.1
	0	0.392	100.0
	−16%	0.255	46.7
	−34%	0.172	16.3
Do not seed	+32%	0.054	335.8
	+16%	0.206	191.1
	0	0.480	100.0
	−16%	0.206	46.7
	+34%	0.054	16.3

General Interest

43. Cats Kimberly Workman has four cats: Riley, Abby, Beastie, and Sylvester. Each cat has a 30% probability of climbing into the chair in which Kimberly is sitting, independent of how many cats are already in the chair with Kimberly.

a. Find the probability distribution for the number of cats in the chair with Kimberly.

b. Find the expected number of cats in the chair with Kimberly using the probability distribution in part a.

c. Find the expected number of cats in the chair with Kimberly using the formula for expected value of the binomial distribution.

44. Postal Service Mr. Statistics (a feature in *Fortune* magazine) investigated the claim of the U.S. Postal Service that 83% of first class mail in New York City arrives by the next day. (The figure is 87% nationwide.) He mailed a letter to himself on 10 consecutive days; only 4 were delivered by the next day. *Source: Fortune.*

a. Find the probability distribution for the number of letters delivered by the next day if the overall probability of next-day delivery is 83%.

b. Using your answer to part a, find the probability that 4 or fewer out of 10 letters would be delivered by the next day.

c. Based on your answer to part b, do you think it is likely that the 83% figure is accurate? Explain.

d. Find the number of letters out of 10 that you would expect to be delivered by the next day if the 83% figure is accurate.

45. Raffle A raffle offers a first prize of $400 and 3 second prizes of $80 each. One ticket costs $2, and 500 tickets are sold. Find the expected payback for a person who buys 1 ticket. Is this a fair game?

46. Raffle A raffle offers a first prize of $1000, 2 second prizes of $300 each, and 20 third prizes of $10 each. If 10,000 tickets are sold at 50¢ each, find the expected payback for a person buying 1 ticket. Is this a fair game?

Find the expected payback for the games of chance described in Exercises 47–52.

47. Lottery A state lottery requires you to choose 4 cards from an ordinary deck: 1 heart, 1 club, 1 diamond, and 1 spade in that order from the 13 cards in each suit. If all four choices are selected by the lottery, you win $5000. It costs $1 to play.

48. Lottery If exactly 3 of the 4 choices in Exercise 47 are selected, the player wins $200. (Ignore the possibility that all 4 choices are selected. It still costs $1 to play.)

49. Roulette In one form of roulette, you bet $1 on "even." If 1 of the 18 even numbers comes up, you get your dollar back, plus another one. If 1 of the 20 noneven (18 odd, 0, and 00) numbers comes up, you lose your dollar.

50. Roulette In another form of roulette, there are only 19 non-even numbers (no 00).

51. Numbers *Numbers* is a game in which you bet $1 on any three-digit number from 000 to 999. If your number comes up, you get $500.

52. Keno In one form of the game *Keno*, the house has a pot containing 80 balls, each marked with a different number from 1 to 80.

You buy a ticket for $1 and mark one of the 80 numbers on it. The house then selects 20 numbers at random. If your number is among the 20, you get $3.20 (for a net winning of $2.20).

53. Contests A magazine distributor offers a first prize of $100,000, two second prizes of $40,000 each, and two third prizes of $10,000 each. A total of 2,000,000 entries are received in the contest. Find the expected payback if you submit one entry to the contest. If it would cost you $1 in time, paper, and stamps to enter, would it be worth it?

54. Contests A contest at a fast-food restaurant offered the following cash prizes and probabilities of winning on one visit. Suppose you spend $1 to buy a bus pass that lets you go to 25 different restaurants in the chain and pick up entry forms. Find your expected value.

Prize	Probability
$100,000	1/176,402,500
$25,000	1/39,200,556
$5000	1/17,640,250
$1000	1/1,568,022
$100	1/282,244
$5	1/7056
$1	1/588

55. The Hog Game In the hog game, each player states the number of dice that he or she would like to roll. The player then rolls that many dice. If a 1 comes up on any die, the player's score is 0. Otherwise, the player's score is the sum of the numbers rolled. *Source: Mathematics Teacher.*

a. Find the expected value of the player's score when the player rolls one die.

b. Find the expected value of the player's score when the player rolls two dice.

c. Verify that the expected nonzero score of a single die is 4, so that if a player rolls n dice that do not result in a score of 0, the expected score is $4n$.

d. Verify that if a player rolls n dice, there are 5^n possible ways to get a nonzero score, and 6^n possible ways to roll the dice. Explain why the expected value, E, of the player's score when the player rolls n dice is then

$$E = \frac{5^n(4n)}{6^n}.$$

56. Football After a team scores a touchdown, it can either attempt to kick an extra point or attempt a two-point conversion. During the 2005 NFL season, two-point conversions were successful 45% of the time and the extra-point kicks were successful 96% of the time. *Source: NFL.*

a. Calculate the expected value of each strategy.

b. Which strategy, over the long run, will maximize the number of points scored?

c. Using this information, should a team always only use one strategy? Explain.

57. Baseball The 2009 National League batting champion was Hanley Ramirez, with an average of 0.342. This can be interpreted as a probability of 0.342 of getting a hit whenever he bats. Assume that each time at bat is an independent event. Suppose he goes to bat four times in a game. *Source: baseball-reference.com.*

a. Find the probability distribution for the number of hits.

b. What is the expected number of hits that Hanley Ramirez gets in a game?

YOUR TURN ANSWERS

1.

x	0	1	2
$P(x)$	6/11	9/22	1/22

2.

x	0	1	2	3
$P(x)$	1/8	3/8	3/8	1/8

3. −$3.25   **4.** 4.08   **5.** 6

8 CHAPTER REVIEW

SUMMARY

In this chapter we continued our study of probability by introducing some elementary principles of counting. Our primary tool is the multiplication principle:

If n choices must be made, with m_1 ways to make choice 1, and for each of these ways, m_2 ways to make choice 2, and so on, with m_n ways to make choice n, then there are $m_1 \cdot m_2 \cdot \ldots \cdot m_n$ ways to make the entire sequence of choices.

We learned two counting ideas to efficiently count the number of ways we can select a number of objects without replacement:

- permutations (when order matters), and
- combinations (when order doesn't matter).

We also considered distinguishable permutations, in which some of the objects are indistinguishable. All of these concepts were then used to calculate the numerator and denominator of various probabilities. We next explored binomial probability, in which the following conditions were satisfied:

- the same experiment is repeated a fixed number of times (n),
- there are only two possible outcomes (success and failure), and

- the trials are independent, so the probability of success remains constant (p).

We showed how to quickly calculate an entire set of combinations for binomial probability using Pascal's triangle. Finally, we introduced the following terms regarding probability distributions:

- random variable (a function assigning a real number to each outcome of an experiment),
- probability distribution (the possible values of a random variable, along with the corresponding probabilities),
- histogram (a bar graph displaying a probability distribution), and
- expected value (the average value of a random variable that we would expect in the long run).

In the next chapter, we will see how probability forms the basis of the field known as statistics.

Factorial Notation $n! = n(n-1)(n-2)\cdots(3)(2)(1)$
$0! = 1$

Permutations $P(n, r) = \dfrac{n!}{(n-r)!}$

Distinguishable Permutations   If there are n_1 objects of type 1, n_2 of type 2, and so on for r different types, then the number of distinguishable permutations is

$$\frac{n!}{n_1! \, n_2! \cdots n_r!}.$$

Combinations $C(n, r) = \dfrac{n!}{(n-r)! \, r!}$

Binomial Probability $P(x) = C(n, x) \, p^x (1-p)^{n-x}$

Expected Value $E(x) = x_1 p_1 + x_2 p_2 + x_3 p_3 + \cdots + x_n p_n$

For binomial probability, $E(x) = np$.

KEY TERMS

8.1
multiplication principle
factorial notation
permutations
distinguishable permutations

8.2
combinations

8.4
Bernoulli trials
binomial experiment

binomial probability
Pascal's triangle

8.5
random variable
probability distribution

probability function
histogram
expected value
fair game

REVIEW EXERCISES

CONCEPT CHECK

Determine whether each of the following statements is true or false, and explain why.

1. Permutations provide a way of counting possibilities when order matters.

2. Combinations provide a way of counting possibilities when order doesn't matter.

3. The number of distinguishable permutations of n objects, when r are indistinguishable and the remaining $n - r$ are also indistinguishable, is the same as the number of combinations of r objects chosen from n.

4. Calculating the numerator or the denominator of a probability can involve either permutations or combinations.

5. The probability of at least 2 occurrences of an event is equal to the probability of 1 or fewer occurrences.

6. The probability of at least two people in a group having the same birthday is found by subtracting the probability of the complement of the event from 1.

7. The trials in binomial probability must be independent.

8. Binomial probability can be used when each trial has three possible outcomes.

9. A random variable can have negative values.

10. The expected value of a random variable must equal one of the values that the random variable can have.

11. The probabilities in a probability distribution must add up to 1.

12. A fair game can have an expected value that is greater than 0.

PRACTICE AND EXPLORATIONS

13. In how many ways can 6 shuttle vans line up at the airport?

14. How many variations in first-, second-, and third-place finishes are possible in a 100-yd dash with 6 runners?

15. In how many ways can a sample of 3 oranges be taken from a bag of a dozen oranges?

16. In how many ways can a committee of 4 be selected from a club with 10 members?

17. If 2 of the 12 oranges in Exercise 15 are rotten, in how many ways can the sample of 3 include

    a. exactly 1 rotten orange?

    b. exactly 2 rotten oranges?

    c. no rotten oranges?

    d. at most 2 rotten oranges?

18. If 6 of the 10 club members in Exercise 16 are males, in how many ways can the sample of 4 include

    a. exactly 3 males?

    b. no males?

    c. at least 2 males?

19. Five different pictures will be arranged in a row on a wall.

    a. In how many ways can this be done?

    b. In how many ways can this be done if a certain one must be first?

20. In how many ways can the 5 pictures in Exercise 19 be arranged if 2 are landscapes and 3 are puppies and if

    a. like types must be kept together?

    b. landscapes and puppies must be alternated?

21. In a Chinese restaurant the menu lists 8 items in column A and 6 items in column B.

    a. To order a dinner, the diner is told to select 3 items from column A and 2 from column B. How many dinners are possible?

    b. How many dinners are possible if the diner can select up to 3 from column A and up to 2 from column B? Assume at least one item must be included from either A or B.

22. A representative is to be selected from each of 3 departments in a small college. There are 7 people in the first department, 5 in the second department, and 4 in the third department.

    a. How many different groups of 3 representatives are possible?

    b. How many groups are possible if any number (at least 1) up to 3 representatives can form a group? (Each department is still restricted to at most one representative.)

23. Explain under what circumstances a permutation should be used in a probability problem, and under what circumstances a combination should be used.

24. Discuss under what circumstances the binomial probability formula should be used in a probability problem.

A basket contains 4 black, 2 blue, and 7 green balls. A sample of 3 balls is drawn. Find the probabilities that the sample contains the following.

25. All black balls

26. All blue balls

27. 2 black balls and 1 green ball

28. Exactly 2 black balls

29. Exactly 1 blue ball

30. 2 green balls and 1 blue ball

Suppose a family plans 6 children, and the probability that a particular child is a girl is 1/2. Find the probabilities that the 6-child family has the following children.

31. Exactly 3 girls

32. All girls

33. At least 4 girls

34. No more than 2 boys

Suppose 2 cards are drawn without replacement from an ordinary deck of 52. Find the probabilities of the following results.

35. Both cards are red.

36. Both cards are spades.

37. At least 1 card is a spade.

38. One is a face card and the other is not.

39. At least one is a face card.

40. At most one is a queen.

In Exercises 41 and 42, (a) give a probability distribution, (b) sketch its histogram, and (c) find the expected value.

41. A coin is tossed 3 times and the number of heads is recorded.

42. A pair of dice is rolled and the sum of the results for each roll is recorded.

In Exercises 43 and 44, give the probability that corresponds to the shaded region of each histogram.

43.

44.

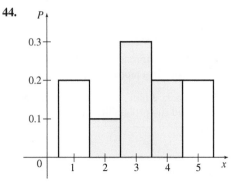

45. You pay $6 to play in a game where you will roll a die, with payoffs as follows: $8 for a 6, $7 for a 5, and $4 for any other results. What are your expected winnings? Is the game fair?

46. Find the expected number of girls in a family of 5 children.

47. Three cards are drawn from a standard deck of 52 cards.

    a. What is the expected number of aces?

    b. What is the expected number of clubs?

48. Suppose someone offers to pay you $100 if you draw 3 cards from a standard deck of 52 cards and all the cards are clubs. What should you pay for the chance to win if it is a fair game?

49. Six students will decide which of them are on a committee by flipping a coin. Each student flips the coin and is on the committee if he or she gets a head. What is the probability that someone is on the committee, but not all 6 students?

50. Find the probability that at most 2 students from Exercise 49 are on the committee.

51. In this exercise we study the connection between sets (from Chapter 7) and combinations (from Chapter 8).

    a. Given a set with n elements, what is the number of subsets of size 0? of size 1? of size 2? of size n?

    b. Using your answer from part a, give an expression for the total number of subsets of a set with n elements.

    c. Using your answer from part b and a result from Chapter 7, explain why the following equation must be true:

$$C(n, 0) + C(n, 1) + C(n, 2) + \cdots + C(n, n) = 2^n.$$

    d. Verify the equation in part c for $n = 4$ and $n = 5$.

    e. Explain what the equation in part c tells you about Pascal's triangle.

In the following exercise, find the digit (0 through 9) that belongs in each box. This exercise is from the 1990 University Entrance Center Examination, given in Japan to all applicants for public universities. *Source: Japanese University Entrance Examination Problems in Mathematics.*

52. The numbers 1 through 9 are written individually on nine cards. Choose three cards from the nine, letting x, y, and z denote the numbers of the cards arranged in increasing order.

    a. There are $\square\square$ such x, y, and z combinations.

    b. The probability of having x, y, and z all even is $\dfrac{\square}{\square\square}$.

    c. The probability of having x, y, and z be consecutive numbers is $\dfrac{\square}{\square\square}$.

    d. The probability of having $x = 4$ is $\dfrac{\square}{\square\square}$.

    e. Possible values of x range from $\square$ to $\square$. If k is an integer such that $\square \leq k \leq \square$, the probability that $x = k$ is $\dfrac{(\square - k)(\square - k)}{\square\square\square}$. The expected value of x is $\dfrac{\square}{\square}$.

APPLICATIONS

Business and Economics

53. Music Players A popular music player is manufactured in 3 different sizes, 8 different colors, and with or without a camera. How many different varieties of this music player are available?

54. Job Qualifications Of the 12 people applying for an entry level position, 9 are qualified and 3 are not. The personnel manager will hire 4 of the applicants.

　a. In how many different ways can she hire the 4 applicants if the jobs are considered the same?

　b. In how many ways can she hire 4 applicants that are qualified?

　c. In how many ways can she hire at most 1 unqualified applicant?

　d. In how many ways can she hire the 4 applicants if the jobs are not the same?

Identity Theft **According to a survey by Javelin Strategy and Research, 1 out of 6 adults in Arizona were victims of identity theft. Suppose that 12 adults are randomly selected from Arizona. Find the probabilities of each of the following results.** *Source: The New York Times.*

55. None of the adults were victims of identity theft.

56. All of the adults were victims of identity theft.

57. Exactly 10 of the adults were victims of identity theft.

58. Exactly 2 of the adults were victims of identity theft.

59. At least 2 of the adults were victims of identity theft.

60. At most 3 of the adults were victims of identity theft.

61. Find the expected number of victims of identity theft in a sample of 12 adults in Arizona.

62. Land Development A developer can buy a piece of property that will produce a profit of $26,000 with probability 0.7, or a loss of $9000 with probability 0.3. What is the expected profit?

63. Insurance Claims An insurance company determines that N, the number of claims received in a week, is a random variable with $P(N = n) = 1/2^{n+1}$, where $n \geq 0$. The company also determines that the number of claims received in a given week is independent of the number of claims received in any other week. Determine the probability that exactly seven claims will be received during a given two-week period. Choose one of the following. *Source: Society of Actuaries.*

　a. 1/256　　**b.** 1/128　　**c.** 7/512　　**d.** 1/64　　**e.** 1/32

64. Injury Claims The number of injury claims per month is modeled by a random variable N with

$$P(N = n) = \frac{1}{(n + 1)(n + 2)}, \quad \text{where } n \geq 0.$$

Determine the probability of at least one claim during a particular month, given that there have been at most four claims during that month. Choose one of the following. *Source: Society of Actuaries.*

　a. 1/3　　**b.** 2/5　　**c.** 1/2　　**d.** 3/5　　**e.** 5/6

65. Product Success A company is considering the introduction of a new product that is believed to have probability 0.5 of

being successful and probability 0.5 of being unsuccessful. Successful products pass quality control 80% of the time. Unsuccessful products pass quality control 25% of the time. If the product is successful, the net profit to the company will be $40 million; if unsuccessful, the net loss will be $15 million. Determine the expected net profit if the product passes quality control. Choose one of the following. *Source: Society of Actuaries.*

　a. $23 million　　**b.** $24 million　　**c.** $25 million

　d. $26 million　　**e.** $27 million

66. Sampling Fruit A merchant buys boxes of fruit from a grower and sells them. Each box of fruit is either Good or Bad. A Good box contains 80% excellent fruit and will earn $200 profit on the retail market. A Bad box contains 30% excellent fruit and will produce a loss of $1000. The a priori probability of receiving a Good box of fruit is 0.9. Before the merchant decides to put the box on the market, he can sample one piece of fruit to test whether it is excellent. Based on that sample, he has the option of rejecting the box without paying for it. Determine the expected value of the right to sample. Choose one of the following. (*Hint:* The a priori probability is the probability before sampling a piece of fruit. If the merchant samples the fruit, what are the probabilities of accepting a Good box, accepting a Bad box, and not accepting the box? What are these probabilities if he does not sample the fruit?) *Source: Society of Actuaries.*

　a. 0　　**b.** $16　　**c.** $34　　**d.** $72　　**e.** $80

67. Overbooking Flights The March 1982 issue of *Mathematics Teacher* included "Overbooking Airline Flights," an article by Joe Dan Austin. In this article, Austin developed a model for the expected income for an airline flight. With appropriate assumptions, the probability that exactly x of n people with reservations show up at the airport to buy a ticket is given by the binomial probability formula. Assume the following: 6 reservations have been accepted for 3 seats, $p = 0.6$ is the probability that a person with a reservation will show up, a ticket costs $400, and the airline must pay $400 to anyone with a reservation who does not get a ticket. Complete the following table.

Number Who Show Up (x)	0	1	2	3	4	5	6
Airline's Income							
$P(x)$							

　a. Use the table to find $E(I)$, the expected airline income from the 3 seats.

　b. Find $E(I)$ for $n = 3$, $n = 4$, and $n = 5$. Compare these answers with $E(I)$ for $n = 6$. For these values of n, how many reservations should the airline book for the 3 seats in order to maximize the expected revenue?

Life Sciences

68. Pharmacology In placebo-controlled trials of Prozac®, a drug that is prescribed to fight depression, 23% of the patients who were taking the drug experienced nausea, whereas 10% of the patients who were taking the placebo experienced nausea. *Source: The New England Journal of Medicine.*

a. If 50 patients who are taking Prozac® are selected, what is the probability that 10 or more will experience nausea?

b. Of the 50 patients in part a, what is the expected number of patients who will experience nausea?

c. If a second group of 50 patients receives a placebo, what is the probability that 10 or fewer will experience nausea?

d. If a patient from a study of 1000 people, who are equally divided into two groups (those taking a placebo and those taking Prozac®), is experiencing nausea, what is the probability that he/she is taking Prozac®?

e. Since 0.23 is more than twice as large as 0.10, do you think that people who take Prozac® are more likely to experience nausea than those who take a placebo? Explain.

Social Sciences

69. Education In Exercise 46 of Section 8.3, we saw that a school in Bangkok requires that students take an entrance examination. After the examination, 5 students are randomly drawn from each group of 40 for automatic acceptance into the school regardless of their performance on the examination. The drawing consists of placing 35 red and 5 green pieces of paper into a box. If the lottery is changed so that each student picks a piece of paper from the box and then returns the piece of paper to the box, find the probability that exactly 5 of the 40 students will choose a green piece of paper. *Source: Mathematics Teacher.*

General Interest

In Exercises 70–73, (a) give a probability distribution, (b) sketch its histogram, and (c) find the expected value.

70. Candy According to officials of Mars, the makers of M&M Plain Chocolate Candies, 20% of the candies in each bag are orange. Four candies are selected from a bag and the number of orange candies is recorded. *Source: Mars, Inc.*

71. Women Athletes Since 1992, the Big 10 collegiate sports conference has been committed to increasing opportunities for women in sports. In the 2007–2008 season, 48% of the conference athletes were women. Suppose 5 athletes are picked at random from Big 10 universities. The number of women is recorded. *Source: Big Ten Conference.*

72. Race In the mathematics honors society at a college, 2 of the 8 members are African American. Three members are selected at random to be interviewed by the student newspaper, and the number of African Americans is noted.

73. Homework In a small class of 10 students, 3 did not do their homework. The professor selects half of the class to present solutions to homework problems on the board, and records how many of those selected did not do their homework.

74. Lottery A lottery has a first prize of $5000, two second prizes of $1000 each, and two $100 third prizes. A total of 10,000 tickets is sold, at $1 each. Find the expected payback of a person buying 1 ticket.

75. Contests At one time, game boards for a United Airlines contest could be obtained by sending a self-addressed, stamped envelope to a certain address. The prize was a ticket for any city to which United flies. Assume that the value of the ticket was $2000 (we might as well go first-class), and that the probability that a particular game board would win was 1/8000. If the stamps to enter the contest cost 44¢ and envelopes cost 4¢ each, find the expected payback for a person ordering 1 game board. (Notice that 2 stamps and envelopes were required to enter.)

76. Lottery On June 23, 2003, an interesting thing happened in the Pennsylvania Lottery's Big 4, in which a four-digit number from 0000 to 9999 is chosen twice a day. On this day, the number 3199 was chosen both times. *Source: Pennsylvania Lottery.*

a. What is the probability of the same number being chosen twice in one day?

b. What is the probability of the number 3199 being chosen twice in one day?

77. Lottery In the Pennsylvania Lottery's Daily Number (Evening) game, a three-digit number between 000 and 999 is chosen each day. The favorite number among players is 000, which on February 13, 2010, was the winning number for the 13th time since 1980. *Source: Pennsylvania Lottery.*

a. Find the number of times that 000 would be expected to win in 30 years of play. (Assume that the game is played 365 days a year.)

b. In 2003, a Daily Number (Midday) drawing was added. The number 000 has only occurred once. Find the number of times that 000 would be expected to win in 7 years of play. (Assume that the game is played 365 days a year.)

78. Lottery New York has a lottery game called Quick Draw, in which the player can pick anywhere from 1 up to 10 numbers from 1 to 80. The computer then picks 20 numbers, and how much you win is based on how many of your numbers match the computer's. For simplicity, we will only consider the two cases in which you pick 4 or 5 numbers. The payoffs for each dollar that you bet are given in the table below.

	How Many Numbers Match the Computer's Numbers					
	0	1	2	3	4	5
You Pick 4	0	0	1	5	55	
You Pick 5	0	0	0	2	20	300

a. According to the Quick Draw playing card, the "Overall Chances of Winning" when you pick 4 are "1:3.86," while the chances when you pick 5 are "1:10.34." Verify these figures.

b. Find the expected value when you pick 4 and when you pick 5, betting $1 each time.

c. Based on your results from parts a and b, are you better off picking 4 numbers or picking 5? Explain your reasoning.

79. Murphy's Law Robert Matthews wrote an article about Murphy's Law, which says that if something can go wrong, it will. He considers Murphy's Law of Odd Socks, which says that if an odd sock can be created it will be, in a drawer of 10 loose pairs of socks. *Source: Sunday Telegraph.*

a. Find the probability of getting a matching pair when the following numbers of socks are selected at random from the drawer.

i. 5 socks **ii.** 6 socks

b. Matthews says that it is necessary to rummage through 30% of the socks to get a matching pair. Using your answers from part a, explain precisely what he means by that.

c. Matthews claims that if you lose 6 socks at random from the drawer, then it is 100 times more likely that you will be left with the worst possible outcome—6 odd socks— than with a drawer free of odd socks. Verify this calculation by finding the probability that you will be left with 6 odd socks and the probability that you will have a drawer free of odd socks.

80. Baseball The number of runs scored in 16,456 half-innings of the 1986 National League Baseball season was analyzed by Hal Stern. Use the table to answer the following questions. *Source: Chance News.*

a. What is the probability that a given team scored 5 or more runs in any given half-inning during the 1986 season?

b. What is the probability that a given team scored fewer than 2 runs in any given half-inning of the 1986 season?

c. What is the expected number of runs that a team scored during any given half-inning of the 1986 season? Interpret this number.

Runs	Frequency	Probability
0	12,087	0.7345
1	2451	0.1489
2	1075	0.0653
3	504	0.0306
4	225	0.0137
5	66	0.0040
6	29	0.0018
7	12	0.0007
8	5	0.0003
9	2	0.0001

81. St. Petersburg Paradox Suppose you play a gambling game in which you flip a coin until you get a head. If you get a head on the first toss, you win $2. You win $4 if the first head occurs on the second toss, $8 if it occurs on the the third toss, and so forth, with a prize of 2^n if the first head occurs on the nth toss. Show that the expected value of this game is infinite. Explain why this is a paradox.*

82. Pit The card game of Pit was introduced by Parker Brothers in 1904 and is still popular. In the version owned by one of the authors of this book, there are 10 suits of 9 identical cards, plus the Bull and the Bear card, for a total of 92 cards. (Newer versions of the game have only 8 suits of cards.) For this problem, assume that all 92 cards are used, and you are dealt 9 cards.

a. What is the probability that you have one card from each of 9 different suits, but neither the Bull nor the Bear?

b. What is the probability that you have a pair of cards from one suit and one card from each of 7 other suits, but neither the Bull nor the Bear?

c. What is the probability that you have two pairs of cards from two different suits and one card from each of 5 other suits, but neither the Bull nor the Bear?

*Many articles have been written in an attempt to explain this paradox, first posed by the Swiss mathematician Daniel Bernoulli when he lived in St. Petersburg. For example, see Székely, Gábor and Donald St. P. Richards, "The St. Petersburg Paradox and the Crash of High-Tech Stocks in 2000," *The American Statistician*, Vol. 58, No. 3, Aug. 2004, pp. 225–231.

EXTENDED APPLICATION

OPTIMAL INVENTORY FOR A SERVICE TRUCK

For many different items it is difficult or impossible to take the item to a central repair facility when service is required. Washing machines, large television sets, office copiers, and computers are only a few examples of such items. Service for items of this type is commonly performed by sending a repair person to the item, with the person driving to the location in a truck containing various parts that might be required in repairing the item. Ideally, the truck should contain all the parts that might be required. However, most parts would be needed only infrequently, so that inventory costs for the parts would be high.

An optimum policy for deciding on which parts to stock on a truck would require that the probability of not being able to repair an item without a trip back to the warehouse for needed parts be as low as possible, consistent with minimum inventory costs. An analysis similar to the one below was developed at the Xerox Corporation. *Source: Management Science.*

To set up a mathematical model for deciding on the optimum truck-stocking policy, let us assume that a broken machine might require one of 5 different parts (we could assume any number of different parts—we use 5 to simplify the notation). Suppose also that the probability that a particular machine requires part 1 is p_1; that it requires part 2 is p_2; and so on. Assume also that failures of different part types are independent, and that at most one part of each type is used on a given job.

Suppose that, on the average, a repair person makes N service calls per time period. If the repair person is unable to make a repair because at least one of the parts is unavailable, there is a penalty cost, L, corresponding to wasted time for the repair person, an extra trip to the parts depot, customer unhappiness, and so on. For each of the parts carried on the truck, an average inventory cost is incurred. Let H_i be the average inventory cost for part i, where $1 \le i \le 5$.

Let M_1 represent a policy of carrying only part 1 on the repair truck, M_{24} represent a policy of carrying only parts 2 and 4, with M_{12345} and M_0 representing policies of carrying all parts and no parts, respectively.

For policy M_{35}, carrying parts 3 and 5 only, the expected cost per time period per repair person, written $C(M_{35})$, is

$$C(M_{35}) = (H_3 + H_5) + NL[1 - (1 - p_1)(1 - p_2)(1 - p_4)].$$

(The expression in brackets represents the probability of needing at least one of the parts not carried, 1, 2, or 4 here.) As further examples,

$$C(M_{125}) = (H_1 + H_2 + H_5) + NL[1 - (1 - p_3)(1 - p_4)],$$

while

$$C(M_{12345}) = (H_1 + H_2 + H_3 + H_4 + H_5) + NL[1 - 1]$$
$$= H_1 + H_2 + H_3 + H_4 + H_5,$$

and

$$C(M_0) = NL[1 - (1 - p_1)(1 - p_2)(1 - p_3)(1 - p_4)(1 - p_5)].$$

To find the best policy, evaluate $C(M_0)$, $C(M_1)$,..., $C(M_{12345})$, and choose the smallest result. (A general solution method is in the *Management Science* paper.)

Example 1

Suppose that for a particular item, only 3 possible parts might need to be replaced. By studying past records of failures of the item, and finding necessary inventory costs, suppose that the following values have been found.

p_1	p_2	p_3	H_1	H_2	H_3
0.09	0.24	0.17	$15	$40	$9

Suppose $N = 3$ and L is $54. Then, as an example,

$$C(M_1) = H_1 + NL[1 - (1 - p_2)(1 - p_3)]$$
$$= 15 + 3(54)[1 - (1 - 0.24)(1 - 0.17)]$$
$$= 15 + 3(54)[1 - (0.76)(0.83)]$$
$$\approx 15 + 59.81 = 74.81.$$

Thus, if policy M_1 is followed (carrying only part 1 on the truck), the expected cost per repair person per time period is $74.81. Also,

$$C(M_{23}) = H_2 + H_3 + NL[1 - (1 - p_1)]$$
$$= 40 + 9 + 3(54)(0.09) = 63.58,$$

so that M_{23} is a better policy than M_1. By finding the expected values for all other possible policies (see the exercises), the optimum policy may be chosen.

EXERCISES

1. Refer to the example and find the following.
   a. $C(M_0)$ b. $C(M_2)$ c. $C(M_3)$ d. $C(M_{12})$
   e. $C(M_{13})$ f. $C(M_{123})$

2. Which policy leads to the lowest expected cost?

3. In the example, $p_1 + p_2 + p_3 = 0.09 + 0.24 + 0.17 = 0.50$. Why is it not necessary that the probabilities add up to 1?

4. Suppose an item to be repaired might need one of n different parts. How many different policies would then need to be evaluated?

DIRECTIONS FOR GROUP PROJECT

Suppose you and three others are employed as service repair persons and that you have some disagreement with your supervisor as to the quantity and type of parts to have on hand for your service calls. Use the answers to Exercises 1–4 to prepare a report with a recommendation to your boss on optimal inventory. Make sure that you describe each concept well since your boss is not mathematically minded.

Appendix A

Solutions to Prerequisite Skills Diagnostic Test   *(with references to Ch. R)*

For more practice on the material in questions 1–4, see *Beginning and Intermediate Algebra* (5th ed.) by Margaret L. Lial, John Hornsby, and Terry McGinnis, Pearson, 2012.

1. $10/50 = 0.20 = 20\%$

2.
$$\frac{13}{7} - \frac{2}{5} = \frac{13}{7} \cdot \frac{5}{5} - \frac{2}{5} \cdot \frac{7}{7} \qquad \text{Get a common denominator.}$$
$$= \frac{65}{35} - \frac{14}{35}$$
$$= \frac{51}{35}$$

3. The total number of apples and oranges is $x + y$, so $x + y = 75$.

4. The sentence can be rephrased as "The number of students is at least four times the number of professors," or $s \geq 4p$.

5.
$$7k + 8 = -4(3 - k)$$
$$7k + 8 = -12 + 4k \qquad\qquad\qquad\qquad\quad \text{Multiply out.}$$
$$7k - 4k + 8 - 8 = -12 - 8 + 4k - 4k \qquad \text{Subtract 8 and } 4k \text{ from both sides.}$$
$$3k = -20 \qquad\qquad\qquad\qquad\qquad\quad \text{Simplify.}$$
$$k = -20/3 \qquad\qquad\qquad\qquad\qquad \text{Divide both sides by 3.}$$

For more practice, see Sec. R.4.

6.
$$\frac{5}{8}x + \frac{1}{16}x = \frac{11}{16} + x$$
$$\frac{5}{8}x + \frac{1}{16}x - x = \frac{11}{16} \qquad\qquad\qquad \text{Subtract } x \text{ from both sides.}$$
$$\frac{5x}{8} \cdot \frac{2}{2} + \frac{x}{16} - x \cdot \frac{16}{16} = \frac{11}{16} \qquad\quad \text{Get a common denominator.}$$
$$\frac{10x}{16} + \frac{x}{16} - \frac{16x}{16} = \frac{11}{16} \qquad\qquad \text{Simplify.}$$
$$\frac{-5x}{16} = \frac{11}{16} \qquad\qquad\qquad\qquad \text{Simplify.}$$
$$x = \frac{11}{16} \cdot \frac{16}{-5} = -\frac{11}{5} \qquad\quad \text{Multiply both sides by the reciprocal of } -5/16.$$

For more practice, see Sec. R.4.

7. The interval $-2 < x \leq 5$ is written as $(-2, 5]$. For more practice, see Sec. R.5.

8. The interval $(-\infty, -3]$ is written as $x \leq -3$. For more practice, see Sec. R.5.

9.
$$5(y - 2) + 1 \leq 7y + 8$$
$$5y - 9 \leq 7y + 8 \qquad\qquad\qquad\qquad\qquad \text{Multiply out and simplify.}$$
$$5y - 7y - 9 + 9 \leq 7y - 7y + 8 + 9 \qquad\quad \text{Subtract } 7y \text{ from both sides and add 9.}$$
$$-2y \leq 17 \qquad\qquad\qquad\qquad\qquad\qquad \text{Simplify.}$$
$$y \geq -17/2 \qquad\qquad\qquad\qquad\qquad\quad \text{Divide both sides by 3.}$$

10.
$$\frac{2}{3}(5p - 3) > \frac{3}{4}(2p + 1)$$
$$\frac{10p}{3} - 2 > \frac{3p}{2} + \frac{3}{4} \qquad\qquad\qquad\qquad \text{Multiply out and simplify.}$$
$$\frac{10p}{3} - \frac{3p}{2} - 2 + 2 > \frac{3p}{2} - \frac{3p}{2} + \frac{3}{4} + 2 \qquad \text{Subtract } 3p/2 \text{ from both sides, and add 2.}$$
$$\frac{10p}{3} \cdot \frac{2}{2} - \frac{3p}{2} \cdot \frac{3}{3} > \frac{3}{4} + 2 \cdot \frac{4}{4} \qquad\qquad \text{Simplify and get a common denominator.}$$
$$\frac{11p}{6} > \frac{11}{4} \qquad\qquad\qquad\qquad\qquad\qquad \text{Simplify.}$$
$$p > \frac{11}{4} \cdot \frac{6}{11} \qquad\qquad\qquad\qquad\qquad \text{Multiply both sides by the reciprocal of } 11/6.$$
$$p > \frac{3}{2} \qquad\qquad\qquad\qquad\qquad\qquad\quad \text{Simplify.}$$

For more practice, see Sec. R.5.

11. $(5y^2 - 6y - 4) - 2(3y^2 - 5y + 1) = 5y^2 - 6y - 4 - 6y^2 + 10y - 2 = -y^2 + 4y - 6$. For more practice, see Sec. R.1.

12. $(x^2 - 2x + 3)(x + 1) = (x^2 - 2x + 3)x + (x^2 - 2x + 3) = x^3 - 2x^2 + 3x + x^2 - 2x + 3 = x^3 - x^2 + x + 3$. For more practice, see Sec. R.1.

13. $(a - 2b)^2 = a^2 - 4ab + 4b^2$. For more practice, see Sec. R.1.

14. $3pq + 6p^2q + 9pq^2 = 3pq(1 + 2p + 3q)$. For more practice, see Sec. R.2.

15. $3x^2 - x - 10 = (3x + 5)(x - 2)$. For more practice, see Sec. R.2.

16.
$$\frac{a^2 - 6a}{a^2 - 4} \cdot \frac{a - 2}{a} = \frac{a(a - 6)}{(a - 2)(a + 2)} \cdot \frac{a - 2}{a} \qquad \text{Factor.}$$

$$= \frac{a - 6}{a + 2} \qquad \text{Simplify.}$$

For more practice, see Sec. R.3.

17. $\dfrac{x + 3}{x^2 - 1} + \dfrac{2}{x^2 + x} = \dfrac{x + 3}{(x - 1)(x + 1)} + \dfrac{2}{x(x + 1)}$ Factor.

$$= \frac{x + 3}{(x - 1)(x + 1)} \cdot \frac{x}{x} + \frac{2}{x(x + 1)} \cdot \frac{x - 1}{x - 1} \qquad \text{Get a common denominator.}$$

$$= \frac{x^2 + 3x}{x(x - 1)(x + 1)} + \frac{2x - 2}{x(x + 1)(x - 1)} \qquad \text{Multiply out.}$$

$$= \frac{x^2 + 5x - 2}{x(x - 1)(x + 1)} \qquad \text{Add fractions.}$$

For more practice, see Sec. R.3.

18.
$$3x^2 + 4x = 1$$
$$3x^2 + 4x - 1 = 0 \qquad \text{Subtract 1 from both sides.}$$

$$x = \frac{-4 \pm \sqrt{4^2 - 4 \cdot 3(-1)}}{2 \cdot 3} \qquad \text{Use the quadratic formula.}$$

$$= \frac{-4 \pm \sqrt{28}}{6} \qquad \text{Simplify.}$$

$$= \frac{-2 \pm \sqrt{7}}{2} \qquad \text{Simplify.}$$

For more practice, see Sec. R.4.

19. First solve the corresponding equation

$$\frac{8x}{z + 3} = 2$$

$$8z = 2(z + 3) \qquad \text{Multiply both sides by } (z + 3).$$
$$8z = 2z + 6 \qquad \text{Multiply out.}$$
$$6z = 6 \qquad \text{Subtract } 2z \text{ from both sides.}$$
$$z = 1 \qquad \text{Divide both sides by 6.}$$

The fraction may also change from being less than 2 to being greater than 2 when the denominator equals 0, namely, at $z = -3$. Testing each of the intervals determined by the numabers -3 and 0 shows that the fraction on the left side of the inequality is less than or equal to 2 on $(-\infty, -3) \cup [1, \infty)$. We do not include $x = -3$ in the solution because that would make the denominator 0. For more practice, see Sec. R.5.

20.
$$\frac{4^{-1}(x^2y^3)^2}{x^{-2}y^5} = \frac{x^2(x^4y^6)}{4y^5} \qquad \text{Simplify.}$$

$$= \frac{x^6y}{4} \qquad \text{Simplify.}$$

For more practice, see Sec. R.6.

21.
$$\frac{4^{1/4}(p^{2/3}q^{-1/3})^{-1}}{4^{-1/4}p^{4/3}q^{4/3}} = \frac{4^{1/2}p^{-2/3}q^{1/3}}{p^{4/3}q^{4/3}} \qquad \text{Simplify.}$$

$$= \frac{2}{p^2q} \qquad \text{Simplify.}$$

For more practice, see Sec. R.6.

22.
$$k^{-1} - m^{-1} = \frac{1}{k}\cdot\frac{m}{m} - \frac{1}{m}\cdot\frac{k}{k} \qquad \text{Get a common denominator.}$$

$$= \frac{m-k}{km} \qquad \text{Simplify.}$$

For more practice, see Sec. R.6.

23. $(x^2 + 1)^{-1/2}(x + 2) + 3(x^2 + 1)^{1/2} = (x^2 + 1)^{-1/2}[x + 2 + 3(x^2 + 1)] = (x^2 + 1)^{-1/2}(3x^2 + x + 5)$. For more practice, see Sec. R.6.

24. $\sqrt[3]{64b^6} = 4b^2$. For more practice, see Sec. R.7.

25. $\dfrac{2}{4 - \sqrt{10}}\cdot\dfrac{4 + \sqrt{10}}{4 + \sqrt{10}} = \dfrac{2(4 + \sqrt{10})}{16 - 10} = \dfrac{4 + \sqrt{10}}{3}$. For more practice, see Sec. R.7.

26. $\sqrt{y^2 - 10y + 25} = \sqrt{(y - 5)^2} = |y - 5|$. For more practice, see Sec. R.7.

Appendix B
Learning Objectives

CHAPTER R: Algebra Reference

R.1: Polynomials

1. Simplify polynomials

R.2: Factoring

1. Factor polynomials

R.3: Rational Expressions

1. Simplify rational expression using properties of rational expressions and order of operations

R.4: Equations

1. Solve linear, quadratic, and rational equations

R.5: Inequalities

1. Solve linear, quadratic, and rational inequalities
2. Graph the solution of linear, quadratic, and rational inequalities
3. Write the solutions of linear, quadratic, and rational inequalities using interval notation

R.6: Exponents

1. Evaluate exponential expressions
2. Simplify exponential expressions

R.7: Radicals

1. Simplify radical expressions
2. Rationalize the denominator in radical expressions
3. Rationalize the numerator in radical expressions

CHAPTER 1: Linear Functions

1.1: Slopes and Equations of Lines

1. Find the slope of a line
2. Find the equation of a line using a point and the slope
3. Find the equation of parallel and perpendicular lines
4. Graph the equation of a line
5. Solve application problems using linear functions

1.2: Linear Functions and Applications

1. Evaluate linear functions
2. Write equations for linear models
3. Solve application problems

1.3: The Least Squares Line

1. Interpret the different value meanings for linear correlation
2. Draw a scatterplot

3. Calculate the correlation coefficient
4. Calculate the least squares line
5. Compute the response variable in a linear model

CHAPTER 2: Systems of Linear Equations and Matrices

2.1: Solution of Linear Systems by the Echelon Method

1. Apply system transformation operations on matrices
2. Solve linear systems using the echelon method
3. Solve application problems

2.2: Solution of Linear Systems by the Gauss-Jordan Method

1. Perform row operations on matrices
2. Solve linear systems by the Gauss-Jordan method
3. Solve application problems

2.3: Addition and Subtraction of Matrices

1. Identify the size of a matrix
2. Add and subtract matrices
3. Solve application problems

2.4: Multiplication of Matrices

1. Multiply a matrix by a constant value
2. Find the product two matrices
3. Simplify matrix expressions
4. Solve application problems

2.5: Matrix Inverses

1. Determine if two matrices are inverses of each other
2. Find the inverse of a matrix (if it exists)
3. Solve a system by using the inverse
4. Solve application problems

2.6: Input-Output Models

1. Find the production matrix for an input-output model
2. Find the demand matrix for an input-output model
3. Solve application problems

CHAPTER 3: Linear Programming: The Graphical Method

3.1: Graphing Linear Inequalities

1. Graph linear inequalities
2. Graph a system of linear inequalities

3. Determine the feasible region for a system of linear inequalities
4. Solve application problems

3.2: Solving Linear Programming Problems Graphically

1. Determine corner points
2. Solve linear programming problems graphically

3.3: Applications of Linear Programming

1. Solve application problems

CHAPTER 4:   Linear Programming: The Simplex Method

4.1: Slack Variables and the Pivot

1. Determine the number of slack variables needed for a linear programming problem
2. Add slack variables to a linear programming problem
3. Generate the initial simplex tableau
4. Identify the pivot and find the resulting matrix
5. Solve linear programming problems using the simplex tableau
6. Solve application problems

4.2: Maximization Problems

1. Solve maximization problems using the simplex tableau and simplex method
2. Solve maximization application problems

4.3: Minimization Problems; Duality

1. Find the transpose of a matrix
2. Generate the dual problem
3. Solve minimization problems using the simplex method
4. Solve minimization application problems

4.4: Nonstandard Problems

1. Solve nonstandard linear programming problems

CHAPTER 5:   Mathematics of Finance

5.1: Simple and Compound Interest

1. Compute the simple and compound interest
2. Compute the effective rate
3. Solve application problems

5.2: Future Value of an Annuity

1. Find terms of a geometric sequence
2. Find the sum of a geometric sequence
3. Find the future value of an annuity

4. Find the future value of an annuity due
5. Find the payment for a sinking fund
6. Solve application problems

5.3: Present Value of an Annuity; Amortization

1. Find the present value of an annuity
2. Find the payment needed for an amortized load
3. Generate an amortization table
4. Solve application problems

CHAPTER 6:   Logic

6.1: Statements

1. Identify statements and compound statements
2. Generate a negation for a statement
3. Convert between statements and symbols
4. Determine the truth value of a compound statement
5. Solve application problems

6.2: Truth Tables and Equivalent Statements

1. Generate a truth table for a compound statement
2. Write the negation for a compound statement
3. Simplify compound statements using De Morgan's law
4. Determine if compound statements are true or false
5. Solve application problems

6.3: The Conditional and Circuits

1. Identify tautologies
2. Identify contradictions
3. Write equivalent statements
4. Simplify circuit problems
5. Draw circuits for statements
6. Solve application problems

6.4: More on the Conditional

1. Generate inverse, converse, and contrapositive statement
2. Solve application problems

6.5: Analyzing Arguments and Proofs

1. Identify valid and invalid arguments
2. Use truth tables to prove rules of logic
3. Solve application problems

6.6: Analyzing Arguments with Quantifiers

1. Use Euler diagrams to test the validity of arguments
2. Construct valid arguments based on Euler diagrams
3. Solve application problems

CHAPTER 7: Sets and Probability

7.1: Sets

1. Understand set notation and terminology
2. Find the union and intersection of sets
3. Solve application problems

7.2: Applications of Venn Diagrams

1. Draw and interpret the Venn diagram for a set
2. Find the number of elements in a set
3. Solve application problems

7.3: Introduction to Probability

1. Generate the sample space for a given experiment
2. Find the probability of an event
3. Identify empirical probabilities
4. Solve application problems

7.4: Basic Concepts of Probability

1. Identify mutually exclusive events
2. Find the probability of an event using probability rules
3. Find the odds of an event
4. Solve application problems

7.5: Conditional Probability; Independent Events

1. Identify independent events
2. Use the product rule to find the probability of an event
3. Find the conditional probability of an event
4. Solve application problems

7.6: Bayes' Theorem

1. Use Bayes' theorem
2. Solve application problems

CHAPTER 8: Counting Principles, Further Probability Topics

8.1: The Multiplication Principle; Permutations

1. Compute the factorial of a number
2. Use the multiplication principle to count outcomes
3. Find the permutation of an outcome
4. Solve application problems

8.2: Combinations

1. Find the combinations of an outcome
2. Solve problems using combinations or permutations
3. Solve application problems

8.3: Probability Applications of Counting Principles

1. Solve probability applications using counting principles

8.4: Binomial Probability

1. Find the probability of binomial experiments
2. Use technology to find binomial probabilities
3. Solve application problems

8.5: Probability Distribution; Expected Value

1. Determine the random variable for a probability distribution
2. Draw a histogram for a probability distribution
3. Generate probability distributions
4. Find the expected value of a probability distribution
5. Solve application problems

CHAPTER 9: Statistics

9.1: Frequency Distributions; Measures of Central Tendency

1. Generate a frequency distribution table
2. Find the mean, median, and mode of a data set
3. Solve application problems

9.2: Measures of Variation

1. Find the range of a data set
2. Find the standard deviation of a data set
3. Solve application problems

9.3: The Normal Distribution

1. Find the area (probability) under the normal curve
2. Understand the standard normal curve
3. Find the z-score associated with a given area (probability) under the normal curve
4. Solve application problems

9.4: Normal Approximation to the Binomial Distribution

1. Use the normal curve distribution to find binomial distribution probabilities
2. Solve application problems

CHAPTER 10: Nonlinear Functions

10.1: Properties of Functions

1. Evaluate nonlinear functions
2. Identify the domain and range of functions
3. Classify functions as odd or even
4. Solve application problems

10.2: Quadratic Functions; Translation and Reflection

1. Complete the square for a given quadratic function
2. Obtain the vertex, y-intercepts and x-intercepts
3. Perform translation and reflection rules to graphs of functions
4. Solve application problems

10.3: Polynomial and Rational Functions

1. Perform translation and reflection rules
2. Identify the degree of a polynomial
3. Find horizontal and vertical asymptotes
4. Solve application problems

10.4: Exponential Functions

1. Evaluate exponential functions
2. Solve exponential equations
3. Graph exponential functions
4. Solve application problems

10.5: Logarithmic Functions

1. Convert expressions between exponential and logarithmic forms
2. Evaluate logarithmic expressions
3. Simplify expressions using logarithmic properties
4. Solve logarithmic equations
5. Identify the domain of a logarithmic function
6. Solve application problems

10.6: Applications: Growth and Decay; Mathematics of Finance

1. Obtain the effective rate
2. Compute future values
3. Solve growth and decay application problems
4. Solve finance application problems

CHAPTER 11:   The Derivative

11.1: Limits

1. Determine if the limit exists
2. Evaluate limits by completing tables and graphically
3. Use limit rules to evaluate limits
4. Solve application problems

11.2: Continuity

1. Identify and apply the conditions for continuity
2. Find points of discontinuity
3. Solve application problems

11.3: Rates of Change

1. Find the average rate of change for functions
2. Find the instantaneous rate of change
3. Solve application problems

11.4: Definition of the Derivative

1. Obtain the slope of the tangent line
2. Obtain the equation of the secant line

3. Find the derivative of a function (using the definition of the derivative)
4. Evaluate the derivative
5. Solve application problems

11.5: Graphical Differentiation

1. Interpret graph of a function and its derivative
2. Sketch the graph of the derivative
3. Solve application problems

CHAPTER 12:   Calculating the Derivative

12.1: Techniques for Finding Derivative

1. Determine the derivative of given functions
2. Find the slope of the tangent line
3. Obtain horizontal tangent points
4. Solve application problems

12.2: Derivative of Products and Quotients

1. Apply the product rule to find the derivative
2. Apply the quotient rule to find the derivative
3. Solve application problems

12.3: The Chain Rule

1. Find the composition of two functions
2. Find the derivative using the chain rule
3. Solve application problems

12.4: Derivatives of Exponential Functions

1. Find the derivative of exponential functions
2. Solve application problems

12.5: Derivatives of Logarithmic Functions

1. Find the derivative of logarithmic functions
2. Solve application problems

CHAPTER 13:   Graphs and the Derivative

13.1: Increasing and Decreasing Functions

1. Identify increasing and decreasing intervals for functions
2. Solve application problems

13.2: Relative Extrema

1. Identify relative extrema points graphically
2. Apply the first derivative test
3. Solve application problems

CHAPTER 17:   Multivariable Calculus

17.1: Functions of Several Variables

1. Evaluate functions with several variables
2. Graph functions with several variables
3. Solve application problems

17.2: Partial Derivatives

1. Find the partial derivative of functions with several variables
2. Find the second partial derivative of functions with several variables
3. Solve application problems

17.3: Maxima and Minima

1. Find relative extrema points
2. Solve application problems

17.4: Lagrange Multipliers

1. Use Lagrange multipliers to find relative extrema points
2. Solve application problems

17.5: Total Differentials and Approximations

1. Find the total differential of functions with several variables
2. Solve application problems

17.6: Double Integrals

1. Evaluate double integrals
2. Find the volume under a given surface
3. Solve application problems

CHAPTER 18:   Probability and Calculus

18.1: Continuous Probability Models

1. Identify probability density functions
2. Find the cumulative distribution function of probability density functions
3. Solve application problems

18.2: Expected Value and Variance of Continuous Random Variables

1. Find the expected value and variance of probability density functions
2. Find the median of a random variable with a given probability density function
3. Solve application problems

18.3: Special Probability Density Functions

1. Find mean and standard deviation of a probability distribution
2. Compute the z-score
3. Solve application problems

Appendix C

MathPrint Operating System for TI-84 and TI-84 Plus Silver Edition

The graphing calculator screens in this text display math in the format of the TI MathPrint operating system. With MathPrint, the math looks more like that seen in a printed book. You can obtain MathPrint and install it by following the instructions in the *Graphing Calculator and Spreadsheet Manual*. Only the TI-84 family of graphing calculators can be updated with the MathPrint operating system. If you own a TI-83 graphing calculator, you can use this brief appendix to help you "translate" what you see in the Classic mode shown on your calculator.

Translating between MathPrint Mode and Classic Mode
The following table compares displays of several types in MathPrint mode and Classic mode (on a calculator without MathPrint installed).

Feature	MathPrint	Classic (MathPrint not installed)
Improper fractions	$\frac{2}{5} - \frac{1}{3}$ $\qquad \frac{1}{15}$ Press **ALPHA** and F1 and select 1: n/d.	2/5 − 1/3 ▶ Frac $\qquad$ 1/15 Enter an expression and press **MATH** and select 1: ▶ Frac.
Mixed fractions	$2\frac{1}{5} * (3\frac{2}{3})$ $\qquad \frac{121}{15}$ Press **ALPHA** and F1 and select 2: Un/d.	Not Supported
Absolute values	$\lvert 10 - 15 \rvert$ $\qquad$ 5 Press **ALPHA** and F2 and select 1:abs(.	abs(10 − 15) $\qquad$ 5 Press **MATH** and ▶ and select 1:abs(.
Summation	$\sum_{I\,=\,1}^{10} (I^2)$ $\qquad$ 385 Press **ALPHA** and F2 and select 2:Σ(.	sum(seq(I^2,I,1,10) $\qquad$ 385 Press **2ND** and LIST and then ▶ twice and select 5:sum(for sum, and press **2ND** and LIST and then ▶ and select 5:seq(for sequence.
Numerical derivatives	$\frac{d}{dX}(X^2)\big\vert_{X\,=\,3}$ $\qquad$ 6 Press **ALPHA** and F2 and select 3:nDeriv(.	nDeriv(X^2,X,3) $\qquad$ 6 Press **MATH** and select 8:nDeriv(.
Numerical values of integrals	$\int_1^5 (X^2)dX$ $\qquad$ 41.33333333 Press **ALPHA** and F2 and select 4:fnInt(.	fnInt(X^2,X,1,5) $\qquad$ 41.33333333 Press **MATH** and select 9:fnInt(.

(continued)

Feature	MathPrint	Classic (MathPrint not installed)
Logarithms	$\log_2(32)$ 5 Press **ALPHA** and F2 and select 5:logBASE(.	Evaluating logs with bases other than 10 or e cannot be done on a graphing calculator if the MathPrint operating system is not installed. To evaluate $\log_2 32$, use the change-of-base formula: $\log(32)/\log(2)$ 5

The $\boxed{Y=}$ Editor

MathPrint features can be accessed from the $\boxed{Y=}$ editor as well as from the home screen. The following table shows examples that illustrate differences between MathPrint in the $\boxed{Y=}$ editor and Classic mode.

Feature	MathPrint	Classic (MathPrint not installed)
Graphing the derivative of $y = x^2$	Plot 1 Plot 2 Plot 3 $\backslash Y_1 \blacksquare \left.\frac{d}{dX}(X^2)\right|_{X=X}$ $\backslash Y_2 =$	Plot 1 Plot 2 Plot 3 $\backslash Y_1 \blacksquare$ nDeriv(X²,X,X) $\backslash Y_2 =$
Graphing an antiderivative of $y = x^2$	Plot 1 Plot 2 Plot 3 $\backslash Y_1 \blacksquare \int_0^X (X^2)dX$ $\backslash Y_2 =$	Plot 1 Plot 2 Plot 3 $\backslash Y_1 \blacksquare$ fnInt(X²,X,0,X) $\backslash Y_2 =$

Appendix D

Table 1 — Formulas from Geometry

PYTHAGOREAN THEOREM
For a right triangle with legs of lengths a and b and hypotenuse of length c, $a^2 + b^2 = c^2$.

CIRCLE
Area: $A = \pi r^2$
Circumference: $C = 2\pi r$

RECTANGLE
Area: $A = lw$
Perimeter: $P = 2l + 2w$

TRIANGLE
Area: $A = \dfrac{1}{2}bh$

SPHERE
Volume: $V = \dfrac{4}{3}\pi r^3$
Surface area: $A = 4\pi r^2$

CONE
Volume: $V = \dfrac{1}{3}\pi r^2 h$

RECTANGULAR BOX
Volume: $V = lwh$
Surface area: $A = 2lh + 2wh + 2lw$

CIRCULAR CYLINDER
Volume: $V = \pi r^2 h$
Surface area: $A = 2\pi r^2 + 2\pi rh$

TRIANGULAR PRISM
Volume: $V = \dfrac{1}{2}bhl$

GENERAL INFORMATION ON SURFACE AREA
To find the surface area of a figure, break down the total surface area into the individual components and add up the areas of the components. For example, a rectangular box has six sides, each of which is a rectangle. A circular cylinder has two ends, each of which is a circle, plus the side, which forms a rectangle when opened up.

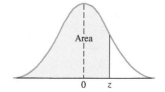

Table 2 — Area Under a Normal Curve to the Left of z, where $z = \dfrac{x - \mu}{\sigma}$

z	0.00	0.01	0.02	0.03	0.04	0.05	0.06	0.07	0.08	0.09
−3.4	0.0003	0.0003	0.0003	0.0003	0.0003	0.0003	0.0003	0.0003	0.0003	0.0002
−3.3	0.0005	0.0005	0.0005	0.0004	0.0004	0.0004	0.0004	0.0004	0.0004	0.0003
−3.2	0.0007	0.0007	0.0006	0.0006	0.0006	0.0006	0.0006	0.0005	0.0005	0.0005
−3.1	0.0010	0.0009	0.0009	0.0009	0.0008	0.0008	0.0008	0.0008	0.0007	0.0007
−3.0	0.0013	0.0013	0.0013	0.0012	0.0012	0.0011	0.0011	0.0011	0.0010	0.0010
−2.9	0.0019	0.0018	0.0017	0.0017	0.0016	0.0016	0.0015	0.0015	0.0014	0.0014
−2.8	0.0026	0.0025	0.0024	0.0023	0.0023	0.0022	0.0021	0.0021	0.0020	0.0019
−2.7	0.0035	0.0034	0.0033	0.0032	0.0031	0.0030	0.0029	0.0028	0.0027	0.0026
−2.6	0.0047	0.0045	0.0044	0.0043	0.0041	0.0040	0.0039	0.0038	0.0037	0.0036
−2.5	0.0062	0.0060	0.0059	0.0057	0.0055	0.0054	0.0052	0.0051	0.0049	0.0048
−2.4	0.0082	0.0080	0.0078	0.0075	0.0073	0.0071	0.0069	0.0068	0.0066	0.0064
−2.3	0.0107	0.0104	0.0102	0.0099	0.0096	0.0094	0.0091	0.0089	0.0087	0.0084
−2.2	0.0139	0.0136	0.0132	0.0129	0.0125	0.0122	0.0119	0.0116	0.0113	0.0110
−2.1	0.0179	0.0174	0.0170	0.0166	0.0162	0.0158	0.0154	0.0150	0.0146	0.0143
−2.0	0.0228	0.0222	0.0217	0.0212	0.0207	0.0202	0.0197	0.0192	0.0188	0.0183
−1.9	0.0287	0.0281	0.0274	0.0268	0.0262	0.0256	0.0250	0.0244	0.0239	0.0233
−1.8	0.0359	0.0352	0.0344	0.0336	0.0329	0.0322	0.0314	0.0307	0.0301	0.0294
−1.7	0.0446	0.0436	0.0427	0.0418	0.0409	0.0401	0.0392	0.0384	0.0375	0.0367
−1.6	0.0548	0.0537	0.0526	0.0516	0.0505	0.0495	0.0485	0.0475	0.0465	0.0455
−1.5	0.0668	0.0655	0.0643	0.0630	0.0618	0.0606	0.0594	0.0582	0.0571	0.0559
−1.4	0.0808	0.0793	0.0778	0.0764	0.0749	0.0735	0.0722	0.0708	0.0694	0.0681
−1.3	0.0968	0.0951	0.0934	0.0918	0.0901	0.0885	0.0869	0.0853	0.0838	0.0823
−1.2	0.1151	0.1131	0.1112	0.1093	0.1075	0.1056	0.1038	0.1020	0.1003	0.0985
−1.1	0.1357	0.1335	0.1314	0.1292	0.1271	0.1251	0.1230	0.1210	0.1190	0.1170
−1.0	0.1587	0.1562	0.1539	0.1515	0.1492	0.1469	0.1446	0.1423	0.1401	0.1379
−0.9	0.1841	0.1814	0.1788	0.1762	0.1736	0.1711	0.1685	0.1660	0.1635	0.1611
−0.8	0.2119	0.2090	0.2061	0.2033	0.2005	0.1977	0.1949	0.1922	0.1894	0.1867
−0.7	0.2420	0.2389	0.2358	0.2327	0.2296	0.2266	0.2236	0.2206	0.2177	0.2148
−0.6	0.2743	0.2709	0.2676	0.2643	0.2611	0.2578	0.2546	0.2514	0.2483	0.2451
−0.5	0.3085	0.3050	0.3015	0.2981	0.2946	0.2912	0.2877	0.2843	0.2810	0.2776
−0.4	0.3446	0.3409	0.3372	0.3336	0.3300	0.3264	0.3228	0.3192	0.3156	0.3121
−0.3	0.3821	0.3783	0.3745	0.3707	0.3669	0.3632	0.3594	0.3557	0.3520	0.3483
−0.2	0.4207	0.4168	0.4129	0.4090	0.4052	0.4013	0.3974	0.3936	0.3897	0.3859
−0.1	0.4602	0.4562	0.4522	0.4483	0.4443	0.4404	0.4364	0.4325	0.4286	0.4247
−0.0	0.5000	0.4960	0.4920	0.4880	0.4840	0.4801	0.4761	0.4721	0.4681	0.4641

(continued)

Table 2 — Area Under a Normal Curve (continued)

z	0.00	0.01	0.02	0.03	0.04	0.05	0.06	0.07	0.08	0.09
0.0	0.5000	0.5040	0.5080	0.5120	0.5160	0.5199	0.5239	0.5279	0.5319	0.5359
0.1	0.5398	0.5438	0.5478	0.5517	0.5557	0.5596	0.5636	0.5675	0.5714	0.5753
0.2	0.5793	0.5832	0.5871	0.5910	0.5948	0.5987	0.6026	0.6064	0.6103	0.6141
0.3	0.6179	0.6217	0.6255	0.6293	0.6331	0.6368	0.6406	0.6443	0.6480	0.6517
0.4	0.6554	0.6591	0.6628	0.6664	0.6700	0.6736	0.6772	0.6808	0.6844	0.6879
0.5	0.6915	0.6950	0.6985	0.7019	0.7054	0.7088	0.7123	0.7157	0.7190	0.7224
0.6	0.7257	0.7291	0.7324	0.7357	0.7389	0.7422	0.7454	0.7486	0.7517	0.7549
0.7	0.7580	0.7611	0.7642	0.7673	0.7704	0.7734	0.7764	0.7794	0.7823	0.7852
0.8	0.7881	0.7910	0.7939	0.7967	0.7995	0.8023	0.8051	0.8078	0.8106	0.8133
0.9	0.8159	0.8186	0.8212	0.8238	0.8264	0.8289	0.8315	0.8340	0.8365	0.8389
1.0	0.8413	0.8438	0.8461	0.8485	0.8508	0.8531	0.8554	0.8577	0.8599	0.8621
1.1	0.8643	0.8665	0.8686	0.8708	0.8729	0.8749	0.8770	0.8790	0.8810	0.8830
1.2	0.8849	0.8869	0.8888	0.8907	0.8925	0.8944	0.8962	0.8980	0.8997	0.9015
1.3	0.9032	0.9049	0.9066	0.9082	0.9099	0.9115	0.9131	0.9147	0.9162	0.9177
1.4	0.9192	0.9207	0.9222	0.9236	0.9251	0.9265	0.9278	0.9292	0.9306	0.9319
1.5	0.9332	0.9345	0.9357	0.9370	0.9382	0.9394	0.9406	0.9418	0.9429	0.9441
1.6	0.9452	0.9463	0.9474	0.9484	0.9495	0.9505	0.9515	0.9525	0.9535	0.9545
1.7	0.9554	0.9564	0.9573	0.9582	0.9591	0.9599	0.9608	0.9616	0.9625	0.9633
1.8	0.9641	0.9649	0.9656	0.9664	0.9671	0.9678	0.9686	0.9693	0.9699	0.9706
1.9	0.9713	0.9719	0.9726	0.9732	0.9738	0.9744	0.9750	0.9756	0.9761	0.9767
2.0	0.9772	0.9778	0.9783	0.9788	0.9793	0.9798	0.9803	0.9808	0.9812	0.9817
2.1	0.9821	0.9826	0.9830	0.9834	0.9838	0.9842	0.9846	0.9850	0.9854	0.9857
2.2	0.9861	0.9864	0.9868	0.9871	0.9875	0.9878	0.9881	0.9884	0.9887	0.9890
2.3	0.9893	0.9896	0.9898	0.9901	0.9904	0.9906	0.9909	0.9911	0.9913	0.9916
2.4	0.9918	0.9920	0.9922	0.9925	0.9927	0.9929	0.9931	0.9932	0.9934	0.9936
2.5	0.9938	0.9940	0.9941	0.9943	0.9945	0.9946	0.9948	0.9949	0.9951	0.9952
2.6	0.9953	0.9955	0.9956	0.9957	0.9959	0.9960	0.9961	0.9962	0.9963	0.9964
2.7	0.9965	0.9966	0.9967	0.9968	0.9969	0.9970	0.9971	0.9972	0.9973	0.9974
2.8	0.9974	0.9975	0.9976	0.9977	0.9977	0.9978	0.9979	0.9979	0.9980	0.9981
2.9	0.9981	0.9982	0.9982	0.9983	0.9984	0.9984	0.9985	0.9985	0.9986	0.9986
3.0	0.9987	0.9987	0.9987	0.9988	0.9988	0.9989	0.9989	0.9989	0.9990	0.9990
3.1	0.9990	0.9991	0.9991	0.9991	0.9992	0.9992	0.9992	0.9992	0.9993	0.9993
3.2	0.9993	0.9993	0.9994	0.9994	0.9994	0.9994	0.9994	0.9995	0.9995	0.9995
3.3	0.9995	0.9995	0.9995	0.9996	0.9996	0.9996	0.9996	0.9996	0.9996	0.9997
3.4	0.9997	0.9997	0.9997	0.9997	0.9997	0.9997	0.9997	0.9997	0.9997	0.9998

Table 3 — Integrals

(*C* is an arbitrary constant.)

1. $\displaystyle\int x^n\,dx = \frac{x^{n+1}}{n+1} + C \quad (\text{if } n \neq -1)$

2. $\displaystyle\int e^{kx}\,dx = \frac{e^{kx}}{k} + C$

3. $\displaystyle\int \frac{a}{x}\,dx = a\ln|x| + C$

4. $\displaystyle\int \ln|ax|\,dx = x(\ln|ax| - 1) + C$

5. $\displaystyle\int \frac{1}{\sqrt{x^2 + a^2}}\,dx = \ln\left|x + \sqrt{x^2 + a^2}\right| + C$

6. $\displaystyle\int \frac{1}{\sqrt{x^2 - a^2}}\,dx = \ln\left|x + \sqrt{x^2 - a^2}\right| + C$

7. $\displaystyle\int \frac{1}{a^2 - x^2}\,dx = \frac{1}{2a}\cdot\ln\left|\frac{a+x}{a-x}\right| + C \quad (a \neq 0)$

8. $\displaystyle\int \frac{1}{x^2 - a^2}\,dx = \frac{1}{2a}\cdot\ln\left|\frac{x-a}{x+a}\right| + C \quad (a \neq 0)$

9. $\displaystyle\int \frac{1}{x\sqrt{a^2 - x^2}}\,dx = -\frac{1}{a}\cdot\ln\left|\frac{a + \sqrt{a^2 - x^2}}{x}\right| + C \quad (a \neq 0)$

10. $\displaystyle\int \frac{1}{x\sqrt{a^2 + x^2}}\,dx = -\frac{1}{a}\cdot\ln\left|\frac{a + \sqrt{a^2 + x^2}}{x}\right| + C \quad (a \neq 0)$

11. $\displaystyle\int \frac{x}{ax + b}\,dx = \frac{x}{a} - \frac{b}{a^2}\cdot\ln|ax + b| + C \quad (a \neq 0)$

12. $\displaystyle\int \frac{x}{(ax + b)^2}\,dx = \frac{b}{a^2(ax + b)} + \frac{1}{a^2}\cdot\ln|ax + b| + C \quad (a \neq 0)$

13. $\displaystyle\int \frac{1}{x(ax + b)}\,dx = \frac{1}{b}\cdot\ln\left|\frac{x}{ax + b}\right| + C \quad (b \neq 0)$

14. $\displaystyle\int \frac{1}{x(ax + b)^2}\,dx = \frac{1}{b(ax + b)} + \frac{1}{b^2}\cdot\ln\left|\frac{x}{ax + b}\right| + C \quad (b \neq 0)$

15. $\displaystyle\int \sqrt{x^2 + a^2}\,dx = \frac{x}{2}\sqrt{x^2 + a^2} + \frac{a^2}{2}\cdot\ln\left|x + \sqrt{x^2 + a^2}\right| + C$

16. $\displaystyle\int x^n\cdot\ln|x|\,dx = x^{n+1}\left[\frac{\ln|x|}{n+1} - \frac{1}{(n+1)^2}\right] + C \quad (n \neq -1)$

17. $\displaystyle\int x^n e^{ax}\,dx = \frac{x^n e^{ax}}{a} - \frac{n}{a}\cdot\int x^{n-1}e^{ax}\,dx + C \quad (a \neq 0)$

Answers to Selected Exercises

Answers to selected writing exercises are provided.

Answers to Prerequisite Skills Diagnostic Test

1. 20%   **2.** 51/35   **3.** $x + y = 75$ **4.** $s \geq 4p$ **5.** $-20/3$ (Sec. R.4)   **6.** $-11/5$ (Sec. R.4)   **7.** $(-2, 5]$ (Sec. R.5)
8. $x \leq -3$ (Sec. R.5)   **9.** $y \geq -17/2$ (Sec. R.5)   **10.** $p > 3/2$ (Sec. R.5)   **11.** $-y^2 + 4y - 6$ (Sec. R.1)
12. $x^3 - x^2 + x + 3$ (Sec. R.1)   **13.** $a^2 - 4ab + 4b^2$ (Sec. R.1)   **14.** $3pq(1 + 2p + 3q)$ (Sec. R.2)   **15.** $(3x + 5)(x - 2)$
(Sec. R.2)   **16.** $(a - 6)/(a + 2)$ (Sec. R.3)   **17.** $(x^2 + 5x - 2)/[x(x - 1)(x + 1)]$ (Sec. R.3)   **18.** $(-2 \pm \sqrt{7})/3$ (Sec. R.4)
19. $[-\infty, -3) \cup [1, \infty)$ (Sec. R.5)   **20.** $x^6 y/4$ (Sec. R.6)   **21.** $2/(p^2 q)$ (Sec. R.6)   **22.** $(m - k)/(km)$ (Sec. R.6)
23. $(x^2 + 1)^{-1/2}(3x^2 + x + 5)$ (Sec. R.6)   **24.** $4b^2$ (Sec. R.7)   **25.** $(4 + \sqrt{10})/3$ (Sec. R.7)   **26.** $|y - 5|$ (Sec. R.7)

Chapter R Algebra Reference

Exercises R.1 (page R-5)

For exercises ...	1–6	7,8,15–22	9–14	23–26
Refer to example ...	2	3	4	5

1. $-x^2 + x + 9$ **2.** $-6y^2 + 3y + 10$ **3.** $-16q^2 + 4q + 6$
4. $9r^2 - 4r + 19$ **5.** $-0.327x^2 - 2.805x - 1.458$ **6.** $0.8r^2 + 3.6r - 1.5$ **7.** $-18m^3 - 27m^2 + 9m$ **8.** $-12x^4 + 30x^2 + 36x$
9. $9t^2 + 9ty - 10y^2$ **10.** $18k^2 - 7kq - q^2$ **11.** $4 - 9x^2$ **12.** $36m^2 - 25$ **13.** $(6/25)y^2 + (11/40)yz + (1/16)z^2$
14. $(15/16)r^2 - (7/12)rs - (2/9)s^2$ **15.** $27p^3 - 1$ **16.** $15p^3 + 13p^2 - 10p - 8$ **17.** $8m^3 + 1$ **18.** $12k^4 + 21k^3 - 5k^2 + 3k + 2$
19. $3x^2 + xy + 2xz - 2y^2 - 3yz - z^2$ **20.** $2r^2 + 2rs - 5rt - 4s^2 + 8st - 3t^2$ **21.** $x^3 + 6x^2 + 11x + 6$ **22.** $x^3 - 2x^2 - 5x + 6$
23. $x^2 + 4x + 4$ **24.** $4a^2 - 16ab + 16b^2$ **25.** $x^3 - 6x^2 y + 12xy^2 - 8y^3$ **26.** $27x^3 + 27x^2 y + 9xy^2 + y^3$

Exercises R.2 (page R-7)

For exercises ...	1–4	5–15	16–20	21–32
Refer to example ...	1	3	2nd CAUTION	4

1. $7a^2(a + 2)$ **2.** $3y(y^2 + 8y + 3)$ **3.** $13p^2 q(p^2 q - 3p + 2q)$
4. $10m^2(6m^2 - 12mn + 5n^2)$ **5.** $(m + 2)(m - 7)$ **6.** $(x + 5)(x - 1)$ **7.** $(z + 4)(z + 5)$ **8.** $(b - 7)(b - 1)$
9. $(a - 5b)(a - b)$ **10.** $(s - 5t)(s + 7t)$ **11.** $(y - 7z)(y + 3z)$ **12.** $(3x + 7)(x - 1)$ **13.** $(3a + 7)(a + 1)$
14. $(5y + 2)(3y - 1)$ **15.** $(7m + 2n)(3m + n)$ **16.** $6(a - 10)(a + 2)$ **17.** $3m(m + 3)(m + 1)$ **18.** $2(2a + 3)(a + 1)$
19. $2a^2(4a - b)(3a + 2b)$ **20.** $12x^2(x - y)(2x + 5y)$ **21.** $(x + 8)(x - 8)$ **22.** $(3m + 5)(3m - 5)$ **23.** $10(x + 4)(x - 4)$
24. Prime   **25.** $(z + 7y)^2$ **26.** $(s - 5t)^2$ **27.** $(3p - 4)^2$ **28.** $(a - 6)(a^2 + 6a + 36)$ **29.** $(3r - 4s)(9r^2 + 12rs + 16s^2)$
30. $3(m + 5)(m^2 - 5m + 25)$ **31.** $(x - y)(x + y)(x^2 + y^2)$ **32.** $(2a - 3b)(2a + 3b)(4a^2 + 9b^2)$

Exercises R.3 (page R-10)

For exercises ...	1–12	13–38
Refer to example ...	1	2

1. $v/7$ **2.** $5p/2$ **3.** $8/9$ **4.** $2/(t + 2)$ **5.** $x - 2$ **6.** $4(y + 2)$ **7.** $(m - 2)/(m + 3)$
8. $(r + 2)/(r + 4)$ **9.** $3(x - 1)/(x - 2)$ **10.** $(z - 3)/(z + 2)$ **11.** $(m^2 + 4)/4$ **12.** $(2y + 1)/(y + 1)$ **13.** $3k/5$
14. $25p^2/9$ **15.** $9/(5c)$ **16.** 2   **17.** $1/4$ **18.** $3/10$ **19.** $2(a + 4)/(a - 3)$ **20.** $2/(r + 2)$ **21.** $(k - 2)/(k + 3)$
22. $(m + 6)/(m + 3)$ **23.** $(m - 3)/(2m - 3)$ **24.** $2(2n - 1)/(3n - 5)$ **25.** 1   **26.** $(6 + p)/(2p)$ **27.** $(12 - 15y)/(10y)$
28. $137/(30m)$ **29.** $(3m - 2)/[m(m - 1)]$ **30.** $(r - 6)/[r(2r + 3)]$ **31.** $14/[3(a - 1)]$ **32.** $23/[20(k - 2)]$
33. $(7x + 1)/[(x - 2)(x + 3)(x + 1)]$ **34.** $(y^2 + 1)/[(y + 3)(y + 1)(y - 1)]$ **35.** $k(k - 13)/[(2k - 1)(k + 2)(k - 3)]$
36. $m(3m - 19)/[(3m - 2)(m + 3)(m - 4)]$ **37.** $(4a + 1)/[a(a + 2)]$ **38.** $(5x^2 + 4x - 4)/[x(x - 1)(x + 1)]$

Exercises R.4 (page R-16)

For exercises ...	1–8	9–26	27–37
Refer to example ...	2	3–5	6,7

1. -12 **2.** $3/4$ **3.** 12   **4.** $-3/8$ **5.** $-7/8$ **6.** $-6/11$ **7.** 4   **8.** $-10/19$ **9.** $-3, -2$
10. $-1, 3$ **11.** 7   **12.** $-2, 5/2$ **13.** $-1/4, 2/3$ **14.** $2, 5$ **15.** $-3, 3$ **16.** $-4, 1/2$ **17.** $0, 4$ **18.** $(5 + \sqrt{13})/6 \approx 1.434$,
$(5 - \sqrt{13})/6 \approx 0.232$ **19.** $(2 + \sqrt{10})/2 \approx 2.581$, $(2 - \sqrt{10})/2 \approx -0.581$ **20.** $(-1 + \sqrt{5})/2 \approx 0.618$, $(-1 - \sqrt{5})/2 \approx$
-1.618 **21.** $5 + \sqrt{5} \approx 7.236$, $5 - \sqrt{5} \approx 2.764$ **22.** $(4 + \sqrt{6})/5 \approx 1.290$, $(4 - \sqrt{6})/5 \approx 0.310$ **23.** $1, 5/2$ **24.** No real
number solutions   **25.** $(-1 + \sqrt{73})/6 \approx 1.257$, $(-1 - \sqrt{73})/6 \approx -1.591$ **26.** $-1, 0$ **27.** 3   **28.** 12   **29.** $-59/6$ **30.** 6
31. 3   **32.** $-5/2$ **33.** $2/3$ **34.** 1   **35.** 2   **36.** No solution   **37.** No solution

Exercises R.5 (page R-21)

For exercises ...	1–14	15–26	27–38	39–42	43–54
Refer to example ...	Figure 1, Example 2	2	3	4	5–7

1. $(-\infty, 4)$

2. $[-3, \infty)$ **3.** $[1, 2)$ **4.** $[-2, 3]$

5. $(-\infty, -9)$ **6.** $[6, \infty)$ **7.** $-7 \leq x \leq -3$ **8.** $4 \leq x < 10$

9. $x \leq -1$ **10.** $x > 3$ **11.** $-2 \leq x < 6$ **12.** $0 < x < 8$ **13.** $x \leq -4$ or $x \geq 4$ **14.** $x < 0$ or $x \geq 3$

15. $(-\infty, 2]$ **16.** $(-\infty, 1)$ **17.** $(3, \infty)$

18. $(-\infty, 1]$

19. $(1/5, \infty)$

20. $(1/3, \infty)$

21. $(-4, 6)$

22. $[7/3, 4]$

23. $[-5, 3)$

24. $[-1, 2]$

25. $[-17/7, \infty)$

26. $(-\infty, 50/9]$

27. $(-5, 3)$

28. $(-\infty, -6] \cup [1, \infty)$

29. $(1, 2)$

30. $(-\infty, -4) \cup (1/2, \infty)$

31. $(-\infty, -4) \cup (4, \infty)$

32. $[-3/2, 5]$

33. $(-\infty, -1] \cup [5, \infty)$

34. $[-1/2, 2/5]$

35. $(-\infty, -1) \cup (1/3, \infty)$

36. $(-\infty, -2) \cup (5/3, \infty)$

37. $(-\infty, -3] \cup [3, \infty)$

38. $(-\infty, 0) \cup (16, \infty)$

39. $[-2, 0] \cup [2, \infty)$

40. $(-\infty, -4] \cup [-3, 0]$

41. $(-\infty, 0) \cup (1, 6)$

42. $(-1, 0) \cup (4, \infty)$

43. $(-5, 3]$ **44.** $(-\infty, -1) \cup (1, \infty)$ **45.** $(-\infty, -2)$

46. $(-2, 3/2)$ **47.** $[-8, 5)$ **48.** $(-\infty, -3/2) \cup [-13/9, \infty)$ **49.** $[2, 3)$ **50.** $(-\infty, -1)$ **51.** $(-2, 0] \cup (3, \infty)$
52. $(-4, -2) \cup (0, 2)$ **53.** $(1, 3/2]$ **54.** $(-\infty, -2) \cup (-2, 2) \cup [4, \infty)$

Exercises R.6 (page R-25)

For exercises . . .	1–8	9–26	27–36	37–50	51–56
Refer to example . . .	1	2	3,4	5	6

1. $1/64$ **2.** $1/81$ **3.** 1 **4.** 1 **5.** $-1/9$ **6.** $1/9$ **7.** 36 **8.** $27/64$
9. $1/64$ **10.** 8^5 **11.** $1/10^8$ **12.** 7 **13.** x^2 **14.** 1 **15.** 2^3k^3 **16.** $1/(3z^7)$ **17.** $x^5/(3y^3)$ **18.** $m^3/5^4$ **19.** a^3b^6
20. $49/(c^6d^4)$ **21.** $(a + b)/(ab)$ **22.** $(1 - ab^2)/b^2$ **23.** $2(m - n)/[mn(m + n^2)]$ **24.** $(3n^2 + 4m)/(mn^2)$
25. $xy/(y - x)$ **26.** $y^4/(xy - 1)^2$ **27.** 11 **28.** 3 **29.** 4 **30.** -25 **31.** $1/2$ **32.** $4/3$ **33.** $1/16$ **34.** $1/5$ **35.** $4/3$
36. $1000/1331$ **37.** 9 **38.** 3 **39.** 64 **40.** 1 **41.** x^4/y^4 **42.** b/a^3 **43.** r **44.** $12^3/y^8$ **45.** $3k^{3/2}/8$ **46.** $1/(2p^2)$
47. $a^{2/3}b^2$ **48.** $y^2/(x^{1/6}z^{5/4})$ **49.** $h^{1/3}t^{1/5}/k^{2/5}$ **50.** m^3p/n **51.** $3x(x^2 + 3x)^2(x^2 - 5)$ **52.** $6x(x^3 + 7)(-2x^3 - 5x + 7)$
53. $5x(x^2 - 1)^{-1/2}(x^2 + 1)$ **54.** $3(6x + 2)^{-1/2}(27x + 5)$ **55.** $(2x + 5)(x^2 - 4)^{-1/2}(4x^2 + 5x - 8)$
56. $(4x^2 + 1)(2x - 1)^{-1/2}(36x^2 - 16x + 1)$

Exercises R.7 (page R-28)

For exercises . . .	1–22	23–26	27–40	41–44
Refer to example . . .	1,2	3	4	5

1. 5 **2.** 6 **3.** -5 **4.** $5\sqrt{2}$ **5.** $20\sqrt{5}$ **6.** $4y^2\sqrt{2y}$ **7.** 9 **8.** 8
9. $7\sqrt{2}$ **10.** $9\sqrt{3}$ **11.** $9\sqrt{7}$ **12.** $-2\sqrt{7}$ **13.** $5\sqrt[3]{2}$ **14.** $3\sqrt[3]{5}$ **15.** $xyz^2\sqrt{2x}$ **16.** $4r^3s^4t^6\sqrt{10rs}$ **17.** $4xy^2z^3\sqrt[3]{2y^2}$
18. $x^2yz^2\sqrt[4]{y^3z^3}$ **19.** $ab\sqrt{ab}(b - 2a^2 + b^3)$ **20.** $p^2\sqrt{pq}(pq - q^4 + p^2)$ **21.** $\sqrt[6]{a^5}$ **22.** $b^2\sqrt[4]{b}$ **23.** $|4 - x|$
24. $|3y + 5|$ **25.** Cannot be simplified **26.** Cannot be simplified **27.** $5\sqrt{7}/7$ **28.** $\sqrt{10}/2$ **29.** $-\sqrt{3}/2$ **30.** $\sqrt{2}$
31. $-3(1 + \sqrt{2})$ **32.** $-5(2 + \sqrt{6})/2$ **33.** $3(2 - \sqrt{2})$ **34.** $(5 - \sqrt{10})/3$ **35.** $(\sqrt{r} + \sqrt{3})/(r - 3)$
36. $5(\sqrt{m} + \sqrt{5})/(m - 5)$ **37.** $\sqrt{y} + \sqrt{5}$ **38.** $(z + \sqrt{5z} - \sqrt{z} - \sqrt{5})/(z - 5)$ **39.** $-2x - 2\sqrt{x(x + 1)} - 1$
40. $[p^2 + p + 2\sqrt{p(p^2 - 1)} - 1]/(-p^2 + p + 1)$ **41.** $-1/[2(1 - \sqrt{2})]$ **42.** $1/(3 + \sqrt{3})$
43. $-1/[2x - 2\sqrt{x(x + 1)} + 1]$ **44.** $2/[p + \sqrt{p(p - 2)}]$

Chapter 1 Linear Functions

Exercises 1.1 (page 13)

For exercises . . .	1–4	5–8	13,29,30	14,31–34	15–17	18,27	19–24	25,26	28	45–60	61–75
Refer to example . . .	1	3	8	9	4	7	5	2	6	11–13	10,14

1. $3/5$ **3.** Not defined **5.** 1
7. $5/9$ **9.** Not defined **11.** 0 **13.** 2 **15.** $y = -2x + 5$ **17.** $y = -7$ **19.** $y = -(1/3)x + 10/3$ **21.** $y = 6x - 7/2$

23. $x = -8$ **25.** $x + 2y = -6$ **27.** $x = -6$ **29.** $3x + 2y = 0$ **31.** $x - y = 7$ **33.** $5x - y = -4$ **35.** No **39.** a **41.** -4

45.   **47.**   **49.**   **51.**

53.   **55.**   **57.**   **59.**

61. a. 12,000 $y = 12{,}000x + 3000$ **b.** 8 years 1 month **63. a.** $y = 4.612t + 86.164$ **b.** 178.4, which is slightly more than the actual CPI. **c.** It is increasing at a rate of approximately 4.6 per year. **65. a.** $u = 0.85(220 - x) = 187 - 0.85x$, $l = 0.7(220 - x) = 154 - 0.7x$ **b.** 140 to 170 beats per minute. **c.** 126 to 153 beats per minute. **d.** The women are 16 and 52. Their pulse is 143 beats per minute. **67.** Approximately 86 yr **69. a.** $y = 0.3444t + 14.1$ **b.** 2022
71. a. $y = 14{,}792.05t - 490{,}416$ **b.** 1,210,670 **73. a.** There appears to be a linear relationship. **b.** $y = 76.9x$ **c.** About 780 megaparsecs (about 1.5×10^{22} mi) **d.** About 12.4 billion yr

75. a.
Yes, the data are approximately linear.
b. $y = 1133.4t + 16{,}072$; the slope 1133.4 indicates that tuition and fees have increased approximately \$1133 per year. **c.** The year 2025 is too far in the future to rely on this equation to predict costs; too many other factors may influence these costs by then.

Exercises 1.2 (page 23)

For exercises …	1–10	19–22	23–26	27–32	33–36,48	37–44	45–47
Refer to example …	1	4	5	2,3	5	6	7

1. -3 **3.** 22 **5.** 0 **7.** -4 **9.** $7 - 5t$ **11.** True
13. True **19.** If $R(x)$ is the cost of renting a snowboard for x hours, then $R(x) = 2.25x + 10$. **21.** If $C(x)$ is the cost of parking a car for x half-hours, then $C(x) = 0.75x + 2$. **23.** $C(x) = 30x + 100$ **25.** $C(x) = 75x + 550$ **27. a.** \$16 **b.** \$11 **c.** \$6
d. 640 watches **e.** 480 watches **f.** 320 watches
g.   **h.** 0 watches **k.**   **l.** 800 watches, \$6
i. About 1333 watches
j. About 2667 watches

29. a. 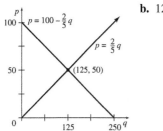 **b.** 125 tubs, \$50 **31.** $D(q) = 6.9 - 0.4q$ **33. a.** $C(x) = 3.50x + 90$ **b.** 17 shirts
c. 108 shirts **35. a.** $C(x) = 0.097x + 1.32$ **b.** \$1.32 **c.** \$98.32
d. \$98.42 **e.** 9.7¢ **f.** 9.7¢, the cost of producing one additional cup of coffee would be 9.7¢. **37. a.** 2 units **b.** \$980 **c.** 52 units
39. Break-even quantity is 45 units; don't produce; $P(x) = 20x - 900$
41. Break-even quantity is -50 units; impossible to make a profit when $C(x) > R(x)$ for all positive x; $P(x) = -10x - 500$ (always a loss)
43. 5 **45. a.** 14.4°C **b.** -28.9°C **c.** 122°C **47.** -40°

Exercises 1.3 (page 32)

For exercises ...	3b,4,10d, 11d,12e,13e, 15b,16d,17b, 18d,19c,20b, 22d,24c,25d, 26a	3c,10a,11a, 12a,13a,15c, 16b,17c,18a, 19a,21c,22a, 23a,24b, 25a,26b	3d,10b,11b, 12c,13c,18b, 21d,22bc,23b, 26c	5ab,6ab, 7a,8a, 14ab,21ab	5c,6c, 15e	10c,11c, 12d,13d, 18c,23c
Refer to example ...	4	1	2	1,4	5	3

3. a. 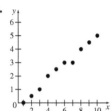 **b.** 0.993 **c.** $Y = 0.555x - 0.5$ **d.** 5.6

5. a. $Y = 0.9783x + 0.0652, 0.9783$ **b.** $Y = 1.5, 0$ **c.** The point $(9,9)$ is an outlier that has a strong effect on the least squares line and the correlation coefficient.

7. a. 0.7746 **b.**

11. a. $Y = -0.1534x + 11.36$ **b.** About 6760 **c.** 2025 **d.** -0.9890 **13. a.** $Y = 97.73x + 1833.3$ **b.** About $97.73 billion per year **c.** $3299 billion **d.** 2023 **e.** 0.9909

15. a. They lie in a linear pattern. **b.** $r = 0.693$; there is a positive correlation between the price and the distance. **c.** $Y = 0.0738x + 111.83$; the marginal cost is 7.38 cents per mile. **d.** In 2000 marginal cost was 2.43 cents per mile; it has increased to 7.38 cents per mile. **e.** Phoenix

17. a. **b.** 0.959, yes **c.** $Y = 3.98x + 22.7$ **19. a.** $Y = -0.1175x + 17.74$ **b.** 14.2 **c.** -0.9326

21. a. $Y = -0.08915x + 74.28$, $r = -0.1035$. The taller the student, the shorter is the ideal partner's height.
b. Females: $Y = 0.6674x + 27.89$, $r = 0.9459$; males: $Y = 0.4348x + 34.04$, $r = 0.7049$

 23. a. **b.** $Y = 0.366x + 0.803$; the line seems to fit the data.

c. $r = 0.995$ indicates a good fit, which confirms the conclusion in part b. **25. a.** -0.995; yes **b.** $Y = -0.0769x + 5.91$ **c.** 2.07 points
27. a. 4.298 miles per hour **b.** ; yes **c.** $Y = 4.317x + 3.419$ **d.** 0.9971; yes **e.** 4.317 miles per hour

Chapter 1 Review Exercises (page 39)

For exercises . . .	1–6,15–44	7–10,13,45–59b,62,63	11,12,14,59c–61,64,65
Refer to section . . .	1	2	3

1. False **2.** False **3.** True **4.** False **5.** True **6.** False **7.** True **8.** False **9.** False **10.** False **11.** False **12.** True
15. 1 **17.** $-2/11$ **19.** $-4/3$ **21.** 0 **23.** 5 **25.** $y = (2/3)x - 13/3$ **27.** $y = -x - 3$ **29.** $y = -10$ **31.** $2x - y = 10$
33. $x = -1$ **35.** $y = -5$

37.   **39.**   **41.**   **43.**

45. a. $E = 352 + 42x$ (where x is in thousands) **b.** $R = 130x$ (where x is in thousands) **c.** More than 4000 chips
47. $S(q) = 0.5q + 10$ **49.** \$41.25, 62.5 diet pills **51.** $C(x) = 180x + 2000$ **53.** $C(x) = 46x + 120$ **55. a.** 40 pounds
b. \$280 **57.** $y = 7.23t + 11.9$ **59. a.** $y = 836x + 7500$ **b.** $y = 795x + 8525$ **c.** $Y = 843.7x + 7662$
d.

f. 0.9995 **61. a.** $Y = 0.9724x + 31.43$ **b.** About 216 **c.** 0.9338 **63.** $y = 1.22t + 48.9$
65. a. 0.6998; yes, but the fit is not very good. **b.**
c. $Y = 3.396x + 117.2$ **d.** \$3396

Chapter 2 Systems of Linear Equations and Matrices

Exercises 2.1 (page 52)

For exercises . . .	1–20	23–26,29–33,40–43	35–39,44–48
Refer to example . . .	1–3	5	4

1. $(3, 2)$ **3.** $(1, 3)$ **5.** $(-2, 0)$ **7.** $(0, 2)$ **9.** $(3, -2)$ **11.** $(2, -2)$
13. No solution **15.** $((2y - 4)/3, y)$ **17.** $(4, 1)$ **19.** $(7, -2)$ **21.** No **23.** 4 **25.** 3 **29.** $(8z - 4, 3 - 5z, z)$
31. $(3 - z, 4 - z, z)$ **35.** \$27 **37.** 400 main floor, 200 balcony **39.** Not possible; inconsistent system **41.** Either 10 buffets,
5 chairs, and no tables, or 11 buffets, 1 chair, and 1 table **43.** $z + 80$ long-sleeve blouses, $260 - 2z$ short-sleeve blouses, and
z sleeveless blouses with $0 \le z \le 130$. **45. a.** March 23, March 19 **b.** 1991 **47.** 36 field goals, 28 foul shots

Exercises 2.2 (page 65)

For exercises . . .	1–8,11–42	44–70
Refer to example . . .	1–5	6

1. $\begin{bmatrix} 3 & 1 & | & 6 \\ 2 & 5 & | & 15 \end{bmatrix}$ **3.** $\begin{bmatrix} 2 & 1 & 1 & | & 3 \\ 3 & -4 & 2 & | & -7 \\ 1 & 1 & 1 & | & 2 \end{bmatrix}$ **5.** $x = 2, y = 3$ **7.** $x = 4, y = -5, z = 1$ **9.** Row operations

11. $\begin{bmatrix} 3 & 7 & 4 & | & 10 \\ 0 & 1 & -5 & | & -8 \\ 0 & 4 & 5 & | & 11 \end{bmatrix}$ **13.** $\begin{bmatrix} 1 & 0 & 0 & | & -3 \\ 0 & 3 & 2 & | & 5 \\ 0 & 5 & 3 & | & 7 \end{bmatrix}$ **15.** $\begin{bmatrix} 1 & 0 & 0 & | & 6 \\ 0 & 5 & 0 & | & 9 \\ 0 & 0 & 4 & | & 8 \end{bmatrix}$ **17.** $(2, 3)$ **19.** $(1, 6)$ **21.** No solution

23. $((3y + 1)/6, y)$ **25.** $(4, 1, 0)$ **27.** No solution **29.** $(-1, 23, 16)$ **31.** $((-9z + 5)/23, (10z - 3)/23, z)$
33. $((-2z + 62)/35, (3z + 5)/7, z)$ **35.** $((9 - 3y - z)/2, y, z)$ **37.** $(0, 2, -2, 1)$; the answers are given in the order x, y, z, w.
39. $(-w - 3, -4w - 19, -3w - 2, w)$ **41.** $(28.9436, 36.6326, 9.6390, 37.1036)$ **43.** row 1: 3/8, 1/6, 11/24; row 2: 5/12, 1/3,
1/4; row 3: 5/24, 1/2, 7/24 **45.** \$2000 in U.S. Savings bonds, \$4000 in mutual funds, \$4000 in money market **47.** 2000 chairs,
1600 cabinets, and 2500 buffets. **49. a.** 5 trucks, 2 vans, and 3 SUVs. **b.** Use 2 trucks, 6 vans, and 1 SUV, or use 5 trucks, 2
vans, and 3 SUVs. **51. a.** \$12,000 at 8%, \$7000 at 9%, and \$6000 at 10% **b.** The amount borrowed at 10% must be less than or
equal to \$9500. If $z = 5000, they borrowed \$11,000 at 8% and \$9000 at 9%. **c.** No solution. **d.** The total annual interest would
be \$2220, not \$2190, as specified as one of the conditions. **53.** The first supplier should send 40 units to Roseville and 35 units to
Akron. The second supplier should send 0 units to Roseville and 40 units to Akron **55. a.** 26 **b.** 0 two-person, 50 four-person,
and 0 six-person tents **c.** 25 two-person, 0 four-person, and 25 six-person tents **57. a.** 400/9 g of group A, 400/3 g of group B,
and 2000/9 g of group C. **b.** For any positive number z of grams of group C, there should be z grams less than 800/3 g of group A

and 400/3 g of group B.   **c.** No   **59.** About 244 fish of species A, 39 fish of species B, and 101 fish of species C.   **61. b.** 7,206,360 white cows, 4,893,246 black cows, 3,515,820 spotted cows, and 5,439,213 brown cows   **63. a.** $r = 175,000, b = 375,000$
65. 8.15, 4.23, 3.15   **67. a.** 24 balls, 57 dolls, and 19 cars   **b.** None   **c.** 48   **d.** 5 balls, 95 dolls, and 0 cars   **e.** 52 balls, 1 doll, and 47 cars   **69. a.** (1, 1, 1, 1); the strategy required to turn all the lights out is to push every button one time.   **b.** (0, 1, 1, 0); the strategy required to turn all the lights out is to push the button in the first row, second column, and push the button in the second row, first column.

Exercises 2.3 (page 74)

For exercises ...	1–6,15–20	7–14	21–32	39,40,43	41,48	42	44–46
Refer to example ...	3	2	4,6	5	1	5,7	7

1. False; not all corresponding elements are equal.
3. True   **5.** True   **7.** 2×2; square   **9.** 3×4 **11.** 2×1; column   **13.** Undefined   **15.** $x = 4, y = -8, z = 1$
17. $s = 10, t = 0, r = 7$ **19.** $a = 20, b = 5, c = 0, d = 4, f = 1$

21. $\begin{bmatrix} 10 & 4 & -5 & -6 \\ 4 & 5 & 3 & 11 \end{bmatrix}$ **23.** Not possible   **25.** $\begin{bmatrix} 1 & 5 & 6 & -9 \\ 5 & 7 & 2 & 1 \\ -7 & 2 & 2 & -7 \end{bmatrix}$ **27.** $\begin{bmatrix} 3 & 4 \\ 4 & 8 \end{bmatrix}$ **29.** $\begin{bmatrix} 10 & -2 \\ 10 & 9 \end{bmatrix}$

31. $\begin{bmatrix} -12x + 8y & -x + y \\ x & 8x - y \end{bmatrix}$ **33.** $\begin{bmatrix} -x & -y \\ -z & -w \end{bmatrix}$ **39. a.** Chicago: $\begin{bmatrix} 4.05 & 7.01 \\ 3.27 & 3.51 \end{bmatrix}$, Seattle: $\begin{bmatrix} 4.40 & 6.90 \\ 3.54 & 3.76 \end{bmatrix}$ **b.** $\begin{bmatrix} 4.42 & 7.43 \\ 3.38 & 3.62 \end{bmatrix}$

41. a. $\begin{bmatrix} 2 & 1 & 2 & 1 \\ 3 & 2 & 2 & 1 \\ 4 & 3 & 2 & 1 \end{bmatrix}$ **b.** $\begin{bmatrix} 5 & 0 & 7 \\ 0 & 10 & 1 \\ 0 & 15 & 2 \\ 10 & 12 & 8 \end{bmatrix}$ **c.** $\begin{bmatrix} 8 \\ 4 \\ 5 \end{bmatrix}$ **43. a.** 8   **b.** 3   **c.** $\begin{bmatrix} 85 & 15 \\ 27 & 73 \end{bmatrix}$ **d.** Yes

45. a. $\begin{bmatrix} 60.0 & 68.3 \\ 63.8 & 72.5 \\ 64.5 & 73.6 \\ 68.3 & 75.2 \end{bmatrix}$ **b.** $\begin{bmatrix} 68.0 & 75.6 \\ 70.7 & 78.1 \\ 72.7 & 79.4 \\ 74.9 & 80.1 \end{bmatrix}$ **c.** $\begin{bmatrix} -8.0 & -7.3 \\ -6.9 & -5.6 \\ -8.2 & -5.8 \\ -6.6 & -4.9 \end{bmatrix}$ **47. a.** $\begin{bmatrix} 51.2 & 7.9 \\ 59.8 & 11.1 \\ 66.2 & 11.3 \\ 73.8 & 13.2 \\ 78.5 & 16.5 \\ 83.0 & 19.6 \end{bmatrix}$ **b.** $\begin{bmatrix} 45.3 & 7.9 \\ 47.9 & 8.5 \\ 50.8 & 9.2 \\ 53.4 & 9.3 \\ 57.0 & 10.6 \\ 62.3 & 13.3 \end{bmatrix}$ **c.** $\begin{bmatrix} 5.9 & 0 \\ 11.9 & 2.6 \\ 15.4 & 2.1 \\ 20.4 & 3.9 \\ 21.5 & 5.9 \\ 20.7 & 6.3 \end{bmatrix}$

Exercises 2.4 (page 83)

For exercises ...	1–6,49,50	7–12	15–31,51	43–48
Refer to example ...	1	4	2,3,5	6

1. $\begin{bmatrix} -4 & 8 \\ 0 & 6 \end{bmatrix}$ **3.** $\begin{bmatrix} 12 & -24 \\ 0 & -18 \end{bmatrix}$ **5.** $\begin{bmatrix} -22 & -6 \\ 20 & -12 \end{bmatrix}$ **7.** 2×2; 2×2

9. 3×4; BA does not exist.   **11.** AB does not exist; 3×2 **13.** columns; rows   **15.** $\begin{bmatrix} 8 \\ -1 \end{bmatrix}$ **17.** $\begin{bmatrix} 14 \\ -23 \end{bmatrix}$ **19.** $\begin{bmatrix} -7 & 2 & 8 \\ 27 & -12 & 12 \end{bmatrix}$

21. $\begin{bmatrix} -2 & 10 \\ 0 & 8 \end{bmatrix}$ **23.** $\begin{bmatrix} 13 & 5 \\ 25 & 15 \end{bmatrix}$ **25.** $\begin{bmatrix} 13 \\ 29 \end{bmatrix}$ **27.** $\begin{bmatrix} 7 \\ -33 \\ 4 \end{bmatrix}$ **29.** $\begin{bmatrix} 22 & -8 \\ 11 & -4 \end{bmatrix}$ **31. a.** $\begin{bmatrix} 16 & 22 \\ 7 & 19 \end{bmatrix}$ **b.** $\begin{bmatrix} 5 & -5 \\ 0 & 30 \end{bmatrix}$ **c.** No   **d.** No

39. a. $\begin{bmatrix} 6 & 106 & 158 & 222 & 28 \\ 120 & 139 & 64 & 75 & 115 \\ -146 & -2 & 184 & 144 & -129 \\ 106 & 94 & 24 & 116 & 110 \end{bmatrix}$ **b.** Does not exist   **c.** No   **41. a.** $\begin{bmatrix} -1 & 5 & 9 & 13 & -1 \\ 7 & 17 & 2 & -10 & 6 \\ 18 & 9 & -12 & 12 & 22 \\ 9 & 4 & 18 & 10 & -3 \\ 1 & 6 & 10 & 28 & 5 \end{bmatrix}$

b. $\begin{bmatrix} -2 & -9 & 90 & 77 \\ -42 & -63 & 127 & 62 \\ 413 & 76 & 180 & -56 \\ -29 & -44 & 198 & 85 \\ 137 & 20 & 162 & 103 \end{bmatrix}$ **c.** $\begin{bmatrix} -56 & -1 & 1 & 45 \\ -156 & -119 & 76 & 122 \\ 315 & 86 & 118 & -91 \\ -17 & -17 & 116 & 51 \\ 118 & 19 & 125 & 77 \end{bmatrix}$ **d.** $\begin{bmatrix} 54 & -8 & 89 & 32 \\ 114 & 56 & 51 & -60 \\ 98 & -10 & 62 & 35 \\ -12 & -27 & 82 & 34 \\ 19 & 1 & 37 & 26 \end{bmatrix}$ **e.** $\begin{bmatrix} -2 & -9 & 90 & 77 \\ -42 & -63 & 127 & 62 \\ 413 & 76 & 180 & -56 \\ -29 & -44 & 198 & 85 \\ 137 & 20 & 162 & 103 \end{bmatrix}$

$$
\begin{array}{cc}
 & \text{A} \quad \text{B} \\
\begin{array}{l}\text{Dept. 1} \\ \text{Dept. 2} \\ \text{Dept. 3} \\ \text{Dept. 4}\end{array} &
\begin{bmatrix} 57 & 70 \\ 41 & 54 \\ 27 & 40 \\ 39 & 40 \end{bmatrix}
\end{array}
$$

f. Yes   **43. a.** (matrix above)   **b.** Supplier A: \$164; Supplier B: \$204; Supplier A   **45. a.** $\begin{bmatrix} 4.24 & 6.95 \\ 3.42 & 3.64 \end{bmatrix}$ **b.** $\begin{bmatrix} 4.41 & 7.17 \\ 3.46 & 3.69 \end{bmatrix}$

47. a. $\begin{bmatrix} 80 & 40 & 120 \\ 60 & 30 & 150 \end{bmatrix}$ **b.** $\begin{bmatrix} 1/2 & 1/5 \\ 1/4 & 1/5 \\ 1/4 & 3/5 \end{bmatrix}$ **c.** $PF = \begin{bmatrix} 80 & 96 \\ 75 & 108 \end{bmatrix}$; the rows give the average price per pair of footwear sold by each store, and the columns give the state.   **d.** \$108

49. a. $\begin{bmatrix} 20 & 52 & 27 \\ 25 & 62 & 35 \\ 30 & 72 & 43 \end{bmatrix}$; the rows give the amounts of fat, carbohydrates, and protein, respectively, in each of the daily meals.

b. $\begin{bmatrix} 75 \\ 45 \\ 70 \\ 168 \end{bmatrix}$; the rows give the number of calories in one exchange of each of the food groups.   **c.** The rows give the number of calories in each meal.

51. $\begin{bmatrix} 66.7 & 74.4 \\ 69.6 & 77.2 \\ 71.3 & 78.4 \\ 73.8 & 79.3 \end{bmatrix}$ **53. a.** $\begin{bmatrix} 0.0346 & 0.0118 \\ 0.0174 & 0.0073 \\ 0.0189 & 0.0059 \\ 0.0135 & 0.0083 \\ 0.0099 & 0.0103 \end{bmatrix}$; $\begin{bmatrix} 361 & 2038 & 286 & 227 & 460 \\ 473 & 2494 & 362 & 252 & 484 \\ 627 & 2978 & 443 & 278 & 499 \\ 803 & 3435 & 524 & 314 & 511 \\ 1013 & 3824 & 591 & 344 & 522 \end{bmatrix}$ **b.**

	Births	Deaths
1970	60.98	27.45
1980	74.80	33.00
1990	90.58	39.20
2000	106.75	45.51
2010	122.57	51.59

Exercises 2.5 (page 94)

For exercises . . .	1–8	11–26,51–55	27–42,56–58	59–63	64,65
Refer to example . . .	1	2,3	4,6	5	7

1. Yes   **3.** No   **5.** No   **7.** Yes   **9.** No; the row of all zeros makes it impossible to get all the 1's in the diagonal of the identity matrix, no matter what matrix is used as an inverse.

11. $\begin{bmatrix} 0 & 1/2 \\ -1 & 1/2 \end{bmatrix}$ **13.** $\begin{bmatrix} 2 & 1 \\ 5 & 3 \end{bmatrix}$ **15.** No inverse   **17.** $\begin{bmatrix} 1 & 0 & 0 \\ 0 & -1 & 0 \\ -1 & 0 & 1 \end{bmatrix}$ **19.** $\begin{bmatrix} 15 & 4 & -5 \\ -12 & -3 & 4 \\ -4 & -1 & 1 \end{bmatrix}$ **21.** No inverse

23. $\begin{bmatrix} -11/2 & -1/2 & 5/2 \\ 1/2 & 1/2 & -1/2 \\ -5/2 & 1/2 & 1/2 \end{bmatrix}$ **25.** $\begin{bmatrix} 1/2 & 1/2 & -1/4 & 1/2 \\ -1 & 4 & -1/2 & -2 \\ -1/2 & 5/2 & -1/4 & -3/2 \\ 1/2 & -1/2 & 1/4 & 1/2 \end{bmatrix}$ **27.** $(5, 1)$ **29.** $(2, 1)$ **31.** $(15, 21)$

33. No inverse, $(-8y - 12, y)$ **35.** $(-8, 6, 1)$ **37.** $(-36, 8, -8)$ **39.** No inverse, no solution for system

41. $(-7, -34, -19, 7)$

51. $\begin{bmatrix} -0.0447 & -0.0230 & 0.0292 & 0.0895 & -0.0402 \\ 0.0921 & 0.0150 & 0.0321 & 0.0209 & -0.0276 \\ -0.0678 & 0.0315 & -0.0404 & 0.0326 & 0.0373 \\ 0.0171 & -0.0248 & 0.0069 & -0.0003 & 0.0246 \\ -0.0208 & 0.0740 & 0.0096 & -0.1018 & 0.0646 \end{bmatrix}$

53. $\begin{bmatrix} 0.0394 & 0.0880 & 0.0033 & 0.0530 & -0.1499 \\ -0.1492 & 0.0289 & 0.0187 & 0.1033 & 0.1668 \\ -0.1330 & -0.0543 & 0.0356 & 0.1768 & 0.1055 \\ 0.1407 & 0.0175 & -0.0453 & -0.1344 & 0.0655 \\ 0.0102 & -0.0653 & 0.0993 & 0.0085 & -0.0388 \end{bmatrix}$ **55.** Yes

57. $\begin{bmatrix} 1.51482 \\ 0.053479 \\ -0.637242 \\ 0.462629 \end{bmatrix}$ **59. a.** $\begin{bmatrix} 72 \\ 48 \\ 60 \end{bmatrix}$ **b.** $\begin{bmatrix} 2 & 4 & 2 \\ 2 & 1 & 2 \\ 2 & 1 & 3 \end{bmatrix} \begin{bmatrix} x_1 \\ x_2 \\ x_3 \end{bmatrix} = \begin{bmatrix} 72 \\ 48 \\ 60 \end{bmatrix}$ **c.** 8 type I, 8 type II, and 12 type III

61. a. $10,000 at 6%, $10,000 at 6.5%, and $5000 at 8%   **b.** $14,000 at 6%, $9000 at 6.5%, and $7000 at 8%   **c.** $24,000 at 6%, $4000 at 6.5%, and $12,000 at 8%   **63. a.** 50 Super Vim, 75 Multitab, and 100 Mighty Mix   **b.** 75 Super Vim, 50 Multitab, and 60 Mighty Mix   **c.** 80 Super Vim, 100 Multitab, and 50 Mighty Mix   **65. a.** 262, −161, −12, 186, −103, −22, 264, −168, −9, 208, −134, −5, 224, −152, 5, 92, −50, −3   **b.** $\begin{bmatrix} 1.75 & 2.5 & 3 \\ -0.25 & -0.5 & 0 \\ -0.25 & -0.5 & -1 \end{bmatrix}$ **c.** happy birthday

Exercises 2.6 (page 102)

For exercises . . .	1–6,9–12,17–25	7,8,26–29	13–16
Refer to example . . .	4	5	3,4

1. $\begin{bmatrix} 60 \\ 50 \end{bmatrix}$ **3.** $\begin{bmatrix} 6.43 \\ 26.12 \end{bmatrix}$ **5.** $\begin{bmatrix} 10 \\ 18 \\ 10 \end{bmatrix}$ **7.** 33 : 47 : 23   **9.** $\begin{bmatrix} 7697 \\ 4205 \\ 6345 \\ 4106 \end{bmatrix}$ (rounded)   **11.** About 1440 metric tons of wheat and 1938 metric tons of oil.   **13.** About 1506 units of agriculture, 1713 units of manufacturing, and 1412 units of transportation.   **15.** About 3077 units of agriculture, about 2564 units of manufacturing, and about 3179 units of transportation **17. a.** 7/4 bushels of yams and 15/8 ≈ 2 pigs   **b.** 167.5 bushels of yams and 153.75 ≈ 154 pigs   **19.** About 848 units of agriculture, about 516 units of manufacturing, and about 2970 units of households   **21.** About 195 million pounds of agriculture, about 26 million pounds of manufacturing, and about 13.6 million pounds of energy   **23.** In millions of dollars, the amounts are about 532 for natural resources, about 481 for manufacturing, about 805 for trade and services, and about 1185 for personal consumption.

25. a. $\begin{bmatrix} 1.67 & 0.56 & 0.56 \\ 0.19 & 1.17 & 0.06 \\ 3.15 & 3.27 & 4.38 \end{bmatrix}$ **b.** These multipliers imply that if the demand for one community's output increases by $1, then the output in the other community will increase by the amount in the row and column of that matrix. For example, if the demand for Hermitage's output increases by $1, then output from Sharon will increase by $0.56, Farrell by $0.06, and Hermitage by $4.38.   **27.** 3 units of coal to every 4 units of steel   **29.** 6 units of mining to every 8 units of manufacturing and 5 units of communication

Chapter 2 Review Exercises (page 106)

For exercises . . .	1,3,10,13, 17,23–28, 67,68,74, 75,79,80,82	2,5,29–33, 36,69,73	4,19–22, 66,77,78, 81,83	6,7,18,34, 35,37–43, 76	8,9,11,12 14,15, 44–62,70, 74	16,63,64, 71,72
Refer to section . . .	2	3	1	4	5	6

1. False   **2.** False   **3.** True   **4.** True   **5.** False   **6.** True   **7.** False   **8.** False   **9.** True   **10.** False   **11.** False   **12.** False **13.** True   **14.** True   **15.** False   **16.** True   **19.** $(1, -4)$ **21.** $((34 - 28z)/50, (53 - z)/25, z)$ **23.** $(-9, 3)$ **25.** $(7, -9, -1)$ **27.** $(6 - 7z/3, 1 + z/3, z)$ **29.** 2×2 (square); $a = 2, b = 3, c = 5, q = 9$ **31.** 1×4 (row); $m = 6, k = 3, z = -3, r = -9$

33. $\begin{bmatrix} 9 & 10 \\ -3 & 0 \\ 10 & 16 \end{bmatrix}$ **35.** $\begin{bmatrix} 23 & 20 \\ -7 & 3 \\ 24 & 39 \end{bmatrix}$ **37.** $\begin{bmatrix} -17 & 20 \\ 1 & -21 \\ -8 & -17 \end{bmatrix}$ **39.** Not possible   **41.** [9]   **43.** $[-14 \ -19]$ **45.** No inverse

47. $\begin{bmatrix} 7 & -3 \\ -2 & 1 \end{bmatrix}$ **49.** No inverse   **51.** $\begin{bmatrix} 2/3 & 0 & -1/3 \\ 1/3 & 0 & -2/3 \\ -2/3 & 1 & 1/3 \end{bmatrix}$ **53.** No inverse   **55.** $X = \begin{bmatrix} 1 \\ -13 \end{bmatrix}$ **57.** $X = \begin{bmatrix} -22 \\ -18 \\ 15 \end{bmatrix}$

59. $(2, 1)$ **61.** $(-1, 0, 2)$ **63.** $\begin{bmatrix} 218.1 \\ 318.3 \end{bmatrix}$ **65. a.** $(2, 3, -1)$ **b.** $(2, 3, -1)$ **c.** $\begin{bmatrix} 1 & 2 & 1 \\ 2 & -1 & -1 \\ 3 & -3 & 2 \end{bmatrix}\begin{bmatrix} x \\ y \\ z \end{bmatrix} = \begin{bmatrix} 7 \\ 2 \\ -5 \end{bmatrix}$

d. $\begin{bmatrix} 5/22 & 7/22 & 1/22 \\ 7/22 & 1/22 & -3/22 \\ 3/22 & -9/22 & 5/22 \end{bmatrix}$ **e.** $(2, 3, -1)$ **67.** 5 blankets, 3 rugs, 8 skirts   **69.** $\begin{bmatrix} 1.33 & 17.6 & 152,000 & 26.75 & +1.88 \\ 1.00 & 20.0 & 238,200 & 32.36 & -1.50 \\ 0.79 & 25.4 & 39,110 & 16.51 & -0.89 \\ 0.27 & 21.2 & 122,500 & 28.60 & +0.75 \end{bmatrix}$

71. a. $\begin{array}{cc} & \begin{array}{cc} c & g \end{array} \\ \begin{array}{c} c \\ g \end{array} & \begin{bmatrix} 0 & 1/2 \\ 2/3 & 0 \end{bmatrix} \end{array}$ **b.** 1200 units of cheese; 1600 units of goats   **73.** $\begin{bmatrix} 8 & 8 & 8 \\ 10 & 5 & 9 \\ 7 & 10 & 7 \\ 8 & 9 & 7 \end{bmatrix}$ **75. a.** No   **b. (i)** 0.23, 0.37, 0.42; A is healthy; B and D are tumorous; C is bone.   **(ii)** 0.33, 0.27, 0.32; A and C are tumorous, B could be healthy or tumorous, D is bone.   **c.** 0.2, 0.4, 0.45, 0.3; A is healthy; B and C are bone; D is tumorous. **d.** One example is to choose beams 1, 2, 3, and 6.   **77.** $W_1 = W_2 = 100\sqrt{3}/3 \approx 58$ lb   **79. a.** $C = 0.010985t^2 + 0.8803t + 317$ **b.** 2095   **81.** There are y girls and $2500 - 1.5y$ boys, where y is any even integer between 0 and 1666.   **83.** A chocolate wafer weighs 4.08 g, and a single layer of vanilla cream weighs 3.17 g.

Chapter 3 Linear Programming: The Graphical Method

Exercises 3.1 (page 118)

For exercises . . .	1–20	21–32	33–36	38–45
Refer to example . . .	1,2	3–5	3	6

1. $x + y \le 2$

3. $x \ge 2 - y$

5. $4x - y < 6$

7. $4x + y < 8$

9. $x + 3y \ge -2$

11. $x \le 3y$

13. 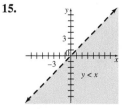 $x + y \le 0$

15. $y < x$

17. $x < 4$

19. $y \le -2$

21. 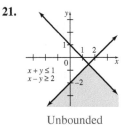 $x + y \le 1$ $x - y \ge 2$
Unbounded

23. $x + 3y \le 6$ $2x + 4y \ge 7$
Unbounded

25. $x + y \le 7$ $x - y \le -4$ $4x + y \ge 0$
Bounded

27. $-2 < x < 3$ $-1 \le y \le 5$ $2x + y < 6$
Bounded

29. $y - 2x \le 4$ $y \ge 2 - x$ $x \ge 0$ $y \ge 0$
Unbounded

31. 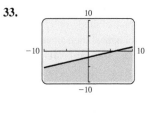 $3x + 4y > 12$ $2x - 3y < 6$ $0 \le y \le 2$ $x \ge 0$
Bounded

33.

35.

37. B: $\le, \le, \le$; **C:** $\ge, \ge, \le$; **D:** $\le, \ge, \le$; **E:** $\le, \le, \ge$; **F:** $\le, \ge, \ge$; **G:** $\ge, \ge, \ge$

39. a.

	Shawls	Afghans		Total
Number Made	x	y		
Spinning Time	1	2	$\le$	8
Dyeing Time	1	1	$\le$	6
Weaving Time	1	4	$\le$	14

b. $x + 2y \le 8$ $x + y \le 6$ $x + 4y \le 14$ $x \ge 0, y \ge 0$

c. Yes; no

41. a. $x \ge 4y$; $0.06x + 0.08y \ge 1.6$; $x + y \le 30$; $x \ge 0$; $y \ge 0$

b. $x \ge 4y$ $0.06x + 0.08y \ge 1.6$ $x + y \le 30$ $x \ge 0$ $y \ge 0$

43. a. $x \le (1/2)y$; $x + y \le 800$; $x \ge 0$; $y \ge 0$

b. $x \le \left(\frac{1}{2}\right)y$ $x + y \le 800$ $x \ge 0$ $y \ge 0$

45. a. $x + y \geq 7$; $2x + y \geq 10$; $x + y \leq 9$; $x \geq 0$; $y \geq 0$ **b.**

Exercises 3.2 (page 124)

For exercises . . .	1–16
Refer to example . . .	3

1. a. Maximum of 29 at $(7, 4)$; minimum of 10 at $(0, 5)$ **b.** Maximum of 35 at $(3, 8)$; minimum of 8 at $(4, 1)$ **3. a.** Maximum of 9 at $(0, 12)$; minimum of 0 at $(0, 0)$ **b.** Maximum of 12 at $(8, 0)$; minimum of 0 at $(0, 0)$ **5. a.** No maximum; minimum of 16 at $(0, 8)$ **b.** No maximum; minimum of 18 at $(3, 4)$ **c.** No maximum; minimum of 21 at $(13/2, 2)$ **d.** No maximum; minimum of 12 at $(12, 0)$ **7.** Minimum of 24 when $x = 6$ and $y = 0$ **9.** Maximum of 46 when $x = 6$ and $y = 8$ **11.** Maximum of 1500 when $x = 150$ and $y = 0$, as well as when $x = 50$ and $y = 100$ and all points on the line between   **13.** No solution   **15. a.** Maximum of 204 when $x = 18$ and $y = 2$ **b.** Maximum of 588/5 when $x = 12/5$ and $y = 39/5$ **c.** Maximum of 102 when $x = 0$ and $y = 17/2$ **17.** b

Exercises 3.3 (page 131)

For exercises . . .	1–6	7–9,16,21–25	10–15,17–20, 26	27
Refer to example . . .	1–3	3	1,2	2

1. Let x be the number of product A produced and y be the number of product B. Then $3x + 5y \leq 60$.   **3.** Let x be the number of calcium carbonate supplements and y be the number of calcium citrate supplements. Then $600x + 250y \geq 1500$.   **5.** Let x be the number of pounds of $8 coffee and y be the number of $10 coffee. Then $x + y \geq 40$.   **7.** 51 to plant I and 32 to plant II, for a minimum cost of $2810   **9. a.** 6 units of policy A and 16 units of policy B, for a minimum premium cost of $940   **b.** 30 units of policy A and 0 units of policy B, for a minimum premium cost of $750   **11. a.** 500 type I and 1000 type II   **b.** Maximum revenue is $275.   **c.** If the price of the type I bolt exceeds 20¢, then it is more profitable to produce 1050 type I bolts and 450 type II bolts.   **13. a.** 120 kg of the half-and-half mix and 120 kg of the other mix, for a maximum revenue of $1980   **b.** 0 kg of the half-and-half mix and 200 kg of the other mix, for a maximum revenue of $2200   **15. a.** 40 gal from dairy I and 60 gal from dairy II, for a maximum butterfat of 3.4 gal   **b.** 10 gal from dairy I and 20 gal from dairy 2. No.   **17.** $10 million in bonds and $20 million in mutual funds, or $5 million in bonds and $22.5 million in mutual funds (or any solution on the line in between those two points), for a maximum annual interest of $2 million   **19.** a   **21. a.** Three of pill 1 and two of pill 2, for a minimum cost of $1.05 per day   **b.** 360 surplus IU of vitamin A. No.   **23.** 4 ounces of fruit and 2 ounces of nuts, for a minimum of 140 calories   **25.** 0 plants and 18 animals, for a minimum of 270 hours

Chapter 3 Review Exercises (page 135)

For exercises . . .	1,6,8,10,12–14,21–36	2,7,9,15–20	3,4,5,37–46	11
Refer to Section . . .	2	1	3	2,3

1. False   **2.** True   **3.** False   **4.** False   **5.** False
6. False   **7.** True   **8.** False   **9.** False   **10.** True   **11.** True   **12.** True   **13.** True

15.

$y \geq 2x + 3$

17.

$2x + 6y \leq 8$

19.

$y \geq x$

21.

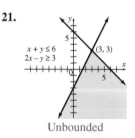

$x + y \leq 6$
$2x - y \geq 3$
Unbounded

23.

$-4 \leq x \leq 2$
$-1 \leq y \leq 3$
$x + y \leq 4$
Bounded

25.

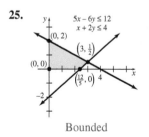

$5x - 6y \leq 12$
$x + 2y \leq 4$
Bounded

27. Maximum of 22 at $(3, 4)$; minimum of 0 at $(0, 0)$
29. Maximum of 24 at $(0, 6)$ **31.** Minimum of 40 at any point on the segment connecting $(0, 20)$ and $(10/3, 40/3)$

35. a.

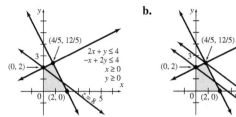

b.

37. Let x = number of batches of cakes and y = number of batches of cookies. Then $x \geq 0$, $y \geq 0$, $2x + (3/2)y \leq 15$, and $3x + (2/3)y \leq 13$.

39. a. 3 batches of cakes and 6 batches of cookies, for a maximum profit of $210 **b.** If the profit per batch of cookies increases by more than $2.50 (to above $22.50), then it will be more profitable to make 10 batches of cookies and no batches of cake.
41. 7 packages of gardening mixture and 2 packages of potting mixture, for a maximum income of $31 **43.** Produce no runs of type I and 7 runs of type II, for a minimum cost of $42,000. **45.** 0 acres for millet and 2 acres for wheat, for a maximum harvest of 1600 lb

Chapter 4 Linear Programming: The Simplex Method

Exercises 4.1 (page 148)

1. $x_1 + 2x_2 + s_1 = 6$ **3.** $2.3x_1 + 5.7x_2 + 1.8x_3 + s_1 = 17$ **5. a.** 3

For exercises . . .	1–14	15–18	19–24	27–31
Refer to example . . .	1	3	4	2

b. s_1, s_2, s_3 **c.** $2x_1 + 3x_2 + s_1 = 15; 4x_1 + 5x_2 + s_2 = 35; x_1 + 6x_2 + s_3 = 20$ **7. a.** 2 **b.** s_1, s_2
c. $7x_1 + 6x_2 + 8x_3 + s_1 = 118; 4x_1 + 5x_2 + 10x_3 + s_2 = 220$

9.
$$\begin{array}{ccccc} x_1 & x_2 & s_1 & s_2 & z \\ \left[\begin{array}{ccccc|c} 4 & 2 & 1 & 0 & 0 & 5 \\ 1 & 2 & 0 & 1 & 0 & 4 \\ \hline -7 & -1 & 0 & 0 & 1 & 0 \end{array}\right] \end{array}$$

11.
$$\begin{array}{cccccc} x_1 & x_2 & s_1 & s_2 & s_3 & z \\ \left[\begin{array}{cccccc|c} 1 & 1 & 1 & 0 & 0 & 0 & 10 \\ 5 & 2 & 0 & 1 & 0 & 0 & 20 \\ 1 & 2 & 0 & 0 & 1 & 0 & 36 \\ \hline -1 & -3 & 0 & 0 & 0 & 1 & 0 \end{array}\right] \end{array}$$

13.
$$\begin{array}{ccccc} x_1 & x_2 & s_1 & s_2 & z \\ \left[\begin{array}{ccccc|c} 3 & 1 & 1 & 0 & 0 & 12 \\ 1 & 1 & 0 & 1 & 0 & 15 \\ \hline -2 & -1 & 0 & 0 & 1 & 0 \end{array}\right] \end{array}$$

15. $x_1 = 0$, $x_2 = 4$, $x_3 = 0$, $s_1 = 0$, $s_2 = 8$, $z = 28$ **17.** $x_1 = 0$, $x_2 = 0$, $x_3 = 8$, $s_1 = 0$, $s_2 = 6$, $s_3 = 7$, $z = 12$
19. $x_1 = 0$, $x_2 = 20$, $x_3 = 0$, $s_1 = 16$, $s_2 = 0$, $z = 60$ **21.** $x_1 = 0$, $x_2 = 0$, $x_3 = 12$, $s_1 = 0$, $s_2 = 9$, $s_3 = 8$, $z = 36$
23. $x_1 = 0$, $x_2 = 250$, $x_3 = 0$, $s_1 = 0$, $s_2 = 50$, $s_3 = 200$, $z = 1000$

27. If x_1 is the number of simple figures, x_2 is the number of figures with additions, and x_3 is the number of computer drawn sketches, find $x_1 \geq 0$, $x_2 \geq 0$, and $x_3 \geq 0$ such that $20x_1 + 35x_2 + 60x_3 \leq 2200$, $x_1 + x_2 + x_3 \leq 400$, $x_3 \leq x_1 + x_2$, $x_1 \geq 2x_2$, and $z = 95x_1 + 200x_2 + 325x_3$ is maximized; $20x_1 + 35x_2 + 60x_3 + s_1 = 2200$, $x_1 + x_2 + x_3 + s_2 = 400$, $-x_1 - x_2 + x_3 + s_3 = 0$, $-x_1 + 2x_2 + s_4 = 0$.

$$\begin{array}{cccccccc} x_1 & x_2 & x_3 & s_1 & s_2 & s_3 & s_4 & z \\ \left[\begin{array}{cccccccc|c} 20 & 35 & 60 & 1 & 0 & 0 & 0 & 0 & 2200 \\ 1 & 1 & 1 & 0 & 1 & 0 & 0 & 0 & 400 \\ -1 & -1 & 1 & 0 & 0 & 1 & 0 & 0 & 0 \\ -1 & 2 & 0 & 0 & 0 & 0 & 1 & 0 & 0 \\ \hline -95 & -200 & -325 & 0 & 0 & 0 & 0 & 1 & 0 \end{array}\right] \end{array}$$

29. If x_1 is the number of redwood tables made, x_2 is the number of stained Douglas fir tables made, and x_3 is the number of stained white spruce tables made, find $x_1 \geq 0$, $x_2 \geq 0$, and $x_3 \geq 0$ such that $8x_1 + 7x_2 + 8x_3 \leq 720$, $2x_2 + 2x_3 \leq 480$, $159x_1 + 138.85x_2 + 129.35x_3 \leq 15,000$, and $z = x_1 + x_2 + x_3$ is maximized; $8x_1 + 7x_2 + 8x_3 + s_1 = 720$, $2x_2 + 2x_3 + s_2 = 480$, $159x_1 + 138.85x_2 + 129.35x_3 + s_3 = 15,000$.

$$\begin{array}{ccccccc} x_1 & x_2 & x_3 & s_1 & s_2 & s_3 & z \\ \left[\begin{array}{ccccccc|c} 8 & 7 & 8 & 1 & 0 & 0 & 0 & 720 \\ 0 & 2 & 2 & 0 & 1 & 0 & 0 & 480 \\ 159 & 138.85 & 129.35 & 0 & 0 & 1 & 0 & 15,000 \\ \hline -1 & -1 & -1 & 0 & 0 & 0 & 1 & 0 \end{array}\right] \end{array}$$

31. If x_1 is the number of newspaper ads run, x_2 is the number of Internet banner ads run, and x_3 is the number of TV ads run, find $x_1 \geq 0$, $x_2 \geq 0$, and $x_3 \geq 0$, such that $400x_1 + 20x_2 + 2000x_3 \leq 8000$, $x_1 \leq 30$, $x_2 \leq 60$, $x_3 \leq 10$, and $z = 4000x_1 + 3000x_2 + 10,000x_3$ is maximized; $400x_1 + 20x_2 + 2000x_3 + s_1 = 8000$, $x_1 + s_2 = 30$, $x_2 + s_3 = 60$, $x_3 + s_4 = 10$.

$$\begin{array}{cccccccc} x_1 & x_2 & x_3 & s_1 & s_2 & s_3 & s_4 & z \\ \left[\begin{array}{cccccccc|c} 400 & 20 & 2000 & 1 & 0 & 0 & 0 & 0 & 8000 \\ 1 & 0 & 0 & 0 & 1 & 0 & 0 & 0 & 30 \\ 0 & 1 & 0 & 0 & 0 & 1 & 0 & 0 & 60 \\ 0 & 0 & 1 & 0 & 0 & 0 & 1 & 0 & 10 \\ \hline -4000 & -3000 & -10,000 & 0 & 0 & 0 & 0 & 1 & 0 \end{array}\right] \end{array}$$

Exercises 4.2 (page 157)

| For exercises . . . | 1–40 |
| Refer to example . . . | 1 |

1. Maximum is 30 when $x_1 = 10$, $x_2 = 0$, $x_3 = 0$, $s_1 = 6$, and $s_2 = 0$.   **3.** Maximum is 8 when $x_1 = 4$, $x_2 = 0$, $s_1 = 8$, $s_2 = 2$, and $s_3 = 0$.   **5.** Maximum is 264 when $x_1 = 16$, $x_2 = 4$, $x_3 = 0$, $s_1 = 0$, $s_2 = 16$, and $s_3 = 0$.   **7.** Maximum is 25 when $x_1 = 0$, $x_2 = 5$, $s_1 = 20$, and $s_2 = 0$.   **9.** Maximum is 120 when $x_1 = 0$, $x_2 = 10$, $s_1 = 0$, $s_2 = 40$, and $s_3 = 4$.   **11.** Maximum is 944 when $x_1 = 118$, $x_2 = 0$, $x_3 = 0$, $s_1 = 0$, and $s_2 = 102$.   **13.** Maximum is 3300 when $x_1 = 240$, $x_2 = 60$, $x_3 = 0$, $x_4 = 0$, $s_1 = 0$, and $s_2 = 0$.   **15.** No maximum   **17.** Maximum is 70,818.18 when $x_1 = 181.82$, $x_2 = 0$, $x_3 = 454.55$, $x_4 = 0$, $x_5 = 1363.64$, $s_1 = 0$, $s_2 = 0$, $s_3 = 0$, and $s_4 = 0$.   **23.** 6 churches and 2 labor unions, for a maximum of $1000 per month   **25. a.** Assemble 1000 Royal Flush poker sets, 3000 Deluxe Diamond poker sets, and 0 Full House poker sets, for a maximum profit of $104,000.   **b.** $s_4 = 1000$; there are 1000 unused dealer buttons.   **27. a.** No racing or touring bicycles and 2700 mountain bicycles   **b.** Maximum profit is $59,400   **c.** No; there are 1500 units of aluminum left; $s_2 = 1500$.   **29. a.** 17 newspaper ads, 60 Internet banner ads, and no TV ads, for a maximum exposure of 248,000   **31. a.** 3   **b.** 4   **c.** 3   **33.** $200, $66.67, $300, $100   **35.** Rachel should run 3 hours, bike 4 hours, and walk 8 hours, for a maximum calorie expenditure of 6313 calories.   **37. a.** None of species A, 114 of species B, and 291 of species C, for a maximum combined weight of 1119.72 kg   **b.** No; there are 346 units of Food II available.   **c.** Many answers are possible.   **d.** Many answers are possible.   **39.** 12 minutes to the senator, 9 minutes to the congresswoman and 6 minutes to the governor, for a maximum of 1,050,000 viewers.

Exercises 4.3 (page 168)

| For exercises . . . | 1–4 | 5–8 | 9–16 | 19–29 |
| Refer to example . . . | 2 | 3 | 4 | 5 |

1. $\begin{bmatrix} 1 & 3 & 1 \\ 2 & 2 & 10 \\ 3 & 1 & 0 \end{bmatrix}$ **3.** $\begin{bmatrix} 4 & 7 & 5 \\ 5 & 14 & 0 \\ -3 & 20 & -2 \\ 15 & -8 & 23 \end{bmatrix}$ **5.** Minimize $w = 5y_1 + 4y_2 + 15y_3$ subject to $y_1 + y_2 + 2y_3 \geq 4$, $y_1 + y_2 + y_3 \geq 3$, $y_1 + 3y_3 \geq 2$, with $y_1 \geq 0$, $y_2 \geq 0$, and $y_3 \geq 0$.   **7.** Maximize $z = 150x_1 + 275x_2$ subject to $x_1 + 2x_2 \leq 3$, $x_1 + 2x_2 \leq 6$, $x_1 + 3x_2 \leq 4$, $x_1 + 4x_2 \leq 1$, with $x_1 \geq 0$ and $x_2 \geq 0$.

9. Minimum is 14 when $y_1 = 0$ and $y_2 = 7$.   **11.** Minimum is 40 when $y_1 = 10$ and $y_2 = 0$.   **13.** Minimum is 30 when $y_1 = 5$ and $y_2 = 0$ or when $y_1 = 0$ and $y_2 = 3$, or any point on the line segment between (5, 0) and (0,3).   **15.** Minimum is 100 when $y_1 = 0$, $y_2 = 100$, and $y_3 = 0$.   **17.** a   **19. a.** 25 units of regular beer and 20 units of light beer, for a minimum cost of $1,800,000   **b.** The shadow cost is $0.10; total production cost is $1,850,000.   **21. a.** Minimize $w = 100y_1 + 20,000y_2$ subject to $y_1 + 400y_2 \geq 120$, $y_1 + 160y_2 \geq 40$, $y_1 + 280y_2 \geq 60$, with $y_1 \geq 0$, $y_2 \geq 0$.   **b.** 52.5 acres of potatoes and no corn or cabbage, for a profit of $6300.   **c.** 47.5 acres of potatoes and no corn or cabbage, for a profit of $5700.   **23.** 8 political interviews and no market interviews are done, for a minimum of 360 minutes.   **25. a.** 1 bag of feed 1 and 2 bags of feed 2   **b.** 1.4 (or 7/5) bags of feed 1 and 1.2 (or 6/5) bags of feed 2 should be used, for a minimum cost of $6.60   **27.** She should spend 30 minutes walking, 197.25 minutes cycling, and 75.75 minutes swimming, for a minimum time of 303 minutes per week.   **29.** 8/3 units of ingredient I and 4 units of ingredient III, for a minimum cost of $30.67.

Exercises 4.4 (page 176)

| For exercises . . . | 1–16 | 17–20,24,27,31,32 | 23,25,26,28,29,30,33 |
| Refer to example . . . | 1 | 3 | 2 |

1. $2x_1 + 3x_2 + s_1 = 8$; $x_1 + 4x_2 - s_2 = 7$
3. $2x_1 + x_2 + 2x_3 + s_1 = 50$; $x_1 + 3x_2 + x_3 - s_2 = 35$; $x_1 + 2x_2 - s_3 = 15$ **5.** Change the objective function to maximize $z = -3y_1 - 4y_2 - 5y_3$. The constraints are not changed.   **7.** Change the objective function to maximize $z = -y_1 - 2y_2 - y_3 - 5y_4$. The constraints are not changed.   **9.** Maximum is 480 when $x_1 = 40$ and $x_2 = 0$.   **11.** Maximum is 750 when $x_1 = 0$, $x_2 = 150$, and $x_3 = 0$.   **13.** Maximum is 135 when $x_1 = 30$ and $x_2 = 5$.   **15.** Minimum is 108 when $y_1 = 0$, $y_2 = 9$, and $y_3 = 0$.   **17.** Maximum is 400/3 when $x_1 = 100/3$ and $x_2 = 50/3$.   **19.** Minimum is 512 when $y_1 = 6$, $y_2 = 8$, and $y_3 = 0$.   **23. a.** Ship 200 barrels of oil from supplier S_1 to distributor D_1; ship 2800 barrels of oil from supplier S_2 to distributor D_1; ship 2800 barrels of oil from supplier S_1 to distributor D_2; ship 2200 barrels of oil from supplier S_2 to distributor D_2. Minimum cost is $180,400.   **b.** $s_3 = 2000$; S_1 could furnish 2000 more barrels of oil.   **25.** Make $3,000,000 in commercial loans and $22,000,000 in home loans, for a maximum return of $2,940,000.   **27.** Use 1500 lb of bluegrass, 2700 lb of rye, and 1800 lb of Bermuda, for a minimum cost of $834.   **29. a.** Ship 2 computers from W_1 to D_1, 20 computers from W_1 to D_2, 30 computers from W_2 to D_1, and 0 computers from W_2 to D_2, for a minimum cost of $628.   **b.** $s_3 = 3$; warehouse W_1 has 3 more computers that it could ship.   **31.** Use 59.21 kg of chemical I, 394.74 kg of chemical II, and 296.05 kg of chemical III, for a minimum cost of $600.39   **33.** 5/3 oz of I, 20/3 oz of II, and 5/3 oz of III, for a minimum cost of $1.55 per gal; 10 oz of the additive should be used per gal of gasoline.

Chapter 4 Review Exercises (page 180)

| For exercises . . . | 1,15,17,18,21–24 | 2,3,5–11,13,37–39,41–43,47 | 4,12 | 14,16,19,20,29–32,40,44 | 25–28,33–36,45,46 |
| Refer to section . . . | 1 | 2 | 3 | 4 | 3, 4 |

1. True   **2.** False   **3.** True   **4.** False   **5.** False   **6.** True   **7.** True   **8.** False   **9.** False   **10.** True   **11.** False   **12.** True   **13.** False   **14.** True   **15.** When the problem has more than two variables   **17. a.** $4x_1 + 6x_2 + s_1 = 60$; $3x_1 + x_2 + s_2 = 18$;

$2x_1 + 5x_2 + s_3 = 20$; $x_1 + x_2 + s_4 = 15$ **b.**

x_1	x_2	s_1	s_2	s_3	s_4	z	
4	6	1	0	0	0	0	60
3	1	0	1	0	0	0	18
2	5	0	0	1	0	0	20
1	1	0	0	0	1	0	15
−2	−7	0	0	0	0	1	0

19. a. $x_1 + x_2 + x_3 + s_1 = 90$; $2x_1 + 5x_2 + x_3 + s_2 = 120$; $x_1 + 3x_2 - s_3 = 80$ **b.**

x_1	x_2	x_3	s_1	s_2	s_3	z	
1	1	1	1	0	0	0	90
2	5	1	0	1	0	0	120
1	3	0	0	0	−1	0	80
−5	−8	−6	0	0	0	1	0

21. Maximum is 33 when $x_1 = 3$, $x_2 = 0$, $x_3 = 3$, $s_1 = 0$, and $s_2 = 0$.   **23.** Maximum is 76.67 when $x_1 = 6.67$, $x_2 = 0$, $x_3 = 21.67$, $s_1 = 0$, $s_2 = 0$, and $s_3 = 35$.   **25. Dual Method** Solve the dual problem: Maximize $17x_1 + 42x_2$ subject to $x_1 + 5x_2 \le 10$, $x_1 + 8x_2 \le 15$.   **Method of Section 4.4** Change the objective function to maximize $z = -10y_1 - 15y_2$. The constraints are not changed. Minimum is 170 when $y_1 = 17$ and $y_2 = 0$.   **27. Dual Method** Solve the dual problem: Maximize $48x_1 + 12x_2 + 10x_3 + 30x_4$ subject to $x_1 + x_2 + 3x_4 \le 7$, $x_1 + x_2 \le 2$, $2x_1 + x_3 + x_4 \le 3$.   **Method of Section 4.4** Change the objective function to maximize $z = -7y_1 - 2y_2 - 3y_3$. The constraints are not changed. Minimum is 98 when $y_1 = 4$, $y_2 = 8$, and $y_3 = 18$.   **29.** Maximum of 480 when $x_1 = 24$ and $x_2 = 0$ **31.** Maximum of 102 when $x_1 = 0$ and $x_2 = 8.5$ **33.** Problems with constraints involving "$\le$" can be solved using slack variables, while those involving "$\ge$" or "$=$" can be solved using surplus and artificial variables, respectively.   **35. a.** Maximize $z = 6x_1 + 7x_2 + 5x_3$, subject to $4x_1 + 2x_2 + 3x_3 \le 9$, $5x_1 + 4x_2 + x_3 \le 10$, with $x_1 \ge 0$, $x_2 \ge 0$, $x_3 \ge 0$.   **b.** The first constraint would be $4x_1 + 2x_2 + 3x_3 \ge 9$.   **c.** $x_1 = 0$, $x_2 = 2.1$, $x_3 = 1.6$, and $z = 22.7$ **d.** Minimize $w = 9y_1 + 10y_2$, subject to $4y_1 + 5y_2 \ge 6$, $2y_1 + 4y_2 \ge 7$, $3y_1 + y_2 \ge 5$, with $y_1 \ge 0$, $y_2 \ge 0$.   **e.** $y_1 = 1.3$, $y_2 = 1.1$, and $w = 22.7$ **37. a.** Let $x_1 = $ number of cake plates, $x_2 = $ number of bread plates, and $x_3 = $ number of dinner plates.   **b.** $z = 15x_1 + 12x_2 + 5x_3$ **c.** $15x_1 + 10x_2 + 8x_3 \le 1500$; $5x_1 + 4x_2 + 4x_3 \le 2700$; $6x_1 + 5x_2 + 5x_3 \le 1200$ **39. a.** Let $x_1 = $ number of gallons of Fruity wine and $x_2 = $ number of gallons of Crystal wine to be made.   **b.** $z = 12x_1 + 15x_2$ **c.** $2x_1 + x_2 \le 110$; $2x_1 + 3x_2 \le 125$; $2x_1 + x_2 \le 90$ **41.** Produce no cake plates, 150 bread plates, and no dinner plates, for a maximum profit of $1800.   **43.** 36.25 gal of Fruity and 17.5 gal of Crystal, for a maximum profit of $697.50
45. a and b Produce 660 cases of corn, 0 cases of beans, and 340 cases of carrots, for a minimum cost of $15,100.   **c.** $16,100
47. Ginger should do $5\frac{1}{3}$ hours of tai chi, $2\frac{2}{3}$ hours of riding a unicycle, and 2 hours of fencing, for a maximum calorie expenditure of $2753\frac{1}{3}$ calories.

Chapter 5 Mathematics of Finance

Exercises 5.1 (page 197)

For exercises . . .	5–10,49,50	11,12	13,14,51–53	19–24,54a,b,55–65	25–28,54c,d,66,77	29–32,67–69	33–38,70,71	41–44	45,46	47,48,63e
Refer to example . . .	1	2	3	4,5	6	7,8	9,10	11	12	13

1. The interest rate and number of compounding periods   **5.** $562.50   **7.** $59.79   **9.** $50.79   **11.** $3176.95; $51.95   **13.** 7.5%
17. t is the number of years, while n is the number of compounding periods.   **19.** $1593.85; $593.85   **21.** $890.82; $420.82
23. $12,630.55; $4130.55   **25.** $4.75%   **27.** 5.75%   **29.** 4.06%   **31.** 7.38%   **33.** $9677.13   **35.** $1246.33   **37.** $6864.08
41. 15 years   **43.** 24 years, 11 months   **45. a.** 21.35 years   **b.** 21.21 years   **47. a.** $7269.94   **b.** 3.15%   **c.** 19.29 years
49. $7534.80; $334.80   **51.** 6.8%   **53.** 11.4%   **55.** $41,325.95   **57.** $1000 now   **59.** $136,110.16   **61.** 9.31×10^{31}
63. a. $16,288.95   **b.** $16,436.19   **c.** $16,470.09   **d.** $16,486.65   **e.** $16,487.21   **65.** 5/4   **67.** 2.48, 5.01, 4.18, 4.43, 5.15
69. 5.64%, 5.63%, Centennial Bank   **71.** $22,829.89   **73.** About 18 years   **75.** About 12 years   **77. a.** 20.7%   **b.** $39.6 billion

Exercises 5.2 (page 207)

For exercises . . .	1–8	9–14	17–26,47–55,65,68	29,30,63,64	31–38,56–58,66,67	39–46,59–62
Refer to example . . .	1	2	3	4	5	6

1. 48   **3.** −648   **5.** 81   **7.** 1
9. 15   **11.** 156/25   **13.** −208   **17.** $437.46   **19.** $2,154,099.15   **21.** $180,307.41; $128,800; $51,507.41   **23.** $28,438.21; $19,200; $9238.21   **25.** $1,145,619.96; $768,000; $377,619.96   **29.** 4.19%   **31.** $628.25   **33.** $952.62   **35.** $7382.54
37. $5970.23   **39.** $6294.79   **41.** $136,785.74   **43.** $26,874.97; $18,000; $8874.97   **45.** $15,662.40; $12,000; $3662.40
47. a. $149,850.69   **b.** $137,895.79   **c.** $11,954.90   **49.** $197,750.47   **51.** $239,315.17   **53.** $312,232.31; $212,232.31
55. $432,548.65; $332,548.65   **57.** $1349.48   **59.** $3777.89   **61.** $67,940.98   **63.** 6.5%   **65. a.** 7 yr **b.** 9 yr   **67. a.** $120
b. $681.83 except the last payment, which is $681.80

Exercises 5.3 (page 215)

For exercises . . .	3–10,41	11–16a,b,27–30,35–40, 42,43,47,48a,49,50a–c, 51a,c,d,52,53	11–16c,21–24,44–46, 54,55	17–20	31–34	48b,49,50d,51b
Refer to example . . .	1	2,3	5	4	6	after Example 3

3. $8994.25 **5.** $209,302.93
7. $170,275.47 **9.** $111,183.87
11. a. $438.81 **b.** $2632.86;
$132.86 **c.** $2632.88; $132.88 **13. a.** $10,734.93 **b.** $128,819.16; $38,819.16 **c.** $128,819.20; $38,819.20 **15. a.** $542.60
b. $9766.80; $2366.80 **c.** $9766.88; $2366.88 **17.** $73,015.71 **19.** $5368.98 **21.** $7.61 **23.** $35.24 **25.** $6699
27. $1407.76; $422,328; $223,328 **29.** $1590.82; $572,695.20; $319,659.20 **31. a.** 8 years **b.** $113,086.84 **c.** $15,732.36
33. a. 11 semiannual periods **b.** $8760.50 **c.** $1006.38 **35.** $1856.49; $114,168.20. The payments are $537.48 more than for the
30-yr loan, but the total interest paid is $140,675.40 less. **37. a.** $335.25 **b.** $2092 **39. a.** $844.95, $30,418.20 **b.** $655.92,
$31,484.16 **41. a.** $623,110.52 **b.** $456,427.28 **c.** $563,757.78 **d.** $392,903.18 **43.** $381.74, $59,522

45.

Payment Number	Amount of Payment	Interest for Period	Portion to Principal	Principal at End of Period
0	—	—	—	$110,000.00
1	$14,794.23	$4400.00	$10,394.23	$99,605.77
2	$14,794.23	$3984.23	$10,810.00	$88,795.77
3	$14,794.23	$3551.83	$11,242.40	$77,553.37
4	$14,794.23	$3102.13	$11,692.10	$65,861.27

47. a. $32.49 **b.** $195.52; $10.97
49. a. $1959.99; $127,798.20
b. $1677.54; $177,609.60 **c.** $1519.22;
$230,766.00 **d.** After 157 payments
51. a. $1121.63; $403,786.80;
$253,786.80 **b.** $115,962.66;
$201,893.40 **c.** $732.96; $267,265.60
d. $1010.16; $186,328.80
53. a. $17,584.58 **b.** $15,069.31
57. a. $25,000 **b.** $40,000

55.

Payment Number	Amount of Payment	Interest for Period	Portion to Principal	Principal at End of Period
0	—	—	—	$4836.00
1	$585.16	$175.31	$409.85	$4426.15
2	$585.16	$160.45	$424.71	$4001.43
3	$585.16	$145.05	$440.11	$3561.32
4	$585.16	$129.10	$456.06	$3105.26
5	$585.16	$112.57	$472.59	$2632.67
6	$585.16	$95.43	$489.73	$2142.94
7	$585.16	$77.68	$507.48	$1635.46
8	$585.16	$59.29	$525.87	$1109.59
9	$585.16	$40.22	$544.94	$564.65
10	$585.12	$20.47	$564.65	$0.00

Chapter 5 Review Exercises (page 219)

1. True **2.** False **3.** True
4. False **5.** True **6.** True

For exercises . . .	1,11–28,64–69,74,75,81a	2–4,29–48,70,71,80,81c,e	5–10,49–63,72,73,76–79,81b,d
Refer to example . . .	1	2	3

7. True **8.** False **9.** False **10.** True **11.** $636.12 **13.** $1290.11 **15.** Compound interest **17.** $33,691.69 **19.** $77,860.80
21. $5244.50 **23.** $4725.22 **25.** $27,624.86 **27.** $1067.71 **29.** 2, 6, 18, 54, 162 **31.** −96 **33.** −120 **35.** 40.56808
39. $23,559.98; $5527.98 **41.** $12,302.78; $1118.78 **43.** $160,224.29; $5524.29 **45.** $955.61 **47.** $6156.14 **49.** $2945.34
51. $56,711.93 **53.** A home loan and an auto loan **55.** $302.59; $431.08 **57.** $1796.20; $5871.40 **59.** $1140.50; $410,580;
$233,470 **61.** $132.99 **63.** $1535.61 **65.** $10,203.80; $383.80 **67.** 8.21% **69.** $2298.58 **71.** $107,892.82; $32,892.82
73. $8751.91; $13,263.37 **75.** 1.50% and 1.46%; Ascencia **77. a.** $266.67, $16,000 (or $16,000.20 using the rounded payments)
b. $249.59, $17,970.48 **c.** $283.64, $13,614.72 **79. a.** $954.42 **b.** $817.92 **c.** Method 1: $109,563.99; Method 2: $109,565.13
d. $9650 **e.** Method 1: $118,786.01; Method 2: $118,784.87 **81. a.** 9.569% **b.** $896.44 **c.** $626,200.88 **d.** $1200.39
e. $478,134.14 **f.** Sue is ahead by $148,066.74.

Chapter 6 Logic

Exercises 6.1 (page 231)

For exercises . . .	1,14, 65,66, 75,76, 78,79	15,16, 67,77, 80	17–20	23–28, 68–72, 83–88	35–46, 49–56, 73,74, 89,90	57–64
Refer to example . . .	1	2	3	4	6	7

1. Statement, not compound **3.** Not a statement **5.** Statement,
compound **7.** Not a statement **9.** Statement, compound
11. Statement, not compound **13.** Statement, compound
15. My favorite flavor is not chocolate. **17.** $y \le 12$ **19.** $q < 5$
23. I'm not getting better. **25.** I'm not getting better or my parrot is dead. **27.** It is not the case that both I'm getting better and my
parrot is not dead. **29.** False **31.** True **33.** Both components are false. **35.** True **37.** True **39.** False **41.** True **43.** True
45. True **47.** Disjunction **49.** True **51.** False **53.** True **55.** True **57.** False **59.** True **61.** True **63.** True **65.** b, c, d

67. An individual has to be your biological child to be a "qualifying" child.   **69.** $a \wedge j$ **71.** $\sim a \vee j$ **73.** 69, 71, and 72
75. b, c, d, e   **77.** You may not find that exercise helps you cope with stress.   **79.** c, d   **83.** $n \wedge \sim m$ **85.** $\sim n \vee m$
87. $\sim n \wedge \sim m$ or $\sim (n \vee m)$ **89.** 85

Exercises 6.2 (page 238)

For exercises . . .	9–18	19–24,42,43,48	25–34,40,41, 44,46,47,49
Refer to example . . .	1,2	3,4	6

1. 4   **3.** 16   **5.** 128   **7.** 6

9.

p	q	$\sim p$	$\sim p \wedge q$
T	T	F	F
T	F	F	F
F	T	T	T
F	F	T	F

11.

p	q	$p \wedge q$	$\sim (p \wedge q)$
T	T	T	F
T	F	F	T
F	T	F	T
F	F	F	T

13.

p	q	$\sim p$	$\sim q$	$q \vee \sim p$	$(q \vee \sim p) \vee \sim q$
T	T	F	F	T	T
T	F	F	T	F	T
F	T	T	F	T	T
F	F	T	T	T	T

In Exercises 15–23, we are using the alternate method to save space.

15.

p	q	$\sim q$	$\wedge$	$(\sim p \vee q)$
T	T	F	F	F T T
T	F	T	F	F F F
F	T	F	F	T T T
F	F	T	T	T T F
		①	④	② ③ ②

17.

p	q	$(p \vee \sim q)$	$\wedge$	$(p \wedge q)$
T	T	T T F	T	T T T
T	F	T T T	F	T F F
F	T	F F F	F	F F T
F	F	F T T	F	F F F
		① ② ①	⑤	③ ④ ③

19.

p	q	r	$(\sim p \wedge q)$	$\wedge$	r
T	T	T	F F T	F	T
T	T	F	F F T	F	F
T	F	T	F F F	F	T
T	F	F	F F F	F	F
F	T	T	T T T	T	T
F	T	F	T T T	F	F
F	F	T	T F F	F	T
F	F	F	T F F	F	F
			① ② ①	④	③

21.

p	q	r	$(\sim p \wedge \sim q)$	$\vee$	$(\sim r \vee \sim p)$
T	T	T	F F F	F	F F F
T	T	F	F F F	T	T T F
T	F	T	F F T	F	F F F
T	F	F	F F T	T	T T F
F	T	T	T F F	T	F T T
F	T	F	T F F	T	T T T
F	F	T	T T T	T	F T T
F	F	F	T T T	T	T T T
			① ② ①	⑤	③ ④ ③

23.

p	q	r	s	$\sim (\sim p \wedge \sim q)$	$\vee$	$(\sim r \vee \sim s)$
T	T	T	T	T F F F	T	F F F
T	T	T	F	T F F F	T	F T T
T	T	F	T	T F F F	T	T T F
T	T	F	F	T F F F	T	T T T
T	F	T	T	T F F T	T	F F F
T	F	T	F	T F F T	T	F T T
T	F	F	T	T F F T	T	T T F
T	F	F	F	T F F T	T	T T T
F	T	T	T	T T F F	T	F F F
F	T	T	F	T T F F	T	F T T
F	T	F	T	T T F F	T	T T F
F	T	F	F	T T F F	T	T T T
F	F	T	T	F T T T	F	F F F
F	F	T	F	F T T T	T	F T T
F	F	F	T	F T T T	T	T T F
F	F	F	F	F T T T	T	T T T
				③ ① ② ①	⑥	④ ⑤ ④

25. It's not a vacation, or I am not having fun.
27. The door was locked and the thief didn't break a window.   **29.** I'm not ready to go, or Naomi Bahary is
31. $12 \leq 4$ and $8 \neq 9$ **33.** Neither Larry nor Moe is out sick today   **35.**

p	q	$p \veebar q$
T	T	F
T	F	T
F	T	T
F	F	F

37. True   **39. a.** False   **b.** True   **c.** False   **d.** True
41. Service will not be performed at the location, and the store may not send the Covered Equipment to an Apple repair service location to be repaired.

43. $s \lor (r \land \sim q)$

s	r	q	s	$\lor$	(r	$\land$	$\sim q$)
T	T	T	T	T	T	F	F
T	T	F	T	T	T	T	T
T	F	T	T	T	F	F	F
T	F	F	T	T	F	F	T
F	T	T	F	F	T	F	F
F	T	F	F	T	T	T	T
F	F	T	F	F	F	F	F
F	F	F	F	F	F	F	T
			①	④	②	③	②

The guarantee would be false if you are not completely satisfied, and they either don't refund your money or ask you questions.
45. Inclusive **47.** Liberty without learning is not always in peril, or learning without liberty is not always in vain.
49. You cannot reroll the die again for your Large Straight and you cannot set aside the 2 Twos and roll for your Twos or for 3 of a Kind.

Exercises 6.3 (page 247)

1. True **3.** True **5.** True **9.** True
11. True **13.** If she dances tonight, then I'm leaving early and he sings loudly.
15. If he doesn't sing loudly, then she dances tonight or I'm not leaving early.

For exercises . . .	9–12	21–30, 91	33–42, 51–68	43–46, 89,90, 92,93	47–50	69–76, 87,88	77–86
Refer to example . . .	3	4	5	6	7	8,9	10

17. $d \lor (f \to g)$ **19.** $\sim f \to g$ **21.** False **23.** False **25.** True **27.** True

33.

p	q	$\sim q$	$\to$	p
T	T	F	T	T
T	F	T	T	T
F	T	F	T	F
F	F	T	F	F
		①	②	①

35.

p	(p	$\lor$	$\sim p)$	$\to$	(p	$\land$	$\sim p)$
T	T	T	F	F	T	F	F
F	F	T	T	F	F	F	T
	①	②	①	⑤	③	④	③

It is a contradiction.

37.

p	q	(p	$\lor$	q)	$\to$	(q	$\lor$	p)
T	T	T	T	T	T	T	T	T
T	F	T	T	F	T	F	T	T
F	T	F	T	T	T	T	T	F
F	F	F	F	F	T	F	F	F
		①	②	①	⑤	③	④	③

It is a tautology.

39.

p	q	r	r	$\to$	(p	$\land$	$\sim q)$
T	T	T	T	F	T	F	F
T	T	F	F	T	T	F	F
T	F	T	T	T	T	T	T
T	F	F	F	T	T	T	T
F	T	T	T	F	F	F	F
F	T	F	F	T	F	F	F
F	F	T	T	F	F	F	T
F	F	F	F	T	F	F	T
			①	④	②	③	②

41.

p	q	r	s	($\sim r$	$\to$	s)	$\lor$	(p	$\to$	$\sim q)$
T	T	T	T	F	T	T	T	T	F	F
T	T	T	F	F	T	F	T	T	F	F
T	T	F	T	T	T	T	T	T	F	F
T	T	F	F	T	F	F	F	T	F	F
T	F	T	T	F	T	T	T	T	T	T
T	F	T	F	F	T	F	T	T	T	T
T	F	F	T	T	T	T	T	T	T	T
T	F	F	F	T	F	F	T	T	T	T
F	T	T	T	F	T	T	T	F	T	F
F	T	T	F	F	T	F	T	F	T	F
F	T	F	T	T	T	T	T	F	T	F
F	T	F	F	T	F	F	T	F	T	F
F	F	T	T	F	T	T	T	F	T	T
F	F	T	F	F	T	F	T	F	T	T
F	F	F	T	T	T	T	T	F	T	T
F	F	F	F	T	F	F	T	F	T	T
				①	②	①	⑤	③	④	③

43. Your eyes are not bad or your whole body will be full of darkness. **45.** I don't have the money or I'd buy that car.
47. You ask me and I do not do it. **49.** You don't love me and I will be happy. **51.** Equivalent **53.** Not equivalent
55. Equivalent **57.** Not equivalent

59.

p	q	p	$\land$	q	$\sim (p$	$\to$	$\sim q)$
T	T	T	T	T	T	T	F	F
T	F	T	F	F	F	T	T	T
F	T	F	F	T	F	F	T	F
F	F	F	F	F	F	F	T	T
		①	②	①	⑤	③	④	③

The columns labeled 2 and 5 are identical.

61.

p	q	p∨q	q∨p
T	T	T T T	T T T
T	F	T T F	F T T
F	T	F T T	T T F
F	F	F F F	F F F
		① ② ①	③ ④ ③

The columns labeled 2 and 4 are identical.

63.

p	q	r	(p∨q)∨r	p∨(q∨r)
T	T	T	T T T T T	T T T T T
T	T	F	T T T T F	T T T T F
T	F	T	T T F T T	T T F T T
T	F	F	T T F T F	T T F F F
F	T	T	F T T T T	F T T T T
F	T	F	F T T T F	F T T T F
F	F	T	F F F T T	F T F T T
F	F	F	F F F F F	F F F F F
			① ② ① ④ ③	⑤ ⑧ ⑥ ⑦ ⑥

The columns labeled 4 and 8 are identical.

65.

p	q	r	p∨(q∧r)	(p∨q)∧(p∨r)
T	T	T	T T T T T	T T T T T T T
T	T	F	T T T F F	T T T T T T F
T	F	T	T T F F T	T T F T T T T
T	F	F	T T F F F	T T F T T T F
F	T	T	F T T T T	F T T T F T T
F	T	F	F F T F F	F T T F F F F
F	F	T	F F F F T	F F F F F T T
F	F	F	F F F F F	F F F F F F F
			① ④ ② ③ ②	⑤ ⑥ ⑤ ⑨ ⑦ ⑧ ⑦

The columns labeled 4 and 9 are identical.

67.

p	q	(p∧q)∨p
T	T	T T T T T
T	F	T F F T T
F	T	F F T F F
F	F	F F F F F
		① ② ① ④ ③

The *p* column and the column labeled 4 are identical.

69. $(p \wedge q) \vee (p \wedge \sim q) \equiv p$ **71.** $p \vee (\sim q \wedge r)$ **73.** $(p \vee q) \vee \sim p \equiv T$ **75.** $[(p \wedge q) \vee (p \wedge p)] \vee (r \wedge \sim r) \equiv p$
77. $p \wedge (q \vee \sim p) \equiv p \wedge p$ **79.** $(p \vee q) \wedge (\sim p \wedge \sim q) \equiv F$ **81.** $\{(p \vee q) \wedge r\} \wedge \sim p \equiv r \wedge (\sim p \wedge q)$

83. $\sim q \rightarrow (\sim p \rightarrow q) \equiv p \vee q$ **85.** $[(p \wedge q) \vee p] \wedge [(p \vee q) \wedge q] \equiv p \wedge q$ **87.** False

89. a. You are not married at the end of the year, or you may file a joint return with your spouse.   **b.** A bequest received by an executor from an estate is compensation for services, or it is tax free.   **c.** A course does not improve your current job skills or does not lead to qualification for a new profession, or the course is not deductible.   **91. a.** $(\nu \vee p) \rightarrow (s \wedge g)$ **b.** True   **d.** The value of my portfolio exceeds \$100,000 or the price of my stock in Ford Motor Company falls below \$50 per share, and I will not sell my shares of Ford stock or I will not give the proceeds to the United Way.   **93. a.** If you cannot file a civil lawsuit yourself, then your attorney can do it for you.   **b.** If your driver's license does not come with restrictions, then restrictions may sometimes be added on later.   **c.** If you can marry when you're not at least 18 years old, then you have the permission of your parents or guardian.

Exercises 6.4 (page 254)

1. a. *Converse:* If I don't see it, then the exit is ahead.   **b.** *Inverse:* If the exit is not ahead, then I see it.   **c.** *Contrapositive:* If I see it, then the exit is not ahead.   **3. a.** *Converse:* If I cleaned the house, then I knew you were coming.   **b.** *Inverse:* If I didn't know you were coming, I wouldn't have cleaned the house.   **c.** *Contrapositive:* If I didn't clean the house, then I didn't know you were coming.   **5. a.** *Converse:* If you wear a pocket protector, then you are a mathematician.
b. *Inverse:* If you are not a mathematician, then you do not wear a pocket protector.   **c.** *Contraposition:* If you do not wear a pocket protector, then you are not a mathematician.   **7. a.** *Converse:* $\sim q \rightarrow p$.   **b.** *Inverse:* $\sim p \rightarrow q$.   **c.** *Contrapositive:* $q \rightarrow \sim p$.
9. a. *Converse:* $(q \vee r) \rightarrow p$.   **b.** *Inverse:* $\sim p \rightarrow \sim (q \vee r)$ or $\sim p \rightarrow (\sim q \wedge \sim r)$.   **c.** *Contrapositive:* $(\sim q \wedge \sim r) \rightarrow \sim p$.
13. If you sign, then you accept the conditions.   **15.** If you can take this course pass/fail, then you have prior permission.   **17.** If the temperature is below 10°, then you can skate on the pond.   **19.** If someone eats 10 hot dogs, then he or she will get sick.   **21.** If you

For exercises . . .	1–10,42,43, 45,47,48	13–29,41,44,46, 55–57	32–38
Refer to example . . .	4	1,2	5

travel to France, then you have a valid passport.   **23.** If a number has a real square root, then it is nonnegative.   **25.** If someone is a bride, then she is beautiful.   **27.** If the sum of a number's digits is divisible by 3, then it is divisible by 3.   **29.** d   **33.** True   **35.** False   **37.** False

39.

p	q	$(\sim p \land q)$			$\leftrightarrow$	$(p \to q)$		
T	T	F	F	T	F	T	T	T
T	F	F	F	F	T	T	F	F
F	T	T	T	T	T	F	T	T
F	F	T	F	F	F	F	T	F
		①	②	①	⑤	③	④	③

41. a. If it is an employee contribution, then it must be reported on From 8889.   **b.** If certain tax benefits may be claimed by married persons, then they file jointly.   **c.** If he or she provides over half of his or her own support, then the child is not a qualifying child.   **43.** *Converse:* If we close your account without notice, then your account is in default. *Inverse:* If your account is not in default, then we may not close your account without notice. *Contrapositive:* If we do not close your account without notice, then your account is not in default. The original statement and the contrapositive are equivalent, and the converse and inverse are equivalent.   **45. a.** $p \to (q \land r)$ **b.** If the most persistent does not stand to gain an extra meal or it does not eat at the expense of another, then there are not triplets.   **47. a.** *Converse:* If you can't get married again, then you are married. *Inverse:* If you aren't married, then you can get married again. *Contrapositive:* If you can get married again, then you are not married.   **b.** *Converse:* If you are protected by the Fair Credit Billing Act, then you pay for your purchase with a credit card. *Inverse:* If you do not pay for your purchase with a credit card, then you are not protected by the Fair Credit Billing Act. *Contrapositive:* If you are not protected by the Fair Credit Billing Act, then you do not pay for your purchase with a credit card.   **c.** *Converse:* If you're expected to make a reasonable effort to locate the owner, then you hit a parked car. *Inverse:* If you did not hit a parked car, then you are not expected to make a reasonable effort to locate the owner. *Contrapositive:* If you are not expected to make a reasonable effort to locate the owner, then you did not hit a parked car. The original statement and the contrapositive are equivalent, and the converse and inverse are equivalent.

49. a. $d \leftrightarrow a$,

d	a	$d \leftrightarrow a$
T	T	T
T	F	F
F	T	F
F	F	T

b. It is false   **51.** If a country has democracy, then it has a high level of education. *Converse:* If a country has a high level of education, then it has democracy. *Inverse:* If a country does not have democracy, then it does not have a high level of education. *Contrapositive:* If a country does not have a high level of education, then it does not have a democracy. The contrapositive is equivalent to the original.   **53.** D, 7   **55. a.** If nothing is ventured, then nothing is gained. If something is gained, then something is ventured. Something is ventured or nothing is gained.   **b.** If something is one of the best things in life, then it is free. If something is not free, then it's not one of the best things in life. Something is not one of the best things in life or it is free.   **c.** If something is a cloud, then it has a silver lining. If something doesn't have a silver lining, then it's not a cloud. Something is not a cloud or it doesn't have a silver lining.   **57.** **a.** If you can score in this box, then the dice show any sequence of four numbers. You cannot score in this box, or the dice show any sequence of four numbers.   **b.** If two or more words are formed in the same play, then each is scored. Two or more words are not formed in the same play, or each is scored. **c.** If words are labeled as a part of speech, then they are permitted. Words are not labeled as parts of speech, or they are permitted.

Exercises 6.5 (page 264)

1. Valid; Reasoning by Transitivity

3. Valid; Modus Ponens

5. Invalid; Fallacy of the Converse

7. Valid; Modus Tollens

For exercises . . .	1,2	3,4	5,6	7,8	9,10	11,12	13–16, 31,32, 35	17–24,29,30, 33,34, 36–44
Refer to example . . .	4	Modus Ponens	1	2	Fallacy of the Inverse	3	5,8	6,7

9. Invalid; Fallacy of the Inverse   **11.** Valid; Disjunctive Syllogism   **13.** Invalid; $p = $ T, $q = $ T   **15.** Invalid; $p = $ F, $q = $ F

17. Valid.

1. $\sim p \to \sim q$	Premise
2. q	Premise
3. p	1, 2, Modus Tollens

19. Valid.

1. $p \to q$	Premise
2. $\sim q$	Premise
3. $\sim p \to r$	Premise
4. $\sim p$	1, 2, Modus Tollens
5. r	3, 4, Modus Ponens

21. Valid.

1. $p \to q$	Premise
2. $q \to r$	Premise
3. $\sim r$	Premise
4. $p \to r$	1, 2, Transitivity
5. $\sim p$	3, 4, Modus Tollens

23. Valid.

1. $p \to q$	Premise
2. $q \to \sim r$	Premise
3. p	Premise
4. $r \lor s$	Premise
5. q	1, 3, Modus Ponens
6. $\sim r$	2, 5, Modus Ponens
7. s	4, 6, Disjunctive Syllogism

25.

p	q	$(p \wedge q) \to p$
T	T	T T T T T
T	F	T F F T T
F	T	F F T T F
F	F	F F F T F
		① ② ① ③ ②

27.

p	q	$(p \wedge q) \to (p \wedge q)$
T	T	T T T T T T T
T	F	T F F T T F F
F	T	F F T T F F T
F	F	F F F T F F F
		① ② ① ⑤ ③ ④ ③

29. Valid. **1.** $a \to s$ Premise
        2. $v \vee a$ Premise
        3. $\sim v$ Premise
        4. a 2, 3, Disjunctive Syllogism
        5. s 1, 4, Modus Ponens

31. Invalid; $b =$ "it is a bear market" $=$ T, $p =$ "prices are rising" $=$ F, $i =$ "investor will sell stocks" $=$ T

33. Valid. **1.** $s \vee i$ Premise
        2. $s \to (l \wedge b)$ Premise
        3. $\sim l \vee \sim b$ Premise
        4. $\sim (l \wedge b)$ 3, DeMorgan's Law
        5. $\sim s$ 2, 4, Modus Tollens
        6. i 1, 5, Disjunctive Syllogism

35. Invalid; $M =$ "I am married to you" $=$ T, $o =$ "we are one" $=$ T, $r =$ "you are really a part of me" $=$ F

37. Valid. **1.** $y \vee \sim p$ Premise
        2. $\sim p \to \sim n$ Premise
        3. n Premise
        4. p 2, 3, Modus Tollens
        5. y 1, 4, Disjunctive Syllogism

39. a. $d \to \sim w$ **b.** $o \to w$ or $\sim w \to \sim o$ **c.** $p \to d$ **d.** $p \to \sim o$, *Conclusion:* If it is my poultry, then it is not an officer. In Lewis Carroll's words, "My poultry are not officers." **41. a.** $b \to \sim t$ or $t \to \sim b$ **b.** $w \to c$ **c.** $\sim b \to h$ **d.** $\sim w \to \sim p$, or $p \to w$ **e.** $c \to t$ **f.** $p \to h$, *Conclusion:* If one is a pawnbroker, then one is honest. In Lewis Carroll's words, "No pawnbroker is dishonest." **43. a.** $d \to p$ **b.** $\sim t \to \sim i$ **c.** $r \to \sim f$ or $f \to \sim r$ **d.** $o \to d$ or $\sim d \to \sim o$ **e.** $\sim c \to i$ **f.** $b \to s$ **g.** $p \to f$ **h.** $\sim o \to \sim c$ or $c \to o$ **i.** $s \to \sim t$ or $t \to \sim s$ **j.** $b \to \sim r$, *Conclusion:* If it is written by Brown, then I can't read it. In Lewis Carroll's words, "I cannot read any of Brown's letters."

Exercises 6.6 (page 272)
1. a. $\exists x \,[b(x) \wedge s(x)]$ **b.** $\forall x \,[b(x) \to \sim s(x)]$
c. No books are bestsellers. **3. a.** $\forall x \,[c(x) \to \sim s(x)]$
b. $\exists x \,[c(x) \wedge s(x)]$ **c.** There is a CEO who sleeps well at night. **5. a.** $\forall x \,[l(x) \to b(x)]$
b. $\exists x \,[l(x) \wedge \sim b(x)]$ **c.** There is a leaf that's not brown.

For exercises . . .	1–6,34,42	7,8,23	9,10, 21	11,12, 24	13–20 37–41 43–48	22,25–32
Refer to example . . .	1	2	4	3	6	5

7. a. $\forall x[g(x) \to f(x)]$
$$\frac{g(t)}{f(t)}$$
b.   Valid

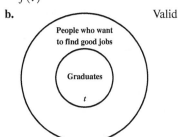

9. a. $\forall x[p(x) \to c(x)]$
$$\frac{c(o)}{p(o)}$$
b.   Invalid

11. a. $\forall x \,[c(x) \to p(x)]$
$$\frac{\sim p(n)}{\sim c(n)}$$
b.   Valid

13. a. $\exists x \, [t(x) \wedge s(x)]$
$\dfrac{\forall x \, [t(x) \rightarrow b(x)]}{\exists x \, [s(x) \wedge b(x)]}$

b.   Valid

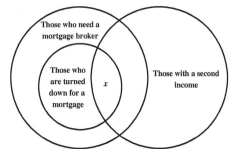

15. a. $\exists x \, [w(x) \wedge l(x)]$
$\dfrac{w(m)}{l(m)}$

b.   Invalid

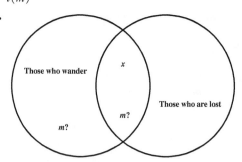

17. a. $\exists x \, [p(x) \wedge u(x)]$ **b.**   Invalid
$\dfrac{\exists x \, [p(x) \wedge r(x)]}{\exists x \, [u(x) \wedge r(x)]}$

19. a. $\forall x \, [a(x) \vee i(x)]$ **b.**   Valid   **21.** Yes
$\dfrac{\exists x \, [\sim a(x)]}{\exists x \, [i(x)]}$

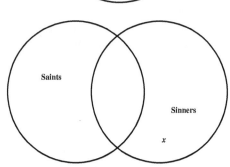

23. All major league baseball players earn at least $300,000 a year.
Ryan Howard is a major league baseball player.
$\overline{\text{Ryan Howard earns at least \$300,000 a year.}}$

25. Valid **27.** Invalid **29.** Invalid **31.** Invalid **37.** a, c, d
39. a. $\forall x \{ r(x) \rightarrow [a(x) \wedge c(x) \wedge i(x)] \}$ **b.** John Boehner
has attained to the age of twenty-five years, and been seven years
a citizen of the United States, and was, when elected, an inhabitant of that State in which he was chosen.

c.

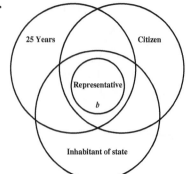

41. a. $\forall x \, \{ s(x) \rightarrow \sim [t(x) \vee a(x) \vee c(x)] \}$ **b.** Texas shall not enter into any treaty,
alliance, or confederation. **c.**

43. Invalid **45.** Invalid **47.** Valid

Chapter 6 Review Exercises (Page 276)
1. True   **3.** False   **5.** False   **7.** False
9. False   **11.** True   **13.** She doesn't pay me and I have enough cash.   **15.** $l \wedge w$
17. $l \to \sim w$ **19.** He doesn't lose the election and he wins the hearts of the voters.   **21.** True   **23.** True

For exercises . . .	15,19–22, 26,60–62, 69,70	14,27 39,40, 66	13,16,17,28, 35–38,41,42, 57–59,63,67	18,23–25, 29–34, 64,65	43–52	53–56,68 71–74
Refer to section . . .	1	2	3	4	5	6

The statement is not a tautology.
29. If someone is a mathematician, then that person is loveable.   **31.** If a system has a unique solution, then it has at least as many equations as unknowns.   **33. a.** If we need to change the way we do business, then the proposed regulations have been approved.
b. If the proposed regulations have not been approved, then we do not need to change the way we do business.   **c.** If we do not need to change the way we do business, then the proposed regulations have not been approved.

27.

p	q	p	$\wedge$	$(\sim p \vee q)$
T	T	T	T	F T T
T	F	T	F	F F F
F	T	F	F	T T T
F	F	F	F	T T F
		①	④	② ③ ②

35. $(p \wedge p) \wedge (\sim p \vee q) \equiv p \wedge q$ **37.**

$(p \wedge q) \vee (p \wedge p) \equiv p$

39.

p	q	$p \vee q$	$(p \vee q) \wedge \sim(p \wedge q)$
T	T	T F T	T T T F F T T T
T	F	T T F	T T F T T T F F
F	T	F T T	F T T T T F F T
F	F	F F F	F F F F T F F F
		① ② ①	③ ④ ③ ⑧ ⑦ ⑤ ⑥ ⑤

The columns labeled 2 and 8 are identical.
41. a. Yes **b.** No   **43.** Valid; Modus Ponens   **45.** Valid; Disjunctive Syllogism   **47.** Invalid; Fallacy of the Converse

49. Valid.

1. $h \to t$	Premise
2. $r \to \sim t$	Premise
3. r	Premise
4. $\sim t$	2, 3, Modus Ponens
5. $\sim h$	1, 4, Modus Tollens

51. Invalid; $p = F, q = F$

53. a. $\forall x \, [d(x) \to l(x)]$ **b.** $\exists x \, [d(x) \wedge \sim l(x)]$ **c.** There is a dog that doesn't have a license.
55. a. $\forall x \, [f(x) \to w(x)]$ **b.**

$$\frac{f(j)}{w(j)}$$

Valid

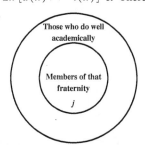

57.

p	q	r	$p \to$	$(q \to r)$	$(p \to q) \to r$
T	T	T	T T	T T T	T T T T T
T	T	F	T F	T F F	T T T F F
T	F	T	T T	F T T	T F F T T
T	F	F	T T	F T F	T F F T F
F	T	T	F T	T T T	F T T T T
F	T	F	F T	T F F	F T T F F
F	F	T	F T	F T T	F T F T T
F	F	F	F T	F T F	F T F F F
			① ④	② ③ ②	⑤ ⑥ ⑤ ⑧ ⑦

No   **59. a.**

p	q	$(p \wedge \sim p) \to q$
T	T	T F F T T
T	F	T F F T F
F	T	F F T T T
F	F	F F T T F
		① ② ① ④ ③

61. b, c

63. You do not use the Tax Table or you do not have to compute your tax mathematically.   **65. a.** If you exercise regularly, then your heart becomes stronger and more efficient.   **b.** If you are a teenager, then you need to be aware of the risks of drinking and driving.   **c.** If you are visiting a country that has a high incidence of infectious diseases, then you may need extra immunizations.   **d.** If you have good health, then you have food.   **67.** $(w \to d) \to v$ **69.** b,c,d   **71. a.** $\sim s \to g$ **b.** $l \to \sim g$ **c.** $w \to l \equiv \sim l \to \sim w$
d. $\sim s \to \sim w$, Conclusion: If the puppy does not lie still, it does not care to do worsted work. In Lewis Carroll's words, "Puppies that will not lie still never care to do worsted work."   **73. a.** $f \to t \equiv \sim t \to \sim f$ **b.** $\sim a \to \sim g \equiv g \to a$ **c.** $w \to f$
d. $t \to \sim g \equiv g \to \sim t$ **e.** $a \to w \equiv \sim w \to \sim a$ **f.** $g \to \sim e$, Conclusion: If the kitten will play with a gorilla, it does not have green eyes. In Lewis Carroll's words, "No kitten with green eyes will play with a gorilla."

Chapter 7 Sets and Probability

Exercises 7.1 (page 290)

For exercises . . .	5–19	21–24,63,69	25–44	47–50,74–76,78,79	53–56,59–62,64–68,71–76,78,79	70
Refer to example . . .	2	4	5,6,7	9	8	3

1. False **3.** True **5.** True **7.** True **9.** False **11.** ⊆ **13.** ⊄ **15.** ⊆ **17.** ⊆ **19.** ⊂;⊂; ⊄; ⊄;⊂; ⊄;⊂; ⊄ **21.** 64 **23.** 8 **25.** ∩ **27.** ∪ **29.** ∩ **31.** ∪ or ∩ **35.** {2, 4, 6} **37.** {1, 3, 5, 7, 9} **39.** {1, 7, 9} **41.** {2, 3, 4, 6} **43.** {7, 8} **45.** {3, 6, 9} = A **47.** All students in this school not taking this course **49.** All students in this school taking accounting and zoology **51.** C and D, B and E, C and E, D and E **53.** B′ is the set of all stocks on the list with a closing price below $60 or above $70; B′ = {AT&T, Coca-Cola, FedEx, Disney}. **55.** (A ∩ B)′ is the set of all stocks on the list that do not have both a high price greater than $50 and a closing price between $60 and $70; A ∩ B = {AT&T, Coca-Cola, FedEx, Disney}. **57. a.** True **b.** True **c.** False **d.** False **e.** True **f.** True **g.** False **59.** {Exxon Mobil, General Electric, JPMorgan Chase & Co.} **61.** {IBM, Hewlett-Packard, Home Depot, Aflac} **63.** $2^9 = 512$ **65.** {i, m, h} **67.** U **69.** $2^{51} \approx 2.252 \times 10^{15}$ **71.** {USA, TLC, TBS} **73.** {Discovery, TNT} **75.** {TNT, USA, TBS, Discovery}; the set of networks that features sports or that have more than 97.6 million viewers.
79. a. The set of states who are not among those whose name contains the letter "e" or who are more than 4 million in population, and who also have an area of more than 40,000 square miles. **b.** {Alaska}

Exercises 7.2 (page 298)

For exercises . . .	1–8,25–28	11–20,29–32	21–24	39,44,45,59	38	40,41,46–58	42,43,60,61
Refer to example . . .	1	2	6	4	5	7	8

9. 8

21. 13 **23.** 18 **25.**

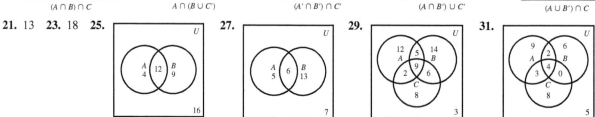

39. a. 12 **b.** 18 **c.** 37 **d.** 97 **41. a.** 2 **b.** 60 **c.** 8 **d.** 100 **e.** 27 **f.** All those who invest in stocks or bonds and are age 18–29 **43. a.** 17 **b.** 2 **c.** 14 **45. a.** 54 **b.** 17 **c.** 10 **d.** 7 **e.** 15 **f.** 3 **g.** 12 **h.** 1 **47. a.** 34 **b.** 16 **c.** 431 **d.** 481 **49.** 110.6 million **51.** 85.4 million **53.** 71.0 million **55.** 25,568,000; Blacks or Hispanics who never married **57.** 203,803,000; Whites or divorced/separated people who are not Asian/Pacific Islanders **59. a.** 342 **b.** 192 **c.** 72 **d.** 86 **61. a.** 89 **b.** 32 **c.** 26 **d.** 30 **e.** 22 **f.** 21

Exercises 7.3 (page 307)

For exercises . . .	3–10,13–18	13–18	19–24	25–34	35–40,53,62,63	41–48,52,56,57–61	51,55,56
Refer to example . . .	1	2,3	6	7	6,7	8	4

3. {January, February, March, . . . , December} **5.** {0, 1, 2, 3, . . . , 79, 80} **7.** {go ahead, cancel} **9.** {(h, 1), (h, 2), (h, 3), (h, 4), (h, 5), (h, 6), (t, 1), (t, 2), (t, 3), (t, 4), (t, 5), (t, 6)} **13.** {AB, AC, AD, AE, BC, BD, BE, CD, CE, DE}, 10, yes **a.** {AC, BC, CD, CE} **b.** {AB, AC, AD, AE, BC, BD, BE, CD, CE} **c.** {AC} **15.** {(1, 2), (1, 3), (1, 4), (1, 5), (2, 3), (2, 4), (2, 5), (3, 4), (3, 5), (4, 5)}, 10, yes **a.** {(2, 4)} **b.** {(1, 2), (1, 4), (2, 3), (2, 5), (3, 4), (4, 5)} **c.** ∅ **17.** {hh, thh, hth, tthh, thth, htth, ttth, ttht, thtt, htit, tttt}, 11, no **a.** {tthh, thth, htth, ttth, ttht, thtt, htit, tttt} **b.** {hh, thh, hth, tthh, thth, htth} **c.** {tttt} **19.** 1/6 **21.** 2/3 **23.** 1/3 **25.** 1/13 **27.** 1/26 **29.** 1/52 **31.** 2/13 **33.** 7/13 **35.** 3/20

37. 1/4 **39.** 3/5 **41.** Not empirical. **43.** Empirical **45.** Empirical **47.** Not empirical. **49.** The outcomes are not equally likely. **51. a.** Worker is male. **b.** Worker is female and has worked less than 5 years. **c.** Worker is female or does not contribute to a voluntary retirement plan. **d.** Worker has worked 5 years or more. **e.** Worker has worked less than 5 years or has contributed to a voluntary retirement plan. **f.** Worker has worked 5 years or more and does not contribute to a voluntary retirement plan. **53. a.** 8/15 **b.** 1/10 **55. a.** Person is not overweight. **b.** Person has a family history of heart disease and is overweight. **c.** Person smokes or is not overweight. **57. a.** 0.2540 **b.** 0.4851 **c.** 0.9225 **59.** 0.17 **61. a.** 0.3151 **b.** 0.3719 **c.** 0.3700 **d.** Calvary **e.** I Corps **63. a.** 25/57 **b.** 32/57 **c.** 4/19

Exercises 7.4 (page 316)

For exercises . . .	9–20,23,24,54,55,	21,22,47,52,53,57–59,61–64	27–32,48,65,70	35–40,49–51,56,66–69	60,71
Refer to example . . .	1,2,3,4	9	5	8	6,7

3. No **5.** No **7.** Yes **9. a.** 1/36 **b.** 1/12 **c.** 1/9 **d.** 5/36 **11. a.** 5/18 **b.** 5/12 **c.** 11/36 **13.** 5/18 **15. a.** 2/13 **b.** 7/13 **c.** 3/26 **d.** 3/4 **e.** 11/26 **17. a.** 5/13 **b.** 7/13 **c.** 3/13 **19. a.** 1/10 **b.** 2/5 **c.** 7/20 **21. a.** 0.51 **b.** 0.25 **c.** 0.10 **d.** 0.84 **23. a.** 5/9 **b.** 5/9 **c.** 5/9 **27.** 1 to 5 **29.** 2 to 1 **31. a.** 1 to 5 **b.** 11 to 7 **c.** 2 to 7 **d.** 7 to 2 **35.** Possible **37.** Not possible; the sum of the probabilities is less than 1. **39.** Not possible; a probability cannot be negative. **41. a.** 0.2778 **b.** 0.4167 **43. a.** 0.0463 **b.** 0.2963 **47.** 0.84 **49. a.** 0.62 **b.** 0.54 **c.** 0.43 **d.** 0.19 **51. a.** 0.061 **b.** 0.761 **c.** 0.822 **d.** 0.535 **53. a.** 0.961 **b.** 0.487 **c.** 0.513 **d.** 0.509 **e.** 0.004 **f.** 0.548 **55. a.** 1/4 **b.** 1/2 **c.** 1/4 **57.** a **59.** c **61. a.** 0.4 **b.** 0.1 **c.** 0.6 **d.** 0.9 **63.** 0 **65.** 2/5 **67. a.** 0.866 **b.** 0.478 **69. a.** 23/55 **b.** 67/220 **c.** 159/220 **71.** 0.0000000051; 0.0000012; 0.0063; 0.0166

Exercises 7.5 (page 330)

For exercises . . .	1–12	13–16	23,24,44–46, 49–53,63,71,72, 79–82,84,87–89	43,69,86	36–40,47, 54–60,62,64–67, 69,73,74,77	29,30,41,42, 75,76	48,61,68,78, 83,85,86
Refer to example . . .	3,4	8	5,6,7	2	1	9	10

1. 0 **3.** 1 **5.** 1/3 **7.** 0 **9.** 4/17 **11.** 11/51 **13.** 8/663 **15.** 25/102 **19.** Independent **21.** Dependent **23. a.** 1/4 **b.** 1/2 **25. a.** Many answers are possible **b.** Many answers are possible **29.** 1/20, 2/5 **31.** Second booth **33.** No, these events are not independent **35.** Yes **37.** The probability that a customer cashing a check will fail to make a deposit is 1/3. **39.** The probability that a customer making a deposit will not cash a check is 1/4. **41. a.** 0.3570 **43.** 0.875 **45.** 0.06 **47.** 2/3 **49.** 1/4 **51.** 1/4 **53.** 1/7 **55.** 0.039 **57.** 0.491 **59.** 0.072 **61.** Yes **63. a.** 0.3367 **b.** 0.6617 **c.** No **65.** 7/229 **67.** 191/229 **69.** e **71. a.** 0.5065 **c.** 0.2872 **d.** $p(1 - P(B)) + (1 - p)(1 - P(B))^2$ **e.** 0.2872 **f.** $2(1 - p)P(B)(1 - P(B))$ **g.** 0.2872 **73. a.** 0.2059 **b.** 0.1489 **c.** 0.0410 **d.** 0.2755 **e.** No **75. a.** 0.58 **77. a.** 0.2713 **b.** 0.3792 **c.** 0.6246 **d.** 0.3418 **e.** 0.6897 **f.** 0.5137 **g.** Not independent **79. a.** 0.052 **b.** 0.476 **81. a.** 7/10 **b.** 2/15 **83.** 10^{-12} **85.** No **87.** 0 points: 0.4; 1 point: 0.24; 2 points: 0.36. **89. c.** They are the same. **d.** The 2-points first strategy has a smaller probability of losing.

Exercises 7.6 (page 340)

For exercises . . .	1,2,9,10–13,23–26, 29–32,36,39	3–8,14–17,19 27,28	18,20–22,33–35, 37,38
Refer to example . . .	1	2	3

1. 1/3 **3.** 3/19 **5.** 21/38 **7.** 8/17 **9.** 85% **11.** 0.0727 **13.** 0.1765 **15.** 0.3636 **17.** 2/7 **19.** d **21.** c **23.** 0.0478 **25. a.** 0.039 **b.** 0.999 **c.** 0.001 **d.** 0.110 **27.** d **29.** b **31. a.** 0.1870 **b.** 0.9480 **33.** 0.1285 **35.** 0.1392 **37.** 0.5549 **39.** 9.9×10^{-5}

Chapter 7 Review Exercises (page 345)

For exercises . . .	1–5,13–28, 59,87,90	6,43–52, 60,61, 69,70,88, 90,103,104	7,8,53,54, 65–68, 71–73, 77,78 91,93, 95,96	9–11,55–58, 62,63,74–76, 86,90,94, 101,102, 107,108	12,79,80, 81–85, 89,97,98	39–42, 92, 99, 105,106, 109
Refer to example . . .	1	3	4	5	6	2

1. True **2.** True **3.** False **4.** False **5.** False **6.** True **7.** False **8.** False **9.** False **10.** True **11.** False **12.** True **13.** False **15.** False **17.** True **19.** False **21.** False **23.** 32 **25.** {a, b, g} **27.** {c, d} **29.** {a, b, e, f, g, h} **31.** U **33.** All female employees in the accounting department **35.** All employees who are in the accounting department or who have MBA degrees **37.** All male employees who are not in the sales department

39.

$A \cup B'$

41.
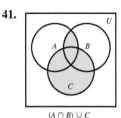
$(A \cap B) \cup C$

43. $\{1, 2, 3, 4, 5, 6\}$ **45.** $\{0, 0.5, 1, 1.5, 2, \ldots, 299.5, 300\}$
47. $\{(3, r), (3, g), (5, r), (5, g), (7, r), (7, g), (9, r), (9, g), (11, r), (11, g)\}$
49. $\{(3, g), (5, g), (7, g), (9, g), (11, g)\}$
51. 1/4 **53.** 11/26 **55.** 1/2 **57.** 1 **63.** No; yes **65.** 1 to 3 **67.** 2 to 11
69. 5/36 **71.** 1/6 **73.** 1/6 **75.** 2/11 **77. a.** 0.66 **b.** 0.29 **c.** 0.71
d. 0.34 **79.** 1/7 **81.** 0.8736 **83.** 0.3077 **85.** 0.87 **87. a.** $(E \cup F)'$ or
$E' \cap F'$ **b.** $E \cup F$ **89. a.** 0.0297 **b.** 0.0909 **c.** 0.2626 **d.** No **91.** b
93. b **95. a.**

	N_2	T_2
N_1	$N_1 N_2$	$N_1 T_2$
T_1	$T_1 N_2$	$T_1 T_2$

b. 1/4 **c.** 1/2 **d.** 1/4 **97.** c **99. a.** 53 **b.** 7 **c.** 12 **d.** 26 **101.** 0.6279
103. 0.90 **105. a.** 4 **b.** 18 **107.** No; 2/3 **109.** d

Chapter 8 Counting Principles; Further Probability Topics

Exercises 8.1 (page 359)

For exercises . . .	1–4,37,39,54,55	5–12,19,20,32,34,40	13–16,30,31,35,43–53	19–24	23,24,33,36,38,41,42
Refer to example . . .	4,5	6	1	9,10	8

1. 720 **3.** 1.308×10^{12}
5. 156 **7.** 1.024×10^{25} **9.** 1 **11.** n **13.** 36 **15.** 20 **19.** one **21. a.** 840 **b.** 180 **c.** 420 **23. a.** 362,880 **b.** 1728
c. 1260 **d.** 24 **e.** 144 **25.** Multiply by 10 **27. a.** 2 **b.** 6 **c.** 18 **29.** Undefined **31. a.** 42 **b.** 28 **33. a.** 39,916,800
b. 172,800 **c.** 86,400 **35.** No; use at least 4 initials **37.** 720 **39.** 3.352×10^{10} **41. a.** 120 **b.** 48 **43. a.** 27,600 **b.** 35,152
c. 1104 **45. a.** 160; 8,000,000 **b.** Some numbers, such as 911, 800, and 900, are reserved for special purposes. **47. a.** 17,576,000
b. 17,576,000 **c.** 456,976,000 **49.** 100,000; 90,000 **51.** 81 **53.** 1,572,864; no **55. a.** 1.216×10^{17} **b.** 43,589,145,600

Exercises 8.2 (page 367)

For exercises . . .	3–10,39,48,58	11,12,33,35,36, 40–42,45,54–56	14,32,37,43,44, 49,53	15,16	17–24	17–24,29–31,34, 38,46,47,50–52,57
Refer to example . . .	1	6	2,3		7	4	5

3. 56 **5.** 1.761×10^{12} **7.** 1
9. n **11.** 1716 **13. a.** 10
b. 7 **15. a.** 9 **b.** 6 **c.** 3; yes, from both **17.** Combinations; **a.** 126 **b.** 462 **c.** 4620 **19.** Permutations; 479,001,600
21. Combinations; **a.** 120 **b.** 1820 **c.** 36 **23.** Combinations; **a.** 10 **b.** 0 **c.** 1 **d.** 10 **e.** 30 **f.** 15 **g.** 0 **27. a.** 30
b. $n(n-1)$ **29.** 336 **31. a.** 720 **b.** 360 **33. a.** 40 **b.** 20 **c.** 7 **35.** 4,115,439,900 **37. a.** 84 **b.** 10 **c.** 40 **d.** 74
39. No; 14,190 **41. a.** 48 **b.** 658,008 **c.** 652,080 **d.** 844,272 **e.** 79,092 **43.** 50 **45. a.** 15,504 **b.** 816 **47.** 558 **49.** a 26
b. 26 **51. a.** 3,089,157,760 **b.** 1,657,656,000 **53. a.** 838 **b.** 20,695,218,670 **55. a.** 84 **b.** 729 **d.** 680 **e.** 120
57. a. 6.402×10^{15} **b.** 3.135×10^{10}

Exercises 8.3 (page 378)

For exercises . . .	1–10,36–41,45,47,65,66,68–71,73	11–18,46–64	19–22,42–44,46,72	25–28,33	29–32
Refer to example . . .	1,2,3	4	5	6	7

1. 7/33 **3.** 14/55
5. 0.008127 **7.** 0.2980 **9.** 0.2214 **11.** 1326 **13.** 33/221 **15.** 52/221 **17.** 130/221 **19.** 8.417×10^{-8} **21.** 18,975/28,561
25. $1 - P(365, 43)/365^{43}$ **27.** 1 **29.** 13/34 **31.** 1/180 **33.** 0.6501 **35.** 3/5 and 2/5 **37.** 36/55 **39.** 21/55 **41.** 7/22
43. 1/3 **45. a.** 225/646 **b.** 15/323 **c.** 225/2584 **d.** 0 **e.** 1/2 **f.** 175/2584 **g.** 503/646 **47. a.** 0.0542 **b.** 0.0111 **c.** 0.0464
d. 0.1827 **e.** 0.3874 **f.** 0.8854 **49.** 1.385×10^{-5} **51.** 0.0039 **53.** 0.0475 **55.** 1.575×10^{-12} **57.** 0.0402 **59.** 0.4728
61. 0.0493 **63.** 0.0306 **65.** 0.0640 **67.** 4.980×10^{-7} **69.** The probability of picking 5 out of 52 is higher, 1/2,598,960 compared
with 1/13,983,816. **71. a.** 0.01642 **b.** 0.01231 **73. a.** 28 **b.** 268,435,456 **c.** 40,320 **d.** 1.502×10^{-4} **e.** $n!/2^{n(n-1)/2}$
75. a. 3.291×10^{-6} **b.** 7.962×10^{-12} **c.** 5.927×10^{-11} **d.** 5.524×10^{26}

Exercises 8.4 (page 386)

For exercises . . .	1–4,9–12,15,16,24,25,29–39,33,34, 37,40,41,43,44,47,59,60	5–8,13,14,17,18,26–28,31,32, 35,36,38,39,42,45,46,48–51, 54,55,57,58,61–63	52,53,64,65
Refer to example . . .	2,3	4,5	7

1. 5/16 **3.** 1/32 **5.** 3/16
7. 13/16 **9.** 4.594×10^{-10}
11. 0.2692 **13.** 0.8748
15. 0.0002441 **17.** 0.9624 **23.** The potential callers are not likely to have birthdates that are evenly distributed throughout the
twentieth century. **25.** 0.6014 **27.** 0.0876 **29.** 0.1721 **31.** 0.7868 **33.** 0.2458 **35.** 0.0170 **37.** 0.3585 **39. a.** 0.1488
b. 0.0213 **c.** 0.9787 **41. a.** 0.0222 **b.** 0.1797 **c.** 0.7766 **43.** 0.0874 **45.** 0.9126 **47.** 0.2183 **49.** 0.0025 **51. a.** 0.0478
b. 0.9767 **c.** 0.8971 **53. a.** 1 chance in 1024 **b.** About 1 chance in 1.1×10^{12} **c.** About 1 chance in 2.587×10^6 **55.** 0.9523
57. e **59.** 0.0305 **61.** 0.8676 **63. a.** 0.2083 **b.** 0.5902 **c.** 0.1250 **d.** 0.8095 **65. a.** 0.5260 **b.** 0.9343 **67. a.** 0.125, 0.25,
0.3125, 0.3125 **b.** 0.2893, 0.3222, 0.2353, 0.1531

Exercises 8.5 (page 395)

For exercises . . .	1–4	5–8,29	9–16,30,32,36,37,42	17,18,26,45,56	19–25,29,31,38,43,44,47–54,57	33,39,40,55,56
Refer to example . . .	1	2	3	5	4,7	8

1.

Number of Heads	0	1	2	3	4
Probability	1/16	1/4	3/8	1/4	1/16

3.

Number of Aces	0	1	2	3
Probability	0.7826	0.2042	0.0130	0.0002

5.   **7.**   **9.** 3.6 **11.** 14.49 **13.** 2.7 **15.** 18 **17.** 0; yes

19. a.   **b.** 9/7 **21. a.**   **b.** 2/3

23. 3/4

25. 1/2

x	0	1	2	3	4
P(x)	625/1296	125/324	25/216	5/324	1/1296

29. a.

Sum	5	6	7	8	9
Probability	1/6	1/6	1/3	1/6	1/6

b. **c.** 1 to 2 **d.** 7

31. $54,000 **33. a.** 30 **b.** 10 **35.** e **37. a.** $68.51; $72.84 **b.** Amoxicillin **39.** 185 **41. a.** 0.007230 **b.** 5.094×10^{-4}
c. 5.5×10^{-5} **d.** 0.1143 **43. a.** **b.** 1.2 **c.** 1.2

Number of Cats	0	1	2	3	4
Probability	0.2401	0.4116	0.2646	0.0756	0.0081

45. −$0.72; no **47.** −$0.82 **49.** −$0.053 **51.** −$0.50 **53.** −$0.90; no **55. a.** 10/3 **b.** 50/9

57. a. **b.** 1.37

x	0	1	2	3	4
P(x)	0.1875	0.3897	0.3038	0.1053	0.0137

Chapter 8 Review Exercises (page 401)

For exercises . . .	1,3,13,14,19,20,53	2,15–18,21,22,54	4–6,25–30,35–40,69 76,78,79,82	7,8,31–34,49,50, 55–60,67,68,70–73	9–12,41–48,61,62, 67,70–75,77,78, 80,81
Refer to section . . .	1	2	3	4	5

1. True **2.** True **3.** True **4.** True **5.** False **6.** True **7.** True **8.** False **9.** True **10.** False **11.** True **12.** False
13. 720 **15.** 220 **17. a.** 90 **b.** 10 **c.** 120 **d.** 220 **19. a.** 120 **b.** 24 **21. a.** 840 **b.** 2045 **25.** 2/143 **27.** 21/143
29. 5/13 **31.** 5/16 **33.** 11/32 **35.** 25/102 **37.** 15/34 **39.** 546/1326

41. a.

Number of Heads	0	1	2	3
Probability	0.125	0.375	0.375	0.125

b.   **c.** 1.5

43. 0.6 **45.** −$0.833; no **47. a.** 0.231 **b.** 0.75 **49.** 31/32 **51. a.** $C(n,0)$, or 1; $C(n,1)$, or n; $C(n,2)$; $C(n,n)$, or 1
b. $C(n,0) + C(n,1) + C(n,2) + \cdots + C(n,n)$ **e.** The sum of the elements in row n of Pascal's triangle is 2^n. **53.** 48
55. 0.1122 **57.** 7.580×10^{-7} **59.** 0.6187 **61.** 2 **63.** d **65.** e

67.

x	0	1	2	3	4	5	6
Income	0	400	800	1200	800	400	0
$P(x)$	0.0041	0.0369	0.1382	0.2765	0.3110	0.1866	0.0467

a. $780.60 **b.** $720; $856.32; $868.22; 5
69. 0.1875

71. a.

Number of Women	0	1	2	3	4	5
Probability	0.0380	0.1755	0.3240	0.2990	0.1380	0.0255

b.

c. 2.4

73. a.

Number Who Did Not Do Homework	0	1	2	3
Probability	1/12	5/12	5/12	1/12

b. 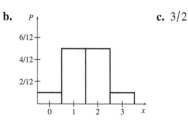 **c.** 3/2

75. −$0.71 **77. a.** 10.95 **b.** 2.56 **79. a.** 0.4799; 0.6533 **c.** 0.3467; 0.003096

Chapter 9 Statistics

Exercises 9.1 (page 415)

For exercises . . .	1a,2a,44a	1b,2b,42a, 44b	7–12,39,40, 47	13–16,42b, 44d	17–22,48b, 50	23,24,45,46, 49	25–30,44c, 44f,48c	36–38,41,43 45,46,48
Refer to example . . .	1	2	3,7	4,5	6,7	9	8	3,6

1. a.–b.

Interval	Frequency
0–24	4
25–49	8
50–74	5
75–99	10
100–124	4
125–149	5

c.–d.

3. a.–b.

Interval	Frequency
0–19	4
20–39	5
40–59	4
60–79	5
80–99	9
100–119	3
120–139	4
140–159	2

c.–d.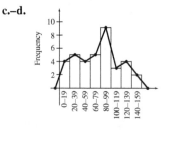

7. 16 **9.** 28,620 **11.** 7.68 **13.** 7.25 **15. a.** 73.81 **b.** 74.5 **17.** 42 **19.** 130 **21.** 29.1 **23.** 73.86, 80.5 **25.** 9 **27.** 55
and 62 **29.** 6.3 **33.** 75–99 **37.** 2095.9 million bushels, 2130 million bushels **39.** $45,794 **41. a.** 348.4, 249.5 **c.** 1.187, 1.215
43. 7.38; 7; 7, 5, 4 **45. a.** 55.5°F; 50.5°F **b.** 28.9°F; 28.5°F **47. a.** $71,349 **49. a.** $8,253,336, $5,500,000, $5,500,000

Exercises 9.2 (page 425)

For exercises . . .	3–8	9,10,25,26,29	11,12	27,28	30–36
Refer to example . . .	1,3	3		4	6	5

1. The standard deviation is the square root of the variance.
3. 33; 12.6 **5.** 46; 16.1 **7.** 24; 8.1 **9.** 40.05 **11.** 39.4 **13.** 8/9 **15.** 24/25 **17.** At least 8/9 **19.** No more than 1/9
25. a. Mean = 25.5 hr; standard deviation = 7.2 hr **b.** Forever Power **c.** Forever Power **27. a.** 1/3; 2; −1/3; 0; 5/3; 7/3; 1;

4/3; 7/3; 2/3 **b.** 2.1; 2.6; 1.5; 2.6; 2.5; 0.6; 1.0; 2.1; 0.6; 1.2 **c.** 1.13 **d.** 1.68 **e.** 4.41; −2.15 **f.** 4.31; 0 **29.** Mean = 1.816 mm; standard deviation = 0.4451 mm. **31. a.** Mean = 7.3571; standard deviation = 0.1326 **b.** 100% **33. a.** 127.7 days; 30.16 days **b.** Seven **35. a.** $9,267,188 **b.** 4%

Exercises 9.3 (page 435)

For exercises . . .	5–14	15–18	22–64
Refer to example . . .	1	2	4

1. the mean **3.** z-scores are found with the formula $z = (x - \mu)/\sigma$. **5.** 45.54%
7. 48.96% **9.** 37.38% **11.** 14.78% **13.** 97.72% **15.** −1.64 or −1.65 **17.** 1.28 **19.** 0.5; 0.5 **21.** 0.8889; 0.9974 **23.** 5000
25. 6247 **27.** 7257 **29.** 0.1587 **31.** 0.0062 **33.** 84.13% **35.** 37.79% **37.** 7.03% **39. a.** 15.87% **b.** 0% **41.** 0.4325
43. About 2 **45.** 1350 units **47.** 1430 units **49.** 60.32 mph **51.** 6.68% **53.** 38.3% **55.** 87 **57.** 71 **59. b.** 55%
61. a. About 0.01; yes **b.** Essentially 0 **63. a.** 0.5596; 0.0188 **b.** Essentially 0; essentially 0 **c.** 0.9265; 0.9554
d. Essentially 0; essentially 0 **e.** Essentially 0; essentially 0

Exercises 9.4 (page 443)

For exercises . . .	3–34
Refer to example . . .	2

1. The number of trials and the probability of success on each trial **3. a.** 0.0278 **b.** 0.0279 **5. a.** 0.0106
b. 0.0122 **7.** 0.0240 **9.** 0.9463 **11.** 0.0956 **13.** 0.8643 **15.** 0.1841 **17. a.** 0.0146 **b.** 0.0537 **19. a.** Essentially 0
b. 0.0018 **21.** 0.0274 **23. a.** 0.9118 **b.** 0.9984 **25. a.** 0.0001 **b.** 0.0002 **c.** 0.0000 **27.** 0.6480 **29.** 0.9554
31. a. The numbers are too large for the calculator to handle. **b.** 0.1742 **33.** 0.0287

Chapter 9 Review Exercises (page 446)

For exercises . . .	4,6,10,13–25	3,5,11,26–33	7,8,12,34–38,44,52–56,58,59	1,2,9,39–41,45,46,48–51	43,47,57
Refer to section . . .	1	2	3	4	1,2

1. True **2.** False **3.** False **4.** True **5.** False **6.** False **7.** False **8.** True **9.** True **10.** True **11.** False **12.** True
15. a.

Sales	Frequency
450–474	5
475–499	6
500–524	5
525–549	2
550–574	2

b.–c.

17. 29.25 **19.** 34.9 **23.** 38; 36 and 38 **25.** 30–39
29. 67; 23.9 **31.** 12.6 **33.** A skewed distribution has the largest frequency at one end. **35.** 0.7995 **37.** 0.0606
39. Because the histogram is skewed, not close to the shape of a normal distribution **41. a.** 2.1; 1.07 **b.** 2; 1
c. Answers to parts a and b should be close to each other.
43. a. Stock I: 8%, 7.9%; Stock II: 8%, 2.6% **b.** Stock II
45. a. 0.8924; 0.8962 **b.** 0.0446; 0.0477 **c.** 0.0196; 0.0150
47. Diet A: $\bar{x} = 2.7$, $s = 2.26$; Diet B: $\bar{x} = 1.3$, $s = 0.95$
a. Diet A **b.** Diet B **49.** 0.9292 **51.** 0.9534 **53.** 43.25% **55.** 56.25% **57. a.** 142.46; 140; no mode **b.** 48.67
c. 38.5% **d.** 100% **59. a.** 0.1020 **b.** 0.3707 **d.** 0.9987 **e.** 0.1336

Chapter 10 Nonlinear Functions

Exercises 10.1 (page 461)

For exercises . . .	1–8	9–16	17–32	33–40	41–56,76,77	57–62	63–70	71–74	75,78	79,80
Refer to example . . .	1,2	3 (b)	3(a), (c)–(e)	2 (d)	4		5	6	7 Dow Jones	8

1. Not a function **3.** Function **5.** Function **7.** Not a function
9. $(-2, -1), (-1, 1), (0, 3), (1, 5), (2, 7), (3, 9)$;
range: $\{-1, 1, 3, 5, 7, 9\}$ **11.** $(-2, 3/2), (-1, 2), (0, 5/2),$ $(1, 3), (2, 7/2), (3, 4)$; range: $\{3/2, 2, 5/2, 3, 7/2, 4\}$ **13.** $(-2, 0), (-1, -1), (0, 0), (1, 3),$ $(2, 8), (3, 15)$; range: $\{-1, 0, 3, 8, 15\}$

15. $(-2, 4), (-1, 1), (0, 0),$
$(1, 1), (2, 4), (3, 9)$; range: $\{0, 1, 4, 9\}$

17. $(-\infty, \infty)$ **19.** $(-\infty, \infty)$ **21.** $[-2, 2]$ **23.** $[3, \infty)$ **25.** $(-\infty, -1) \cup (-1, 1) \cup (1, \infty)$
27. $(-\infty, -4) \cup (4, \infty)$ **29.** $(-\infty, -1] \cup [5, \infty)$ **31.** $(-\infty, -1) \cup (1/3, \infty)$ **33.** Domain:
$[-5, 4)$; range: $[-2, 6]$ **35.** Domain: $(-\infty, \infty)$; range: $(-\infty, 12]$ **37.** Domain: $[-2, 4]$; range: $[0, 4]$
a. 0 **b.** 4 **c.** 3 **d.** −1.5, 1.5, 2.5 **39.** Domain: $[-2, 4]$; range: $[-3, 2]$ **a.** −3 **b.** −2
c. −1 **d.** 2.5 **41. a.** 33 **b.** 15/4 **c.** $3a^2 - 4a + 1$ **d.** $12/m^2 - 8/m + 1$ or
$(12 - 8m + m^2)/m^2$ **e.** 0, 4/3 **43. a.** 7 **b.** 0 **c.** $(2a + 1)/(a - 4)$ if $a \neq 4$, 7 if $a = 4$

d. $(4 + m)/(2 - 4m)$ if $m \neq 1/2$, 7 if $m = 1/2$ **e.** -5 **45.** $6t^2 + 12t + 4$ **47.** $r^2 + 2rh + h^2 - 2r - 2h + 5$
49. $9/q^2 - 6/q + 5$ or $(9 - 6q + 5q^2)/q^2$ **51. a.** $2x + 2h + 1$ **b.** $2h$ **c.** 2 **53. a.** $2x^2 + 4xh + 2h^2 - 4x - 4h - 5$
b. $4xh + 2h^2 - 4h$ **c.** $4x + 2h - 4$ **55. a.** $1/(x + h)$ **b.** $-h/[x(x + h)]$ **c.** $-1/[x(x + h)]$ **57.** Function
59. Not a Function   **61.** Function   **63.** Odd   **65.** Even   **67.** Even   **69.** Odd   **71.** **a.** $36   **b.** $36   **c.** $64   **d.** $120
e. $120   **f.** $148   **g.** $148   **i.** x, the number of full and partial days   **j.** S, the cost of renting a saw   **73. a.** $93,300. Attorneys
can receive a maximum of $93,300 on a jury award of $250,000.   **b.** $124,950. Attorneys can receive a maximum of $124,950 on a
jury award of $350,000.   **c.** $181,950. Attorneys can receive a maximum of $181,950 on a jury award of $550,000.
d.

75. a. About 140 m   **b.** About 250 m   **77. a. i.** 3.6 kcal/km   **ii.** 61 kcal/km
b. $x = g(z) = 1000z$ **c.** $y = 4.4z^{0.88}$ **79. a.** $P(w) = 1000/w + 2w$ **b.** $(0, \infty)$
c.

Exercises 10.2 (page 472)

For exercises . . .	3–8	9–24,58–62,64–67	25–38,47,48	39–46	49–53	54–57,68,69
Refer to example . . .	1–3	4	8	Before Example 8	7	6

3. D   **5.** A   **7.** C
9. $y = 3(x + 3/2)^2 - 7/4$, $(-3/2, -7/4)$ **11.** $y = -2(x - 2)^2 - 1$, $(2,-1)$ **13.** Vertex is $(-5/2, -1/4)$; axis is $x = -5/2$;
x-intercepts are -3 and -2; y-intercept is 6.
15. Vertex is $(-3, 2)$; axis is $x = -3$; x-intercepts are -4
and -2; y-intercept is -16.

17. Vertex is $(-2, -16)$; axis is $x = -2$;   **19.** Vertex is $(1, 3)$;   **21.** Vertex is $(4, 11)$; axis is $x = 4$; x-intercepts are
x-intercepts are $-2 \pm 2\sqrt{2} \approx 0.83$ axis is $x = 1$; no x-intercepts; $4 \pm \sqrt{22}/2 \approx 6.35$ or 1.65; y-intercept is -21.
or -4.83; y-intercept is -8. y-intercept is 5.

      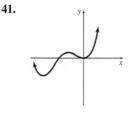

23. Vertex is $(4, -5)$; axis is $x = 4$;   **25.** D   **27.** C   **29.** E   **31.**   **33.**
x-intercepts are $4 \pm \sqrt{15} \approx 7.87$
or 0.13; y-intercept is 1/3.

35.   **37.**   **39.**   **41.**

43.   **45.**   **47. a.** r **b.** $-r$ **c.** $-r$ **49. a.**   **b.** 1 batch
c. $16,000
d. $4000

51. a.   **b.** 2.5 batches **c.** $31,250 **d.** $5000 **53.** Maximum revenue is $9225; 35 seats are unsold.
55. a. $R(x) = x(500 - x) = 500x - x^2$ **b.**   **c.** $250 **d.** $62,500

57. a. $800 + 25x$ **b.** $80 - x$ **c.** $R(x) = 64,000 + 1200x - 25x^2$ **d.** 24 **e.** $78,400 **59. a.** 87 yr **b.** 98 yr
61. a. 28.5 weeks **b.** 0.81 **c.** 0 weeks or 57 weeks of gestation; no
63. a.   **b.** Quadratic **c.** $y = 0.002726x^2 - 0.3113x + 29.33$;
d. $f(x) = 0.003(x - 60)^2 + 20.3$

e.

65. 49 yr; 3.98 **67. a.** 61.70 ft **b.** 43.08 mph **69.** 9025 ft^2

71. $y = (4/27)x^2$; $6\sqrt{3}$ ft ≈ 10.39 ft

Exercises 10.3 (page 481)

3.   **5.**

For exercises . . .	3–6	7–15,21–26	16–20,27–42,57,58	46,47,50–52	54–56,59
Refer to example . . .	1	4	6	7	2,3

7. D **9.** E **11.** I **13.** G **15.** A **17.** D **19.** E **21.** 4, 6, etc.
(true degree $= 4$); $+$ **23.** 5, 7, etc. (true degree $= 5$); $+$
25. 7, 9, etc. (true degree $= 7$); $-$

27. Horizontal asymptote: $y = 0$; vertical asymptote: $x = -2$; no x-intercept; y-intercept $= -2$

29. Horizontal asymptote: $y = 0$; vertical asymptote: $x = -3/2$; no x-intercept; y-intercept $= 2/3$

31. Horizontal asymptote: $y = 2$; vertical asymptote: $x = 3$; x-intercept $= 0$; y-intercept $= 0$

33. Horizontal asymptote: $y = 1$; vertical asymptote: $x = 4$; x-intercept $= -1$; y-intercept $= -1/4$

35. Horizontal asymptote: $y = -1/2$; vertical asymptote: $x = -5$; x-intercept $= 3/2$; y-intercept $= 3/20$

37. Horizontal asymptote: $y = -1/3$; vertical asymptote: $x = -2$; x-intercept $= -4$; y-intercept $= -2/3$

39. No asymptotes; hole at $x = -4$; x-intercept $= -3$; y-intercept $= 3$

41. One possible answer is $y = 2x/(x - 1)$.   **43. a.** 0   **b.** 2, -3 **d.** $(x + 1)(x - 1)(x + 2)$ **e.** $3(x + 1)(x - 1)(x + 2)$
f. $(x - a)$ **45. a.** Two; one at $x = -1.4$ and one at $x = 1.4$ **b.** Three; one at $x = -1.414$, one at $x = 1.414$, and one at $x = 1.442$ **47. a.** \$440; \$419; \$383; \$326; \$284; \$251   **b.** Vertical asymptote at $x = -475$; horizontal asymptote at $y = 0$
c. $y = 463.2$ **d.**

49. $f_1(x) = x(100 - x)/25$,
$f_2(x) = x(100 - x)/10$,
$f(x) = x^2(100 - x)^2/250$

$f(x) = \dfrac{x^2(100 - x)^2}{250}$

51. a. \$6700; \$15,600; \$26,800; \$60,300; \$127,300; \$328,300; \$663,300   **b.** No
c.

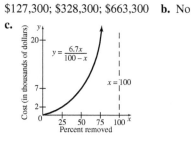

53. a. $a = 337/d$ **b.** 8.32 (using $k = 337$)   **55. a.**

$A(x) = 0.003631x^3 - 0.03746x^2 + 0.1012x + 0.009$

b. Close to 2 hours   **c.** About 1.1 to 2.7 hours

57. a. $[0, \infty)$ **b.**

c.

d. The population of the next generation, $f(x)$, gets smaller when the current generation, x, is larger.
59. a. 220 g; 602.5 g; 1220 g   **b.** $c < 19.68$
c.

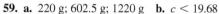

d. 41.9 cm

61. a. 1.80, 0.812, 0.366 **b.**

c. 2.48 sec **d.** The period increases by a factor of $\sqrt{2}$.
e. $L = 0.822T^2$, which is very close to the function found in part b.

Exercises 10.4 (page 494)

For exercises . . .	3–11,29–32	13–28	37–45,46	47–49	50–55
Refer to example . . .	1,2	3	4,5	6	7

1. 2, 4, 8, 16, 32, . . . , 1024; $1.125899907 \times 10^{15}$ **3.** E **5.** C **7.** F
9. A **11.** C **13.** 5 **15.** -4 **17.** -3 **19.** 21/4 **21.** $-12/5$ **23.** 2, -2 **25.** 0, -1 **27.** 0, 1/2
29.

31.

37. a. $2166.53 **b.** $2189.94 **c.** $2201.90 **d.** $2209.97 **e.** $2214.03
39. He should choose the 5.9% investment, which would yield $23.74 additional
interest. **41. a.** $10.94 **b.** $11.27 **c.** $11.62 **43.** 6.30%
45. a. 1, 0.92, 0.85, 0.78, 0.72, 0.66, 0.61, 0.56, 0.51, 0.47, 0.43
b.

c. About $384,000 **d.** About $98
47. a. The function gives a population of about
3660 million, which is close to the actual population.
b. 6022 million **c.** 7725 million

49. a. 41.93 million **b.** 12.48 million **c.** 2.1%, 2.3%; Asian **d.** 37.99 million **51. a.**
e. Hispanic: 2039;   Asian: 2036;   Black: 2079

exponentially

b. $f(x) = 534(1.026)^x$ **c.** 2.6%

d.

2026 **53. a.** $P = 1013e^{-1.34 \times 10^{-4}x}$; $P = -0.0748x + 1013$; $P = 1/(2.79 \times 10^{-7}x + 9.87 \times 10^{-4})$
b. $P = 1013e^{-1.34 \times 10^{-4}x}$ is the best fit.
c. 829 millibars, 232 millibars
d. $P = 1038(0.99998661)^x$. This is
slightly different from the function
found in part b, which can be rewritten as $P = 1013(0.99998660)^x$.

55. a. $C = 16,861t + 7461, C = 1686t^2 + 22,636, C = 19,231(1.2647)^t$ **b.**
c. $C = 19,250(1.2579)^t$; this is close to the function found in part b.
d. 176,100, 191,200, 201,300, 190,900

$C = 19,231(1.2647)^t$
is the best fit.

Exercises 10.5 (page 506)

For exercises . . .	1–12	13–24	27–36	37–40	41–56	57–64	65–68	69–70	75–77,79,87	75d,76c,78	81–83
Refer to example . . .	1	2	3	4	5	6	7	first CAUTION	8	9	10

1. $\log_5 125 = 3$ **3.** $\log_3 81 = 4$ **5.** $\log_3(1/9) = -2$ **7.** $2^5 = 32$ **9.** $e^{-1} = 1/e$ **11.** $10^5 = 100{,}000$ **13.** 2 **15.** 3
17. -4 **19.** $-2/3$ **21.** 1 **23.** 5/3 **25.** $\log_3 4$ **27.** $\log_5 3 + \log_5 k$ **29.** $1 + \log_3 p - \log_3 5 - \log_3 k$
31. $\ln 3 + (1/2)\ln 5 - (1/3)\ln 6$ **33.** $5a$ **35.** $2c + 3a + 1$ **37.** 2.113 **39.** -0.281 **41.** $x = 1/6$ **43.** $z = 4/3$
45. $r = 25$ **47.** $x = 1$ **49.** No solution **51.** $x = 3$ **53.** $x = 5$ **55.** $x = 1/\sqrt{3e} \approx 0.3502$ **57.** $x = (\ln 6)/(\ln 2) \approx 2.5850$
59. $k = 1 + \ln 6 \approx 2.7918$ **61.** $x = (\ln 3)/(\ln(5/3)) \approx 2.1507$ **63.** $x = (\ln 1.25)/(\ln 1.2) \approx 1.224$ **65.** $e^{(\ln 10)(x+1)}$
67. 20.09^x **69.** $x < 5$ **75. a.** 23.4 yr **b.** 11.9 yr **c.** 9.0 yr **d.** 23.3 yr; 12 yr; 9 yr **77.** 6.25% **79.** 2035
81. a. About 0.693 **b.** $\ln 2$ **c.** Yes **83. a.** About 1.099 **b.** About 1.386 **85.** About every 7 hr, $T = (3\ln 5)/\ln 2$
87. a. 2039 **b.** 2036 **89.** $s/n = 2^{C/B} - 1$ **91.** No; 1/10 **93. a.** 1000 times greater **b.** 1,000,000 times greater

Exercises 10.6 (page 515)

For exercises . . .	6,28b,29b	7–10,15–17,21c	11–14,18–20	19d,20d	23,24	25–28,30,31,42	21d,e,22,29,41	32–40
Refer to example . . .	3	4	6	7	8	1	5	2

7. 4.06% **9.** 8.33% **11.** $6209.93 **13.** $6283.17 **15.** 9.20% **17.** 6.17% **19. a.** $257,107.67 **b.** $49,892.33
c. $68,189.54 **d.** 14.28% **21. a.** The 8% investment compounded quarterly. **b.** $759.26 **c.** 8.24% and 8.06% **d.** 3.71 yr
e. 3.75 yr **23. a.** 200 **b.** About 1/2 year **c.** No **d.** Yes; 1000 **25. a.** $0.003285e^{0.007232t}$ **b.** 3300 **c.** No; it is too small.
Exponential growth does not accurately describe population growth for the world over a long period of time.
27. a. $y = 25{,}000e^{0.047t}$ **b.** $y = 25{,}000(1.048)^t$ **c.** About 18.6 hours **29. a.** 17.9 days **b.** January 17 **31. a.** 2, 5, 24, and
125 **b.** 0.061 **c.** 0.24 **d.** No, the values of k are different. **e.** Between 3 and 4 **33.** About 13 years
35. a. 0.0193 gram **b.** 69 years **37. a.** $y = 500e^{-0.0863t}$ **b.** $y = 500(386/500)^{t/3}$ **c.** 8.0 days **39. a.** 19.5 watts
b. 173 days **41. a.** 67% **b.** 37% **c.** 23 days **d.** 46 days **43.** 18.02° **45.** 1 hour

Chapter 10 Review Exercises (page 521)

1. True **2.** False **3.** True
4. True **5.** False **6.** False
7. True **8.** False **9.** False
10. False **11.** False **12.** False
13. False **14.** True **15.** False
16. False **17.** True **18.** True

For exercises . . .	1,2,6,20,21, 35–42,87,110, 115,122	3,4,31–34, 105,109	5,9,43–46, 51–54,83, 88–93,101,108, 111,112,114, 116–118,120	7,10–17,22, 29,30,47–50, 55–82,84, 94–95,121	8,23–28,86	18,96–100. 102–104
Refer to section . . .	3	2	4	5	1	6

23. $(-3, 14), (-2, 5), (-1, 0), (0, -1), (1, 2), (2, 9), (3, 20)$; **25. a.** 17 **b.** 4 **c.** $5k^2 - 3$ **d.** $-9m^2 + 12m + 1$
range: $\{-1, 0, 2, 5, 9, 14, 20\}$ **e.** $5x^2 + 10xh + 5h^2 - 3$ **f.** $-x^2 - 2xh - h^2 + 4x + 4h + 1$
g. $10x + 5h$ **h.** $-2x - h + 4$ **27.** $(-\infty, 0) \cup (0, \infty)$
29. $(-7, \infty)$ **31.** **33.**

35. **37.** **39.** **41.**

43.

45.

47.

49.

51. -5 **53.** -6 **55.** $\log_3 243 = 5$ **57.** $\ln 2.22554 = 0.8$ **59.** $2^5 = 32$ **61.** $e^{4.41763} = 82.9$ **63.** 4 **65.** 3/2
67. $\log_5(21k^4)$ **69.** $\log_3(y^4/x^2)$ **71.** $p = 1.581$ **73.** $m = -1.807$ **75.** $x = -3.305$ **77.** $m = 2.156$ **79.** $k = 2$
81. $p = 3/4$ **83. a.** $(-\infty, \infty)$ **b.** $(0, \infty)$ **c.** 1 **d.** $y = 0$ **e.** Greater than 1 **f.** Between 0 and 1 **87. a.** \$28,000
b. \$7000 **c.** \$63,000 **d.**

e. No. **89.** \$921.95 **91.** \$15,510.79 **93.** \$17,901.90 **95.** 70 quarters or 17.5
years; 111 quarters or 27.75 years **97.** 6.17% **99.** \$1494.52 **101.** \$17,339.86
103. About 9.59% **105. a.** $n = 1500 - 10p$ **b.** $R = p(1500 - 10p)$
c. $50 \le p \le 150$ **d.** $R = (1500n - n^2)/10$ **e.** $0 \le n \le 1000$ **f.** \$75
g. 750 **h.** \$56,250 **i.**

j. The revenue starts at \$50,000
when the price is \$50, rises to a
maximum of \$56,250 when the
price is \$75, and falls to 0 when
the price is \$150.

107. a.

b. $2x + 5$ **c.** $A(x) = x + 4 + 7/x$
d. $1 - 7/[x(x + 1)]$ **109.** The third
day; 104.2°F

111. a.

b. $y = 2.384t^2 - 42.55t + 269.2$, $y = -0.4931t^3 + 11.26t^2 - 82.00t + 292.9$, $y = 213.8(0.9149)^t$
d. 372, -788, 36 **113.** 187.9 cm; 345 kg
115. a. 10.915 billion; this is about
4.006 billion more than the estimate of
6.909 billion. **b.** 26.56 billion; 96.32 billion
117. 0.25; 0.69 minutes

119. a. $S = -3.404 + 103.2 \ln A$ **b.** $S = 81.26 A^{0.3011}$ **c.** 1800 ... 2200

d. 234, 163

121. a. 0 yr **b.** 1.85×10^9 yr
c. As r increases, t increases, but at a slower and slower rate.
As r decreases, t decreases at a faster and faster rate.

Chapter 11 The Derivative

Exercises 11.1 (page 543) For exercises . . .

	1,7b, 8b,9a, 82–84	2,7a, 10a, 53–56	3,5a, 6a, 17–20	4	5a,6b, 8a,9b, 10b,15,16	11, 12	21–30	31–38, 41,42	39,40	43–52, 75–81, 84–93	57–63, 65, 71–74
Refer to example . . .	5	3	2	4	1	11	6	8	9	12	10

1. c **3.** b **5. a.** 3 **b.** 1 **7. a.** 0 **b.** Does not exist **9. a. i.** -1; **ii.** $-1/2$ **iii.** Does not exist; **iv.** Does not exist
b. i. $-1/2$ **ii.** $-1/2$ **iii.** $-1/2$ **iv.** $-1/2$ **11.** 3 **15.** 4 **17.** 10 **19.** Does not exist **21.** -18 **23.** 1/3 **25.** 3
27. 512 **29.** 2/3 **31.** 6 **33.** 3/2 **35.** -5 **37.** $-1/9$ **39.** 1/10 **41.** $2x$ **43.** 3/7 **45.** 3/2 **47.** 0 **49.** ∞ (does not
exist) **51.** $-\infty$ (does not exist) **53.** 1 **55. a.** 2 **b.** Does not exist **57.** 6 **59.** 1.5 **61. a.** Does not exist **b.** $x = -2$
c. If $x = a$ is a vertical asymptote for the graph of $f(x)$, then $\lim\limits_{x \to a} f(x)$ does not exist. **65. a.** 0 **b.** $y = 0$ **67. a.** $-\infty$ (does
not exist) **b.** $x = 0$ **71.** 5 **73.** 0.3333 or 1/3 **75. a.** 1.5 **77. a.** -2 **79. a.** 8 **83. a.** 3 cents **b.** 7.25 cents
c. 8.25 cents **d.** Does not exist **e.** 8.25 cents **85.** \$6; the average cost approaches \$6 as the number of DVDs produced
becomes very large. **87.** 63 items; the number of items a new employee produces gets closer and closer to 63 as the number of

days of training increases. **89.** $R/(i - g)$ **91. a.** 36.2 cm; the depth of the sediment layer deposited below the bottom of the lake in 1970 is 36.2 cm. **b.** 155 cm; the depth of the sediment approaches 155 cm going back in time. **93. a.** 0.572 **b.** 0.526 **c.** 0.503 **d.** 0.5; the numbers in a, b, and c give the probability that the legislator will vote yes on the second, fourth, and eighth votes. In d, as the number of roll calls increases, the probability of a yes vote approaches 0.5 but is never less than 0.5.

Exercises 11.2 (page 554)

For exercises . . .	1–6,34,35	7–18,31–33	19–28	36–41
Refer to example . . .	1	2	3	4

1. $a = -1$: **a.** $f(-1)$ does not exist. **b.** 1/2 **c.** 1/2 **d.** 1/2
e. $f(-1)$ does not exist. **3.** $a = 1$: **a.** 2 **b.** -2 **c.** -2 **d.** -2
e. $f(1)$ does not equal the limit. **5.** $a = -5$: **a.** $f(-5)$ does not exist **b.** ∞ (does not exist) **c.** $-\infty$ (does not exist)
d. Limit does not exist. **e.** $f(-5)$ does not exist and the limit does not exist; $a = 0$: **a.** $f(0)$ does not exist. **b.** 0 **c.** 0
d. 0 **e.** $f(0)$ does not exist. **7.** $a = 0$, limit does not exist; $a = 2$, limit does not exist. **9.** $a = 2$, limit is 4 **11.** Nowhere
13. $a = -2$, limit does not exist. **15.** $a < 1$, limit does not exist. **17.** $a = 0$, $-\infty$ (limit does not exist); $a = 1$, ∞ (limit does not exist).
19. a. **b.** 2 **c.** 1, 5 **21. a.** **b.** -1 **c.** 11, 3 **23. a.**

b. None **25.** 2/3 **27.** 4 **31. a.** Discontinuous at $x = 1.2$ **33.** a **35. a.** $500 **b.** $1500 **c.** $1000 **d.** Does not exist
e. Discontinuous at $x = 10$; a change in shifts **f.** 15 **37. a.** $100 **b.** $150 **c.** $125 **d.** At $x = 100$ **39. a.** $2.92 **b.** $3.76
c. Does not exist **d.** $2.92 **e.** $10.56 **f.** $10.56 **g.** $10.56 **h.** $10.56 **i.** 1, 2, 3, 4, 5, 6, 7, 8, 12, 16, 20, 24, 28, 32, 36, 40,
44, 48, 52, 56, 60 **41.** About 687 g **b.** No **c.**

Exercises 11.3 (page 566)

For exercises . . .	1–8	9–18,33, 36,38,44	19–22, 28,29,37	25–27	30–32, 34,35, 39–41	42,43
Refer to example . . .	1	3	6	4 and 5	2	7

1. 6 **3.** -15 **5.** 1/3 **7.** 0.4323 **9.** 17
11. 18 **13.** 5 **15.** 2 **17.** 2 **19.** 6.773
21. 1.121 **25. a.** $700 per item **b.** $500 per item
c. $300 per item **d.** $1100 per item **27. a.** -25 boxes per dollar **b.** -20 boxes per dollar **c.** -30 boxes per dollar
d. Demand is decreasing. Yes, a higher price usually reduces demand. **29. a.** $56.81 per year **b.** $72.94 per year **c.** $64.20
per year **31. a.** 17.7 cents per gallon per month **b.** -48.0 cents per gallon per month **c.** -11.2 cents per gallon per month
33. a. 6% per day **b.** 7% per day **35. a.** 2; from 1 min to 2 min, the population of bacteria increases, on the average, 2 million
per min. **b.** -0.8; from 2 min to 3 min, the population of bacteria decreases, on the average, 0.8 million or 800,000 per min.
c. -2.2; from 3 min to 4 min, the population of bacteria decreases, on the average, 2.2 million per min. **d.** -1; from 4 min to 5 min,
the population decreases, on the average, 1 million per min. **e.** 2 min **f.** 3 min **37. a.**
b. 81.51 kilojoules per hour per hour **c.** 18.81 kilojoules per hour per hour
d. 1.3 hours **39. a.** $-15,760$ immigrants per year **b.** 17,680 immigrants per year
c. 960 immigrants per year **d.** They are equal; no **e.** 1,126,000 immigrants
41. a. 4° per 1000 ft **b.** 1.75° per 1000 ft **c.** $-4/3$° per 1000 ft **d.** 0° per 1000 ft
e. 3000 ft; 1000 ft; if 7000 ft is changed to 10,000 ft, the lowest temperature would be at
10,000 ft. **f.** 9000 ft **43. a.** 50 mph **b.** 44 mph

Exercises 11.4 (page 584)

For exercises . . .	5–10, 54,55, 58–61	11–14	15, 16	17, 18	19, 20	21–26	27–34, 42–45, 53	35–38	49–52, 56–57
Refer to example . . .	3	4	6	7	5	1 and 9	2	10	8

1. a. 0 **b.** 1 **c.** -1 **d.** Does not exist
e. m **3.** At $x = -2$ **5.** 2 **7.** 1/4 **9.** 0
11. 3; 3; 3; 3 **13.** $-8x + 9$; 25; 9; -15

15. $-12/x^2$; -3; does not exist; $-4/3$ **17.** $1/(2\sqrt{x})$; does not exist; does not exist; $1/(2\sqrt{3})$ **19.** $6x^2$; 24; 0; 54
21. a. $y = 10x - 15$ **b.** $y = 8x - 9$ **23. a.** $y = -(1/2)x + 7/2$ **b.** $y = -(5/4)x + 5$ **25. a.** $y = (4/7)x + 48/7$
b. $y = (2/3)x + 6$ **27.** -5; -117; 35 **29.** 7.389; 8,886,112; 0.0498 **31.** 1/2; 1/128; 2/9 **33.** $1/(2\sqrt{2})$; 1/8; does not exist

35. 0 **37.** $-3; -1; 0; 2; 3; 5$ **39. a.** $(a, 0)$ and (b, c) **b.** $(0, b)$ **c.** $x = 0$ and $x = b$ **41. a.** Distance **b.** Velocity
43. 56.66 **45.** -0.0158 **49. a.** $-4p - 4$ **b.** -44; demand is decreasing at a rate of about 44 items for each increase in price
of \$1. **51. a.** \$16 per table **b.** \$15.996 (or \$16) **c.** \$15.998 (or \$16) **d.** The marginal revenue gives a good approximation of
the actual revenue from the sale of the 1001st table. **53.** Answers are in trillion of dollars. **a.** 2.54; 2.03; 1.02 **b.** 0.061;
$-0.019; -0.079; -0.120; -0.133$ **55.** 1000; the population is increasing at a rate of 1000 shellfish per time unit. 570; the population is increasing more slowly at 570 shellfish per time unit. 250; the population is increasing at a much slower rate of 250 shellfish
per time unit. **57. a.** 1690 m per sec **b.** 4.84 days per m per sec; an increase in velocity from 1700 m per sec to 1701 m per sec
indicates an approximate increase in the age of the cheese of 4.84 days. **59. a.** About 270; the temperature was increasing at a rate
of about 270° per hour at 9:00 a.m. **b.** About -150; the temperature was decreasing at a rate of about 150° per hour at 11:30 a.m.
c. About 0; the temperature was staying constant at 12:30 p.m. **d.** About 11:15 a.m. **61. a.** 0; about 0.5 mph/oz

Exercises 11.5 (page 592)

For exercises . . .	2–6	7–24
Refer to example . . .	4	1,2, and 3

3. $f:Y_2; f':Y_1$ **5.** $f:Y_1; f':Y_2$

7.
9.
11.
13.

15.
17.
19.

21.
23.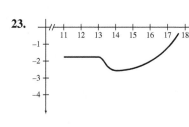
About 9 cm; about 2.6 cm less per year

Chapter 11 Review Exercises (page 596)

For exercises . . .	1–3, 17–34, 45–46, 61,66	4–6,15, 35–44, 63,74	7–9, 47–50, 63–65	10–12,16, 51–58,62, 68–69,73	59–60,67, 70–72,74
Refer to section . . .	1	2	3	4	5

1. True **2.** True **3.** True **4.** False **5.** True **6.** False
7. False **8.** True **9.** True **10.** True **11.** False **12.** False
17. a. 4 **b.** 4 **c.** 4 **d.** 4 **19. a.** ∞ **b.** $-\infty$
c. Does not exist **d.** Does not exist **21.** ∞ **23.** 19/9
25. 8 **27.** -13 **29.** 1/6 **31.** 2/5 **33.** 3/8 **35.** Discontinuous at x_2 and x_4 **37.** 0, does not exist, does not exist; $-1/3$, does
not exist, does not exist **39.** -5, does not exist, does not exist **41.** Continuous everywhere **43. a.**
b. 1 **c.** 0, 2 **45.** 2 **47.** 126; 18 **49.** 9/77; 18/49 **51. a.** $y = 13x - 17$ **b.** $y = 7x - 5$
53. a. $y = -x + 9$ **b.** $y = -3x + 15$ **55.** $8x + 3$ **57.** 1.332 **59.**
61. e **63. a.** \$150 **b.** \$187.50 **c.** \$189
d.
e. Discontinuous at $x = \$125$
f. \$1.50 **g.** \$1.50 **h.** \$1.35
i. 1.5; when 100 lb are purchased, an
additional pound will cost about \$1.50 more. **j.** 1.35; when 140 lb are purchased, an additional
pound will cost about \$1.35 more. **65. b.** $x = 7.5$ **c.** The marginal cost equals the average cost
at the point where the average cost is smallest.

67.

; about 5.8; about 2

69. a.

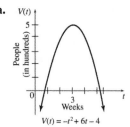

$V(t) = -t^2 + 6t - 4$

b. $[0.8, 5.2]$ **c.** 3 weeks; 500 cases

d. $V'(t) = -2t + 6$ **e.** 0

f. $+; -$

71. a.

b.

73. a. Nowhere   **b.** 50, 130, 230, 770

c.

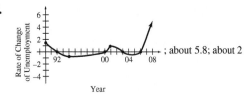

Chapter 12 Calculating the Derivative

Exercises 12.1 (page 615)

For exercises . . .	1–22,27–30	47,55,56	51,53	52,54	57,58,60–62, 64,68–75	59,63, 65,67	31–43
Refer to example . . .	1,2,3,5	6	7	8	9	4	1 (in 4th section of previous chapter)

1. $dy/dx = 36x^2 - 16x + 7$ **3.** $dy/dx = 12x^3 - 18x^2 + (1/4)x$ **5.** $f'(x) = 21x^{2.5} - 5x^{-0.5}$ or $21x^{2.5} - 5/x^{0.5}$
7. $dy/dx = 4x^{-1/2} + (9/2)x^{-1/4}$ or $4/x^{1/2} + 9/(2x^{1/4})$ **9.** $dy/dx = -30x^{-4} - 20x^{-5} - 8$ or $-30/x^4 - 20/x^5 - 8$
11. $f'(t) = -7t^{-2} + 15t^{-4}$ or $-7/t^2 + 15/t^4$ **13.** $dy/dx = -24x^{-5} + 21x^{-4} - 3x^{-2}$ or $-24/x^5 + 21/x^4 - 3/x^2$
15. $p'(x) = 5x^{-3/2} - 12x^{-5/2}$ or $5/x^{3/2} - 12/x^{5/2}$ **17.** $dy/dx = (-3/2)x^{-5/4}$ or $-3/(2x^{5/4})$
19. $f'(x) = 2x - 5x^{-2}$ or $2x - 5/x^2$ **21.** $g'(x) = 256x^3 - 192x^2 + 32x$ **23.** b   **27.** $-(9/2)x^{-3/2} - 3x^{-5/2}$ or
$-9/(2x^{3/2}) - 3/x^{5/2}$ **29.** $-25/3$ **31.** $-28; y = -28x + 34$ **33.** 25/6   **35.** $(4/9, 20/9)$ **37.** $-5, 2$ **39.** $(4 \pm \sqrt{37})/3$
41. $(-1/2, -19/2)$ **43.** $(-2, -24)$ **45.** 7   **51. a.** 30   **b.** 0   **c.** -10 **53.** \$990   **55. a.** 100   **b.** 1   **57. a.** 18¢; 36¢
b. 0.755¢ per year; 1.09¢ per year   **c.** $C(t) = -0.0001549t^3 + 0.02699t^2 - 0.6484t + 3.212$; 0.889¢ per year; 0.853¢ per year
59. a. 0.4824   **b.** 2.216   **61. a.** 1232.62 cm³   **b.** 948.08 cm³/yr   **63.** $5.00l^{0.86}$ **65. a.** 3 minutes, 58.1 seconds   **b.** 0.118
sec/m; at 100 meters, the fastest possible time increases by 0.118 seconds for each additional meter.   **c.** Yes   **67. a.** 27.5
b. 23 pounds   **c.** $-175,750/h^3$ **d.** -0.64; for a 125-lb female with a height of 65 in. (5'5"), the BMI decreases by 0.64 for each
additional inch of height.   **69. a.** $v(t) = 36t - 13$ **b.** $-13; 167; 347$ **71. a.** $v(t) = -9t^2 + 8t - 10$ **b.** $-10; -195; -830$
73. 0 ft/sec; -32 ft/sec   **b.** 2 seconds   **c.** 64 ft   **75. a.** 35, 36   **b.** When $x = 5$, $dy_1/dx = 4.13$ and $dy_2/dx \approx 4.32$. These
values are fairly close and represent the rate of change of four years for a dog for one year of a human, for a dog that is actually
5 years old.   **c.** $y = 4x + 16$

Exercises 12.2 (page 624)

For exercises . . .	1–10,29,34,39, 42,44–47,50	11–26,31–33,35,40, 43,45,48,49,51–54	27,28,30	41,42
Refer to example . . .	1,2	3	4	5

1. $dy/dx = 18x^2 - 6x + 4$ **3.** $dy/dx = 8x - 20$
5. $k'(t) = 4t^3 - 4t$
7. $dy/dx = (3/2)x^{1/2} + (1/2)x^{-1/2} + 2$ or $3x^{1/2}/2 + 1/(2x^{1/2}) + 2$ **9.** $p'(y) = -8y^{-5} + 15y^{-6} + 30y^{-7}$
11. $f'(x) = 57/(3x + 10)^2$ **13.** $dy/dt = -17/(4 + t)^2$ **15.** $dy/dx = (x^2 - 2x - 1)/(x - 1)^2$
17. $f'(t) = 2t/(t^2 + 3)^2$ **19.** $g'(x) = (4x^2 + 2x - 12)/(x^2 + 3)^2$ **21.** $p'(t) = [-\sqrt{t}/2 - 1/(2\sqrt{t})]/(t - 1)^2$ or
$(-t - 1)/[2\sqrt{t}(t - 1)^2]$ **23.** $dy/dx = (5/2)x^{-1/2} - 3x^{-3/2}$ or $(5x - 6)/(2x\sqrt{x})$
25. $h'(z) = (-z^{4.4} + 11z^{1.2})/(z^{3.2} + 5)^2$ **27.** $f'(x) = (60x^3 + 57x^2 - 24x + 13)/(5x + 4)^2$ **29.** 77
31. In the first step, the numerator should be $(x^2 - 1)2 - (2x + 5)(2x)$.   **33.** $y = -2x + 9$

35. a. $f'(x) = (7x^3 - 4)/x^{5/3}$ **b.** $f'(x) = 7x^{4/3} - 4x^{-5/3}$ **39.** $0, -1.307$, and 1.307 **41. a.** \$22.86 per unit
b. \$12.92 per unit **c.** $(3x + 2)/(x^2 + 4x)$ per unit **d.** $\bar{C}'(x) = (-3x^2 - 4x - 8)/(x^2 + 4x)^2$
43. a. $M'(d) = 2000d/(3d^2 + 10)^2$ **b.** 8.3; the new employee can assemble about 8.3 additional bicycles per day after 2 days
of training. 1.4; the new employee can assemble about 1.4 additional bicycles per day after 5 days of training.
47. Increasing at a rate of \$0.03552 per gallon per month **49. a.** $AK/(A + x)^2$ **b.** $K/(4A)$ **51. a.** 8.57 min
b. 16.36 min **c.** 6.12 min²/kcal; 2.48 min²/kcal **53. a.** -100 facts/hr **b.** -0.01 facts/hr

Exercises 12.3 (page 633)

For exercises ...	1–6	7–14,53,59	15–20	21–28,54,57, 62,63,66,67	29–34,64	35–40,56	58,65	55	60,61	45–50
Refer to example ...	1	2	3	5,6	7	8	9	10	4	1 (in 3rd section of previous chapter)

1. 1767 **3.** 131 **5.** $320k^2 + 224k + 39$ **7.** $(6x + 55)/8; (3x + 164)/4$ **9.** $1/x^2; 1/x^2$ **11.** $\sqrt{8x^2 - 4}; 8x + 10$
13. $\sqrt{(x - 1)/x}; -1/\sqrt{x + 1}$ **15.** If $f(x) = x^{3/5}$ and $g(x) = 5 - x^2$, then $y = f[g(x)]$.
17. If $f(x) = -\sqrt{x}$ and $g(x) = 13 + 7x$, then $y = f[g(x)]$. **19.** If $f(x) = x^{1/3} - 2x^{2/3} + 7$ and $g(x) = x^2 + 5x$, then
$y = f[g(x)]$. **21.** $dy/dx = 4(8x^4 - 5x^2 + 1)^3(32x^3 - 10x)$ **23.** $k'(x) = 288x(12x^2 + 5)^{-7}$
25. $s'(t) = (1215/2)t^2(3t^3 - 8)^{1/2}$ **27.** $g'(t) = -63t^2/(2\sqrt{7t^3 - 1})$ **29.** $m'(t) = -6(5t^4 - 1)^3(85t^4 - 1)$
31. $dy/dx = 3x^2(3x^4 + 1)^3(19x^4 + 64x + 1)$ **33.** $q'(y) = 2y(y^2 + 1)^{1/4}(9y^2 + 4)$ **35.** $dy/dx = 60x^2/(2x^3 + 1)^3$
37. $r'(t) = 2(5t - 6)^3(15t^2 + 18t + 40)/(3t^2 + 4)^2$ **39.** $dy/dx = (-18x^2 + 2x + 1)/(2x - 1)^6$ **43. a.** -2 **b.** $-24/7$
45. $y = (3/5)x + 16/5$ **47.** $y = x$ **49.** 1, 3 **53.** $D(c) = (-c^2 + 10c + 12,475)/25$ **55. a.** \$101.22 **b.** \$111.86
c. \$117.59 **57. a.** $-\$10,500$ **b.** $-\$4570.64$ **59.** $P[f(a)] = 18a^2 + 24a + 9$ **61. a.** $A[r(t)] = A(t) = 4\pi t^2$; this function
gives the area of the pollution in terms of the time since the pollutants were first emitted. **b.** 32π; at 12 P.M. the area of pollution is
changing at the rate of 32π mi² per hour **63. a.** -0.5 **b.** $-1/54 \approx -0.02$ **c.** $-1/128 \approx -0.008$ **d.** Always decreasing; the
derivative is negative for all $t \geq 0$. **65. a.** 34 minutes **b.** $-(108/17)\pi$ mm³ per minute, $-(72/17)\pi$ mm² per minute
67. a. $12x^{11}$ **b.** $x^{12}; 12x^{11}$

Exercises 12.4 (page 640)

For exercises ...	1–12,25–30,33,34, 38,41,44–45,48,50, 51–54,56,59–63	13–16,23,24, 39,40,42, 49	17–22,31,32,51	43,46,47,55,57	58
Refer to example ...	1	2	3	5	4

1. $dy/dx = 4e^{4x}$ **3.** $dy/dx = -24e^{3x}$ **5.** $dy/dx = -32e^{2x+1}$ **7.** $dy/dx = 2xe^{x^2}$ **9.** $dy/dx = 12xe^{2x^2}$
11. $dy/dx = 16xe^{2x^2-4}$ **13.** $dy/dx = xe^x + e^x = e^x(x + 1)$ **15.** $dy/dx = 2(x + 3)(2x + 7)e^{4x}$
17. $dy/dx = (2xe^x - x^2e^x)/e^{2x} = x(2 - x)/e^x$ **19.** $dy/dx = [x(e^x - e^{-x}) - (e^x + e^{-x})]/x^2$
21. $dp/dt = 8000e^{-0.2t}/(9 + 4e^{-0.2t})^2$ **23.** $f'(z) = 4(2z + e^{-z})(1 - ze^{-z})$ **25.** $dy/dx = 3(\ln 7)7^{3x+1}$
27. $dy/dx = 6x(\ln 4)4^{x^2+2}$ **29.** $ds/dt = (\ln 3)3^{\sqrt{t}}/\sqrt{t}$ **31.** $dy/dt = [(1 - t)e^{3t} - 4e^{2t} + (1 + t)e^t]/(e^{2t} + 1)^2$
33. $f'(x) = (9x + 4)e^{x\sqrt{3x+2}}/[2\sqrt{3x + 2}]$ **39. a.** \$3.81 **b.** \$0.20 **c.** $C'(x)$ approaches zero. **41. a.** 100% **b.** 94%
c. 89% **d.** 83% **e.** -3.045 **f.** -2.865 **g.** The percent of these cars on the road is decreasing but at a slower rate as they age.
43. a. $G(t) = 250/(1 + 124e^{-0.45t})$ **b.** 17.8 million; 7.4 million/yr **c.** 105.2 million; 27.4 million/yr **d.** 246.2 million; 1.7
million/yr **e.** It increases for a while and then gradually decreases to 0. **45. a.** 51,600,000 **b.** 1,070,000 people/year
47. a. $5200/(1 + 12e^{-0.52t})$ **b.** 639, 292 **c.** 2081, 649 **d.** 4877, 157 **e.** It increases for a while and then gradually
decreases to 0. **49. a.** 3.857 cm³ **b.** 0.973 cm **c.** 18 years **d.** 1100 cm³ **e.** 0.282; at 240 months old, the tumor is
increasing in volume at the instantaneous rate of 0.282 cm³/month. **51. a.** 0.180 **b.** 2024 **c.** The marginal increase in the
proportion per year in 2010 is approximately 0.023. **53. a.** 509.7 kg, 498.4 kg **b.** 1239 days, 1095 days **c.** 0.22 kg/day,
0.22 kg/day **d.** The growth patterns of the two functions are **e.** The graphs of the rates of change of the two functions are
very similar.

also very similar.

55. a. $G(t) = 1/(1 + 270e^{-3.5t})$ **b.** 0.109, 0.341 per century **c.** 0.802, 0.555 per century **d.** 0.993, 0.0256 per century
e. It increases for a while and then gradually decreases to 0. **57. a.** $G(t) = 6.8/(1 + 3.242e^{-0.2992t})$ **b.** 2.444 million
students; 0.468 million students/yr **c.** 3.435 million students; 0.509 million students/yr **d.** 5.247 million students; 0.359 million
students/yr **e.** The rate increases at first and then decreases toward 0. **59. a.** $(V/R)e^{-t/RC}$ **b.** 1.35×10^{-7} amps
61. a. 218.5 seconds **b.** The record is decreasing by 0.034 seconds per year at the end of 2010. **c.** 218 seconds. If the
estimate is correct, then this is the least amount of time that it will ever take for a human to run a mile. **63. a.** 625.14 ft
b. 0; yes **c.** −1.476 ft per ft from center

Exercises 12.5 (page 648)

For exercises . . .	1,2,59,62,66	3,4,7–10,31,32,56,67	5,6,11–30,33–44, 57,58,60,61,64,65	68
Refer to example . . .	1	2	3	4

1. $dy/dx = 1/x$ **3.** $dy/dx = -3/(8 - 3x)$
or $3/(3x - 8)$ **5.** $dy/dx = (8x - 9)/(4x^2 - 9x)$
7. $dy/dx = 1/[2(x + 5)]$ **9.** $dy/dx = 3(2x^2 + 5)/[x(x^2 + 5)]$ **11.** $dy/dx = -15x/(3x + 2) - 5\ln(3x + 2)$
13. $ds/dt = t + 2t\ln|t|$ **15.** $dy/dx = [2x - 4(x + 3)\ln(x + 3)]/[x^3(x + 3)]$
17. $dy/dx = (4x + 7 - 4x\ln x)/[x(4x + 7)^2]$ **19.** $dy/dx = (6x\ln x - 3x)/(\ln x)^2$ **21.** $dy/dx = 4(\ln|x + 1|)^3/(x + 1)$
23. $dy/dx = 1/(x\ln x)$ **25.** $dy/dx = e^x/x + 2xe^{x^2}\ln x$ **27.** $dy/dx = (xe^x\ln x - e^x)/[x(\ln x)^2]$
29. $g'(z) = 3(e^{2z} + \ln z)^2(2ze^{2z} + 1)/z$ **31.** $dy/dx = 1/(x\ln 10)$ **33.** $dy/dx = -1/[(\ln 10)(1 - x)]$ or $1/[(\ln 10)(x - 1)]$
35. $dy/dx = 5/[(2\ln 5)(5x + 2)]$ **37.** $dy/dx = 3(x + 1)/[(\ln 3)(x^2 + 2x)]$ **39.** $dw/dp = (\ln 2)2^p/[(\ln 8)(2^p - 1)]$
41. $f'(x) = e^{\sqrt{x}}\{1/[2\sqrt{x}(\sqrt{x} + 5)] + \ln(\sqrt{x} + 5)/[2\sqrt{x}]\}$
43. $f'(t) = [(t^2 + 1)\ln(t^2 + 1) - t^2 + 2t + 1]/\{(t^2 + 1)[\ln(t^2 + 1) + 1]^2\}$

55. $h(x) = (x^2 + 1)^{5x}\left[\dfrac{10x^2}{x^2 + 1} + 5\ln(x^2 + 1)\right]$ **57. a.** $dR/dq = 100 + 50(\ln q - 1)/(\ln q)^2$ **b.** $112.48

c. To decide whether it is reasonable to sell additional items. **59. a.** −0.19396 **b.** −0.06099 **61. a.** $N(t) = 1000e^{9.8901e^{-e^{2.54197 - 0.2167t}}}$
b. 1,307,416 bacteria per hour; the number of bacteria is increasing at a rate of 1,307,416 per hour, 20 hours after the experiment began.

c.

d.

e. 9.8901; $1000e^{9.8901} \approx 19,734,033$
63. b. i. 3.343 **ii.** 1.466 **c. i.** −0.172 **ii.** −0.0511 **65.** 26.9; 13.1
67. a. 1.567×10^{11} kWh **b.** 63.4 months **c.** 4.14×10^{-6}
d. dM/dE decreases and approac.hes zero.

Chapter 12 Review Exercises (page 652)

For exercises . . .	1,2,4,11–16, 53,54,73,79–81	3,17–20,55,56, 74,75,88	5,21–30,51,52, 57,58,67–70,76,91	6–7,31–36,43–46,59,60, 71,77,82–87,89,90	8–10,37–42,47–50, 61,62,72,78
Refer to section . . .	1	2	3	4	5

1. False **2.** True **3.** False **4.** True **5.** False **6.** False **7.** False **8.** True **9.** True **10.** False
11. $dy/dx = 15x^2 - 14x - 9$ **13.** $dy/dx = 24x^{5/3}$ **15.** $f'(x) = -12x^{-5} + 3x^{-1/2}$ or $-12/x^5 + 3/x^{1/2}$
17. $k'(x) = 21/(4x + 7)^2$ **19.** $dy/dx = (x^2 - 2x)/(x - 1)^2$ **21.** $f'(x) = 24x(3x^2 - 2)^3$ **23.** $dy/dt = 7t^6/(2t^7 - 5)^{1/2}$
25. $dy/dx = 3(2x + 1)^2(8x + 1)$ **27.** $r'(t) = (-15t^2 + 52t - 7)/(3t + 1)^4$ **29.** $p'(t) = t(t^2 + 1)^{3/2}(7t^2 + 2)$
31. $dy/dx = -12e^{2x}$ **33.** $dy/dx = -6x^2e^{-2x^3}$ **35.** $dy/dx = 10xe^{2x} + 5e^{2x} = 5e^{2x}(2x + 1)$ **37.** $dy/dx = 2x/(2 + x^2)$
39. $dy/dx = (x - 3 - x\ln|3x|)/[x(x - 3)^2]$ **41.** $dy/dx = [e^x(x + 1)(x^2 - 1)\ln(x^2 - 1) - 2x^2e^x]/[(x^2 - 1)[\ln(x^2 - 1)]^2]$
43. $ds/dt = 2(t^2 + e^t)(2t + e^t)$ **45.** $dy/dx = -6x(\ln 10) \cdot 10^{-x^2}$ **47.** $g'(z) = (3z^2 + 1)/[(\ln 2)(z^3 + z + 1)]$
49. $f'(x) = (x + 1)e^{3x}/(xe^x + 1) + 2e^{2x}\ln(xe^x + 1)$ **51. a.** −3/2 **b.** −24/11 **53.** −2; $y = -2x - 4$
55. −3/4; $y = -(3/4)x - 9/4$ **57.** 3/4; $y = (3/4)x + 7/4$ **59.** 1; $y = x + 1$ **61.** 1; $y = x - 1$ **63.** No points if $k > 0$;
exactly one point if $k = 0$ or if $k < -1/2$; exactly two points if $-1/2 \le k < 0$. **65.** 5%; 5.06%
67. $\overline{C}'(x) = (-x - 2)/[2x^2(x + 1)^{1/2}]$ **69.** $\overline{C}'(x) = (x^2 + 3)^2(5x^2 - 3)/x^2$ **71.** $\overline{C}'(x) = [e^{-x}(x + 1) - 10]/x^2$
73. a. 22; sales will increase by $22 million when $1000 more is spent on research. **b.** 19.5; sales will increase by $19.5 million
when $1000 more is spent on research. **c.** 18; sales will increase by $18 million when $1000 more is spent on research.
d. As more is spent on research, the increase in sales is decreasing. **75. a.** −2.201; costs will decrease by $2201 for the next $100
spent on training. **b.** −0.564; costs will decrease by $564 for the next $100 spent on training. **c.** Decreasing
77. $218.65. The balance increases by roughly $218.65 for every 1% increase in the interest rate when the rate is 5%.

79. a. 4.839 billion/yr; the volume of mail is increasing by about 4,839,000,000 pieces per year   **b.** –2.582 billion/yr; the volume of mail is decreasing by about 2,582,000,000 pieces per year   **81. a.** $y = 1.799 \times 10^{-5}t^3 + 3.177 \times 10^{-4}t^2 - 0.06866t + 2.504$, $y = -1.112 \times 10^{-6}t^4 + 2.920 \times 10^{-4}t^3 - 0.02238t^2 + 0.6483t - 4.278$ **b.** \$0.59/yr, \$0.46/yr
83. a. $G(t) = 30,000/(1 + 14e^{-0.15t})$ **b.** 4483; 572   **85. a.** 3493.76 grams   **b.** 3583 grams   **c.** 84 days   **d.** 1.76 g/day
e.

Growth is initially rapid, then tapers off.   **f.**

Day	Weight	Rate
50	904	24.90
100	2159	21.87
150	2974	11.08
200	3346	4.59
250	3494	1.76
300	3550	0.66

87. a. 14,612 megawatts/yr   **b.** 47,276 megawatts/yr   **c.** 152,960 megawatts/yr   **89.** 0.242; the production of corn is increasing at a rate of 0.242 billion bushels a year in 2000.   **91. a.** −0.4677 fatalities per 1000 licensed drivers per 100 million miles per year; at the age of 20, each extra year results in a decrease of 0.4677 fatalities per 1000 licensed drivers per 100 million miles.
b. 0.003672 fatalities per 1000 licensed drivers per 100 million miles per year; at the age of 60, each extra year results in an increase of 0.003672 fatalities per 1000 licensed drivers per 100 million miles.

Chapter 13 Graphs and the Derivative

Exercises 13.1 (page 668)

1. a. $(1, \infty)$ **b.** $(-\infty, 1)$ **3. a.** $(-\infty, -2)$
b. $(-2, \infty)$ **5. a.** $(-\infty, -4), (-2, \infty)$
b. $(-4, -2)$ **7. a.** $(-7, -4), (-2, \infty)$
b. $(-\infty, -7), (-4, -2)$

For exercises . . .	1–8, 43,44 50,51, 60,61	13–22,25, 29–34,38, 39,42,49, 52,53,56–59	21–24	26–28, 35,36	45,54,55	46–48
Refer to example . . .	1	2	4	3	6	5

9. a. $(-\infty, -1), (3, \infty)$ **b.** $(-1, 3)$ **11. a.** $(-\infty, -8), (-6, -2.5), (-1.5, \infty)$ **b.** $(-8, -6), (-2.5, -1.5)$ **13. a.** 17/12
b. $(-\infty, 17/12)$ **c.** $(17/12, \infty)$ **15. a.** −3, 4   **b.** $(-\infty, -3), (4, \infty)$ **c.** $(-3, 4)$ **17. a.** −3/2, 4
b. $(-\infty, -3/2), (4, \infty)$ **c.** $(-3/2, 4)$ **19. a.** −2, −1, 0   **b.** $(-2, -1), (0, \infty)$ **c.** $(-\infty, -2), (-1, 0)$ **21. a.** None
b. None   **c.** $(-\infty, \infty)$ **23. a.** None   **b.** None   **c.** $(-\infty, -1), (-1, \infty)$ **25. a.** 0   **b.** $(0, \infty)$ **c.** $(-\infty, 0)$ **27. a.** 0
b. $(0, \infty)$ **c.** $(-\infty, 0)$ **29. a.** 7   **b.** $(7, \infty)$ **c.** $(3, 7)$ **31. a.** 1/3   **b.** $(-\infty, 1/3)$ **c.** $(1/3, \infty)$ **33. a.** 0, 2/ln 2
b. $(0, 2/\ln 2)$ **c.** $(-\infty, 0), (2/\ln 2, \infty)$ **35. a.** 0, 2/5   **b.** $(0, 2/5)$ **c.** $(-\infty, 0), (2/5, \infty)$ **39.** Vertex: $(-b/(2a),$
$(4ac - b^2)/(4a))$; increasing on $(-\infty, -b/(2a))$, decreasing on $(-b/(2a), \infty)$ **41.** On $(0, \infty)$; nowhere; nowhere
43. a. About $(567, \infty)$ **b.** About $(0, 567)$ **45. a.** Nowhere   **b.** $(0, \infty)$ **47.** $(0, 2200)$ **49. a.** Increasing on $(0, 7.4)$ or from 2000 to about the middle of 2007   **b.** Decreasing on $(7.4, 50)$ or from about the middle of 2007 to 2050   **51. a.** Yes   **b.** April to July; July to November; January to April and November to December   **c.** January to April and November to December
53. a. $(0, 1.85)$ **b.** $(1.85, 5)$ **55. a.** $(0, 1)$ **b.** $(1, \infty)$ **57. a.** $F'(t) = 175.9e^{-t/1.3}(1 - 0.769t)$ **b.** $(0, 1.3); (1.3, \infty)$
59. $(-\infty, 0); (0, \infty)$ **61. a.** $(2500, 5750)$ **b.** $(5750, 6000)$ **c.** $(2800, 4800)$ **d.** $(2500, 2800)$ and $(4800, 6000)$

Exercises 13.2 (page 679)

1. Relative minimum of −4 at 1   **3.** Relative maximum of 3 at −2   **5.** Relative maximum of 3 at −4; relative minimum of 1 at −2   **7.** Relative maximum

For exercises . . .	1–8, 37–39, 50	13–20, 35,36, 51	21–24	25–34, 52–54, 56	41–44, 46–49	45,55,57
Refer to example . . .	2	3a	3b	3c	4	1

of 3 at −4; relative minimum of −2 at −7 and −2   **9.** Relative maximum at −1; relative minimum at 3   **11.** Relative maxima at −8 and −2.5; relative minimum at −6 and −1.5   **13.** Relative minimum of 8 at 5   **15.** Relative maximum of −8 at −3; relative minimum of −12 at −1   **17.** Relative maximum of 827/96 at −1/4; relative minimum of −377/6 at −5   **19.** Relative maximum of −4 at 0; relative minimum of −85 at 3 and −3   **21.** Relative maximum of 3 at −8/3   **23.** Relative maximum of 1 at −1; relative minimum of 0 at 0   **25.** No relative extrema   **27.** Relative maximum of 0 at 1; relative minimum of 8 at 5   **29.** Relative maximum of −2.46 at −2; relative minimum of −3 at 0   **31.** No relative extrema   **33.** Relative minimum of $e \ln 2$ at $1/\ln 2$
35. $(3, 13)$ **37.** Relative maximum of 6.211 at 0.085; relative minimum of −57.607 at 2.161
39. Relative minimum at $x = 5$

41. a. 13   **b.** \$44   **c.** \$258   **43. a.** 100   **b.** \$14.72
c. \$635.76   **45.** Relative maximum of 20,470 megawatts at midnight $(t = 0)$; relative minimum of 20,070 megawatts at 1:40 A.M.; relative maximum of 30,060 megawatts at 4:44 P.M.; relative minimum of 20,840 megawatts at midnight $(t = 24)$.   **47.** $q = 10; p \approx \$73.58$
49. 120 units   **51.** 5:04 P.M.; 6:56 A.M.   **53.** 4.96 years; 458.22 kg
55. 10   **57. a.** 28 ft   **b.** 2.57 sec

Exercises 13.3 (page 691)

For exercises . . .	1–16	17–26, 76,77	27–48,54, 65–68, 70,80, 85–88	57–64,79, 81,82, 90,92,93	72–75 78, 83,84	91,92, 94,95
Refer to example . . .	2	3	5	6	7	4

1. $f''(x) = 30x - 14$; -14; 46
3. $f''(x) = 48x^2 - 18x - 4$; -4; 152
5. $f''(x) = 6$; 6; 6
7. $f''(x) = 2/(1 + x)^3$; 2; $2/27$
9. $f''(x) = 4/(x^2 + 4)^{3/2}$; $1/2$; $1/(4\sqrt{2})$ 11. $f''(x) = -6x^{-5/4}$ or $-6/x^{5/4}$; $f''(0)$ does not exist; $-3/2^{1/4}$
13. $f''(x) = 20x^2 e^{-x^2} - 10e^{-x^2}$; -10; $70e^{-4} \approx 1.282$ 15. $f''(x) = (-3 + 2\ln x)/(4x^3)$; does not exist; -0.050
17. $f'''(x) = 168x + 36$; $f^{(4)}(x) = 168$ 19. $f'''(x) = 300x^2 - 72x + 12$; $f^{(4)}(x) = 600x - 72$ 21. $f'''(x) = 18(x + 2)^{-4}$
or $18/(x + 2)^4$; $f^{(4)}(x) = -72(x + 2)^{-5}$ or $-72/(x + 2)^5$ 23. $f'''(x) = -36(x - 2)^{-4}$ or $-36/(x - 2)^4$;
$f^{(4)}(x) = 144(x - 2)^{-5}$ or $144/(x - 2)^5$ 25. **a.** $f'(x) = 1/x$; $f''(x) = -1/x^2$; $f'''(x) = 2/x^3$; $f^{(4)}(x) = -6/x^4$;
$f^{(5)}(x) = 24/x^5$ **b.** $f^{(n)}(x) = (-1)^{n-1}[1 \cdot 2 \cdot 3 \cdots (n - 1)]/x^n$ or, using factorial notation, $f^{(n)}(x) = (-1)^{n-1}(n - 1)!/x^n$
27. Concave upward on $(2, \infty)$; concave downward on $(-\infty, 2)$; inflection point at $(2, 3)$ 29. Concave upward on $(-\infty, -1)$
and $(8, \infty)$; concave downward on $(-1, 8)$; inflection points at $(-1, 7)$ and $(8, 6)$ 31. Concave upward on $(2, \infty)$; concave
downward on $(-\infty, 2)$; no inflection points   33. Always concave upward; no inflection points   35. Concave upward on
$(-\infty, 3/2)$; concave downward on $(3/2, \infty)$; inflection point at $(3/2, 525/2)$ 37. Concave upward on $(5, \infty)$;
concave downward on $(-\infty, 5)$; no inflection points   39. Concave upward on $(-10/3, \infty)$; concave downward on
$(-\infty, -10/3)$; inflection point at $(-10/3, -250/27)$ 41. Never concave upward; always concave downward; no inflection points
43. Concave upward on $(-\infty, 0)$ and $(1, \infty)$; concave downward on $(0, 1)$; inflection points at $(0, 0)$ and $(1, -3)$
45. Concave upward on $(-1, 1)$; concave downward on $(-\infty, -1)$ and $(1, \infty)$; inflection points at $(-1, \ln 2)$ and $(1, \ln 2)$
47. Concave upward on $(-\infty, -e^{-3/2})$ and $(e^{-3/2}, \infty)$; concave downward on $(-e^{-3/2}, 0)$ and $(0, e^{-3/2})$; inflection points at
$(-e^{-3/2}, -3e^{-3}/(2\ln 10))$ and $(e^{-3/2}, -3e^{-3}/(2\ln 10))$ 49. Concave upward on $(-\infty, 0)$ and $(4, \infty)$; concave downward on
$(0, 4)$; inflection points at 0 and 4   51. Concave upward on $(-7, 3)$ and $(12, \infty)$; concave downward on $(-\infty, -7)$ and $(3, 12)$;
inflection points at -7, 3, and 12   53. Choose $f(x) = x^k$ where $1 < k < 2$. For example, $f(x) = x^{4/3}$ has a relative minimum at
$x = 0$, and $f(x) = x^{5/3}$ has an inflection point at $x = 0$.   55. **a.** Close to 0   **b.** Close to 1   57. Relative maximum at -5.
59. Relative maximum at 0; relative minimum at $2/3$.   61. Relative minimum at -3 63. Relative maximum at $-4/7$; relative
minimum at 0   65. **a.** Minimum at about -0.4 and 4.0; maximum at about 2.4   **b.** Increasing on about $(-0.4, 2.4)$ and about
$(4.0, \infty)$; decreasing on about $(-\infty, -0.4)$ and $(2.4, 4.0)$ **c.** About 0.7 and 3.3   **d.** Concave upward on about $(-\infty, 0.7)$ and
$(3.3, \infty)$; concave downward on about $(0.7, 3.3)$ 67. **a.** Maximum at 1; minimum at -1 **b.** Increasing on $(-1, 1)$; decreasing
on $(-\infty, -1)$ and $(1, \infty)$ **c.** About -1.7, 0, and about 1.7   **d.** Concave upward on about $(-1.7, 0)$ and $(1.7, \infty)$; concave downward on about $(-\infty, -1.7)$ and $(0, 1.7)$ 71. 45.6; mid 2045   73. $(22, 6517.9)$ 75. $(2.06, 20.8)$ 79. **a.** 4 hours   **b.** 1160
million   81. **a.** After 2 hours   **b.** $3/4\%$ 83. $(38.92, 5000)$ 85. Inflection point at $t = (\ln c)/k \approx 2.96$ years; this signifies the
time when the rate of growth begins to slow down, since L changes from concave up to concave down at this inflection point.
87. Always concave down   89. $f(t)$ is decreasing and concave up; $f'(t) < 0$, $f''(t) > 0$.   91. **a.** -96 ft/sec   **b.** -160 ft/sec
c. -256 ft/sec   **d.** -32 ft/sec^2 93. $v(t) = 256 - 32t$; $a(t) = -32$; 1024 ft; 16 seconds after being thrown   95. $t = 6$

Exercises 13.4 (page 702)

For exercises . . .	3–10,29–30	11,12	13–20	21–28
Refer to example . . .	1	2	3	4

1. 0   **3.**

$f(x) = -2x^3 - 9x^2 + 108x - 10$

5.

$f(x) = -3x^3 + 6x^2 - 4x - 1$

7.

$f(x) = x^4 - 24x^2 + 80$

9.

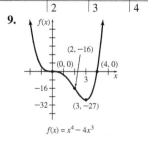

$f(x) = x^4 - 4x^3$

11.

$f(x) = 2x + \frac{10}{x}$

13.

$f(x) = \frac{-x + 4}{x + 2}$

15.

$f(x) = \frac{1}{x^2 + 4x + 3}$

17.

$f(x) = \frac{x}{x^2 + 1}$

19.

$f(x) = \dfrac{1}{x^2 - 9}$

21.

$f(x) = x \ln|x|$

23.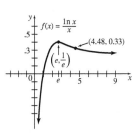

$f(x) = \dfrac{\ln x}{x}$

25.

$f(x) = xe^{-x}$

27.

$f(x) = (x - 1)e^{-x}$

29.

$f(x) = x^{2/3} - x^{5/3}$

31. 3, 7, 9, 11, 15   **33.** 17, 19, 23, 25, 27

In Exercises 35–39, other answers are possible.   **35.**

37.

39.

Chapter 13 Review Exercises (page 705)

1. True   **2.** False   **3.** False   **4.** True   **5.** False
6. True   **7.** False   **8.** False   **9.** False
10. False   **11.** True   **12.** False

For exercises . . .	1,2,12,13, 17–24,70	3,4,14,15, 25–32,63,64, 72,73a,74b,c	5–9,16,33–38, 61,62,65,66,71, 73b,74a	10,11, 39–60,63e, 67–69
Refer to section . . .	1	2	3	4

17. Increasing on $(-9/2, \infty)$; decreasing on $(-\infty, -9/2)$ **19.** Increasing on $(-5/3, 3)$; decreasing on $(-\infty, -5/3)$ and $(3, \infty)$
21. Never decreasing; increasing on $(-\infty, 3)$ and $(3, \infty)$ **23.** Decreasing on $(-\infty, -1)$ and $(0, 1)$; increasing on $(-1, 0)$ and
$(1, \infty)$ **25.** Relative maximum of -4 at 2   **27.** Relative minimum of -7 at 2   **29.** Relative maximum of 101 at -3; relative
minimum of -24 at 2   **31.** Relative maximum at $(-0.618, 0.206)$; relative minimum at $(1.618, 13.203)$
33. $f''(x) = 36x^2 - 10$; 26; 314   **35.** $f''(x) = 180(3x - 6)^{-3}$ or $180/(3x - 6)^3$; $-20/3$; $-4/75$
37. $f''(t) = (t^2 + 1)^{-3/2}$ or $1/(t^2 + 1)^{3/2}$; $1/2^{3/2} \approx 0.354$; $1/10^{3/2} \approx 0.032$

39.

$f(x) = -2x^3 - \tfrac{1}{2}x^2 + x - 3$

41.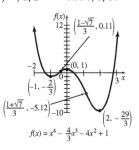

$f(x) = x^4 - \tfrac{4}{3}x^3 - 4x^2 + 1$

43.

$f(x) = \dfrac{x - 1}{2x + 1}$

45.

$f(x) = -4x^3 - x^2 + 4x + 5$

47.

$f(x) = x^4 + 2x^2$

49.

$f(x) = \dfrac{x^2 + 4}{x}$

51.

$f(x) = \dfrac{2x}{3 - x}$

53.

$f(x) = xe^{2x}$

55.

$f(x) = \ln(x^2 + 4)$

57.

$f(x) = 4x^{1/3} + x^{4/3}$

In Exercise 59, other answers are possible. **59.**

61. a. Both are negative. **63. a.** $P(q) = -q^3 + 7q^2 + 49q$ **b.** 7 brushes **c.** $229 **d.** $343 **e.** $q = 7/3$; between 2 and 3 brushes **65. a.** The first derivative has many critical numbers **b.** The curve is always decreasing except at frequent inflection points. **67.** **69.** **71.** 7.405 yr; the age at which the rate of learning to pass the test begins to slow down **73. a.** At 1965, 1973, 1976, 1983, 1986, and 1988 **b.** Concave upward; this means that the stockpile was increasing at an increasingly rapid rate.

Chapter 14 Applications of the Derivative

Exercises 14.1 (page 717)

For exercises ...	1–6,31–38	7,8,11–30,39	41–46,51–60	47–50
Refer to example ...	2	1	3	On Graphical Optimization

1. Absolute maximum at x_3; no absolute minimum
3. No absolute extrema **5.** Absolute minimum at x_1; no absolute maximum **7.** Absolute maximum at x_1; absolute minimum at x_2 **11.** Absolute maximum of 12 at $x = 5$; absolute minimum of -8 at $x = 0$ and $x = 3$ **13.** Absolute maximum of 19.67 at $x = -4$; absolute minimum of -1.17 at $x = 1$ **15.** Absolute maximum of 1 at $x = 0$; absolute minimum of -80 at $x = -3$ and $x = 3$ **17.** Absolute maximum of 1/3 at $x = 0$; absolute minimum of $-1/3$ at $x = 3$ **19.** Absolute maximum of 0.21 at $x = 1 + \sqrt{2} \approx 2.4$; absolute minimum of 0 at $x = 1$ **21.** Absolute maximum of 1.710 at $x = 3$; absolute minimum of -1.587 at $x = 0$ **23.** Absolute maximum of 7 at $x = 1$; absolute minimum of 0 at $x = 0$ **25.** Absolute maximum of 4.910 at $x = 4$; absolute minimum of -1.545 at $x = 2$ **27.** Absolute maximum of 19.09 at $x = -1$; absolute minimum of 0.6995 at $x = (\ln 3)/3$ **29.** Absolute maximum of 1.356 at $x = 0.6085$; absolute minimum of 0.5 at $x = -1$ **31.** Absolute minimum of 7 at $x = 2$; no absolute maximum **33.** Absolute maximum of 137 at $x = 3$; no absolute minimum **35.** Absolute maximum of 0.1 at $x = 4$; absolute minimum of -0.5 at $x = -2$ **37.** Absolute maximum of 0.1226 at $x = e^{1/3}$; no absolute minimum
39. a. Absolute minimum of -5 at $x = -1$; absolute maximum of 0 at $x = 0$ **b.** Absolute maximum of about -0.76 at $x = 2$; absolute minimum of -1 at $x = 1$ **41. a.** Relative maxima of 8496 in 2001, 7556 in 2004, 6985 in 2006, and 6700 in 2008; relative minima of 7127 in 2000, 7465 in 2003, 6748 in 2005, 5933 in 2007, and 5943 in 2009. **b.** Absolute maximum of 8496 in 2001 and absolute minimum of 5933 in 2007. **43.** The maximum profit is $700,000 when 1,000,000 tires are sold. **45. a.** 112 **b.** 162 **47.** About 11.5 units **49.** 100 units **51.** 6 mo; 6% **53.** About 7.2 mm **55.** Maximum of 25 mpg at 45 mph; minimum of 16.1 mpg at 65 mph **57.** The piece formed into a circle should have length $12\pi/(4 + \pi)$ ft, or about 5.28 ft.

Exercises 14.2 (page 726)

For exercises ...	1–8,15–18, 33,34,37,44	9–14, 19–24,47	25–30	31,32,41, 42,45,46	35,36, 38–40,43
Refer to example ...	1	3	4	2	5

1. a. $y = 180 - x$ **b.** $P = x(180 - x)$
c. $[0, 180]$ **d.** $dP/dx = 180 - 2x; x = 90$
e. $P(0) = 0$; $P(180) = 0$; $P(90) = 8100$ **f.** 8100; 90 and 90 **3. a.** $y = 90 - x$ **b.** $P = x^2(90 - x)$ **c.** $[0, 90]$
d. $dP/dx = 180x - 3x^2; x = 0, x = 60$ **e.** $P(0) = 0, P(60) = 108,000, P(90) = 0$ **f.** 108,000; 60 and 30
5. $\overline{C}(x) = x^2/2 + 2x - 3 + 35/x; x = 2.722$ **7. a.** $R(x) = 160,000x - 100x^2$ **b.** 800 **c.** $640,000 **9. a.** $1400 - 2x$
b. $A(x) = 1400x - 2x^2$ **c.** 350 m **d.** 245,000 m^2 **11.** 405,000 m^2 **13.** $960 **15. a.** 125 passengers **b.** $156,250
17. In 10 days; $960 **19.** 4 in. by 4 in. by 2 in. **21.** 2/3 ft (or 8 in.) **23.** 20 cm by 20 cm by 40 cm; $7200
27. Radius $= 5.206$ cm, height $= 11.75$ cm **29.** Radius $= 5.242$ cm; height $= 11.58$ cm **31.** 1 mile from point A
33. a. 15 days **b.** 16.875% **35.** 12.98 thousand **37. a.** 12 days **b.** 50 per ml **c.** 1 day **d.** 81.365 per ml

39. 49.37 **41.** Point P is $3\sqrt{7}/7 \approx 1.134$ mi from Point A **43. a.** Replace a with e^r and b with r/P.
b. Shepherd: $f'(S) = a[1 + (1 - c)(S/b)^c]/[1 + (S/b)^c]^2$; Ricker: $f'(S) = ae^{-bS}(1 - bS)$; Beverton-Holt:
$f'(S) = a/[1 + (S/b)]^2$ **c.** Shepherd: a; Ricker: a; Beverton-Holt: a; the constant a represents the slope of the graph of
$f(S)$ at $S = 0$. **d.** 194,000 tons **e.** 256,000 tons **45.** $(56 - 2\sqrt{21})/7 \approx 6.7$ mi **47.** 36 in. by 18 in. by 18 in.

Exercises 14.3 (page 737)

3. c **5.** It is negative. **9.** 10,000 **11.** 10

For exercises . . .	1,2,9–12, 15–18	3,13,14	4,27,32	5,7,8,25,26, 28–30	19–24,31
Refer to example . . .	1	2	3	4	5

13. 4899 **19. a.** $E = p/(200 - p)$ **b.** 25
21. a. $E = 2p^2/(7500 - p^2)$ **b.** 25,000 **23. a.** $E = 5/q$ **b.** 5 **25. a.** $E = 0.5$; inelastic; total revenue increases as price
increases. **b.** $E = 8$; elastic; total revenue decreases as price increases. **27.** 0.06; the demand is inelastic. **29.** 2.826; the
demand is elastic. **31. a.** 0.071 **b.** Inelastic **c.** $1255

Exercises 14.4 (page 742)

For exercises . . .	1–16,38–40	17–37	41–50
Refer to example . . .	1,2	3	4

1. $dy/dx = -6x/(5y)$ **3.** $dy/dx = (8x - 5y)/(5x - 3y)$
5. $dy/dx = 15x^2/(6y + 4)$ **7.** $dy/dx = -3x(2 + y)^2/2$
9. $dy/dx = \sqrt{y}/[\sqrt{x}(5\sqrt{y} - 2)]$ **11.** $dy/dx = (4x^3y^3 + 6x^{1/2})/(9y^{1/2} - 3x^4y^2)$ **13.** $dy/dx = (5 - 2xye^{x^2y})/(x^2e^{x^2y} - 4)$
15. $dy/dx = y(2xy^3 - 1)/(1 - 3x^2y^3)$ **17.** $y = (3/4)x + 25/4$ **19.** $y = x + 2$ **21.** $y = x/64 + 7/4$
23. $y = (11/12)x - 5/6$ **25.** $y = -(37/11)x + 59/11$ **27.** $y = (5/2)x - 1/2$ **29.** $y = 1$ **31.** $y = -2x + 7$
33. $y = -x + 2$ **35.** $y = (8/9)x + 10/9$ **37. a.** $y = -(3/4)x + 25/2$; $y = (3/4)x - 25/2$
b.

39. a. $du/dv = -2u^{1/2}/(2v + 1)^{1/2}$ **b.** $dv/du = -(2v + 1)^{1/2}/(2u^{1/2})$ **c.** They are reciprocals.
41. $dy/dx = -x/y$; there is no function $y = f(x)$ that satisfies $x^2 + y^2 + 1 = 0$.
43. a. $0.94; the approximate increase in cost of an additional unit
b. $0; the approximate change in revenue for a unit increase in sales **45 a.** 0.44; inelastic
b. 0.44 **47.** $1/(3\sqrt{3})$ **49.** $ds/dt = (4s - 6t^2 + 5)/(3s^2 - 4t)$

Exercises 14.5 (page 749)

For exercises . . .	1–8, 16–22	9–14	15	23,24, 29,31,32	25	26–28,30
Refer to example . . .	1	5	6	3	2	4

1. -64 **3.** $-9/7$ **5.** $1/5$ **7.** $-3/2$ **9.** $384 per month
11. a. Revenue is increasing at a rate of $180 per day.
b. Cost is increasing at a rate of $50 per day. **c.** Profit is
increasing at a rate of $130 per day. **13.** Demand is decreasing at a rate of approximately 98 units per unit time.
15. 0.067 mm per min **17.** About 1.9849 g per day **19. a.** $105.15 \text{ m}^{-0.25} \, dm/dt$ **b.** About 52.89 kcal per day^2
21. 25.6 crimes per month **23.** 24/5 ft/min **25.** 16π ft^2/min **27.** 2/27 cm/min **29.** 62.5 ft per min **31.** $\sqrt{2} \approx 1.41$ ft per sec

Exercises 14.6 (page 756)

For exercises . . .	1–8	9–16	17–20	21–35	36–41
Refer to example . . .	1	2	3	4	5

1. 1.9 **3.** 0.1 **5.** 0.060 **7.** -0.023 **9.** 12.0417; 12.0416; 0.0001
11. 0.995; 0.9950; 0 **13.** 1.01; 1.0101; 0.0001 **15.** 0.05; 0.0488; 0.0012 **17. a.** -4.4 thousand lb **b.** -52.2 thousand lb
19. $60 **21.** About 9600 in^3 **23. a.** 0.007435 **b.** -0.005105 **25. a.** 0.347 million **b.** -0.022 million **27.** 1568π mm^3
29. 80π mm^2 **31. a.** About 9.3 kg **b.** About 9.5 kg **33.** -7.2π cm^3 **35.** 0.472 cm^3 **37.** 0.00125 cm **39.** ± 1.273 in^3
41. ± 0.116 in^3

Chapter 14 Review Exercises (page 758)

For exercises . . .	1–3, 11–18	4,5, 49–54	6, 19–30, 43,44,56	7,8, 31–38, 55,59–61	9,10, 39–42, 62,63	45–48, 57,58, 64–68
Refer to section . . .	1	3	4	5	6	2

1. False **2.** True **3.** False **4.** True **5.** True
6. True **7.** True **8.** True **9.** True **10.** True
11. Absolute maximum of 33 at 4; absolute minimum of 1 at 0
and 6 **13.** Absolute maximum of 39 at -3; absolute minimum of $-319/27$ at 5/3 **17. a.** Maximum $= 0.37$; minimum $= 0$
b. Maximum $= 0.35$; minimum $= 0.13$ **21.** $dy/dx = (2x - 9x^2y^4)/(8y + 12x^3y^3)$ **23.** $dy/dx = 6\sqrt{y} - 1/[x^{1/3}(1 - \sqrt{y} - 1)]$
25. $dy/dx = -(30 + 50x)/3$ **27.** $dy/dx = (2xy^4 + 2y^3 - y)/(x - 6x^2y^3 - 6xy^2)$ **29.** $y = (-16/23)x + 94/23$ **33.** 272
35. -2 **37.** $-8e^3$ **41.** 0.00204 **43. a.** $(2, -5)$ and $(2, 4)$ **b.** $(2, -5)$ is a relative minimum; $(2, 4)$ is a relative maximum.
c. No **45. a.** 600 boxes **b.** $720 **47.** 3 in. **49.** 1789 **51.** 80 **53.** 0.47; inelastic **55.** 56π ft^2 per min
57. a.
b. About the 15th day **59.** 8/3 ft per min **61.** $21/16 = 1.3125$ ft per min **63.** ± 0.736 in^2
65. $1.25 + 2\ln 1.5$ **67.** 10 ft; 18.67 sec

Chapter 15 Integration

Exercises 15.1 (page 774)

1. They differ only by a constant.

5. $6k + C$ **7.** $z^2 + 3z + C$

9. $2t^3 - 4t^2 + 7t + C$

11. $z^4 + z^3 + z^2 - 6z + C$

13. $10z^{3/2}/3 + \sqrt{2}z + C$

15. $5x^4/4 - 20x^2 + C$

17. $8v^{3/2}/3 - 6v^{5/2}/5 + C$

For exercises . . .	5–24, 27,28,	25,26, 29–32, 35,36, 41,42, 60,63, 66	33,34, 37–40, 61	43,44	45–52, 57–59, 65	53–56	67–74
Refer to example . . .	4,5	7,8	6	12	9	10	11

19. $4u^{5/2} - 4u^{7/2} + C$ **21.** $-7/z + C$ **23.** $-\pi^3/(2y^2) - 2\sqrt{\pi y} + C$ **25.** $6t^{-1.5} - 2 \ln|t| + C$ **27.** $-1/(3x) + C$
29. $-15e^{-0.2x} + C$ **31.** $-3 \ln|x| - 10e^{-0.4x} + e^{0.1}x + C$ **33.** $(1/4)\ln|t| + t^3/6 + C$ **35.** $e^{2u}/2 + 2u^2 + C$
37. $x^3/3 + x^2 + x + C$ **39.** $6x^{7/6}/7 + 3x^{2/3}/2 + C$ **41.** $10^x/(\ln 10) + C$ **43.** $f(x) = 3x^{5/3}/5$
45. $C(x) = 2x^2 - 5x + 8$ **47.** $C(x) = 3e^{0.01x} + 5$ **49.** $C(x) = 3x^{5/3}/5 + 2x + 114/5$
51. $C(x) = 5x^2/2 - \ln|x| - 153.50$ **53.** $p = 175 - 0.01x - 0.01x^2$ **55.** $p = 500 - 0.1\sqrt{x}$
57. a. $f(t) = 3.75t^2 - 16.8t + 0.05$ **b.** Approximately 152.6 billion monthly text messages **59. a.** $P(x) = 25x^4/2 + 10x^3 - 40$
b. $240 **61.** $a \ln x - bx + C$ **63. a.** $N(t) = 155.3e^{0.3219t} + 144.7$ **b.** 7537
65. a. $B(t) = 0.02016t^3 - 0.6460t^2 + 15.86t + 839.7$ **b.** About 2,082,000 **67.** $v(t) = 5t^3/3 + 4t + 6$
69. $s(t) = -16t^2 + 6400$; 20 sec **71.** $s(t) = 2t^{5/2} + 3e^{-t} + 1$ **73.** 160 ft/sec, 12 ft

Exercises 15.2 (page 782)

3. $2(2x + 3)^5/5 + C$

5. $-(2m + 1)^{-2}/2 + C$

7. $-(x^2 + 2x - 4)^{-3}/3 + C$

For exercises . . .	3,4,29, 33,34	5–8, 21,22	9,10,27, 28,30	11–16, 31,35, 36	17–20, 32	23–26	39–44
Refer to example . . .	1	3	2	5	4	6	7

9. $(4z^2 - 5)^{3/2}/12 + C$ **11.** $e^{2x^3}/2 + C$ **13.** $e^{2t-t^2}/2 + C$ **15.** $-e^{1/z} + C$ **17.** $[\ln(t^2 + 2)]/2 + C$
19. $[\ln(x^4 + 4x^2 + 7)]/4 + C$ **21.** $-1/[2(x^2 + x)^2] + C$ **23.** $(p + 1)^7/7 - (p + 1)^6/6 + C$
25. $2(u - 1)^{3/2}/3 + 2(u - 1)^{1/2} + C$ **27.** $(x^2 + 12x)^{3/2}/3 + C$ **29.** $(1 + 3 \ln x)^3/9 + C$ **31.** $(1/2) \ln(e^{2x} + 5) + C$
33. $(\ln 10)(\log x)^2/2 + C$ **35.** $8^{3x^2+1}/(6 \ln 8) + C$ **39. a.** $R(x) = 6(x^2 + 27,000)^{1/3} - 180$ **b.** 150 players
41. a. $C(x) = 6 \ln(5x^2 + e) + 4$ **b.** Yes **43. a.** $f(t) = 4.0674 \times 10^{-4}[(t - 1970)^{2.4}/2.4 +$
$1970(t - 1970)^{1.4}/1.4] + 61.298$ **b.** About 181,000

Exercises 15.3 (page 791)

3. a. 88 **b.** $\int_0^8 (2x + 5)\, dx$

For exercises . . .	5–14,17–22	15,16,24–30, 33–35,39	31,32,36–38
Refer to example . . .	1,2	3	4

5. a. 21 **b.** 23 **c.** 22 **d.** 22 **7. a.** 10 **b.** 10 **c.** 10 **d.** 11 **9. a.** 8.22 **b.** 15.48 **c.** 11.85 **d.** 10.96 **11. a.** 6.70
b. 3.15 **c.** 4.93 **d.** 4.17 **13. a.** 4 **b.** 4 **15. a.** 4 **b.** 5 **17.** 4π **19.** 24 **21. b.** 0.385 **c.** 0.33835 **d.** 0.334334
e. 0.333333 **25.** Left: 1410 trillion BTUs; right: 3399 trillion BTUs; average: 2404.5 trillion BTUs **27. a.** Left: about 582,000
cases; right: about 580,000 cases; average: about 581,000 cases **b.** Left: about 146,000 cases; right: about 144,000 cases; average:
about 145,000 cases **29.** About 1300 ft; yes **31.** 2751 ft, 3153 ft, 2952 ft **33. a.** About 660 BTU/ft^2 **b.** About 320 BTU/ft^2
35. a. 9 ft **b.** 2 sec **c.** 4.6 ft **d.** Between 3 and 3.5 sec **37.** 22.5 and 18 ft **39. a.** About 75,600 **b.** About 77,300

Exercises 15.4 (page 803)

1. -18 **3.** $-3/2$ **5.** $28/3$ **7.** 13

9. $-16/3$ **11.** 76 **13.** $4/5$ **15.** $108/25$

17. $20e^{0.3} - 20e^{0.2} + 3 \ln 2 - 3 \ln 3 \approx 1.353$

For exercises . . .	1–6,9–12, 15–20, 23,24	7,8,13,14, 21,22, 27–30,54	31–44,47	55–61, 63–72
Refer to example . . .	1,2,3	4	5, 6	7

19. $e^8/4 - e^4/4 - 1/6 \approx 731.4$ **21.** 91/3
23. $447/7 \approx 63.86$ **25.** $(\ln 2)^2/2 \approx 0.2402$ **27.** 49 **29.** $1/8 - 1/[2(3 + e^2)] \approx 0.07687$ **31.** 10 **33.** 76 **35.** 41/2
37. $e^2 - 3 + 1/e \approx 4.757$ **39.** $e - 2 + 1/e \approx 1.086$ **41.** 23/3 **43.** $e^2 - 2e + 1 \approx 2.952$

45. $\int_a^c f(x)\, dx = \int_a^b f(x)\, dx + \int_b^c f(x)\, dx$ **47.** -8 **51.** -12 **53. a.** $x^5/5 - 1/5$ **c.** $f'(1) \approx 2.746$, and $g(1) = e \approx 2.718$

55. a. $(9000/8)(17^{4/3} - 2^{4/3}) \approx \$46,341$ **b.** $(9000/8)(26^{4/3} - 17^{4/3}) \approx \$37,477$ **c.** It is slowly increasing without bound.

57. No **59. a.** 0.8778 ft **b.** 0.6972 ft **61. a.** 18.12 **b.** 8.847 **63. b.** $\int_0^{60} n(x)\, dx$ **c.** $2(51^{3/2} - 26^{3/2})/15 \approx 30.89$ million

65. a. $Q(R) = \pi k R^4/2$ **b.** $0.04k$ mm per min **67. b.** About 505,000 kJ/$W^{0.67}$ **69. a.** About 286 million; the total population aged 0 to 90 **b.** About 64 million **71. a.** $c'(t) = 1.2e^{0.04t}$ **b.** $\int_0^{10} 1.2e^{0.04t}\, dt$ **c.** $30e^{0.4} - 30 \approx 14.75$ billion **d.** About 12.8 yr **e.** About 14.4 yr

Exercises 15.5 (page 813)

1. 21 **3.** 20 **5.** 23/3 **7.** 366.2
9. 4/3 **11.** $2 \ln 2 - \ln 6 + 3/2 \approx 1.095$
13. $6 \ln(3/2) - 6 + 2e^{-1} + 2e \approx 2.605$

For exercises ...	1,2	3–6, 11–18,20, 23,24	7–10, 19,21,22, 25,26,41,42	27–30, 39,40	31–37
Refer to example ...	1	3	2	4	5

15. $(e^{-2} + e^4)/2 - 2 \approx 25.37$ **17.** 1/2 **19.** 1/20 **21.** $3(2^{4/3})/2 - 3(2^{7/3})/7 \approx 1.620$ **23.** $(e^9 + e^6 + 1)/3 \approx 2836$
25. $-1.9241, -0.4164, 0.6650$ **27. a.** 8 yr **b.** About \$148 **c.** About \$771 **29. a.** 39 days **b.** \$3369.18 **c.** \$484.02
d. \$2885.16 **31.** 12,931.66 **33.** 54
35. a.

b. $(15, 375)$ **c.** \$4500 **d.** \$3375 **37. a.** 12 **b.** \$5616, \$1116 **c.** \$1872, \$1503
d. \$387 **39. a.** About 71.25 gal **b.** About 25 hr **c.** About 105 gal **d.** About 47.91 hr
41. a. 0.019; the lower 10% of the income producers earn 1.9% of the total income of the population. **b.** 0.184; the lower 40% of the income producers earn 18.4% of the total income of the population. **c.**

d. 0.15 **e.** Income is distributed less equally in 2008 than in 1968.

Exercises 15.6 (page 821)

1. a. 12.25 **b.** 12 **c.** 12 **3. a.** 3.35 **b.** 3.3
c. $3 \ln 3 \approx 3.296$ **5. a.** 11.34 **b.** 10.5 **c.** 10.5
7. a. 0.9436 **b.** 0.8374 **c.** $4/5 = 0.8$ **9. a.** 1.236
b. 1.265 **c.** $2 - 2e^{-1} \approx 1.264$ **11. a.** 5.991 **b.** 6.167
c. 6.283; Simpson's rule **13.** b is true. **15. a.** 0.2 **b.** 0.220703, 0.205200, 0.201302, 0.200325, 0.020703, 0.005200, 0.001302, 0.000325 **c.** $p = 2$ **17. a.** 0.2 **b.** 0.2005208, 0.2000326, 0.2000020, 0.2000001, 0.0005208, 0.0000326, 0.0000020, 0.0000001
c. $p = 4$ **19.** $M = 0.7355$; $S = 0.8048$

For exercises ...	1a–12a,15, 23a–24a,29	1b–12b,17,19,20, 23b–24b,29,30, 33–35	21,22,25–28, 31,32
Refer to example ...	1	2	3

21. a.

b. 6.3 **c.** 6.27 **23. a.** 1.831 **b.** 1.758 **25.** About 30 mcg(h)/ml; this represents the total amount of drug available to the patient for each ml of blood. **27.** About 9 mcg(h)/ml; this represents the total effective amount of the drug available to the patient for each ml of blood.
29. a. $y = b_0(t/7)^{b_1}e^{-b_2 t/7}$ **b.** About 1212 kg; about 1231 kg **c.** About 1224 kg; about 1250 kg
31. a. **b.** 71.5 **c.** 69.0 **33.** 3979 **35. a.** 0.6827 **b.** 0.9545 **c.** 0.9973

Chapter 15 Review Exercises (page 825)

1. True **2.** False **3.** False **4.** True
5. True **6.** False **7.** False **8.** True
9. True **10.** False **11.** True **12.** False
13. False **14.** True **19.** $x^2 + 3x + C$

For exercises ...	1–4, 19–30, 79,80, 84	5,16,17, 31–40, 87,94	6–8,15, 41–43, 81,92,96	9,10, 45–62, 82,83, 89–91, 95	11,12, 63–66, 85,86	13,14, 18, 44, 67–77, 93
Refer to section ...	1	2	3	4	5	6

21. $x^3/3 - 3x^2/2 + 2x + C$ **23.** $2x^{3/2} + C$ **25.** $2x^{3/2}/3 + 9x^{1/3} + C$ **27.** $2x^{-2} + C$ **29.** $-3e^{2x}/2 + C$ **31.** $e^{3x^2}/6 + C$
33. $(3 \ln |x^2 - 1|)/2 + C$ **35.** $-(x^3 + 5)^{-3}/9 + C$ **37.** $-e^{-3x^4}/12 + C$ **39.** $(3 \ln x + 2)^5/15 + C$ **41.** 20 **43.** 24
45. a. $s(T) - s(0)$ **b.** $\int_0^T v(t)\, dt = s(T) - s(0)$ is equivalent to the Fundamental Theorem with $a = 0$ and $b = T$ because $s(t)$ is an antiderivative of $v(t)$. **47.** 12 **49.** $3 \ln 5 + 12/25 \approx 5.308$ **51.** 19/15 **53.** $3(1 - e^{-4})/2 \approx 1.473$ **55.** $\pi/32$
57. $25\pi/4$ **59.** 13/3 **61.** $(e^4 - 1)/2 \approx 26.80$ **63.** 64/3 **65.** 149/3 **67.** 0.5833; 0.6035 **69.** 4.187; 4.155 **71.** 0.6011
73. 4.156 **75. a.** 4/3 **b.** 1.146 **c.** 1.252 **77. a.** 0 **b.** 0 **79.** $C(x) = (2x - 1)^{3/2} + 145$ **81.** \$96,000 **83.** \$38,000
85. a. \$916.67 **b.** \$666.67 **87. a.** 17.718 billion barrels **b.** 17.718 billion barrels **d.** $y = -0.03545x + 2.1347$; 17.777
billion barrels **89.** 782 **91. a.** 0.2784 **b.** 0.2784 **93. a.** About 8208 kg **b.** About 8430 kg **c.** About 8558 kg
95. $s(t) = t^3/3 - t^2 + 8$.

Chapter 16 Further Techniques and Applications of Integration

Exercises 16.1 (page 840)

For exercises . . .	1–4,36,40,41,43,44	5,6,35,39,42	7–10,20–22	13–19	23–28
Refer to example . . .	1,3	2	4	1–3	5

1. $xe^x - e^x + C$ **3.** $(-x/2 + 23/16)\,e^{-8x} + C$ **5.** $(x^2 \ln x)/2 - x^2/4 + C$ **7.** $-5e^{-1} + 3 \approx 1.161$
9. $26 \ln 3 - 8 \approx 20.56$ **11.** $e^4 + e^2 \approx 61.99$ **13.** $x^2 e^{2x}/2 - xe^{2x}/2 + e^{2x}/4 + C$
15. $(2/7)(x + 4)^{7/2} - (16/5)(x + 4)^{5/2} + (32/3)(x + 4)^{3/2} + C$ or $(2/3)x^2(x + 4)^{3/2} - (8/15)x(x + 4)^{5/2} + (16/105)(x + 4)^{7/2} + C$
17. $(4x^2 + 10x) \ln 5x - 2x^2 - 10x + C$ **19.** $(-e^2/4)(3e^2 + 1) \approx -42.80$ **21.** $2\sqrt{3} - 10/3 \approx 0.1308$
23. $16 \ln |x + \sqrt{x^2 + 16}| + C$ **25.** $-(3/11) \ln |(11 + \sqrt{121 - x^2})/x| + C$ **27.** $-1/(4x + 6) - (1/6) \ln |x/(4x + 6)| + C$
31. -18 **33.** 15 **37. a.** $(2/3)x(x + 1)^{3/2} - (4/15)(x + 1)^{5/2} + C$ **b.** $(2/5)(x + 1)^{5/2} - (2/3)(x + 1)^{3/2} + C$
39. $(169/2) \ln 13 - 42 \approx \$174.74$ **41.** $15e^6 + 3 \approx 6054$ **43.** About 219 kJ

Exercises 16.2 (page 847)

For exercises . . .	1–23,32,33,40,43	24–31,34–37,39,41,42	38
Refer to example . . .	1–3	4	Derivation of volume formula

1. 9π **3.** $364\pi/3$ **5.** $386\pi/27$ **7.** $15\pi/2$ **9.** 18π **11.** $\pi(e^4 - 1)/2 \approx 84.19$ **13.** $4\pi \ln 3 \approx 13.81$ **15.** $3124\pi/5$
17. $16\pi/15$ **19.** $4\pi/3$ **21.** $4\pi r^3/3$ **23.** $\pi r^2 h$ **25.** $13/3 \approx 4.333$ **27.** $38/15 \approx 2.533$ **29.** $e - 1 \approx 1.718$
31. $(5e^4 - 1)/8 \approx 34.00$ **33.** 3.758 **35.** $\$42.49$ **37.** 200 cases   **39. a.** $110e^{-0.1} - 120e^{-0.2} \approx 1.284$
b. $210e^{-1.1} - 220e^{-1.2} \approx 3.640$ **c.** $330e^{-2.3} - 340e^{-2.4} \approx 2.241$ **41. a.** $9(6 \ln 6 - 5) \approx 51.76$ **b.** $5(10 \ln 10 - 9) \approx 70.13$
c. $3(31 \ln 31 - 30)/2 \approx 114.7$ **43.** $1.083 \times 10^{21} \, \text{m}^3$

Exercises 16.3 (page 855)

For exercises . . .	1(a)–8(a),16	1(b)–8(b),15,17,18	9–14,19,20
Refer to example . . .	2	3,4	5

1. a. $\$6883.39$ **b.** $\$15,319.26$ **3. a.** $\$3441.69$ **b.** $\$7659.63$ **5. a.** $\$3147.75$ **b.** $\$7005.46$ **7. a.** $\$32,968.35$
b. $\$73,372.42$ **9. a.** $\$746.91$ **b.** $\$1662.27$ **11. a.** $\$688.64$ **b.** $\$1532.59$ **13. a.** $\$11,351.78$ **b.** $\$25,263.84$
15. $\$63,748.43$ **17.** $\$28,513.76, \$54,075.81$ **19.** $\$4560.94$

Exercises 16.4 (page 860)

For exercises . . .	1–26,31–34,37	27–30,35,36	42–47,50	48,49,51,52
Refer to example . . .	1	2	4	3

1. $1/3$ **3.** Divergent   **5.** -1 **7.** $10,000$ **9.** $1/10$
11. $3/5$ **13.** 1 **15.** 1000 **17.** Divergent   **19.** 1 **21.** Divergent
23. Divergent   **25.** Divergent   **27.** 0 **29.** Divergent   **31.** Divergent   **33.** 1 **35.** 0 **39. a.** $2.808, 3.724, 4.417, 6.720, 9.022$
b. Divergent   **c.** $0.8770, 0.9070, 0.9170, 0.9260, 0.9269$ **d.** Convergent   **41. a.** $9.9995, 49.9875, 99.9500, 995.0166$
b. Divergent   **c.** $100,000$ **43.** $\$20,000,000$ **45.** $\$30,000$ **47.** $\$30,000$ **49.** $Na/[b(b + k)]$ **51.** About 833.3

Exercises 16.5 (page 871)

For exercises . . .	1,2	3,4,17–20	5–16,21–32, 38,39,53	35	36,37,41,42, 49–51,54	40,47,48,52	43–46,56–59
Refer to example . . .	1	3	4,5,6	2	5	7	6

1. $y = -2x^2 + 2x^3 + C$ **3.** $y = x^4/2 + C$ **5.** $y^2 = 2x^3/3 + C$ **7.** $y = ke^{x^2}$ **9.** $y = ke^{x^3-x^2}$ **11.** $y = Cx$
13. $\ln(y^2 + 6) = x + C$ **15.** $y = -1/(e^{2x}/2 + C)$ **17.** $y = x^2 - x^3 + 5$ **19.** $y = -2xe^{-x} - 2e^{-x} + 44$ **21.** $y^2 = x^4/2 + 25$
23. $y = e^{x^2 + 3x}$ **25.** $y^2/2 - 3y = x^2 + x - 4$ **27.** $y = -3/(3 \ln |x| - 4)$ **29.** $y = (e^{x-1} - 3)/(e^{x-1} - 2)$ **35. a.** $\$1011.75$
b. $\$1024.52$ **c.** No   **37.** About 13.9 yr   **39.** $q = C/p^2$ **41.** d   **43. a.** $I = 2.4 - 1.4e^{-0.088W}$ **b.** I approaches 2.4.
45. a. $dw/dt = k(C - 17.5w)$; the calorie intake per day is constant.   **b.** lb/calorie   **c.** $dw/dt = (C - 17.5w)/3500$
d. $w = C/17.5 - e^{-0.005M}e^{-0.005t}/17.5$ **e.** $w = C/17.5 + (w_0 - C/17.5)e^{-0.005t}$

47. a.   **b.** $y = \dfrac{25,538}{1 + 110.28e^{-0.01819t}}$ **c.**   **d.** $25,538$

49. $y = 35.6e^{0.02117t}$ **51. a.** $k \approx 0.8$ **b.** 11 **c.** 55 **d.** About 3000 **53.** About 10 **55.** 7:22:55 A.M. **57.** The temperature approaches T_M, the temperature of the surrounding medium. **59. a.** $T = 88.6e^{-0.24t} + 10$ **b.**

c. Just after death—the graph shows that the most rapid decrease occurs in the first few hours. **d.** About 43.9°F **e.** About 4.5 hours

Chapter 16 Review Exercises (page 876)

For exercises . . .	1–4,18–29	5–7,70–39,91	8,9,48,65–75,81	10,40–47,76,82	11–14,49–64,71–80,83–90,92,93
Refer to section . . .	1	2	3	4	5

1. False **2.** True **3.** False **4.** True **5.** False **6.** False **7.** True **8.** True **9.** True **10.** False **11.** True
12. False **13.** True **14.** True **19.** $6x(x - 2)^{1/2} - 4(x - 2)^{3/2} + C$ **21.** $-(x + 2)e^{-3x} - (1/3)e^{-3x} + C$
23. $(x^2/2 - x)\ln |x| - x^2/4 + x + C$ **25.** $(1/8)\sqrt{16 + 8x^2} + C$ **27.** $10e^{1/2} - 16 \approx 0.4872$ **29.** $234/7 \approx 33.43$
31. $81\pi/2 \approx 127.2$ **33.** $\pi \ln 3 \approx 3.451$ **35.** $64\pi/5 \approx 40.21$ **39.** 2,391,484/3 **41.** 1/5 **43.** $6/e \approx 2.207$ **45.** Divergent
47. 3 **51.** $y = x^3 + 3x^2 + C$ **53.** $y = 2e^{2x} + C$ **55.** $y^2 = 3x^2 + 2x + C$ **57.** $y = (Cx^2 - 1)/2$ **59.** $y = x^3/3 - 3x^2 + 3$
61. $y = -\ln[5 - (x + 2)^4/4]$ **63.** $y^2 + 6y = 2x - 2x^2 + 352$ **65.** $16,250/3 \approx \$5416.67$ **67.** \$174,701.45 **69.** \$15.58
71. \$5354.97 **73.** \$30,035.17 **75.** \$176,919.15 **77. a.** \$10,099 **b.** \$71,196 **79. a.** $dA/dt = 0.05A - 20,000$ **b.** \$235,127.87
81. 0.4798 **83. a.** About 40 **b.** About 1.44×10^{10} hours **87. a.** $N = 329, b = 7.23; k = 0.247$ **b.** $y \approx 268$ million, which is less
than the table value of 308.7 million. **c.** About 289 million for 2030, about 303 million for 2050 **89. a.** $x = 1/k + Ce^{-kt}$ **b.** $1/k$
91. a. 158.3° **b.** 125° **c.** 133.3° **93.** 93.3 hr

Chapter 17 Multivariable Calculus

Exercises 17.1 (page 891)

For exercises . . .	1–4,27,28,32, 33,38–45,48	5–12	13–16	21–26		23–28	31,34–36
Refer to example . . .	1–3	4–6	7,8	material after Example 8		5	8

1. a. 12 **b.** −6 **c.** 10 **d.** −19 **3. a.** $\sqrt{43}$ **b.** 6 **c.** $\sqrt{19}$ **d.** $\sqrt{11}$
5.

7.

9.

11.

13.

15.

21. c **23.** e **25.** b **27. a.** $8x + 4h$
b. $-4y - 2h$ **c.** $8x$ **d.** $-4y$ **29. a.** $3e^2$;
slope of tangent line in the direction of x at
$(1, 1)$ **b.** $3e^2$; slope of tangent line in the
direction of y at $(1, 1)$ **31. a.** 1987
(rounded) **b.** 595 (rounded) **c.** 359,768
(rounded) **33.** 1.416; the IRA account
grows faster.

35. $y = 500^{5/2}/x^{3/2} \approx 5,590,170/x^{3/2}$

37. $C(x, y, z) = 250x + 150y + 75z$ **39. a.** 1.89 m² **b.** 1.62 m² **c.** 1.78 m²
41. a. 8.7% **b.** 48% **c.** Multiple solutions: $W = 19.75, R = 0, A = 0$ or
$W = 10, R = 10, A = 4.59$ **d.** Wetland percentage **43. a.** 397 accidents
45. a. $T = 242.257 \, C^{0.18}/F^3$ **b.** 58.82; a tethered sow spends nearly 59% of the time doing
repetitive behavior when she is fed 2 kg of food a day and neighboring sows spend 40% of the
time doing repetitive behavior. **47.** $g(L, W, H) = 2LW + 2WH + 2LH$ ft²

Exercises 17.2 (page 902)

For exercises ...	1,2,33–36,43,44	3–20	21–32	37–42	45–47,53–67	48–52
Refer to example ...	3	1–3	6,7	8	4	5

1. a. $12x - 4y$ **b.** $-4x + 18y$ **c.** 12 **d.** -40 **3.** $f_x(x, y) = -4y; f_y(x, y) = -4x + 18y^2; 4; 178$ **5.** $f_x(x, y) = 10xy^3;$
$f_y(x, y) = 15x^2y^2; -20; 2160$ **7.** $f_x(x, y) = e^{x+y}; f_y(x, y) = e^{x+y}; e^1$ or $e; e^{-1}$ or $1/e$ **9.** $f_x(x, y) = -24e^{4x-3y}; f_y(x, y) = 18e^{4x-3y};$
$-24e^{11}; 18e^{-25}$ **11.** $f_x(x, y) = (-x^4 - 2xy^2 - 3x^2y^3)/(x^3 - y^2)^2; f_y(x, y) = (3x^3y^2 - y^4 + 2x^2y)/(x^3 - y^2)^2; -8/49; -1713/5329$
13. $f_x(x, y) = 15x^2y^2/(1 + 5x^3y^2); f_y(x, y) = 10x^3y/(1 + 5x^3y^2); 60/41; 1920/2879$ **15.** $f_x(x, y) = e^{x^2y}(2x^2y + 1);$
$f_y(x, y) = x^3e^{x^2y}; -7e^{-4}; -64e^{48}$ **17.** $f_x(x, y) = (1/2)(4x^3 + 3y)/(x^4 + 3xy + y^4 + 10)^{1/2};$
$f_y(x, y) = (1/2)(3x + 4y^3)/(x^4 + 3xy + y^4 + 10)^{1/2}; 29/(2\sqrt{21}); 48/\sqrt{311}$
19. $f_x(x, y) = [6xy(e^{xy} + 2) - 3x^2y^2e^{xy}]/(e^{xy} + 2)^2; f_y(x, y) = [3x^2(e^{xy} + 2) - 3x^3ye^{xy}]/(e^{xy} + 2)^2; -24(e^{-2} + 1)/(e^{-2} + 2)^2;$
$(624e^{-12} + 96)/(e^{-12} + 2)^2$ **21.** $f_{xx}(x, y) = 8y^2 - 32; f_{yy}(x, y) = 8x^2; f_{xy}(x, y) = f_{yx}(x, y) = 16xy$
23. $R_{xx}(x, y) = 8 + 24y^2; R_{yy}(x, y) = -30xy + 24x^2; R_{xy}(x, y) = R_{yx}(x, y) = -15y^2 + 48xy$
25. $r_{xx}(x, y) = 12y/(x + y)^3; r_{yy}(x, y) = -12x/(x + y)^3; r_{xy}(x, y) = r_{yx}(x, y) = (6y - 6x)/(x + y)^3$
27. $z_{xx} = 9ye^x; z_{yy} = 0; z_{xy} = z_{yx} = 9e^x$ **29.** $r_{xx} = -1/(x + y)^2; r_{yy} = -1/(x + y)^2; r_{xy} = r_{yx} = -1/(x + y)^2$
31. $z_{xx} = 1/x; z_{yy} = -x/y^2; z_{xy} = z_{yx} = 1/y$ **33.** $x = -4, y = 2$ **35.** $x = 0, y = 0;$ or $x = 3, y = 3$ **37.** $f_x(x, y, z) = 4x^3;$
$f_y(x, y, z) = 2z^2; f_z(x, y, z) = 4yz + 4z^3; f_{yz}(x, y, z) = 4z$ **39.** $f_x(x, y, z) = 6/(4z + 5); f_y(x, y, z) = -5/(4z + 5);$
$f_z(x, y, z) = -4(6x - 5y)/(4z + 5)^2; f_{yz}(x, y, z) = 20/(4z + 5)^2$ **41.** $f_x(x, y, z) = (2x - 5z^2)/(x^2 - 5xz^2 + y^4);$
$f_y(x, y, z) = 4y^3/(x^2 - 5xz^2 + y^4); f_z(x, y, z) = -10xz/(x^2 - 5xz^2 + y^4); f_{yz}(x, y, z) = 40xy^3z/(x^2 - 5xz^2 + y^4)^2$
43. a. 6.773 **b.** 3.386 **45. a.** 80 **b.** 150 **c.** 80 **d.** 440 **47. a.** \$902,100 **b.** $f_p(p, i) = 99 - 0.5i - 0.005p; f_i(p, i) = -0.5p;$
the rate at which weekly sales are changing per unit of change in price when the interest rate remains constant $(f_p(p, i))$ or per unit change in
interest rate when the price remains constant $(f_i(p, i))$ **c.** A weekly sales decrease of \$9700 **49. a.** 50.57 hundred units
b. $f_x(16, 81) = 1.053$ hundred units and is the rate at which production is changing when labor changes by 1 unit (from 16 to 17) and capital
remains constant; $f_y(16, 81) = 0.4162$ hundred units and is the rate at which production is changing when capital changes by 1 unit (from 81
to 82) and labor remains constant. **c.** Production would increase by approximately 105 units. **51.** $0.4x^{-0.6}y^{0.6}; 0.6x^{0.4}y^{-0.4}$
53. a. 1279 kcal per hr **b.** 2.906 kcal per hr per g; the instantaneous rate of change of energy usage for a 300-kg animal traveling
at 10 km per hr is about 2.9 kcal per hr per g. **55. a.** 0.0142 m² **b.** 0.00442 m² **57. a.** 4.125 lb **b.** $\partial f/\partial n = n/4$; the rate of
change of weight loss per unit change in workouts **c.** An additional loss of 3/4 lb **59. a.** $(2ax - 3x^2)t^2e^{-t}$
b. $x^2(a - x)(2t - t^2)e^{-t}$ **c.** $(2a - 6x)t^2e^{-t}$ **d.** $(2ax - 3x^2)(2t - t^2)e^{-t}$ **e.** $\partial R/\partial x$ gives the rate of change of the reaction
per unit of change in the amount of drug administered. $\partial R/\partial t$ gives the rate of change of the reaction for a 1-hour change in the time
after the drug is administered. **61. a.** $-24.9°F$ **b.** 15 mph **c.** $W_V(20, 10) = -1.114$; while holding the temperature fixed at 10°F,
the wind chill decreases approximately 1.1°F when the wind velocity increases by 1 mph; $W_T(20, 10) = 1.429$; while holding the wind
velocity fixed at 20 mph, the wind chill increases approximately 1.429°F if the actual temperature increases from 10°F to 11°F.
d. Sample table

T\W	5	10	15	20
30	27	16	9	4
20	16	3	-5	-11
10	6	-9	-18	-25
0	-5	-21	-32	-39

63. -10 ml per year, 100 ml per in. **65. a.** $F_m = gR^2/r^2$; the rate
of change in force per unit change in mass while the distance is held
constant; $F_r = -2mgR^2/r^3$; the rate of change in force per unit
change in distance while the mass is held constant
67. a. 1055 **b.** $T_s(3, 0.5) = 127.4$ msec per ft. If the distance to
move an object increases from 3 ft to 4 ft, while keeping w fixed
at 0.5, the approximate increase in movement time is 127.4 msec.
$T_w(3, 0.5) = -764.6$ msec per ft. If the width of the target area increases by 1 ft, while keeping s fixed at 3 ft, the approximate
decrease in movement time is 764.6 msec.

Exercises 17.3 (page 912)

For exercises ...	1–18,21–28	34–40,42
Refer to example ...	1–3	4

1. Saddle point at $(-1, 2)$ **3.** Relative minimum at $(-3, -3)$
5. Relative minimum at $(-2, -2)$ **7.** Relative minimum at $(15, -8)$ **9.** Relative maximum at $(2/3, 4/3)$ **11.** Saddle point
at $(2, -2)$ **13.** Saddle point at $(0, 0)$; relative minimum at $(27, 9)$ **15.** Saddle point at $(0, 0)$; relative minimum at $(9/2, 3/2)$
17. Saddle point at $(0, -1)$ **21.** Relative maximum of 9/8 at $(-1, 1)$; saddle point at $(0, 0)$; a **23.** Relative minima of $-33/16$
at $(0, 1)$ and at $(0, -1)$; saddle point at $(0, 0)$; b **25.** Relative maxima of 17/16 at $(1, 0)$ and $(-1, 0)$; relative minima of $-15/16$
at $(0, 1)$ and $(0, -1)$; saddle points at $(0, 0), (-1, 1), (1, -1), (1, 1)$, and $(-1, -1)$; e **31. a.** all values of k **b.** $k \geq 0$
35. Minimum cost of \$59 when $x = 4, y = 5$ **37.** Sell 12 spas and 7 solar heaters for a maximum revenue of \$166,600.
39. \$2000 on quality control and \$1000 on consulting, for a minimum time of 8 hours
41. a. $r = -1.722, s = 0.3652, y = 0.1787(1.441)^t$ **b.** Same as a **c.** Same as a

Exercises 17.4 (page 922)

For exercises . . .	1–8,11,12,15,21	9,10,13,14,37–42	23–26	27–36
Refer to example . . .	1	3	material after Example 3	2

1. $f(8,8) = 256$ **3.** $f(5,5) = 125$ **5.** $f(5,3) = 28$ **7.** $f(20,2) = 360$ **9.** $f(3/2, 3/2, 3) = 81/4 = 20.25$
11. $x = 8, y = 16$ **13.** 30, 30, 30 **15.** Minimum value of 128 at $(2,5)$, maximum value of 160 at $(-2,7)$
21. a. Minimum value of -5 at $(3,-2)$. **d.** $(3,-2)$ is a saddle point. **23.** Purchase 20 units of x and 20 units of y for a maximum utility of 8000. **25.** Purchase 20 units of x and 5 units of y for a maximum utility of 4,000,000.
27. 60 feet by 60 feet **29.** 10 large kits and no small kits **31.** 167 units of labor and 178 units of capital **33.** 125 m by 125 m **35.** Radius = 5 in.; height = 10 in. **37.** 12.91 m by 12.91 m by 6.455 m **39.** 5 m by 5 m by 5 m
41. b. 2 yd by 1 yd by 1/2 yd

Exercises 17.5 (page 926)

For exercises . . .	1–6,18–20,23–28	7–14	15–17,21,22,29–32	33,34
Refer to example . . .	1	2	3	4

1. 0.12 **3.** 0.0311 **5.** -0.335
7. 10.022; 10.0221; 0.0001 **9.** 2.0067; 2.0080; 0.0013 **11.** 1.07; 1.0720; 0.0020 **13.** -0.02; -0.0200; 0 **15.** 20.73 cm^3
17. 86.4 in^3 **19.** 0.07694 unit **21.** 6.65 cm^3 **23.** 2.98 liters **25. a.** 0.2649 **b.** Actual 0.2817; approximation 0.2816
27. a. 87% **b.** 75% **d.** 89%; 87% **29.** 26.945 cm^2 **31.** 3% **33.** 8

Exercises 17.6 (page 937)

For exercises . . .	1–10	11–20	21–28,61–64,66–71	29–38,65	39–46	47–56	57,58
Refer to example . . .	1	2,3	4	5,6	7	8	9

1. $630y$ **3.** $(2x/9)[(x^2 + 15)^{3/2} - (x^2 + 12)^{3/2}]$ **5.** $6 + 10y$ **7.** $(1/2)(e^{12+3y} - e^{4+3y})$ **9.** $(1/2)(e^{4x+9} - e^{4x})$ **11.** 945
13. $(2/45)(39^{5/2} - 12^{5/2} - 7533)$ **15.** 21 **17.** $(\ln 3)^2$ **19.** $8 \ln 2 + 4$ **21.** 171 **23.** $(4/15)(33 - 2^{5/2} - 3^{5/2})$
25. $-3 \ln(3/4)$ or $3 \ln(4/3)$ **27.** $(1/2)(e^7 - e^6 - e^3 + e^2)$ **29.** 96 **31.** 40/3 **33.** $(2/15)(2^{5/2} - 2)$
35. $(1/4) \ln(17/8)$ **37.** $e^2 - 3$ **39.** 97,632/105 **41.** 128/9 **43.** $\ln 16$ or $4 \ln 2$ **45.** 64/3 **47.** 34 **49.** 10/3
51. $7(e - 1)/3$ **53.** 16/3 **55.** $4 \ln 2 - 2$ **57.** 1 **61.** 49 **63.** $(e^6 + e^{-10} - e^{-4} - 1)/60$ **65.** 9 in^3 **67.** 14,753 units
69. $34,833 **71.** $32,000

Chapter 17 Review Exercises (page 942)

For exercises . . .	1–5,17–26,87	6,13,14,27–44, 89,98–101	7,8,45–53,90, 103,104	9,54–57, 91,92	10–12,67–86, 100	15,59–66,88, 93–96,98
Refer to section . . .	1	2	3	4	6	5

1. True **2.** True **3.** True **4.** True **5.** False **6.** False **7.** False **8.** True **9.** False **10.** False **11.** True **12.** False
17. $-19; -255$ **19.** $-5/9; -4/3$ **21.**

23.

25.

27. a. $9x^2 + 8xy$ **b.** -12 **c.** 16 **29.** $f_x(x, y) = 12xy^3; f_y(x, y) = 18x^2y^2 - 4$ **31.** $f_x(x, y) = 4x/(4x^2 + y^2)^{1/2}$;
$f_y(x, y) = y/(4x^2 + y^2)^{1/2}$ **33.** $f_x(x, y) = 3x^2e^{3y}; f_y(x, y) = 3x^3e^{3y}$ **35.** $f_x(x, y) = 4x/(2x^2 + y^2); f_y(x, y) = 2y/(2x^2 + y^2)$
37. $f_{xx}(x, y) = 30xy; f_{xy}(x, y) = 15x^2 - 12y$ **39.** $f_{xx}(x, y) = 12y/(2x - y)^3; f_{xy}(x, y) = (-6x - 3y)/(2x - y)^3$
41. $f_{xx}(x, y) = 8e^{2y}; f_{xy}(x, y) = 16xe^{2y}$ **43.** $f_{xx}(x, y) = (-2x^2y^2 - 4y)/(2 - x^2y)^2; f_{xy}(x, y) = -4x/(2 - x^2y)^2$
45. Saddle point at (0, 2) **47.** Relative minimum at (2, 1) **49.** Saddle point at (3, 1) **51.** Saddle point at $(-1/3, 11/6)$;
relative minimum at $(1, 1/2)$ **55.** Minimum of 18 at $(-3, 3)$ **57.** $x = 25, y = 50$ **59.** 1.22 **61.** 13.0846; 13.0848; 0.0002
63. $8y - 6$ **65.** $(3/2)[(100 + 2y^2)^{1/2} - (2y^2)^{1/2}]$ **67.** 1232/9 **69.** $(2/135)[(42)^{5/2} - (24)^{5/2} - (39)^{5/2} + (21)^{5/2}]$
71. $2 \ln 2$ or $\ln 4$ **73.** 110 **75.** $(4/15)(782 - 8^{5/2})$ **77.** 105/2 **79.** 1/2 **81.** 1/48 **83.** $\ln 2$ **85.** 3
87. a. $\$(325 + \sqrt{10}) \approx \$328.16$ **b.** $\$(800 + \sqrt{15}) \approx \$803.87$ **c.** $\$(2000 + \sqrt{20}) \approx \$2004.47$ **89. a.** $0.7y^{0.3}/x^{0.3}$
b. $0.3x^{0.7}/y^{0.7}$ **91.** Purchase 10 units of x and 15 units of y for a maximum utility of 33,750. **93.** Decrease by $243.82
95. 4.19 ft^3 **97. a.** $200 spent on fertilizer and $80 spent on seed will produce a maximum profit of $266 per acre.
b. Same as a **c.** Same as a **99. a.** 49.68 liters **b.** -0.09, the approximate change in total body water if age is increased by 1 yr and mass and height are held constant is -0.09 liters; 0.34, the approximate change in total body water if mass is increased by 1 kg and age and height are held constant is 0.34 liters; 0.25, the approximate change in total body water if height is increased by 1 cm and age and mass are held constant is 0.25 liters. **101. a.** 50; in 1900, 50% of those born 60 years earlier are still alive.
b. 75; in 2000, 75% of those born 70 years earlier are still alive. **c.** -1.25; in 1900, the percent of those born 60 years earlier who are still alive was dropping at a rate of 1.25 percent per additional year of life. **d.** -2; in 2000, the percent of those born 70 years earlier who are still alive was dropping at a rate of 2 percent per additional year of life. **103.** 5 in. by 5 in. by 5 in.

Chapter 18 Probability and Calculus

Exercises 18.1 (page 957)

For exercises . . .	1–10	11–18,29–34	19–24,35c,d,36c,d, 48d,e,49d,e	35a,b,36a,b,39–42,44–47, 48a,b,c,49a,b,c,50	43,51
Refer to example . . .	1	2	5	3	4

1. Yes **3.** Yes **5.** No; $\int_0^3 4x^3\,dx \neq 1$
7. No; $\int_{-2}^2 x^2/16\,dx \neq 1$
9. No; $f(x) < 0$ for some x values in $[-1, 1]$. **11.** $k = 3/14$ **13.** $k = 3/125$ **15.** $k = 2/9$ **17.** $k = 1/12$
19. $F(x) = (x^2 - x - 2)/18, 2 \leq x \leq 5$ **21.** $F(x) = (x^3 - 1)/63, 1 \leq x \leq 4$ **23.** $F(x) = (x^{3/2} - 1)/7, 1 \leq x \leq 4$
25. 1 **29. a.** 0.4226 **b.** 0.2071 **c.** 0.4082 **31. a.** 0.3935 **b.** 0.3834 **c.** 0.3679 **33. a.** 1/3 **b.** 2/3 **c.** 295/432
35. a. 0.9975 **b.** 0.0024 **c.** $F(t) = 1 - e^{-t/2}, t \geq 0$ **d.** 0.9502 **37.** c **39. a.** 0.2679 **b.** 0.4142 **c.** 0.3178
41. a. 0.8131 **b.** 0.4901

43. a. polynomial function **b.** $N(t) = -0.00007445t^4 + 0.01243t^3 - 0.7419t^2 + 18.18t - 137.5$

 Yes

c. $S(t) = \dfrac{1}{466.26}(-0.00007445t^4 + 0.01243t^3 - 0.7419t^2 + 18.18t - 137.5)$ **d.** Estimates: 0.1688, 0.5896, 0.1610; actual:
0.1730, 0.5865, 0.1325 **45. a.** 0.2 **b.** 0.6 **c.** 0.6 **47. a.** 0.1640 **b.** 0.1353 **49. a.** 0.2829 **b.** 0.4853 **c.** 0.2409
d. $F(t) = 1.8838(0.5982 - e^{-0.03211t}), 16 \leq t \leq 84$ **e.** 0.1671

51. a. A polynomial function **b.** $T(t) = -2.564t^3 + 99.11t^2 - 964.6t + 5631$

c. $S(t) = \dfrac{1}{101,370}(-2.564t^3 + 99.11t^2 - 964.6t + 5631)$ **d.** 0.09457; 0.07732

Exercises 18.2 (page 967)

For exercises . . .	1–6,11–14	7,8	11d,e–14d,e,24–26,31–33, 34,35,38–42	15a–20a,24d,26d,31d, 33d,36,40d,41d	37,43
Refer to example . . .	1	2	3	5	4

1. $\mu = 5$; $\text{Var}(X) \approx 1.33$; $\sigma \approx 1.15$
3. $\mu = 14/3 \approx 4.67$; $\text{Var}(X) \approx 0.89$; $\sigma \approx 0.94$ **5.** $\mu = 2.83$; $\text{Var}(X) \approx 0.57$; $\sigma \approx 0.76$
7. $\mu = 4/3 \approx 1.33$; $\text{Var}(X) = 2/9 \approx 0.22$; $\sigma \approx 0.47$ **11. a.** 5.40 **b.** 5.55 **c.** 2.36 **d.** 0.5352 **e.** 0.6043 **13. a.** 1.6
b. 0.11 **c.** 0.33 **d.** 0.5904 **e.** 0.6967 **15. a.** 5 **b.** 0 **17. a.** 4.828 **b.** 0.0553 **19. a.** $\sqrt[4]{2} \approx 1.189$ **b.** 0.1836
21. 16/5; does not exist; does not exist **23.** d **25. a.** 6.409 yr **b.** 1.447 yr **c.** 0.4910 **27.** c **29.** c **31. a.** 6.342 seconds
b. 5.135 sec **c.** 0.7518 **d.** 4.472 sec **33. a.** 2.333 cm **b.** 0.8692 cm **c.** 0 **d.** 2.25 cm **35.** 111 **37.** 31.75 years; 11.55
years **39. a.** 1.806 **b.** 1.265 **c.** 0.1886 **41. a.** 38.51 years **b.** 17.56 years **c.** 0.1656 **d.** 34.26 years **43.** About 1 pm

Exercises 18.3 (page 979)

For exercises . . .	1,2,29,35,39,48	3–6,30,31,36–38,40, 41,43–45,47,49–51	7–14,32–34,42,52	46
Refer to example . . .	1	2	3	4

1. a. 3.7 cm **b.** 0.4041 cm **c.** 0.2886
3. a. 0.25 years **b.** 0.25 years **c.** 0.2325
5. a. 3 days **b.** 3 days **c.** 0.2325 **7.** 49.98% **9.** 8.01% **11.** -1.28 **13.** 0.92 **19.** $m = (-\ln 0.5)/a$ or $(\ln 2)/a$
23. a. 1.00000 **b.** 1.99999 **c.** 8.00000 **25. a.** $\mu \approx 0$ **b.** $\sigma = 0.9999999251 \approx 1$ **27.** $F(x) = (x - a)/(b - a), a \leq x \leq b$
29. a. \$47,500 **b.** 0.4667 **31. a.** $f(x) = 0.235e^{-0.235x}$ on $[0, \infty)$ **b.** 0.0954 **33. a.** 0.1587 **b.** 0.7698 **35.** c **37.** d
39. a. 28 days **b.** 0.375 **41. a.** 1 hour **b.** 0.3935 **43. a.** 58 minutes **b.** 0.0907 **45. a.** 0.1967 **b.** 0.2468
47. a. 4.37 millennia; 4.37 millennia **b.** 0.6325 **49. a.** 0.2865 **b.** 0.2212 **51. a.** 0.5457 **b.** 0.0039

Chapter 18 Review Exercises (page 983)
1. True **2.** True **3.** True **4.** False **5.** False **6.** True
7. True **8.** True **9.** False **10.** False **11.** probabilities
13. 1. $f(x) \geq 0$ for all x in $[a, b]$; 2. $\int_a^b f(x)\,dx = 1$

For exercises . . .	1–4,11–22,41, 46a–47a,60a-d	5,6,23–31,42, 46b,c–47b,c,52, 55,60e,f,61	7–10,33–40,43, 48–51,53,54,56, 57–59,62
Refer to section . . .	1	2	3

15. Not a probability density function **17.** Probability density function **19.** $k = 1/21$ **21. a.** $1/5 = 0.2$ **b.** $9/20 = 0.45$
c. 0.54 **25. a.** 4 **b.** 0.5 **c.** 0.7071 **d.** 4.121 **e.** $F(x) = (x - 2)^2/9, 2 \leq x \leq 5$ **27. a.** 5/4 **b.** $5/48 \approx 0.1042$
c. 0.3227 **d.** 1.149 **e.** $F(x) = 1 - 1/x^5, x \geq 1$ **29. a.** 0.5833 **b.** 0.2444 **c.** 0.4821 **d.** 0.6114 **31. a.** 100
b. 100 **c.** 0.8647 **33.** 33.36% **35.** 34.31% **37.** 11.51% **39.** −0.05 **41. a.** Uniform **b.** Domain: [10, 30], range: {0.05}

c.

$f(x) = 0.05$ for [10, 30]

d. $\mu = 20; \sigma \approx 5.77$ **e.** 0.577 **43. a.** Normal **b.** Domain: $(-\infty, \infty)$, range: $(0, 1/\sqrt{\pi}\,]$

c.

$f(x) = \dfrac{e^{-x^2}}{\sqrt{\pi}}$

d. $\mu = 0; \sigma = 1/\sqrt{2}$ **e.** 0.6826 **45. b.** 0.6819 **c.** 0.9716
d. 1; yes **47. a.** 0.9107 **b.** 13.57 years **c.** 6.68 years
49. a. $f(x) = e^{-x/8}/8; [0, \infty)$ **b.** 8 **c.** 8 **d.** 0.2488 **51.** d
53. 0.6321 **55. a.** 40.07°C **b.** 0.4928 **57.** 0.2266
59. a. 0.2921 **b.** 0.1826 **61.** 3650.1 days; 3650.1 days

Credits

Text Credits

Photo Credits

page R-1 Ng Yin Chern/Shutterstock   **page 1** Stockbyte/Getty Images   **page 37** Comstock/Thinkstock   **page 42** Forster Forest/Shutterstock   **page 44** Kelly-Mooney Photography/Corbis   **page 76** Courtesy of Raymond N. Greenwell   **page 86** John and Karen Hollingsworth/U.S. Fish and Wildlife Service   **page 109** Photos/Thinkstock   **page 110** Tischenko Irina/Shutterstock   **page 112** F11 Photo/Shutterstock   **page 119** Neftall/Fotolia   **page 128** Ondrejschaumann/Dreamstime   **page 137** Jordache/Shutterstock   **page 142** Ewwwgenich1/Fotolia   **page 167** Courtesy of Raymond N. Greenwell   **page 169** Iko/Shutterstock   **page 174** Alma Sacra/Fotolia   **page 183** Semen Lixodeev/Shutterstock   **page 187** Mangostock/Shutterstock   **page 216** AP Images   **page 222** Hleib/Shutterstock   **page 224** Hightowernrw/Shutterstock   **page 283** Liquidlibrary/Thinkstock   **page 351** Avava/Shutterstock   **page 352** Stephen Coburn/Shutterstock   **page 406** Lisa F. Young/Shutterstock   **page 407** Kletr/Shutterstock   **page 452** Photos/Thinkstock   **page 485** Olga Miltsova/Shutterstock   **page 508** Cuson/Shutterstock   **page 525** Andrea Danti/Shutterstock   **page 526** John Good/National Park Service   **page 529** Digital Vision/Thinkstock   **page 565** Courtesy of Raymond N. Greenwell   **page 580** Courtesy of Raymond N. Greenwell   **page 586** Tony Brindley/Shutterstock   **page 601** BananaStock/Thinkstock   **page 604** Comstock/Thinkstock   **page 626** Pack-Shot/Shutterstock   **page 649** AardLumens/Fotolia   **page 659** Wallenrock/Shutterstock   **page 694** Theroff97/Dreamstime   **page 708** Stockbyte/Thinkstock   **page 711** John R. Smith/Shutterstock   **page 762** Auremar/Shutterstock   **page 763** Maureen Plainfield/Shutterstock   **page 772** Rudy Balasko/Shutterstock   **page 795** (left) Courtesy of Raymond N. Greenwell; (right) Gary Kemper/AP Images   **page 833** B.W. Folsom/Shutterstock   **page 867** Randal Sedler/Shutterstock   **page 883** Specta/Shutterstock   **page 949** U.S. Geological Survey Photographic Library   **page 978** Library Congress Prints and Photographs Division [LC-USZC4-2109]

Chapter opener photos are repeated at a smaller size on table of contents and preface pp. iii–vii, ix.

Index of Applications

Index

Note: A complete Index of Applications appears on pp. I-1.

Sources

This is a sample of the comprehensive source list available for the tenth edition of Calculus with Applications. The complete list is available at the Downloadable Student Resources site, www.pearsonhighered.com/mathstatsresources, as well as to qualified instructors within MyMathLab or through the Pearson Instructor Resource Center, www.pearsonhighered.com/irc.

Chapter 1

Section 1.1

1. Example 10 from *Morbidity and Mortality Weekly Report*, Centers for Disease Control and Prevention, Vol. 58, No. 44, Nov. 13, 2009, p. 1227.
2. Example 14 from http://www.trends-collegeboard.com/college_ pricing/1_3_over_ time_current_dollars.html.
3. Exercise 62 from *Time Almanac 2010*, p. 150.
4. Exercise 63 from *Time Almanac 2010*, pp. 637–638.
5. Exercise 64 from Alcabes, P., A. Munoz, D. Vlahov, and G. Friedland, "Incubation Period of Human Immunodeficiency Virus," *Epidemiologic Review*, Vol. 15, No. 2, The Johns Hopkins University School of Hygiene and Public Health, 1993, pp. 303–318.
6. Exercise 65 from Hockey, Robert V., *Physical Fitness: The Pathway to Healthful Living*, Times Mirror/ Mosby College Publishing, 1989, pp. 85–87.
7. Exercise 66 from *Science*, Vol. 253, No. 5017, July 19, 1991, pp. 306–308.
8. Exercise 67 from *Science*, Vol. 254, No. 5034, Nov. 15, 1991, pp. 936–938, and http://www.cdc.gov/nchs/data.
9. Exercise 68 from *World Health Statistics 2010*, World Health Organization, pp. 56–57.
10. Exercise 69 from *The New York Times,* Sept. 11, 2009, p. A12.
11. Exercise 70 from U. S. Census Bureau, http://www.census.gov/ population/socdemo/ hh-fam/ms2.pdf.
12. Exercise 71 from *2008 Yearbook of Immigration Statistics,* Office of Immigration Statistics, Aug. 2009, p. 5.
13. Exercise 72 from *Science News,* June 23, 1990, p. 391.
14. Exercise 73 from Acker, A. and C. Jaschek, *Astronomical Methods and Calculations*, John Wiley & Sons, 1986; Karttunen, H. (editor), *Fundamental Astronomy*, Springer-Verlag, 1994.
15. Exercise 74 from http://www.stateofthemedia .org/2009/narrative_audio_audience.php? media=10&cat=2#1listeningtoradio.
16. Exercise 75 from http://www.trends-collegeboard.com/college_ pricing/1_3_ over_time_current_dollars.html.

Section 1.2

1. Page 18 from http://www.agmrc.org/media/ cms/oceanspray_4BB99D38246C8.pdf.
2. Exercise 46 from *Science News,* Sept. 26, 1992, p. 195, *Science News,* Nov. 7, 1992, p. 399.
3. Exercise 48 from http://www.calstate.edu/ budget/fybudget/2009-2010/supportbook2/ challenges-off-campus-costs.shtml.

Section 1.3

1. Page 25 from U.S. Dept. of Health and Human Services, National Center for Health Statistics, found in *New York Times 2010 Almanac,* p. 394.
2. Example 5 from *Public Education Finances 2007,* U.S. Census Bureau, July 2009, Table 8. http://www2.census.gov/govs/school/07f33pub .pdf; *The Nation's Report Card: Reading 2007,* National Center for Education Statistics, U.S. Department of Education, Sept. 2007, Table 11. http://nces.ed.gov/ nationsreportcard/pdf/main2007/2007496.pdf.
3. Exercise 4 from "November 1989 Course 120 Examination Applied Statistical Methods" of the *Education and Examination Committee of The Society of Actuaries.* Reprinted by permission of The Society of Actuaries.
4. Exercise 10 from http://www.bea.gov/ national/FA2004/SelectTable.asp.
5. Exercise 11 from http://www2.fdic.gov/ hsob/hsobRpt.asp.
6. Exercise 12 from http://www.ncta.com/Stats/ CableAvailableHomes.aspx.
7. Exercise 13 from http://www.federalreserve .gov/releases/g19/Current/.
8. Exercise 14 from http://www.nada.org/NR/ rdonlyres/0FE75B2C-69F0-4039-89FE-1366B5B86C97/0/NADAData08_no.pdf.
9. Exercise 15 from American Airlines, http:// www.aa.com.
10. Exercise 15 from *The New York Times*, Jan. 7, 2000.
11. Exercise 16 from www.nctm.org/wlme/ wlme6/five.htm.
12. Exercise 17 from Stanford, Craig B., "Chimpanzee Hunting Behavior and Human Evolution," *American Scientist,* Vol. 83, May–June 1995, pp. 256–261, and Goetz, Albert, "Using Open-Ended Problems for Assessment," *Mathematics Teacher,* Vol. 99, No. 1, August 2005, pp. 12–17.
13. Exercise 18 from Pierce, George W., *The Songs of Insects*, Cambridge, Mass., Harvard University Press, Copyright © 1948 by the President and Fellows of Harvard College.
14. Exercise 19 from *Digest of Education Statistics 2006,* National Center for Education Statistics, Table 63.
15. Exercise 20 from *Historical Poverty Tables*, U.S. Census Bureau.
16. Exercise 21 from Lee, Grace, Paul Velleman, and Howard Wainer, "Giving the Finger to Dating Services," *Chance,* Vol. 21, No. 3, 2008, pp. 59–61.
17. Exercise 23 from data provided by Gary Rockswold, Mankato State University, Minnesota.
18. Exercise 25 from Carter, Virgil and Robert E. Machol, *Operations Research*, Vol. 19, 1971, pp. 541–545.

19. Exercise 26 from Whipp, Brian J. and Susan Ward, "Will Women Soon Outrun Men?" *Nature,* Vol. 355, Jan. 2, 1992, p. 25. The data are from Peter Matthews, *Track and Field Athletics: The Records*, Guinness, 1986, pp. 11, 44; from Robert W. Schultz and Yuanlong Liu, in *Statistics in Sports,* edited by Bennett, Jay and Jim Arnold, 1998, p. 189; and from *The World Almanac and Book of Facts 2006*, p. 880.
20. Exercise 27 from http://www.run100s.com/HR/.

Review Exercises

1. Exercises 56 and 57 from TradeStats Express™, http://tse.export.gov.
2. Exercise 58 from U.S. Census Bureau, Historical Income Tables–Households, Table H-6, 2008.
3. Exercise 59 from *Chicago Tribune*, Feb. 4, 1996, Sec. 5, p. 4, and NADA Industry Analysis Division, 2006.
4. Exercise 60 from Food and Agriculture Organization Statistical Yearbook, Table D1, Table G5, http://www.fao.org/economic/ess/ publications-studies/statistical-yearbook/ fao-statistical-yearbook-2009/en/.
5. Exercise 62 from http://www.ers.usda.gov/ Data/FoodConsumption/spreadsheets/mtpcc.xls.
6. Exercise 63 from http://www.census.gov/ population/socdemo/hh-fam/ms1.xls.
7. Exercise 64 from http://www.census.gov/ hhes/www/poverty/histpov/famindex.html.
8. Exercise 65 from http://www.census.gov/ popest/states/NST-ann-est.html; http://doa .alaska.gov/dop/fileadmin/socc/pdf/bkgrnd_ socc23.pdf.
9. Exercise 66 from Moore, Thomas L., "Paradoxes in Film Rating," *Journal of Statistics Education,* Vol. 14, 2006, http://www. amstat.org/publications/jse/v14n1/datasets. moore.html

Extended Application

1. Page 43 from *Health, United States, 2009,* National Center for Health Statistics, U.S. Department of Health and Human Services, Table 24, http://www.cdc.gov/nchs/data/hus/ hus09.pdf.

Chapter 2

Section 2.1

1. Exercise 44 from Goetz, Albert, "Basic Economics: Calculating Against Theatrical Disaster," *The Mathematics Teacher,* Vol. 89, No. 1, Jan. 1996, pp. 30–32.
2. Exercise 45 from Inouye, David, Billy Barr, Kenneth Armitage, and Brian Inouye, "Climate Change Is Affecting Altitudinal Migrants and Hibernating Species," *Proceedings of the National Academy of Science*, Vol. 97, No. 4, Feb. 15, 2000, pp. 1630–1633.

3. Exercise 46 from *National Traffic Safety Institute Student Workbook*, 1993, p. 7.
4. Exercise 47 from "Kobe's 81-Point Game Second Only to Wilt," http://sports.espn.go.com.
5. Exercise 48 from Suntex Int. Inc., Easton, PA, http://www.24game.com. Copied with permission. 24® is a registered trademark of Suntex International Inc., all rights reserved.

Section 2.2

1. Exercise 46 was provided by Prof. Nathan Borchelt, Clayton State University.
2. Exercise 55 from L. L. Bean, http://www.llbean.com.
3. Exercise 60 from Paredes, Miguel, Mohammad Fatehi, and Richard Hinthorn, "The Transformation of an Inconsistent Linear System into a Consistent System," *The AMATYC Review*, Vol. 13, No. 2, Spring 1992.
4. Exercise 61 from Dorrie, Heinrich, *100 Great Problems of Elementary Mathematics, Their History and Solution*, New York: Dover Publications, 1965, pp. 3–7.
5. Exercise 62 from *The New York Times 2010 Almanac*, p. 392.
6. Exercise 63 from Bellany, Ian, "Modeling War," *Journal of Peace Research*, Vol. 36, No. 6, 1999, pp. 729–739.
7. Exercise 65 from Szydlik, Stephen D., "The Problem with the Snack Food Problem," *The Mathematics Teacher*, Vol. 103, No. 1, Aug. 2009, pp. 18–28.
8. Exercise 66 from "Kobe's 81-Point Game Second Only to Wilt," http://sports.espn.go.com.
9. Exercise 68 from Guinard, J., C. Zoumas-Morse, L. Mori, B. Uatoni, D. Panyam, and A. Kilar, "Sugar and Fat Effects on Sensory Properties of Ice Cream," *Journal of Food Science*, Vol. 62, No. 4, Sept./Oct. 1997, pp. 1087–1094.
10. Exercise 69 from Anderson, Marlow and Todd Feil, "Turning Lights Out with Linear Algebra," *Mathematics Magazine*, Vol. 71, No. 4, 1998, pp. 300–303.
11. Exercise 70 from http://www.baseball-almanac.com.

Section 2.3

1. Exercise 44 from *Traffic Safety Facts Research Note*, NHTSA, December 2009.
2. Exercise 45 from *The New York Times 2010 Almanac*, p. 394.
3. Exercise 46 from U.S. Census Bureau Educational Attainment, Table A-2, http://www.census.gov/population/www/socdemo/educ-attn.html.
4. Exercise 47 from U.S. Census Bureau Educational Attainment, Table A-2, http://www.census.gov/population/www/socdemo/educ-attn.html.

Section 2.4

1. Exercise 52 from David I. Schneider, University of Maryland, based on the article "A Dynamic Analysis of Northern Spotted Owl Viability in a Fragmented Forest Landscape," by Lamberson, R., R. McKelvey, B. Noon, and C. Voss, *Conservation Biology*, Vol. 6, No. 4, Dec. 1992, pp. 505–512.
2. Exercise 53 from http://www.census.gov/ipc/www/idb/region.php and https://www.census.gov/ipc/prod/wp02/tabA-01.xls

Section 2.5

1. Exercise 66 from Isaksen, Daniel, "Linear Algebra on the Gridiron," *The College Mathematics Journal*, Vol. 26, No. 5, Nov. 1995, pp. 358–360.

Section 2.6

1. Page 102 from http://www.bea.gov/industry/.
2. Exercise 19 from Leontief, Wassily, Input-Output Economics, 2nd ed., Oxford University Press, 1966, pp. 20–27.
3. Exercise 20 from Ibid, pp. 6–9.
4. Exercise 21 from Ibid, pp. 174–177
5. Exercise 22 from *Input-Output Tables of China, 1981*, China Statistical Information and Consultancy Service Centre, 1987, pp. 17–19.
6. Exercise 23 and 24 from Chase, Robert, Philip Bourque, and Richard Conway Jr., "The 1987 Washington State Input-Output Study," Report to the Graduate School of Business Administration, University of Washington, Sept. 1993.
7. Exercise 25 from an example created by Thayer Watkins, Department of Economics, San Jose State University, www.sjsu.edu/faculty/watkins/inputoutput.htm.

Review Exercises

1. Exercise 72 from Lamphear, F. Charles and Theodore Roesler, "1970 Nebraska Input-Output Tables," *Nebraska Economic and Business Report No. 10*, Bureau of Business Research, University of Nebraska-Lincoln, 1971.
2. Exercises 74 and 75 are based on the article "Medical Applications of Linear Equations" by David Jabon, Gail Nord, Bryce W. Wilson, and Penny Coffman, *The Mathematics Teacher*, Vol. 89, No. 5, May 1996, p. 398.
3. Exercise 76 from Benson, Brian, Nicholas Nohtadi, Sarah Rose, and Willem Meeuwisse, "Head and Neck Injuries Among Ice Hockey Players Wearing Full Face Shields vs. Half Face Shields," *JAMA*, Vol. 282, No. 24, Dec. 22/29, 1999, pp. 2328–2332.
4. Exercise 77 from Hibbeler, R., *Structural Analysis*, Prentice-Hall, 1995.
5. Exercise 79 from Atmospheric Carbon Dioxide Record from Mauna Loa, Scripps Institution of Oceanography http://cdiac.esd.ornl.gov/ftp/trends/co2/maunaloa.co2.
6. Exercise 80 from Alberty, Robert, "Chemical Equations Are Actually Matrix Equations," *Journal of Chemical Education*, Vol. 68, No. 12, Dec. 1991, p. 984.
7. Exercise 82 from http://www.baseball-reference.com.

Extended Application

1. Page 110 from Grossman, Stanley, "First and Second Order Contact to a Contagious Disease." *Finite Mathematics with Applications to Business, Life Sciences, and Social Sciences*, WCB/McGraw-Hill, 1993.

Chapter 3

Section 3.2

1. Exercise 17 from Problem 5 from "November 1989 Course 130 Examination Operations Research" of the *Education and Examination Committee of The Society of Actuaries*. Reprinted by permission of The Society of Actuaries.

Section 3.3

1. Page 133 from *Uniform CPA Examinations and Unofficial Answers*, copyright © 1973, 1974, 1975 by the American Institute of Certified Public Accountants, Inc.; reprinted with permission.
2. Exercise 25 from Reidhead, Van A., "Linear Programming Models in Archaeology," *Annual Review of Anthropology*, Vol. 8, 1979, pp. 543–578.

Review Exercise

1. Exercise 45 from Joy, Leonard, "Barth's Presentation of Economic Spheres in Darfur," in *Themes in Economic Anthropology*, edited by Raymond Firth, Tavistock Publications, 1967, pp. 175–189.

Chapter 4

Section 4.1

1. Exercise 29 was provided by Professor Karl K. Norton, Husson University.

Section 4.2

1. Exercise 31 from *Uniform CPA Examination Questions and Unofficial Answers*, copyright ©1973, 1974, 1975 by the American Institute of Certified Public Accountants, Inc., is reprinted with permission.
2. Exercise 35 from http://www.nutristrategy.com/activitylist4.htm.
3. Exercise 36 from http://www.nutristrategy.com/activitylist4.htm.

Section 4.3

1. Exercise 17 from Problem 2 from "November 1989 Course 130 Examination Operations Research" of the *Education and Examination Committee of The Society of Actuaries*. Reprinted by permission of The Society of Actuaries.
2. Exercise 27 from http://www.brianmac.demon.co.uk/energyexp.htm.

Section 4.4

1. Exercise 30 from http://www.nutristrategy
.com/activitylist4.htm.

Review Exercise

1. Exercise 47 from http://www.nutristrategy
.com/activitylist4.htm.

Extended Application

1. This application based on material from the
following online sources: The website of the
Optimization Technology Center at
Northwestern University at http://
www.ece.nwu.edu/OTC/. There is a link to a
thorough explanation of the stock-cutting
problem. Home page of the Special Interest
Group on Cutting and Packing at http://prodlog
.wiwi.uni-halle.de/sicup/index.html. The linear
programming FAQ at http://www.faqs.org/faqs/
linear-programming-faq/.

Chapter 5

Section 5.1

1. Exercise 54 from *The New York Times*, July
20, 1997, Sec. 4, p. 2.
2. Exercise 54 b from http://money.cnn.com.
3. Exercise 54 d from http://www.forbes.com/
lists/2006/10/BH69.html and http://www
.forbes.com/lists/2010/10/billionaires-2010_
William-Gates-III_BH69.html.
4. Exercise 55 from SallieMae: http://www
.salliemae.com/get_student_loan/find_student
_loan/undergrad_student_loan/federal_student
_loans/.
5. Exercise 58 from *The New York Times*, Dec.
31, 1995, Sec. 3. p. 5.
6. Exercise 65 adapted from Problem 5 from
"Course 140 Examination, Mathematics of
Compound Interest" of the *Education and
Examination Committee of The Society of
Actuaries*. Reprinted by permission of The
Society of Actuaries.
7. Exercise 66 from *The New York Times*, March
30, 1995.
8. Exercise 67 from http://www.ibankmarine.com.
9. Exercise 68 from http://us.etrade.com.
10. Exercise 69 from https://www.bankrate.com.
11. Exercise 77 from *The New York Times*, March
11, 2007, p. 27.
12. Exercise 77 b from http://www.american
.com/archive/2006/december/mitt-romney/

Section 5.2

1. Exercise 49 from http://articles.moneycentral
.msn.com/Insurance/InsureYourHealth/High
CostOfSmoking.aspx
2. Exercise 65 from *The Washington Post*,
March 10, 1992, p. A1

Section 5.3

1. Exercise 39 from http://www.cars.com/go/
advice/incentives/incentivesAll.jsp,
http://www.cars.com/go/buyIndex.jsp.

2. Exercise 40 from http://www.cars.com/go/
advice/incentives/incentivesAll.jsp,
http://www.cars.com/go/buyIndex.jsp.
3. Exercise 41 from Gould, Lois, "Ticket to
Trouble," *The New York Times Magazine*,
April 23, 1995, p. 39.
4. Page 216 from http://www.direct.ed.gov/
RepayCalc/dlindex2.html.
5. Exercise 47 from *The New York Times,* Nov.
12, 1996, pp. A1, A22.

Review Exercises

1. Exercise 70 from "Pocket That Pension,"
Smart Money, Oct. 1994, p. 33.
2. Exercise 75 from http://www.bankrate.com
3. Exercise 77 from http://www.cars.com/go/
advice/incentives/incentivesAll.jsp,
http://www.cars.com/go/buyIndex.jsp
4. Exercise 78 from http://www.cars.com/go/
advice/incentives/incentivesAll.jsp,
http://www.cars.com/go/buyIndex.jsp
5. Exercise 80 from Problem 16 from "Course
140 Examination, Mathematics of Compound
Interest" of the *Education and Examination
Committee of The Society of Actuaries*.
Reprinted by permission of The Society of
Actuaries.
6. Exercise 81 from *The New York Times,* Sept.
27, 1998, p. BU 10.

Extended Application

1. Page 218 from COMAP, copyright COMAP
"Consortium" 1991. COMAP, Inc. 57 Bedford
Street #210, Lexington, MA 02420.

Chapter 6

Section 6.1

1. Page 225 from http://research.microsoft.com/
2. Page 231 from J.K. Lasser Institute, *Your
Income Tax 2010,* New York: John Wiley &
Sons, pp. 10, 562, 487, 435.
3. Page 232 from Goldman, D. R., ed.,
*American College of Physicians Complete
Home Medical Guide*, 2nd ed., New York: DK
Publishing, 2003, p. 57.
4. Page 232 from Ventura, John, *Law for
Dummies*, Indianapolis, IN: Wiley Publishing,
Inc. 2005, pp. 113, 20, 12, 55, 10.
5. Page 232 from Frost, S. E., ed., *Masterworks
of Philosophy*, New York: McGraw-Hill,
1946.
6. Page 232 from *TNIV Bible*, Zondervan, 2005.

Section 6.2

1. Exercise 40 from J.K. Lasser Institute, *Your
Income Tax 2010,* New York: John Wiley &
Sons, p. 489.
2. Exercise 41 from "AppleCare Protection
Plan for iPhone," Apple Inc., 2009, p. 11.
3. Exercise 42 from eBay.
4. Exercise 44 from Goldman, David R., ed.,
*American College of Physicians Complete
Home Medical Guide,* 2nd ed., New York: DK
Publishing, 2003, p. 223.

5. Exercise 46 from Ventura, John, *Law for
Dummies*, Indianapolis, IN: Wiley Publishing,
Inc. 2005, p. 21.
6. Exercise 47 from http://www.drmardy.com/
chiasmus/masters/kennedyl.shtml.
7. Exercise 49 from Milton Bradley Company,
East Longmeadow, MA, 1996.
8. Exercise 50 from Smullyan, Raymond, *The
Lady or the Tiger? And Other Logic Puzzles,
Including a Mathematical Novel That
Features Godel's Great Discovery*, New York:
Knopf, 1982.

Section 6.3

1. Exercise 89 from J.K. Lasser Institute, *Your
Income Tax 2010,* New York: John Wiley &
Sons, pp. 13, 41, 576.
2. Exercise 90 from "AppleCare Protection
Plan for iPhone," Apple Inc., 2009, p. 11.
3. Exercise 92 from Goldman, David R., ed.,
*American College of Physicians Complete
Home Medical Guide*, 2nd ed., New York: DK
Publishing, 2003, p. 59.
4. Exercise 93 from Ventura, John, *Law for
Dummies*, Indianapolis, IN: Wiley Publishing,
Inc. 2005, pp. 12, 110, 5.

Section 6.4

1. Exercise 41 from J.K. Lasser Institute, *Your
Income Tax 2010,* New York: John Wiley &
Sons, p. 55, 13, 435.
2. Exercise 42 from J.K. Lasser Institute, *Your
Income Tax 2010,* New York: John Wiley &
Sons, p. 271.
3. Exercise 43 from JP Morgan Chase & Co.
4. Exercise 44 from Goldman, David R., ed.,
*American College of Physicians Complete
Home Medical Guide*, 2nd ed., New York: DK
Publishing, 2003, p. 72.
5. Exercise 45 from Rosing, Norbert, "Bear
Beginnings: New Life on the Ice," *National
Geographic*, December 2000, p. 33.
6. Exercise 46 from Ventura, John, *Law for
Dummies*, Indianapolis, IN: Wiley Publishing,
Inc. 2005, p. 115.
7. Exercise 47 from Ventura, John, *Law for
Dummies*, Indianapolis, IN: Wiley Publishing,
Inc. 2005, p. 55, 190, 114.
8. Exercise 48 from Bartlett, John, *Bartlett's
Familiar Quotations*, 15th ed., Boston: Little,
Brown and Company, 1980.
9. Exercise 49 from Fisher, William E., "An
Analysis of the Deutsch Sociocausal
Paradigm of Political Integration,"
International Organizational, Vol. 23, No. 2,
Spring 1969, pp. 254–290.
10. Exercise 50 from *The New York Times,* May
29, 2002, p. A1.
11. Exercise 51 from Lipset, Seymour Martin,
Political Man, 1960, quoted by Hildebrand,
David K., James D. Laing, and Howard
Rosenthal, "Prediction Analysis in Political
Research," *The American Political Science
Review*, Vol. 70, No. 2, June 1976, pp.
509–535.

12. Exercise 52 from Rosenthal, Howard, "The Electoral Politics of Gaullists in the Fourth French Republic: Ideology or Constituency Interest?" *The American Political Science Review*, Vol. 63, June 1969, pp. 476–487.
13. Exercise 53 from Bower, Bruce, "Roots of Reason," *Science News*, Vol. 145, Jan. 29, 1994, pp. 72–73.
14. Exercise 57 from Directions for Scrabble® and Yahtzee®, Milton Bradley Company, East Longmeadow, MA.

Section 6.5

1. Page 62 and Exercises 39–44 from *The Complete Works of Lewis Carroll,* Vintage Books, 1976.

Section 6.6

1. Example 6 from www.fec.gov/pubrec/fe2000/prespop.htm.
2. Exercise 40 from *United States v. Brown*, 381 U.S. 437 (1965).
3. Exercise 42 from NIV Bible.

Review Exercise

1. Exercise 42 from *Formal Logic: Its Scope and Limits*, 2nd ed., by Richard Jeffrey, New York: McGraw-Hill, 1981.
2. From page 274 from J.K. Lasser Institute, *Your Income Tax 2010*, New York: John Wiley & Sons, pp. 561, 450, 399, 435.
3. Exercise 65 from Goldman, David R., ed., *American College of Physicians Complete Home Medical Guide*, 2nd ed., New York: DK Publishing, 2003, p. 55, 32, 45, 48.
4. Exercise 66 from Ventura, John, *Law for Dummies*, Indianapolis, IN: Wiley Publishing, Inc. 2005, p. 315, 348, 314.
5. Exercise 67 from Tilly, Charles, "Processes and Mechanisms of Democratization," *Sociological Theory*, Vol. 18, No. 1, March 2000, pp. 1–16.
6. Exercise 68 from Estling, Ralph, "It's a Good Thing Cows Can't Fly in Mobile," *Skeptical Inquirer*, Nov./Dec. 2002, pp. 57–58.
7. Exercise 68c from Chambers, Timothy, "On Venn Diagrams," *The Mathematics Teacher*, Vol. 97, No. 1, Jan. 2004, p. 3.
8. Page 278 from Milton Bradley Company.
9. Page 278 from *The Complete Works of Lewis Carroll,* Vintage Books, 1976.

Extended Application

1. From page 279 from *World-Class Logic Problems, Penny Press,* Autumn, 2003.
2. Exercise 1 from *World-Class Logic Problems Special,* Summer 2003, p. 6.
3. Exercise 2 from *World-Class Logic Problems Special,* October 2003, p. 23.
4. Exercise 3 from *World-Class Logic Problems Special,* Autumn 2003, p. 20.
5. Exercise 4 from *World-Class Logic Problems Special,* Autumn 2003, p. 6.
6. Exercise 5 from *World-Class Logic Problems Special,* Autumn 2003, p. 7.

Chapter 7

Section 7.1

1. Page 291 from *The Merck Manual of Diagnosis and Therapy,* 16th ed., Merck Research Laboratories, 1992, pp. 1075 and 1080.
2. Page 292 from *The New York Times 2010 Almanac,* page 408.
3. Exercise 77 from Stewart, Ian, "Mathematical Recreations: A Strategy for Subsets," *Scientific American*, Mar. 2000, pp. 96–98.
4. Page 292 from *The New York Times 2010 Almanac,* pp. 187–207.

Section 7.2

1. Example 7 from U.S. Fish and Wildlife Service, http://ecos.fws.gov.
2. Exercise 46 from *National Vital Statistics Reports,* Vol. 57, No. 14, April 17, 2009, p.18.
3. Exercise 47 from Benson, Brian, Nicholas Nohtaki, M. Sarah Rose, Willem Meeuwisse, "Head and Neck Injuries Among Ice Hockey Players Wearing Full Face Shields vs. Half Face Shields," *JAMA*, Vol. 282, No. 24, Dec. 22/29, 1999, pp. 2328–2332.
4. Exercise 48 from usa.gov.
5. Page 301 from *Population Projections of the United States by Age, Sex, Race, and Hispanic Origin: 1995 to 2050*, U.S. Bureau of the Census, Feb. 1996, pp. 16–17.
6. Page 301 from *The New York Times 2010 Almanac,* p. 296.

Section 7.3

1. Example 4 from www.epi.org.
2. Example 8 from National Safety Council, Itasca, IL, *Injury Facts,* 2007.
3. Exercise 50 from http://www.cartalk.com/content/puzzler/transcripts/200107/. Cartalk.com is a production of Dewey, Cheetham and Howe. Contents © 2007, Dewey, Cheetham and Howe.
4. Exercise 52 from www.nsf.gov/statistics.
5. Exercise 54 from www.bls.gov.
6. Exercise 57 from www.cdc.gov.
7. Exercise 58 from *Population Projections of the United States by Age, Sex, Race, and Hispanic Origin: 1995 to 2050*, Bureau of the Census, Feb. 1996, p. 12.
8. Exercise 59 from *Roll Call*, March 1, 2010.
9. Exercises 60 and 61 from Busey, John and David Martin, *Regimental Strengths and Losses at Gettysburg*, Hightstown, N.J., Longstreet House, 1986, p. 270.

Section 7.4

1. Example 8 from *The New York Times 2010 Almanac,* p. 365.
2. Exercise 24 from *Parade* magazine, Nov. 6, 1994, p. 11. © 1994 Marilyn vos Savant. Initially published in *Parade* magazine. All rights reserved.
3. Exercise 26 from Staubach, Roger, *First Down, Lifetime to Go,* Word Incorporated, Dallas, 1976.
4. Exercise 45 from Menand, Louis, "Everybody's an Expert: Putting Predictions to the Test," *New Yorker*, Dec. 5, 2005, pp. 98–101.
5. Exercise 46 from Problem 3 from the 2005 Sample Exam P of the *Education and Examination Committee of the Society of Actuaries*. Reprinted by permission of the Society of Actuaries.
6. Exercise 50 from www.bls.gov.
7. Exercise 51 from www.bls.gov.
8. Exercise 53: The probabilities of a person being male or female are from *The World Almanac and Book of Facts*, 1995. The probabilities of a male and female being color-blind are from *Parsons' Diseases of the Eye* (18th ed.) by Stephen J. H. Miller, Churchill Livingstone, 1990, p. 269. This reference gives a range of 3 to 4% for the probability of gross color blindness in men; we used the midpoint of this range.
9. Exercise 56 from Wright, J. R., "An Analysis of Variability in Guinea Pigs," *Genetics,* Vol. 19, pp. 506–536.
10. Exercise 57 from Problem 2 from the 2005 Sample Exam P of the *Education and Examination Committee of the Society of Actuaries*. Reprinted by permission of the Society of Actuaries.
11. Exercise 58 from Problem 8 from the 2005 Sample Exam P of the *Education and Examination Committee of the Society of Actuaries*. Reprinted by permission of the Society of Actuaries.
12. Exercise 59 from Problem 15 from the 2005 Sample Exam P of the *Education and Examination Committee of the Society of Actuaries*. Reprinted by permission of the Society of Actuaries.
13. Exercise 60 from Safire, William, "The Henry Poll," *The New York Times*, June 25, 2001, p. A17 and http://abcnews.go.com.
14. Exercise 66 from usa.gov.
15. Exercises 67 and 68 from Gibson, J. L., "Putting Up with Fellow Russians: An Analysis of Political Tolerance in the Fledgling Russian Democracy," *Political Research Quarterly*, Vol. 51, No. 1, Mar. 1998, pp. 37–68.
16. Exercise 69 from *The New York Times*, Feb. 23, 2006, p. D3.
17. Exercise 70 from bookofodds.com.
18. Exercise 71 from bookofodds.com.

Section 7.5

1. Page 325 from Pringle, David, "Who's the DNA Fingerprinting Pointing At?" *New Scientist*, Jan. 29, 1994, pp. 51–52.
2. Exercise 31 from *Parade* magazine, June 12, 1994, p. 18. © 1994 Marilyn vos Savant. Initially published in *Parade* magazine. All rights reserved.

3. Exercise 32 from *Chance News* 10.01, Jan 16, 2001.

4. Exercise 35: This problem is based on the "Puzzler of the Week: Prison Marbles" from the week of Sept. 7, 1996, on National Public Radio's *Car Talk*.

5. Exercise 41 from airconsumer.dot.gov.

6. Exercise 43 from *Chicago Tribune,* Dec. 18, 1995, Sec. 4, p. 1.

7. Exercise 63 from American Medical Association, 2010.

8. Page 332 from Benson, Brian, Nicholas Nohtaki, M. Sarah Rose, and Willem Meeuwisse, "Head and Neck Injuries Among Ice Hockey Players Wearing Full Face Shields vs. Half Face Shields," *JAMA*, Vol. 282, No. 24, Dec. 22/29, 1999, pp. 2328–2332.

9. Exercise 69 from Problem 12 from the 2005 Sample Exam P of the *Education and Examination Committee of the Society of Actuaries.* Reprinted by permission of the Society of Actuaries.

10. Exercise 70 from Falk, Ruma, *Chance News*, July 23, 1995.

11. Exercise 73 from cdc.gov.

12. Exercise 74 from Matthews, Robert A. J., *Nature*, Vol. 382, Aug. 29, 1996, p. 3.

13. Exercise 75 from *Science News*, Vol. 169, April 15, 2006, pp. 234–236.

14. Exercise 77 from Takis, Sandra L., "Titanic: A Statistical Exploration," *Mathematics Teacher*, Vol. 92, No. 8, Nov. 1999, pp. 660–664.

15. Exercise 87 from Goodman, Terry, "Shooting Free Throws, Probability, and the Golden Ratio," Mathematics Teacher, Vol. 103, No. 7, March, 2010, pp. 482–487.

16. Exercise 88 from Goodman, Terry, "Shooting Free Throws, Probability, and the Golden Ratio," *Mathematics Teacher,* Vol. 103, No. 7, March, 2010, pp. 482–487.

17. Exercise 89 from Schielack, Vincent P., Jr., "The Football Coach's Dilemma: Should We Go for 1 or 2 Points First?" *The Mathematics Teacher*, Vol. 88, No. 9, Dec. 1995, pp. 731–733.

Section 7.6

1. Exercise 18 from Problem 8 from May 2003 Course 1 Examination of the *Education and Examination Committee of the Society of Actuaries.* Reprinted by permission of the Society of Actuaries.

2. Exercise 19 from Problem 20 from the 2005 Sample Exam P of the *Education and Examination Committee of the Society of Actuaries.* Reprinted by permission of the Society of Actuaries.

3. Exercise 20 from Problem 23 from the 2005 Sample Exam P of the *Education and Examination Committee of the Society of Actuaries.* Reprinted by permission of the Society of Actuaries.

4. Exercise 21 from Uniform CPA Examination, Nov. 1989.

5. Exercise 23 from Hoffrage, Ulrich, Samuel Lindsey, Ralph Hertwig, and Gerd Gigerenzer, *Science*, Vol. 290, Dec. 22, 2000, pp. 2261–2262.

6. Exercise 25 from *"Mammography facility characteristics associated with interpretive accuracy of screening mammography,"* National Cancer Institute, www.cancer.gov.

7. Exercise 26 from www.cdc.gov.

8. Exercise 27 from Problem 31 from May 2003 Course 1 Examination of the *Education and Examination Committee of the Society of Actuaries.* Reprinted by permission of the Society of Actuaries.

9. Exercise 28 from Problem 21 from the 2005 Sample Exam P of the *Education and Examination Committee of the Society of Actuaries.* Reprinted by permission of the Society of Actuaries.

10. Exercise 29 from Problem 25 from the 2005 Sample Exam P of the *Education and Examination Committee of the Society of Actuaries.* Reprinted by permission of the Society of Actuaries.

11. Exercise 30 from Problem 26 from the 2005 Sample Exam P of the *Education and Examination Committee of the Society of Actuaries.* Reprinted by permission of the Society of Actuaries.

12. Exercise 31 from "Binge-Drinking Trends," Harvard School of Public Health, Vol 50, March 2002, p. 209.

13. Exercise 32 from Good, I. J., "When Batterer Turns Murderer," *Nature*, Vol. 375, No. 15, June 15, 1995, p. 541.

14. Page 342 from www.uscensus.gov.

15. Exercise 36 from "Factors Related to the Likelihood of a Passenger Vehicle Occupant Being Ejected in a Fatal Crash," National Highway Traffic Safety Administration, U.S. Department of Transportation, December, 2009.

16. Page 343 from "Cigarette Smoking Among Adults—United States, 2007," www.cdc.gov.

17. Exercise 39 from http://abcnews.go.com/ Technology/WhosCounting/story?id= 1560771.

18. Exercise 40 from Shimojo, Shinsuke, and Shin'ichi Ichikawa, "Intuitive Reasoning About Probability: Theoretical and Experimental Analyses of the 'Problem of Three Prisoners,'" *Cognition*, Vol. 32, 1989, pp. 1–24.

Review Exercises

1. Exercise 64 from *Parade* magazine, Sept. 9, 1990, p. 13. © 1990 Marilyn vos Savant. Initially published in *Parade* magazine. All rights reserved.

2. Exercise 78 from Problem 4 from the 2005 Sample Exam P of the *Education and Examination Committee of the Society of Actuaries.* Reprinted by permission of the Society of Actuaries.

3. Exercise 91 from Problem 5 from May 2003 Course 1 Examination of the *Education and Examination Committee of the Society of Actuaries.* Reprinted by permission of the Society of Actuaries.

4. Exercise 92 from Problem 5 from the 2005 Sample Exam P of the *Education and Examination Committee of the Society of Actuaries.* Reprinted by permission of the Society of Actuaries.

5. Exercise 93 from Problem 11 from the 2005 Sample Exam P of the *Education and Examination Committee of the Society of Actuaries.* Reprinted by permission of the Society of Actuaries.

6. Exercise 94 from Problem 18 from May 2003 Course 1 Examination of the *Education and Examination Committee of the Society of Actuaries.* Reprinted by permission of the Society of Actuaries.

7. Exercise 96 from Young, Victoria, "A Matter of Survival," *The Mathematics Teacher*, Vol. 95, No. 2, Feb. 2002, pp. 100–112.

8. Exercise 97 from Problem 13 from the 2005 Sample Exam P of the *Education and Examination Committee of the Society of Actuaries.* Reprinted by permission of the Society of Actuaries.

9. Exercise 98 from www.uscensus.gov and "Election Results 2008," *The New York Times,* November 5, 2008.

10. Exercise 100 from Warner, Stanley, "Randomized Response: A Survey Technique for Eliminating Evasive Answer Bias," *The Journal of the American Statistical Association*, Vol. 60, No. 309, Mar. 1965, pp. 63–69.

11. Exercise 101 from John Allen Paulos, "Coins and Confused Eyewitnesses: Calculating the Probability of Picking the Wrong Guy," *Who's Counting*, Feb. 1, 2001. http://more.abcnews .go.com/sections/science/ whoscounting_ index/whoscounting_index.html.

12. Exercise 102 from *Science*, Vol. 309, July 22, 2005, p. 543.

13. Exercise 103 from *The San Francisco Chronicle*, June 8, 1994, p. A1.

14. Exercise 104 from Carter, Virgil and Robert Machols, "Optimal Strategies on Fourth Down," *Management Science,* Vol. 24, No. 16, Dec. 1978. Copyright © 1978 by The Institute of Management Sciences.

15. Exercise 107 from http://www.cartalk.com/ content/puzzler/2002.html.

16. Exercise 108 from Clancy, Tom, *Debt of Honor*, New York: G. P. Putnam's Sons, 1994, pp. 686–687.

17. Exercise 109 from Problem 1 from May 2003 Course 1 Examination of the *Education and Examination Committee of the Society of Actuaries.* Reprinted by permission of the Society of Actuaries.

KEY DEFINITIONS, THEOREMS, AND FORMULAS

2.2 Row Operations

For any augmented matrix of a system of equations, the following operations produce the augmented matrix of an equivalent system:

1. interchanging any two rows;

2. multiplying the elements of a row by any nonzero real number;

3. adding a nonzero multiple of the elements of one row to the corresponding elements of a nonzero multiple of some other row.

2.5 Finding a Multiplicative Inverse Matrix

To obtain A^{-1} for any $n \times n$ matrix A for which A^{-1} exists, follow these steps.

1. Form the augmented matrix $[A|I]$, where I is the $n \times n$ identity matrix.

2. Perform row operations on $[A|I]$ to get a matrix of the form $[I|B]$ if this is possible.

3. Matrix B is A^{-1}.

4.2 Simplex Method for Standard Maximization Problems

1. Determine the objective function.

2. Write all necessary constraints.

3. Convert each constraint into an equation by adding a slack variable in each.

4. Set up the initial simplex tableau.

5. Locate the most negative indicator. If there are two such indicators, choose the one farther to the left.

6. Form the necessary quotients to find the pivot. Disregard any quotients with 0 or a negative number in the denominator. The smallest nonnegative quotient gives the location of the pivot. If all quotients must be disregarded, no maximum solution exists. If two quotients are both equal and smallest, choose the pivot in the row nearest the top of the matrix.

7. Use row operations to change all other numbers in the pivot column to zero by adding a suitable multiple of the pivot row to a positive multiple of each row.

8. If the indicators are all positive or 0, this is the final tableau. If not, go back to Step 5 and repeat the process until a tableau with no negative indicators is obtained.

9. Read the solution from this final tableau.

5.1 Compound Amount

$$A = P(1 + i)^n$$

where $i = \dfrac{r}{m}$ and $n = mt$,

A is the future (maturity) value;
P is the principal;
r is the annual interest rate;
m is the number of compounding periods per year;
t is the number of years;
n is the number of compounding periods;
i is the interest rate per period.

5.2 Future Value of an Ordinary Annuity

$$S = R\left[\frac{(1 + i)^n - 1}{i}\right] \qquad \text{or} \qquad S = Rs_{\overline{n}|i}$$

where

S is the future value;

R is the payment;

i is the interest rate per period;

n is the number of periods.

6.1, 6.3 Truth Tables

The following truth table defines the logical operators in this chapter.

p	q	$\sim p$	$p \wedge q$	$p \vee q$	$p \to q$	$p \leftrightarrow q$
T	T	F	T	T	T	T
T	F	F	F	T	F	F
F	T	T	F	T	T	F
F	F	T	F	F	T	T

7.3 Basic Probability Principle

Let S be a sample space of equally likely outcomes, and let event E be a subset of S. Then the probability that event E occurs is

$$P(E) = \frac{n(E)}{n(S)}.$$

7.4 Union Rule

For any two events E and F from a sample space S,

$$P(E \cup F) = P(E) + P(F) - P(E \cap F).$$

7.5 Product Rule

If E and F are events, then $P(E \cap F)$ may be found by either of these formulas.

$$P(E \cap F) = P(F) \cdot P(E|F) \qquad \text{or} \qquad P(E \cap F) = P(E) \cdot P(F|E)$$

7.6 Bayes' Theorem

$$P(F_i|E) = \frac{P(F_i) \cdot P(E|F_i)}{P(F_1) \cdot P(E|F_1) + P(F_2) \cdot P(E|F_2) + \cdots + P(F_n) \cdot P(E|F_n)}$$

8.2 Permutations and Combinations

Permutations Different orderings or arrangements of the r objects are different permutations.

$$P(n, r) = \frac{n!}{(n - r)!}$$

Clue words: arrangement, schedule, order
Order matters!

Combinations Each choice or subset of r objects gives one combination. Order within the group of r objects does not matter.

$$C(n, r) = \frac{n!}{(n - r)!r!}$$

Clue words: group, committee, set, sample
Order does not matter!

8.4 Binomial Probability

If p is the probability of success in a single trial of a binomial experiment, the probability of x successes and $n - x$ failures in n independent repeated trials of the experiment, known as binomial probability, is

$$P(x \text{ successes in } n \text{ trials}) = C(n, x) \cdot p^x \cdot (1-p)^{n-x}.$$

8.5 Expected Value

Suppose the random variable x can take on the n values $x_1, x_2, x_3, \ldots, x_n$. Also, suppose the probabilities that these values occur are, respectively, $p_1, p_2, p_3, \ldots, p_n$. Then the expected value of the random variable is

$$E(x) = x_1 p_1 + x_2 p_2 + x_3 p_3 + \cdots + x_n p_n.$$

9.2 Variance and Standard Deviation

The variance of a sample of n numbers $x_1, x_2, x_3, \ldots, x_n$, with mean $\bar{x}$, is

$$s^2 = \frac{\Sigma x^2 - n\bar{x}^2}{n - 1}.$$

The standard deviation of a sample of n numbers $x_1, x_2, x_3, \ldots, x_n$, with mean $\bar{x}$, is

$$s = \sqrt{\frac{\Sigma x^2 - n\bar{x}^2}{n - 1}}.$$

11.4 Derivative

The derivative of the function f at x, written $f'(x)$, is defined as

$$f'(x) = \lim_{h \to 0} \frac{f(x + h) - f(x)}{h}, \quad \text{provided this limit exists.}$$

Rules for Derivatives

The following rules for derivatives are valid when all the indicated derivatives exist.

12.1 *Constant Rule* If $f(x) = k$ where k is any real number, then $f'(x) = 0$.

12.1 *Power Rule* If $f(x) = x^n$ for any real number n, then $f'(x) = nx^{n-1}$.

12.1 *Constant Times a Function* Let k be a real number. Then the derivative of $f'(x) = k \cdot g(x)$ is

$$f'(x) = k \cdot g'(x).$$

12.1 *Sum or Difference Rule* If $f(x) = u(x) \pm v(x)$ then

$$f'(x) = u'(x) \pm v'(x).$$

12.2 *Product Rule* If $f(x) = u(x) \cdot v(x)$ then

$$f'(x) = u(x) \cdot v'(x) + v(x) \cdot u'(x).$$

12.2 *Quotient Rule* If $f(x) = u(x)/v(x)$, and $v(x) \neq 0$, then

$$f'(x) = \frac{v(x) \cdot u'(x) - u(x) \cdot v'(x)}{[v(x)]^2}.$$

12.3 *Chain Rule* If y is a function of u, say $y = f(u)$, and if u is a function of x, say $u = g(x)$, then $y = f(u) = f[g(x)]$, and

$$\frac{dy}{dx} = \frac{dy}{du} \cdot \frac{du}{dx},$$

12.3 *Chain Rule* (Alternate Form) If $y = f[g(x)]$, then $dy/dx = f'[g(x)] \cdot g'(x)$.

12.4 *Exponential Function*

$$\frac{d}{dx}[a^{g(x)}] = (\ln a)a^{g(x)}g'(x)$$

$$\frac{d}{dx}[e^{g(x)}] = e^{g(x)}g'(x)$$

12.5 *Logarithmic Function*

$$\frac{d}{dx}[\log_a|g(x)|] = \frac{1}{\ln a} \cdot \frac{g'(x)}{g(x)}$$

$$\frac{d}{dx}[\ln|g(x)|] = \frac{g'(x)}{g(x)}$$

15.2 Substitution

Each of the following forms can be integrated using the substitution $u = f(x)$.

Form of the Integral   **Result**

1. $\int [f(x)]^n f'(x)\,dx, \quad n \neq -1$ $\int u^n\,du = \dfrac{u^{n+1}}{n+1} + C = \dfrac{[f(x)]^{n+1}}{n+1} + C$

2. $\int \dfrac{f'(x)}{f(x)}\,dx$ $\int \dfrac{1}{u}\,du = \ln|u| + C = \ln|f(x)| + C$

3. $\int e^{f(x)} f'(x)\,dx$ $\int e^u\,du = e^u + C = e^{f(x)} + C$

15.4 Fundametal Theorem of Calculus

Let f be continuous on the interval $[a, b]$, and let F be *any* antiderivative of f. Then

$$\int_a^b f(x)\,dx = F(b) - F(a) = F(x)\Big|_a^b .$$

17.3 Test for Relative Extrema

For a function $z = f(x, y)$ let $f_{xx}, f_{yy},$ and f_{xy} all exist in a circular region contained in the xy-plane with center (a, b) Further, let

$$f_x(a, b) = 0 \quad \text{and} \quad f_x(a, b) = 0.$$

Define the number D by

$$D = f_{xx}(a, b) + f_{xx}(a, b) - [f_{xx}(a, b)]^2.$$

Then

(a) $f(a, b)$ is a relative maximum if $D > 0$ and $f_{xx}(a, b) < 0$;

(b) $f(a, b)$ is a relative minimum if $D > 0$ and $f_{xx}(a, b) > 0$;

(c) $f(a, b)$ is a saddle point (neither a maximum nor a minimum) if $D < 0$;

(d) if $D = 0$, the test gives no information.